James Herriot (a pseudo                           d as
a veterinary surgeon                    College. Shortly
afterwards he took up a position as an assistant in a North Yorkshire
practice where he remained for the rest of his life, with the exception
of his wartime service in the RAF.

James Herriot's interests extended beyond writing and veterinary
work to music, and dog-walking in the Dales. He was married, with
a son who is also a veterinary surgeon and a daughter who is a doctor.

Britain's best loved vet died in 1995.

*Also by James Herriot in Pan*

If Only They Could Talk
It Shouldn't Happen to a Vet
Let Sleeping Vets Lie
Vets Might Fly
Vet in a Spin

*and*

The Lord God Made them All

*and*

All Creatures Great and Small
All Things Bright and Beautiful
All Things Wise and Wonderful
(Omnibus editions)

James Herriot's Dog Stories

# JAMES HERRIOT

# Vet In Harness
# Vet In A Spin
# Vets Might Fly

PAN BOOKS
*in association with*
MICHAEL JOSEPH

*Vet In Harness* first published 1974 by Michael Joseph Ltd
and first published by Pan Books 1975 in association with Michael Joseph Ltd.
*Vet In A Spin* first published 1977 by Michael Joseph Ltd
and first published by Pan Books 1978 in association with Michael Joseph Ltd.
*Vets Might Fly* first published 1976 by Michael Joseph Ltd
and first published by Pan Books 1977 in association with Michael Joseph Ltd.

This combined edition published 1995 by Pan Books
an imprint of Macmillan General Books
25 Eccleston Place, London SW1W 9NF
in association with Michael Joseph Ltd.

Associated companies throughout the world

ISBN 0 330 34598 2

The four lines from *If I Only Had Wings* on p.78 of *Vets Might Fly*
are reproduced by permission of The Peter Maurice Music Co. Ltd,
138–140 Charing Cross Road, London WC2H 0LD

1 3 5 7 9 8 6 4 2

A CIP catalogue record for this book is available from
the British Library

Printed and bound in Great Britain by
Cox & Wyman Ltd, Reading, Berkshire

# Vet In Harness

With love to my mother
in dear old Glasgow town

# 1

As I crawled into bed and put my arm around Helen it occurred to me, not for the first time, that there are few pleasures in this world to compare with snuggling up to a nice woman when you are half frozen.

There weren't any electric blankets in the thirties. Which was a pity because nobody needed the things more than country vets. It is surprising how deeply bone-marrow cold a man can get when he is dragged from his bed in the small hours and made to strip off in farm buildings when his metabolism is at a low ebb. Often the worst part was coming back to bed; I often lay exhausted for over an hour, longing for sleep but kept awake until my icy limbs and feet had thawed out.

But since my marriage such things were but a dark memory. Helen stirred in her sleep – she had got used to her husband leaving her in the night and returning like a blast from the North Pole – and instinctively moved nearer to me. With a sigh of thankfulness I felt the blissful warmth envelop me and almost immediately the events of the last two hours began to recede into unreality.

It had started with the aggressive shrilling of the bedside phone at one a.m. And it was Sunday morning, a not unusual time for some farmers after a late Saturday night to have a look round their stock and decide to send for the vet.

This time it was Harold Ingledew. And it struck me right away that he would have just about had time to get back to his farm after his ten pints at the Four Horse Shoes where they weren't too fussy about closing time.

And there was a significant slur in the thin croak of his voice.

'I 'ave a ewe amiss. Will you come ?'

'Is she very bad ?' In my semi-conscious state I always clung to the faint hope that one night somebody would say it would wait till morning. It had never happened yet and it didn't happen now: Mr Ingledew was not to be denied.

'Aye, she's in a bad way. She'll have to have summat done for 'er soon.'

Not a minute to lose, I thought bitterly. But she had probably been in a bad way all the evening when Harold was out carousing.

Still, there were compensations. A sick sheep didn't present any great threat. It was worst when you had to get out of bed facing the prospect of a spell of sheer hard labour in your enfeebled state. But in this case I was confident that I would be able to adopt my half-awake technique; which meant simply that I would be able to go out there and deal with the emergency and return between the sheets while still enjoying many of the benefits of sleep.

There was so much night work in country practice that I had been compelled to perfect this system as, I suspect, had many of my fellow practitioners. I had done some sterling work while in a somnambulistic limbo.

So, eyes closed, I tiptoed across the carpet and pulled on my working clothes. I effortlessly accomplished the journey down the long flights of stairs but when I opened the side door the system began to crumble, because even in the shelter of the high-walled garden the wind struck at me with savage force. It was difficult to stay asleep. In the yard as I backed out of the garage the high branches of the elms groaned in the darkness as they bent before the blast.

Driving from the town I managed to slip back into my trance and my mind played lazily with the phenomenon of Harold Ingledew. This drinking of his was so out of character. He was a tiny mouse of a man about seventy years old and when he came into the surgery on an occasional market day it was difficult to extract more than a few muttered words from him. Dressed in his best suit, his scrawny neck protruding from a shirt collar several sizes too big for him, he was the very picture of a meek and solid citizen; the watery blue eyes and fleshless cheeks added to the effect and only the brilliant red colouration of the tip of his nose gave any hint of other possibilities.

His fellow smallholders in Therby village were all steady

characters and did not indulge beyond a social glass of beer now and then, and his next door neighbour had been somewhat bitter when he spoke to me a few weeks ago.

'He's nowt but a bloody nuisance is awd Harold.'

'How do you mean?'

'Well, every Saturday night and every market night he's up roarin' and singin' till four o'clock in the mornin'.'

'Harold Ingledew? Surely not! He's such a quiet little chap.'

'Aye, he is for the rest of t'week.'

'But I can't imagine him singing!'

'You should live next door to 'im, Mr Herriot. He makes a 'ell of a racket. There's no sleep for anybody till he settles down.'

Since then I had heard from another source that this was perfectly true and that Mrs Ingledew tolerated it because her husband was entirely submissive at all other times.

The road to Therby had a few sharp little switchbacks before it dipped to the village and looking down I could see the long row of silent houses curving away to the base of the fell which by day hung in peaceful green majesty over the huddle of roofs but now bulked black and menacing under the moon.

As I stepped from the car and hurried round to the back of the house the wind caught at me again, jerking me to wakefulness as though somebody had thrown a bucket of water over me. But for a moment I forgot the cold in the feeling of shock as the noise struck me. Singing . . . loud raucous singing echoing around the old stones of the yard.

It was coming from the lighted kitchen window.

'JUST A SONG AT TWILIGHT, WHEN THE LIGHTS ARE LOW!'

I looked inside and saw little Harold sitting with his stockinged feet extended towards the dying embers of the fire while one hand clutched a bottle of brown ale.

'AND THE FLICKERING SHADOWS SOFTLY COME AND GO!' He was really letting it rip, head back, mouth wide.

I thumped on the kitchen door.

'THOUGH THE HEART BE WEARY, SAD THE DAY AND LONG!'

9

replied Harold's reedy tenor and I banged impatiently at the woodwork again.

The noise ceased and I waited an unbelievably long time till I heard the key turning and the bolt rattling back. The little man pushed his nose out and gave me a questioning look.

'I've come to see your sheep,' I said.

'Oh aye.' He nodded curtly with none of his usual diffidence. 'Ah'll put me boots on.' He banged the door in my face and I heard the bolt shooting home.

Taken aback as I was I realised that he wasn't being deliberately rude. Bolting the door was proof that he was doing everything mechanically. But for all that he had left me standing in an uncharitable spot. Vets will tell you that there are corners in farmyards which are colder than any hill top and I was in one now. Just beyond the kitchen door was a stone archway leading to the open fields and through this black opening there whistled a Siberian draught which cut effortlessly through my clothes.

I had begun to hop from one foot to the other when the singing started again.

'THERE'S AN OLD MILL BY THE STREAM, NELLIE DEAN!'

Horrified, I rushed back to the window. Harold was back in his chair, pulling on a vast boot and taking his time about it. As he bellowed he poked owlishly at the lace holes and occasionally refreshed himself from the bottle of brown ale.

I tapped on the window. 'Please hurry, Mr Ingledew.'

'WHERE WE USED TO SIT AND DREAM, NELLIE DEAN!' bawled Harold in response.

My teeth had begun to chatter before he got both boots on but at last he reappeared in the doorway.

'Come on then,' I gasped. 'Where is this ewe? Have you got her in one of these boxes?'

The old man raised his eyebrows. 'Oh, she's not 'ere.'

'Not here?'

'Nay, she's up at t'top buildings.'

'Right back up the road, you mean?'

'Aye, ah stopped off on t'way home and had a look at 'er.'

I stamped and rubbed my hands. 'Well, we'll have to drive back up. But there's no water, is there? You'd better bring a bucket of warm water, some soap and a towel.'

'Very good.' He nodded solemnly and before I knew what was happening the door was slammed shut and bolted and I was alone again in the darkness. I trotted immediately to the window and was not surprised to see Harold seated comfortably again. He leaned forward and lifted the kettle from the hearth and for a dreadful moment I thought he was going to start heating the water on the ashes of the fire. But with a gush of relief I saw him take hold of a ladle and reach into the primitive boiler in the old black grate.

'AND THE WATERS AS THEY FLOW SEEM TO MURMUR SWEET AND LOW!' he warbled, happy at his work, as he unhurriedly filled a bucket.

I think he had forgotten I was there when he finally came out because he looked at me blankly as he sang.

'YOU'RE MY HEART'S DESIRE, I LOVE YOU, NELLIE DEAN!' he informed me at the top of his voice.

'All right, all right,' I grunted. 'Let's go.' I hurried him into the car and we set off on the way I had come.

Harold held the bucket at an angle on his lap, and as we went over the switchbacks the water slopped gently on to my knee. The atmosphere in the car soon became so highly charged with beer fumes that I began to feel lightheaded.

'In 'ere!' the old man barked suddenly as a gate appeared in the headlights. I pulled on to the grass verge and stood on one leg for a few moments till I had shaken a surplus pint or two of water from my trousers. We went through the gate and I began to hurry towards the dark bulk of the hillside barn, but I noticed that Harold wasn't following me. He was walking aimlessly around the field.

'What are you doing, Mr Ingledew?'

'Lookin' for t'ewe.'

'You mean she's outside?' I repressed an impulse to scream.

'Aye, she lambed this afternoon and ah thowt she'd be right enough out 'ere.' He produced a torch, a typical farmer's torch

– tiny and with a moribund battery – and projected a fitful beam into the darkness. It made not the slightest difference.

As I stumbled across the field a sense of hopelessness assailed me. Above, the ragged clouds scurried across the face of the moon but down here I could see nothing. And it was so cold. The recent frosts had turned the ground to iron and the crisp grass cowered under the piercing wind. I had just decided that there was no way of finding an animal in this black waste land when Harold piped up.

'She's over 'ere.'

And sure enough when I groped my way towards the sound of his voice he was standing by an unhappy looking ewe. I don't know what instinct had brought him to her but there she was. And she was obviously in trouble; her head hung down miserably and when I put my hand on her fleece she took only a few faltering steps instead of galloping off as a healthy sheep would. Beside her, a tiny lamb huddled close to her flank.

I lifted her tail and took her temperature. It was normal. There were no signs of the usual post-lambing ailments; no staggering to indicate a deficiency, no discharge or accelerated respirations. But there was something very far wrong.

I looked again at the lamb. He was an unusually early arrival in this high country and it seemed unfair to bring the little creature into the inhospitable world of a Yorkshire March. And he was so small ... yes ... it was beginning to filter through to me. He was too damn small for a single lamb.

'Bring me that bucket, Mr Ingledew!' I cried. I could hardly wait to see if I was right. But as I balanced the receptacle on the grass the full horror of the situation smote me. I was going to have to strip off.

They don't give vets medals for bravery but as I pulled off my overcoat and jacket and stood shivering in my shirt sleeves on that black hillside I felt I deserved one.

'Hold her head,' I gasped and soaped my arm quickly. By the light of the torch I felt my way into the vagina and I didn't have to go very far before I found what I expected; a woolly

12

little skull. It was bent downwards with the nose under the pelvis and the legs were back.

'There's another lamb in here,' I said. 'It's laid wrong or it would have been born with its mate this afternoon.'

Even as I spoke my fingers had righted the presentation and I drew the little creature gently out and deposited him on the grass. I hadn't expected him to be alive after his delayed entry but as he made contact with the cold ground his limbs gave a convulsive twitch and almost immediately I felt his ribs heaving under my hand.

For a moment I forgot the knife-like wind in the thrill which I always found in new life, the thrill that was always fresh, always warm. The ewe, too, seemed stimulated because in the darkness I felt her nose pushing interestedly at the new arrival.

But my pleasant ruminations were cut short by a scuffling from behind me and some muffled words.

'Bugger it!' mumbled Harold.

'What's the matter?'

'Ah've kicked bucket ower.'

'Oh no! Is the water all gone?'

'Aye, nowt left.'

Well this was great. My arm was smeared with mucus after being inside the ewe. I couldn't possibly put my jacket on without a wash.

Harold's voice issued again from the darkness. 'There's some watter ower at building.'

'Oh good. We've got to get this ewe and lambs over there anyway.' I threw my clothes over my shoulder, tucked a lamb under each arm and began to blunder over the tussocks of grass to where I thought the barn lay. The ewe, clearly feeling better without her uncomfortable burden, trotted behind me.

It was Harold again who had to give me directions.

'Ower 'ere!' he shouted.

When I reached the barn I cowered thankfully behind the massive stones. It was no night for a stroll in shirt sleeves. Shaking uncontrollably I peered at the old man. I could just see his form in the last faint radiance of the torch and I wasn't quite sure what he was doing. He had lifted a stone from the pasture and was bashing something with it; then I realised he was bending over the water trough, breaking the ice.

When he had finished he plunged the bucket into the trough and handed it to me.

'There's your watter,' he said triumphantly.

I thought I had reached the ultimate in frigidity but when I plunged my hands into the black liquid with its floating icebergs I changed my mind. The torch had finally expired and I lost the soap very quickly. When I found I was trying to work up a lather with one of the pieces of ice I gave it up and dried my arms.

Somewhere nearby I could hear Harold humming under his breath, as comfortable as if he was by his own fireside. The vast amount of alcohol surging through his bloodstream must have made him impervious to the cold.

We pushed the ewe and lambs into the barn which was piled high with hay and before leaving I struck a match and looked at the little sheep and her new family settled comfortably among the fragrant clover. They would be safe and warm in there till morning.

My journey back to the village was less hazardous because the bucket on Harold's knee was empty. I dropped him outside his house, then I had to drive to the bottom of the village to turn; and as I came past the house again the sound forced its way into the car.

'IF YOU WERE THE ONLY GIRL IN THE WORLD AND I WERE THE ONLY BOY!'

I stopped, wound the window down and listened in wonder. It was incredible how the noise reverberated around the quiet street and if it went on till four o'clock in the morning as the neighbours said, then they had my sympathy.

'NOTHING ELSE WOULD MATTER IN THE WORLD TODAY!'

It struck me suddenly that I could soon get tired of Harold's singing. His volume was impressive but for all that he would never be in great demand at Covent Garden; he constantly

14

wavered off key and there was a grating quality in his top notes which set my teeth on edge.

'WE WOULD GO ON LOVING IN THE SAME OLD WAY!'

Hurriedly I wound the window up and drove off. As the heaterless car picked its way between the endless flitting pattern of walls I crouched in frozen immobility behind the wheel. I had now reached the state of total numbness and I can't remember much about my return to the yard at Skeldale House, nor my automatic actions of putting away the car, swinging shut the creaking doors of what had once been the old coach house, and trailing slowly down the long garden.

But a realisation of my blessings began to return when I slid into bed and Helen, instead of shrinking away from me as it would have been natural to do, deliberately draped her feet and legs over the human ice block that was her husband. The bliss was unbelievable. It was worth getting out just to come back to this.

I glanced at the luminous dial of the alarm clock. It was three o'clock and as the warmth flowed over me and I drifted away, my mind went back to the ewe and lambs, snug in their scented barn. They would be asleep now, I would soon be asleep, everybody would be asleep.

Except, that is, Harold Ingledew's neighbours. They still had an hour to go.

# 2

I had only to sit up in bed to look right across Darrowby to the hills beyond.

I got up and walked to the window. It was going to be a fine morning and the early sun glanced over the weathered reds and greys of the jumbled roofs, some of them sagging under their burden of ancient tiles, and brightened the tufts of green where trees pushed upwards from the gardens among the bristle of chimney pots. And behind everything the calm bulk of the fells.

It was my good fortune that this was the first thing I saw every morning; after Helen, of course, which was better still.

Following our unorthodox tuberculin testing honeymoon we had set up our first home on the top of Skeldale House. Siegfried, my boss up to my wedding and now my partner, had offered us free use of these empty rooms on the third storey and we had gratefully accepted; and though it was a makeshift arrangement there was an airy charm, an exhilaration in our high perch that many would have envied.

It was makeshift because everything at that time had a temporary complexion and we had no idea how long we would be there. Siegfried and I had both volunteered for the R.A.F. and were on deferred service but that is all I am going to say about the war. This book is not about such things which in any case were so very far from Darrowby; it is the story of the months I had with Helen between our marriage and my call-up and is about the ordinary things which have always made up our lives; my work, the animals, the Dales.

This front room was our bed-sitter and though it was not luxuriously furnished it did have an excellent bed, a carpet, a handsome side table which had belonged to Helen's mother and two armchairs. It had an ancient wardrobe, too, but the lock didn't work and the only way we kept the door closed was by jamming one of my socks in it. The toe always dangled outside but it never seemed of any importance.

I went out and across a few feet of landing to our kitchen-dining room at the back. This apartment was definitely spartan. I clumped over bare boards to a bench we had rigged against the wall by the window. This held a gas ring and our crockery and cutlery. I seized a tall jug and began my long descent to the main kitchen downstairs because one minor snag was that there was no water at the top of the house. Down two flights to the three rooms on the first storey then down two more and a final gallop along the passage to the big stone-flagged kitchen at the end.

I filled the jug and returned to our eyrie two steps at a time. I wouldn't like to do this now whenever I needed water but at that time I didn't find it the least inconvenience.

Helen soon had the kettle boiling and we drank our first cup of tea by the window looking down on the long garden. From up here we had an aerial view of the unkempt lawns, the fruit trees, the wistaria climbing the weathered brick towards our window, and the high walls with their old stone copings stretching away to the cobbled yard under the elms. Every day I went up and down that path to the garage in the yard but it looked so different from above.

'Wait a minute, Helen,' I said. 'Let me sit on that chair.'

She had laid the breakfast on the bench where we ate and this was where the difficulty arose. Because it was a tall bench and our recently acquired high stool fitted it but our chair didn't.

'No, I'm all right, Jim, really I am.' She smiled at me reassuringly from her absurd position, almost at eye level with her plate.

'You can't be all right,' I retorted. 'Your chin's nearly in among your cornflakes. Please let me sit there.'

She patted the seat of the stool. 'Come on, stop arguing. Sit down and have your breakfast.'

This, I felt, just wouldn't do. I tried a different tack.

'Helen!' I said severely. 'Get off that chair!'

'No!' she replied without looking at me, her lips pushed forward in a characteristic pout which I always found enchanting but which also meant she wasn't kidding.

I was at a loss. I toyed with the idea of pulling her off the chair, but she was a big girl. We had had a previous physical try-out when a minor disagreement had escalated into a wrestling match and though I thoroughly enjoyed the contest and actually won in the end I had been surprised by her sheer strength. At this time in the morning I didn't feel up to it. I sat on the stool.

17

After breakfast Helen began to boil water for the washing-up, the next stage in our routine. Meanwhile I went downstairs, collected my gear, including suture material for a foal which had cut its leg and went out the side door into the garden. Just about opposite the rockery I turned and looked up at our window. It was open at the bottom and an arm emerged holding a dishcloth. I waved and the dishcloth waved back furiously. It was the start to every day.

And, driving from the yard, it seemed a good start. In fact everything was good. The raucous cawing of the rooks in the elms above as I closed the double doors, the clean fragrance of the air which greeted me every morning, and the challenge and interest of my job.

The injured foal was at Robert Corner's farm and I hadn't been there long before I spotted Jock, his sheepdog. And I began to watch the dog because behind a vet's daily chore of treating his patients there is always the fascinating kaleidoscope of animal personality and Jock was an interesting case.

A lot of farm dogs are partial to a little light relief from their work. They like to play and one of their favourite games is chasing cars off the premises. Often I drove off with a hairy form galloping alongside and the dog would usually give a final defiant bark after a few hundred yards to speed me on my way. But Jock was different.

He was really dedicated. Car chasing to him was a deadly serious art which he practised daily without a trace of levity. Corner's farm was at the end of a long track, twisting for nearly a mile between its stone walls down through the gently sloping fields to the road below and Jock didn't consider he had done his job properly until he had escorted his chosen vehicle right to the very foot. So his hobby was an exacting one.

I watched him now as I finished stitching the foal's leg and began to tie on a bandage. He was slinking about the buildings, a skinny little creature who, without his mass of black and white hair would have been an almost invisible mite, and he was playing out a transparent charade of pretending he was taking no notice of me – wasn't the least bit interested in my presence, in fact. But his furtive glances in the direction of the stable, his repeated criss-crossing of my line of vision gave him away. He was waiting for his big moment.

When I was putting on my shoes and throwing my wellingtons into the boot I saw him again. Or rather part of him; just a long nose and one eye protruding from beneath a broken door. It wasn't till I had started the engine and begun to move off that he finally declared himself, stealing out from his hiding place, body low, tail trailing, eyes fixed intently on the car's front wheels, and as I gathered speed and headed down the track he broke into an effortless lope.

I had been through this before and was always afraid he might run in front of me so I put my foot down and began to hurtle downhill. This was where Jock came into his own. I often wondered how he'd fare against a racing greyhound because by golly he could run. That sparse frame housed a perfect physical machine and the slender limbs reached and flew again and again, devouring the stony ground beneath, keeping up with the speeding car with joyful ease.

There was a sharp bend about half way down and here Jock invariably sailed over the wall and streaked across the turf, a little dark blur against the green, and having craftily cut off the corner he reappeared like a missile zooming over the grey stones lower down. This put him into a nice position for the run to the road and when he finally saw me on to the tarmac my last view of him was of a happy panting face looking after me. Clearly he considered it was a job well done and he would wander contentedly back up to the farm to await the next session, perhaps with the postman or the baker's van.

And there was another side to Jock. He was an outstanding performer at the sheepdog trials and Mr Corner had won many trophies with him. In fact the farmer could have sold the little animal for a lot of money but couldn't be persuaded to part with him. Instead he purchased a bitch, a scrawny little female counterpart of Jock and a trial winner in her own right. With this combination Mr Corner thought he could breed some world-beating types for sale. On my visits to the farm the bitch joined in the car-chasing but it seemed as though she was doing it more or less to humour her new mate and she always gave up at the first bend leaving Jock in command. You could see her heart wasn't in it.

When the pups arrived, seven fluffy black balls tumbling about the yard and getting under everybody's feet, Jock watched indulgently as they tried to follow him in his pursuit of my vehicle and you could almost see him laughing as they fell over their feet and were left trailing far behind.

It happened that I didn't have to go there for about ten months but I saw Robert Corner in the market occasionally and he told me he was training the pups and they were shaping well. Not that they needed much training; it was in their blood and he said they had tried to round up the cattle and sheep nearly as soon as they could walk. When I finally saw them they were like seven Jocks – meagre, darting little creatures flitting noiselessly about the buildings – and it didn't take me long to find out that they had learned more than sheep herding from their father. There was something very evocative about the way they began to prowl around in the background as I prepared to get into my car, peeping furtively from behind straw bales, slinking with elaborate nonchalance into favourable positions for a quick getaway. And as I settled in my seat I could sense they were all crouched in readiness for the off.

I revved my engine, let in the clutch with a bump and shot across the yard and in a second the immediate vicinity erupted in a mass of hairy forms. I roared on to the track and put my foot down and on either side of me the little animals pelted along shoulder to shoulder, their faces all wearing the intent fanatical expression I knew so well. When Jock cleared the wall the seven pups went with him and when they reappeared and entered the home straight I noticed something different. On past occasions Jock had always had one eye on the car – this was what he considered his opponent; but now on that last quarter mile as he hurtled along at the head of a shaggy phalanx he was glancing at the pups on either side as though they were the main opposition.

And there was no doubt he was in trouble. Superbly fit though he was, these stringy bundles of bone and sinew which he had fathered had all his speed plus the newly minted energy of youth and it was taking every shred of his power to keep up with them. Indeed there was one terrible moment when he stumbled and was engulfed by the bounding creatures around him; it seemed that all was lost but there was a core of steel in Jock. Eyes popping, nostrils dilated, he fought his way through the pack until by the time we reached the road he was once more in the lead.

But it had taken its toll. I slowed down before driving away and looked down at the little animal standing with lolling tongue and heaving flanks on the grass verge. It must have been like this with all the other vehicles and it wasn't a merry game any more. I suppose it sounds silly to say you could read a dog's thoughts but everything in his posture betrayed the mounting apprehension that his days of supremacy were numbered. Just round the corner lay the unthinkable ignominy of being left trailing in the rear of that litter of young upstarts and as I drew away Jock looked after me and his expression was eloquent.

'How long can I keep this up?'

I felt for the little dog and on my next visit to the farm about two months later I wasn't looking forward to witnessing the final degradation which I felt was inevitable. But when I drove into the yard I found the place strangely unpopulated.

Robert Corner was forking hay into the cow's racks in the byre. He turned as I came in.

'Where are all your dogs?' I asked.

He put down his fork. 'All gone. By gaw, there's a market for good workin' sheepdogs. I've done right well out of t'job.'

'But you've still got Jock?'

'Oh aye, ah couldn't part with t'awd lad. He's over there.'

And so he was, creeping around as of old, pretending he wasn't watching me. And when the happy time finally arrived and I drove away it was like it used to be with the lean little animal haring along by the side of the car, but relaxed, enjoying the game, winging effortlessly over the wall and beating the car down to the tarmac with no trouble at all.

I think I was as relieved as he was that he was left alone with his supremacy unchallenged; that he was still top dog.

# 3

You could hardly expect to find a more unlikely character in Darrowby than Roland Partridge. The thought came to me for the hundredth time as I saw him peering through the window which looked on to Trengate just a little way up the other side of the street from our surgery.

He was tapping the glass and beckoning to me and the eyes behind the thick spectacles were wide with concern. I waited and when he opened the door I stepped straight from the street into his living room because these were tiny dwellings with only a kitchen in the rear and a single small bedroom overlooking the street above. But when I went in I had the familiar feeling of surprise. Because most of the other occupants of the row were farmworkers and their furnishings were orthodox; but this place was a studio.

An easel stood in the light from the window and the walls were covered from floor to ceiling with paintings. Unframed canvases were stacked everywhere and the few ornate chairs and the table with its load of painted china and other bric-à-brac added to the artistic atmosphere.

The simple explanation was, of course, that Mr Partridge was in fact an artist. But the unlikely aspect came into it when you learned that this middle-aged velvet-jacketed aesthete was the son of a small farmer, a man whose forebears had been steeped in the soil for generations.

'I happened to see you passing there, Mr Herriot,' he said. 'Are you terribly busy?'

'Not too busy, Mr Partridge. Can I help you?'

He nodded gravely. 'I wonder whether you could spare a moment to look at Percy. I'd be most grateful.'

'Of course,' I replied. 'Where is he?'

He was ushering me towards the kitchen when there was a bang on the outer door and Bert Hardisty the postman burst in. Bert was a rough-hewn character and he dumped a parcel unceremoniously on the table.

'There y'are, Rolie!' he shouted and turned to go.

Mr Partridge gazed with unruffled dignity at the retreating back. 'Thank you very much indeed, Bertram, good day to you.'

Here was another thing. The postman and the artist were both Darrowby born and bred, had the same social background, had gone to the same school, yet their voices were quite different. Roland Partridge, in fact, spoke with the precise, well-modulated syllables of a barrister-at-law.

We went into the kitchen. This was where he cooked for himself in his bachelor state. When his father died many years ago he had sold the farm immediately. Apparently his whole nature was appalled by the earthy farming scene and he could not get out quickly enough. At any rate he had got sufficient money from the sale to indulge his interests and he had taken up painting and lived ever since in this humble cottage, resolutely doing his own thing. This had all happened long before I came to Darrowby and the dangling lank hair was silver now. I always had the feeling that he was happy in his way because I couldn't imagine that small, rather exquisite figure plodding round a muddy farmyard.

It was probably in keeping with his nature that he had never married. There was a touch of asceticism in the thin cheeks and pale blue eyes and it was possible that this self-contained imperturbable personality might denote a lack of warmth. But that didn't hold good with regard to his dog, Percy.

He loved Percy with a fierce protective passion and as the

23

little animal trotted towards him he bent over him, his face alight with tenderness.

'He looks pretty bright to me,' I said. 'He's not sick, is he?'

'No...no...' Mr Partridge seemed strangely ill at ease. 'He's perfectly well in himself, but I want you to look at him and see if you notice anything.'

I looked. And I saw only what I had always seen, the snow-white, shaggy-haired little object regarded by local dog breeders and other *cognoscenti* as a negligible mongrel but nevertheless one of my favourite patients. Mr Partridge, looking through the window of a pet shop in Brawton about five years ago had succumbed immediately to the charms of two soulful eyes gazing up at him from a six-week-old tangle of white hair and had put down his five bob and rushed the little creature home. Percy had been described in the shop somewhat vaguely as a 'terrier' and Mr Partridge had flirted fearfully with the idea of having his tail docked; but such was his infatuation that he couldn't bring himself to cause such a mutilation and the tail had grown in a great fringed curve almost full circle over the back.

To me, the tail nicely balanced the head which was undoubtedly a little too big for the body but Mr Partridge had been made to suffer for it. His old friends in Darrowby who, like all country folks, considered themselves experts with animals, were free with their comments. I had heard them at it. When Percy was young it was:

'Time ye had that tail off, Rolie. Ah'll bite it off for ye if ye like.' And later, again and again. 'Hey Rolie, you should've had that dog's tail off when he were a pup. He looks bloody daft like that.'

When asked Percy's breed Mr Partridge always replied haughtily, 'Sealyham Cross', but it wasn't as simple as that; the tiny body with its luxuriant bristling coat, the large, rather noble head with high, pricked ears, the short, knock-kneed legs and that tail made him a baffling mixture.

Mr Partridge's friends again were merciless, referring to Percy as a 'tripe-'ound' or a 'mouse-'ound' and though the little artist received these railleries with a thin smile I knew they bit

24

deep. He had a high regard for me based simply on the fact that the first time I saw Percy I exclaimed quite spontaneously, 'What a beautiful little dog!' And since I have never had much time for the points and fads of dog breeding I really meant it.

'Just what is wrong, Mr Partridge?' I asked. 'I can't see anything unusual.'

Again the little man appeared to be uneasy. 'Well now, watch as he walks across the floor. Come, Percy my dear.' He moved away from me and the dog followed him.

'No ... no ... I don't quite understand what you mean.'

'Watch again.' He set off once more. 'It's at his ... his er ... back end.'

I crouched down. 'Ah now, yes, wait a minute. Just hold him there, will you?'

I went over and had a close look. 'I see it now. One of his testicles is slightly enlarged.'

'Yes ... yes ... quite.' Mr Partridge's face turned a shade pinker. 'That is ... er ... what I thought.'

'Hang on to him a second while I examine it.' I lifted the scrotum and palpated gently. 'Yes, the left one is definitely bigger and it is harder too.'

'Is it ... anything serious?'

I paused. 'No, I shouldn't think so. Tumours of the testicles are not uncommon in dogs and fortunately they aren't inclined to metastasise – spread through the body – very readily. So I shouldn't worry too much.'

I added the last bit hastily because at the mention of the word 'tumour' the colour had drained from his face alarmingly.

'That's a growth, isn't it?' he stammered.

'Yes, but there are all kinds and a lot of them are not malignant. So don't worry but please keep an eye on him. It may not grow much but if it does you must let me know immediately.'

'I see ... and if it does grow?'

'Well the only thing would be to remove the testicle.'

'An operation?' The little man stared at me and for a moment I thought he would faint.

'Yes, but not a serious one. Quite straightforward, really.' I bent down and felt the enlargement again. It was very slight. From the front end, Percy kept up a continuous musical growling. I grinned. He always did that – when I took his temperature, cut his nails, anything; a nonstop grumble and it didn't mean a thing. I knew him well enough to realise there was no viciousness in him; he was merely asserting his virility, reminding me what a tough fellow he was, and it was not idle boasting because for all his lack of size he was a proud, mettlesome little dog, absolutely crammed with character.

After I had left the house I looked back and saw Mr Partridge standing there watching me. He was clasping and unclasping his hands.

And even when I was back in the surgery half of me was still in that odd little studio. I had to admire Mr Partridge for doing exactly what he wanted to do because in Darrowby he would never get any credit for it. A good horseman or cricketer would be revered in the town but an artist . . . never. Not even if he became famous, and Mr Partridge would never be famous. A few people bought his paintings but he could not have lived on the proceeds. I had one of them hanging in our bed-sitter and to my mind he had a definite gift. In fact I would have tried to afford more of them but for the fact that he obviously shrank from that aspect of the Yorkshire Dales which I loved most.

If I had been able to paint I would have wanted to show how the walls climbed everywhere over the stark fell-sides. I would have tried to capture the magic of the endless empty moors with the reeds trembling over the black bog pools. But Mr Partridge went only for the cosy things; willows hanging by a rustic bridge, village churches, rose-covered cottages.

Since Percy was a near neighbour I saw him nearly every day, either from our bed-sitter at the top of the house or from the surgery below. His master exercised him with great zeal and regularity and it was a common sight to see the artist passing on the other side of the road with the little animal trotting proudly beside him. But from that distance it was impossible to see if the tumour was progressing, and since I heard nothing from Mr Partridge I assumed that all was well. Maybe that thing had grown no more. Sometimes it happened that way.

Keeping a close watch on the little dog reminded me of other incidents connected with him, particularly the number of times he was involved in a fight. Not that Percy ever started a brawl – at ten inches high he wasn't stupid enough for that – but somehow big dogs when they saw that dainty white figure prancing along were inclined to go for him on sight. I witnessed some of these attacks from our windows and the same thing happened every time; a quick flurry of limbs, a snarling and yelping and then the big dog retreated bleeding.

Percy never had a mark on him – that tremendous thick coat gave him complete protection – but he always got a nip in from underneath. I had stitched up several of the local street fighters after Percy had finished with them.

It must have been about six weeks later when Mr Partridge came in again. He looked tense.

'I'd like you to have a look at Percy again, Mr Herriot.'

I lifted the dog on to the surgery table and I didn't need to examine him very closely.

'It's quite a lot bigger, I'm afraid.' I looked across the table at the little man.

'Yes, I know.' He hesitated. 'What do you suggest?'

'Oh there's no doubt at all he'll have to come in for an operation. That thing must come off.'

Horror and despair flickered behind the thick spectacles.

'An operation!' He leaned on the table with both hands.

'I hate the idea, I just can't bear the thought of it!'

I smiled reassuringly. 'I know how you feel, but honestly there's nothing to worry about. As I told you before, it's quite a simple procedure.'

'Oh I know, I know,' he moaned. 'But I don't want him to be . . . cut about, you understand . . . it's just the idea of it.'

And I couldn't persuade him. He remained adamant and marched resolutely from the surgery with his pet. I watched him crossing the road to his house and I knew he had let himself in for a load of worry, but I didn't realise just how bad it was going to be.

It was to be a kind of martyrdom.

# 4

I do not think martyrdom is too strong a word for what Mr Partridge went through over the next few weeks, because with the passage of time that testicle became more and more massive and due to the way Percy carried his tail the thing was lamentably conspicuous.

People used to turn and stare as man and dog made their way down the street, Percy trotting bravely, his master, eyes rigidly to the front, putting up a magnificent pretence of being quite unaware of anything unusual. It really hurt me to see them and I found the sight of the smart little dog's disfigurement particularly hard to bear.

Mr Partridge's superior facade had always made him a natural target for a certain amount of legpulling which he bore stoically; but the fact that it now involved his pet pierced him to the soul.

One afternoon he brought him over to the surgery and I could see that the little man was almost in tears. Gloomily I examined the offending organ which was now about six inches long; gross, pendulous, undeniably ludicrous.

'You know, Mr Herriot,' the artist gasped. 'Some boys chalked on my window, "Roll up and see the famous Chinese dog, Wun Hung Lo." I've just been wiping it off.'

I rubbed my chin. 'Well that's an ancient joke, Mr Partridge. I shouldn't worry about that.'

'But I do worry! I can't sleep because of the thing!'

'For heaven's sake, then, why don't you let me operate? I could put the whole business right for you.'

'No! No! I can't do that!' His head rolled on his shoulders; he was the very picture of misery as he stared at me. 'I'm frightened, that's what it is. I'm frightened he'll die under the anaesthetic.'

'Oh come now! He's a strong little animal. There's no reason at all for such fears.'

'But there is a risk, isn't there?'

I looked at him helplessly. 'Well there's a slight risk in all operations if you come right down to it, but honestly in this case . . .'

'No! That's enough. I won't hear of it,' he burst out and seizing Percy's lead he strode away.

Things went from bad to worse after that. The tumour grew steadily, easily visible now from my vantage point in the surgery window as the dog went by on the other side of the street, and I could see too that the stares and occasional ridicule were beginning to tell on Mr Partridge. His cheeks had hollowed and he had lost some of his high colour.

But I didn't have words with him till one market day several weeks later. It was early afternoon – the time the farmers often came in to pay their bills. I was showing one of them out when I saw Percy and his master coming out of the house. And I noticed immediately that the little animal now had to swing one leg slightly to clear the massive obstruction.

On an impulse I called out and beckoned to Mr Partridge.

'Look,' I said as he came across to me. 'You've just got to let me take that thing off. It's interfering with his walking – making him lame. He can't go on like this.'

The artist didn't say anything but stared back at me with hunted eyes. We were standing there in silence when Bill Dalton came round the corner and marched up to the surgery steps, cheque book in hand. Bill was a large beefy farmer who spent most of market day in the bar of the Black Swan and he was preceded by an almost palpable wave of beer fumes.

'Nah then, Rolie lad, how ista?' he roared, slapping the little man violently on the back.

'I am quite well, William, thank you, and how are you?'

But Bill didn't answer. His attention was all on Percy who had strolled a few paces along the pavement. He watched him intently for a few moments then, repressing a giggle, he turned back to Mr Partridge with a mock-serious expression.

'Tha knows, Rolie,' he said, 'that blood 'ound of your reminds me of the young man of Devizes, whose balls were of different sizes. The one was so small it was no ball at all, but the other one won several prizes.' He finished with a shout of laughter which went on and on till he collapsed weakly against the iron railings.

For a moment I thought Mr Partridge was going to strike him. He glared up at the big man and his chin and mouth trembled with rage, then he seemed to gain control of himself and turned to me.

'Can I have a word with you, Mr Herriot?'

'Certainly.' I walked a few yards with him down the street.

'You're right,' he said. 'Percy will have to have that operation. When can you do him?'

'Tomorrow,' I replied. 'Don't give him any more food and bring him in at two in the afternoon.'

It was with a feeling of intense relief that I saw the little dog stretched on the table the next day. With Tristan as anaesthetist I quickly removed the huge testicle, going well up the spermatic cord to ensure the complete excision of all tumour tissue. The only thing which troubled me was that the scrotum itself had become involved due to the long delay in operating. This is the sort of thing that can lead to a recurrence and as I carefully cut away the affected parts of the scrotal wall I cursed Mr Partridge's procrastination. I put in the last stitch with my fingers crossed.

The little man was in such transports of joy at seeing his pet alive after my efforts and rid of that horrid excrescence that I didn't want to spoil everything by voicing my doubts; but I wasn't entirely happy. If the tumour did recur I wasn't sure just what I could do about it.

But in the meantime I enjoyed my own share of pleasure at my patient's return to normality. I felt a warm rush of satisfaction whenever I saw him tripping along, perky as ever and free from the disfigurement which had bulked so large in his master's life. Occasionally I used to stroll casually behind him on the way down Trengate into the market place, saying nothing to Mr Partridge but shooting some sharp glances at the region beneath Percy's tail.

In the meantime I had sent the removed organ off to the pathology department at Glasgow Veterinary College and their report told me that it was a Sertoli Cell Tumour. They also added the comforting information that this type was usually benign and that metastasis into the internal organs occurred in only a very small proportion of cases. Maybe this lulled me into a deeper security than was warranted because I stopped following Percy around and in fact, in the nonstop rush of new cases, forgot all about his spell of trouble.

So that when Mr Partridge brought him round to the surgery I thought it was for something else and when his master lifted him on to the table and turned him round to show his rear end I stared uncomprehendingly for a moment. But I leaned forward anxiously when I spotted the ugly swelling on the left side of the scrotum. I palpated quickly, with Percy's growls and grousings providing an irritable obbligato, and there was no doubt about it, the tumour was growing again. It meant business, too, because it was red, angry-looking, painful; a dangerously active growth if ever I had seen one.

'It's come up quite quickly, has it?' I asked.

Mr Partridge nodded. 'Yes, indeed. I can almost see it getting bigger every day.'

We were in trouble. There was no hope of trying to cut this lot away; it was a great diffuse mass without clear boundaries and I wouldn't have known where to start. Anyway, if I began any more poking about it would be just what was needed to start a spread into the internal organs, and that would be the end of Percy.

'It's worse this time, isn't it?' The little man looked at me and gulped.

'Yes ... yes ... I'm afraid so.'

'Is there anything at all you can do about it ?' he asked.

I was trying to think of a painless way of telling him that there wasn't when I remembered something I had read in the Veterinary Record a week ago. It was about a new drug, Stilboestrol, which had just come out and was supposed to be useful for hormonal therapy in animals; but the bit I was thinking about was a small print extract which said it had been useful in cancer of the prostate in men. I wondered . . .

'There's one thing I'd like to try,' I said, suddenly brisk, 'I can't guarantee anything, of course, because it's something new. But we'll see what a week or two's course does.'

'Oh good, good,' Mr Partridge breathed, snatching gratefully at the straw.

I rang May and Baker's and they sent the Stilboestrol to me immediately.

I injected Percy with 10 mg of the oily suspension and put him on to 10 mg tablets daily. They were big doses for a little dog but in a desperate situation I felt they were justified. Then I sat back and waited.

For about a week the tumour continued to grow and I nearly stopped the treatment, then there was a spell lasting several days during which I couldn't be sure; but then with a surge of relief I realised there could be no further doubt – the thing wasn't getting any bigger. I wasn't going to throw my hat in the air and I knew anything could still happen but I had done something with my treatment; I had halted that fateful progress.

The artist's step acquired a fresh spring as he passed on his daily walk and then as the ugly mass actually began to diminish he would wave towards the surgery window and point happily at the little white animal trotting by his side.

Poor Mr Partridge. He was on the crest of the wave but just ahead of him was the second and more bizarre phase of his martyrdom.

At first neither I nor anybody else realised what was going on. All we knew was there suddenly seemed to be a lot of dogs in Trengate – dogs we didn't usually see, from other parts of the town; big ones, small ones, shaggy mongrels and sleek aristo-

crats all hanging around apparently aimlessly, but then it was
noticed that there was a focal point of attraction. It was Mr
Partridge's house.

And it hit me blindingly one morning as I looked out of our
bedroom window. They were after Percy. For some reason he
had taken on the attributes of a bitch in heat. I hurried downstairs and got out my pathology book. Yes, there it was. The
Sertoli Cell tumour occasionally made dogs attractive to other
male dogs. But why should it be happening now when the thing
was reducing and not when it was at its height? Or could it be
the Stilboestrol? The new drug was said to have a feminising
effect, but surely not to that extent.

Anyway, whatever the cause, the undeniable fact remained
that Percy was under siege, and as the word got around the pack
increased, being augmented by several of the nearby farm dogs,
a Great Dane who had made the journey from Houlton, and
Magnus, the little dachshund from the Drovers' Arms. The
queue started forming almost at first light and by ten o'clock
there would be a milling throng almost blocking the street.
Apart from the regulars the odd canine visitor passing through
would join the company, and no matter what his breed or size
he was readily accepted into the club, adding one more to the
assortment of stupid expressions, lolling tongues and waving
tails; because, motley crew though they were, they were all
happily united in the roisterous, bawdy camaraderie of lust.

The strain on Mr Partridge must have been almost intolerable. At times I noticed the thick spectacles glinting balefully
at the mob through his window but most of the time he kept
himself in hand, working calmly at his easel as though he were
oblivious that every one of the creatures outside had evil designs
on his treasure.

Only rarely did his control snap. I witnessed one of these
occasions when he rushed screaming from his doorway, laying
about him with a walking stick; and I noticed that the polished
veneer slipped from him and his cries rang out in broadest
Yorkshire.

'Gerrout, ye bloody rotten buggers! Gerrout of it!'

33

He might as well have saved his energy because the pack scattered only for a few seconds before taking up their stations again.

I felt for the little man but there was nothing I could do about it. My main feeling was of relief that the tumour was going down but I had to admit to a certain morbid fascination at the train of events across the street.

Percy's walks were fraught with peril. Mr Partridge always armed himself with his stick before venturing from the house and kept Percy on a short lead, but his precautions were unavailing as the wave of dogs swept down on him. The besotted creatures, mad with passion, leapt on top of the little animal as the artist beat vainly on the shaggy backs and yelled at them; and the humiliating procession usually continued right across the market place to the great amusement of the inhabitants.

At lunch time most of the dogs took a break and at nightfall they all went home to bed, but there was one little brown spaniel type who, with the greatest dedication, never left his post. I think he must have gone almost without food for about two weeks because he dwindled practically to a skeleton and I think he might have died if Helen hadn't taken pieces of meat over to him when she saw him huddled trembling in the doorway in the cold darkness of the evening. I know he stayed there all night because every now and then a shrill yelping wakened me in the small hours and I deduced that Mr Partridge had got home on him with some missile from his bedroom window. But it made no difference; he continued his vigil undaunted.

I don't quite know how Mr Partridge would have survived if this state of affairs had continued indefinitely; I think his reason might have given way. But mercifully signs began to appear that the nightmare was on the wane. The mob began to thin as Percy's condition improved and one day even the little brown dog reluctantly left his beat and slunk away to his unknown home.

That was the very day I had Percy on the table for the last time. I felt a thrill of satisfaction as I ran a fold of the scrotal skin between my fingers.

'There's nothing there now, Mr Partridge. No thickening, even. Not a thing.'

The little man nodded. 'Yes, it's a miracle, isn't it! I'm very grateful to you for all you've done. I've been so terribly worried.'

'Oh, I can imagine. You've been through a bad time. But I'm really as pleased as you are yourself – it's one of the most satisfying things in practice when an experiment like this comes off.'

But often over the subsequent years, as I watched dog and master pass our window, Mr Partridge with all his dignity restored, Percy as trim and proud as ever, I wondered about that strange interlude.

Did the Stilboestrol really reduce that tumour or did it regress naturally? And were the extraordinary events caused by the treatment or the condition or both?

I could never be quite sure of the answer, but of the outcome I could be happily certain. That unpleasant growth never came back ... and neither did all those dogs.

# 5

This was the real Yorkshire with the clean limestone wall riding the hill's edge and the path cutting brilliant green through the crowding heather. And, walking face on to the scented breeze I felt the old tingle of wonder at being alone on the wide moorland where nothing stirred and the spreading miles of purple blossom and green turf reached away till it met the hazy blue of the sky.

But I wasn't really alone. There was Sam, and he made all the difference. Helen had brought a lot of things into my life and Sam was one of the most precious; he was a Beagle and her own personal pet. He would be about two years old when I first saw him and I had no way of knowing that he was to be my faithful companion, my car dog, my friend who sat by my side through the lonely hours of driving till his life ended at the age of fourteen. He was the first of a series of cherished dogs whose comradeship have warmed and lightened my working life.

Sam adopted me on sight. It was as though he had read the *Faithful Hound Manual* because he was always near me; paws on the dash as he gazed eagerly through the windscreen on my rounds, head resting on my foot in our bed-sitting room, trotting just behind me wherever I moved. If I had a beer in a pub he would be under my chair and even when I was having a haircut you only had to lift the white sheet to see Sam crouching beneath my legs. The only place I didn't dare take him was to the cinema and on these occasions he crawled under the bed and sulked.

Most dogs love car riding but to Sam it was a passion which never waned – even in the night hours; he would gladly leave his basket when the world was asleep, stretch a couple of times and follow me out into the cold. He would be on to the seat before I got the car door fully open and this action became so much a part of my life that for a long time after his death I still held the door open unthinkingly, waiting for him. And I still remember the pain I felt when he did not bound inside.

And having him with me added so much to the intermissions I granted myself on my daily rounds. Whereas in offices and factories they had tea breaks I just stopped the car and stepped out into the splendour which was always at hand and walked for a spell down hidden lanes, through woods, or as today, along one of the grassy tracks which ran over the high tops.

This thing which I had always done had a new meaning now. Anybody who has ever walked a dog knows the abiding satisfaction which comes from giving pleasure to a loved animal, and the sight of the little form trotting ahead of me lent a depth which had been missing before.

Round the curve of the path I came to where the tide of heather lapped thickly down the hillside on a little slope facing invitingly into the sun. It was a call I could never resist. I looked at my watch; oh I had a few minutes to spare and there was nothing urgent ahead, just Mr Dacre's tuberculin test. In a moment I was stretched out on the springy stems, the most wonderful natural mattress in the world.

Lying there, eyes half closed against the sun's glare, the heavy heather fragrance around me, I could see the cloud shadows racing across the flanks of the fells, throwing the gulleys and crevices into momentary gloom but trailing a fresh flaring green in their wake.

Those were the days when I was most grateful I was in country practice; the shirt sleeve days when the bleak menace of the bald heights melted into friendliness, when I felt at one with all the airy life and growth about me and was glad that I had become what I never thought I would be, a doctor of farm animals.

My partner, Siegfried, would be somewhere out there, thrashing round the practice and Tristan his student brother would probably be studying in Skeldale House. This latter was quite a thought because I had never seen Tristan open a text book until lately. He had been blessed with the kind of brain which made swotting irrelevant but he would take his finals this year and even he had to get down to it. I had little doubt he would soon be a qualified man and in a way it seemed a shame that his free spirit should be shackled by the realities of veterinary practice. It would be the end of a luminous chapter.

A long-eared head blotted out the sunshine as Sam came and sat on my chest. He looked at me questioningly. He didn't hold with this laziness but I knew if I didn't move after a few minutes he would curl up philosophically on my ribs and have a sleep until I was ready to go. But this time I answered the unspoken appeal by sitting up and he leaped around me in delight as I rose and began to make my way back to the car and Mr Dacre's test.

'Move over, Bill!' Mr Dacre cried some time later as he tweaked the big bull's tail.

Nearly every farmer kept a bull in those days and they were all called Billy or Bill. I suppose it was because this was a very mature animal that he received the adult version. Being a docile beast he responded to the touch on his tail by shuffling his great bulk to one side, leaving me enough space to push in between him and the wooden partition against which he was tied by a chain.

I was reading a tuberculin test and all I wanted to do was to measure the intradermal reaction. I had to open my calipers very wide to take in the thickness of the skin on the enormous neck.

'Thirty,' I called out to the farmer.

He wrote the figure down on the testing book and laughed. 'By heck, he's got some pelt on 'im.'

'Yes,' I said, beginning to squeeze my way out. 'But he's a big fellow, isn't he?'

Just how big he was was brought home to me immediately because the bull suddenly swung round, pinning me against the partition. Cows did this regularly and I moved them by bracing my back against whatever was behind me and pushing them away. But it was different with Bill.

Gasping, I pushed with all my strength against the rolls of fat which covered the vast roan-coloured flank, but I might as well have tried to shift a house.

The farmer dropped his book and seized the tail again but this time the bull showed no response. There was no malice in his behaviour – he was simply having a comfortable lean against the boards and I don't suppose he even noticed the morsel of puny humanity wriggling frantically against his rib-cage.

Still, whether he meant it or not, the end result was the same; I was having the life crushed out of me. Pop-eyed, groaning, scarcely able to breathe, I struggled with everything I had, but I couldn't move an inch. And just when I thought things couldn't get any worse, Bill started to rub himself up and down against the partition. So that was what he had come round for; he had an itch and he just wanted to scratch it.

The effect on me was catastrophic. I was certain my internal organs were being steadily ground to pulp and as I thrashed about in complete panic the huge animal leaned even more heavily.

I don't like to think what would have happened if the wood behind me had not been old and rotten, but just as I felt my senses leaving me there was a cracking and splintering and I fell through into the next stall. Lying there like a stranded fish on a bed of shattered timbers I looked up at Mr Dacre, waiting till my lungs started to work again.

The farmer, having got over his first alarm, was rubbing his upper lip vigorously in a polite attempt to stop himself laughing. His little girl who had watched the whole thing from her vantage point in one of the hay racks had no such inhibitions. Screaming with delight, she pointed at me.

'Ooo, Dad, Dad, look at that man! Did you see him, Dad, did you see him? Ooo what a funny man!' She went into helpless convulsions. She was only about five but I had a feeling she would remember my performance all her life.

At length I picked myself up and managed to brush the matter off lightly, but after I had driven a mile or so from the farm I stopped the car and looked myself over. My ribs ached pretty uniformly as though a light road roller had passed over them and there was a tender area on my left buttock where I had landed on my calipers but otherwise I seemed to have escaped damage. I removed a few spicules of wood from my trousers, got back into the car and consulted my list of visits.

And when I read my next call a gentle smile of relief spread over my face. 'Mrs Tompkin, 14, Jasmine Terrace. Clip budgie's beak.'

Thank heaven for the infinite variety of veterinary practice. After that bull I needed something small and weak and harmless and really you can't ask for much better in that line than a budgie.

Number 14 was one of a row of small mean houses built of the cheap bricks so beloved of the jerry builders after the First World War. I armed myself with a pair of clippers and stepped on to the narrow strip of pavement which separated the door from the road. A pleasant looking red-haired woman answered my knock.

'I'm Mrs Dodds from next door,' she said. 'I keep an eye on

t'old lady. She's over eighty and lives alone. I've just been out gettin' her pension for her.'

She led me into the cramped little room. 'Here y'are, love,' she said to the old woman who sat in a corner. She put the pension book and money on the mantelpiece. 'And here's Mr Herriot come to see Peter for you.'

Mrs Tompkin nodded and smiled. 'Oh that's good. Poor little feller can't hardly eat with 'is long beak and I'm worried about him. He's me only companion, you know.'

'Yes, I understand, Mrs Tompkin.' I looked at the cage by the window with the green budgie perched inside. 'These little birds can be wonderful company when they start chattering.'

She laughed. 'Aye, but it's a funny thing. Peter never has said owt much. I think he's lazy! But I just like havin' him with me.'

'Of course you do,' I said. 'But he certainly needs attention now.'

The beak was greatly overgrown, curving away down till it touched the feathers of the breast. I would be able to revolutionise his life with one quick snip from my clippers. The way I was feeling this job was right up my street.

I opened the cage door and slowly inserted my hand.

'Come on, Peter,' I wheedled as the bird fluttered away from me. And I soon cornered him and enclosed him gently in my fingers. As I lifted him out I felt in my pocket with the other hand for the clippers, but as I poised them I stopped.

The tiny head was no longer poking cheekily from my fingers but had fallen loosely to one side. The eyes were closed. I stared at the bird uncomprehendingly for a moment then opened my hand. He lay quite motionless on my palm. He was dead.

Dry mouthed, I continued to stare; at the beautiful iridescence of the plumage, the long beak which I didn't have to cut now, but mostly at the head dropping down over my forefinger. I hadn't squeezed him or been rough with him in any way but he was dead. It must have been sheer fright.

Mrs Dodds and I looked at each other in horror and I hardly dared turn my head towards Mrs Tompkin. When I did, I was surprised to see that she was still nodding and smiling.

I drew her neighbour to one side. 'Mrs Dodds, how much does she see?'

'Oh, she's very short-sighted but she's right vain despite her age. Never would wear glasses. She's hard of hearin', too.'

'Well look,' I said. My heart was still pounding. 'I just don't know what to do. If I tell her about this the shock will be terrible. Anything could happen.'

Mrs Dodds nodded, stricken-faced. 'Aye, you're right. She's that attached to the little thing.'

'I can only think of one alternative,' I whispered. 'Do you know where I can get another budgie?'

Mrs Dodds thought for a moment. 'You could try Jack Almond at t'town end. I think he keeps birds.'

I cleared my throat but even then my voice came out in a dry croak. 'Mrs Tompkin, I'm just going to take Peter along to the surgery to do this job. I won't be long.'

I left her still nodding and smiling and, cage in hand, fled into the street. I was at the town end and knocking at Jack Almond's door within three minutes.

'Mr Almond?' I asked the stout, shirtsleeved man who answered.

'That's right, young man.' He gave me a slow, placid smile. 'Do you keep birds?'

He drew himself up with dignity. 'I do, and I'm t'president of the Darrowby and Houlton Cage Bird Society.'

'Fine,' I said breathlessly. 'Have you got a green budgie?'

'Ah've got Canaries, Budgies, Parrots, Parakeets. Cockatoos ...'

'I just want a budgie.'

'Well ah've got Albinos, Blue-greens, Barreds, Litinos ...'

'I just want a green one.'

A slightly pained expression flitted across the man's face as though he found my attitude of haste somewhat unseemly.

'Aye ... well, we'll go and have a look,' he said.

I followed him as he paced unhurriedly through the house into the back yard which was largely given over to a long shed containing a bewildering variety of birds.

Mr Almond gazed at them with gentle pride and his mouth opened as though he was about to launch into a dissertation then he seemed to remember that he had an impatient chap to deal with and dragged himself back to the job in hand.

'There's a nice little green 'un here. But he's a bit older than t'others. Matter of fact I've got 'im talkin'.'

'All the better, just the thing. How much do you want for him?'

'But . . . there's some nice 'uns along here. Just let me show you . . .'

I put a hand on his arm. 'I want that one. How much?'

He pursed his lips in frustration then shrugged his shoulders. 'Ten bob.'

'Right. Bung him in this cage.'

As I sped back up the road I looked in the driving mirror and could see the poor man regarding me sadly from his doorway.

Mrs Dodds was waiting for me back at Jasmine Terrace.

'Do you think I'm doing the right thing?' I asked her in a whisper.

'I'm sure you are,' she replied. 'Poor awd thing, she hasn't much to think about and I'm sure she'd fret over Peter.'

'That's what I thought.' I made my way into the living room.

Mrs Tompkin smiled at me as I went in. 'That wasn't a long job, Mr Herriot.'

'No,' I said, hanging the cage with the new bird up in its place by the window. 'I think you'll find all is well now.'


It was months before I had the courage to put my hand into a budgie's cage again. In fact to this day I prefer it if the owners will lift the birds out for me. People look at me strangely when I ask them to do this; I believe they think I am scared the little things might bite me.

It was a long time, too, before I dared go back to Mrs Tompkin's but I was driving down Jasmine Terrace one day and on an impulse I stopped outside Number 14.

The old lady herself came to the door.

'How . . .' I said. 'How is . . . er . . . ?'

She peered at me closely for a moment then laughed. 'Oh I see who it is now. You mean Peter, don't you, Mr Herriot. Oh 'e's just grand. Come in and see 'im.'

In the little room the cage still hung by the window and Peter the Second took a quick look at me then put on a little act for my benefit; he hopped around the bars of the cage, ran up and down his ladder and rang his little bell a couple of times before returning to his perch.

His mistress reached up, tapped the metal and looked lovingly at him.

'You know, you wouldn't believe it,' she said. 'He's like a different bird.'

I swallowed. 'Is that so? In what way?'

'Well he's so active now. Lively as can be. You know 'e chatters to me all day long. It's wonderful what cuttin' a beak can do.'

# 6

This was one for Granville Bennett. I liked a bit of small animal surgery and was gradually doing more as time went on but this one frightened me. A twelve-year-old spaniel bitch in the last stages of pyometritis, pus dripping from her vulva on to the surgery table, temperature a hundred and four, panting, trembling, and, as I held my stethoscope against her chest I could hear the classical signs of valvular insufficiency. A dicky heart was just what I needed on top of everything else.

'Drinking a lot of water, is she?' I asked.

Old Mrs Barker twisted the strings of her shopping bag anxiously. 'Aye, she never seems to be away from the water bowl. But she won't eat – hasn't had a bite for the last four days.'

'Well I don't know,' I took off my stethoscope and stuffed it in my pocket. 'You should have brought her in long ago. She must have been ill for weeks.'

'Not rightly ill, but a bit off it. I thought there was nothing to worry about as long as she was eating.'

I didn't say anything for a few moments. I had no desire to upset the old girl but she had to be told.

'I'm afraid this is rather serious, Mrs Barker. The condition has been building up for a long time. It's in her womb, you see, a bad infection, and the only cure is an operation.'

'Well will you do it, please ?' The old lady's lips quivered.

I came round the table and put my hand on her shoulder.

'I'd like to, but there are snags. She's in poor shape and twelve years old. Really a poor operation risk. I'd like to take her through to the Veterinary Hospital at Hartington and let Mr Bennett operate on her.'

'All right,' she said, nodding eagerly. 'I don't care what it costs.'

'Oh we'll keep it down as much as possible.' I walked along the passage with her and showed her out of the door. 'Leave her with me – I'll look after her, don't worry. What's her name, by the way ?'

'Dinah,' she replied huskily, still peering past me down the passage.

I went through and lifted the phone. Thirty years ago country practitioners had to turn to the small animal experts when anything unusual cropped up in that line. It is different nowadays when our practices are more mixed. In Darrowby now we have the staff and equipment to tackle any type of small animal surgery but it was different then. I had heard it said that sooner or later every large animal man had to scream for help from Granville Bennett and now it was my turn.

'Hello, is that Mr Bennett ?'

'It is indeed.' A big voice, friendly, full of give.

'Herriot here. I'm with Farnon in Darrowby.'

'Of course! Heard of you, laddie, heard of you.'

'Oh . . . er . . . thanks. Look, I've got a bit of a sticky job here. I wonder if you'd take it on for me ?'

'Delighted, laddie, what is it ?'

'A real stinking pyo.'

'Oh lovely!'

'The bitch is twelve years old.'

'Splendid!'

'And toxic as hell.'

'Excellent!'

'And one of the worst hearts I've heard for a long time.'

'Fine, fine! When are you coming through ?'

'This evening, if it's OK with you. About eight.'

'Couldn't be better, laddie. See you.'

Hartington was a fair-sized town – about 200,000 inhabitants – but as I drove into the centre the traffic had thinned and only a few cars rolled past the rows of shop fronts. I hoped my twenty-five mile journey had been worth it. Dinah, stretched out on a blanket in the back looked as if she didn't care either way. I glanced behind me at the head drooping over the edge of the seat, at the white muzzle and the cataracts in her eyes gleaming palely in the light from the dash. She looked so old. Maybe I was wasting my time, placing too much faith in this man's reputation.

There was no doubt Granville Bennett had become something of a legend in northern England. In those days when specialisation was almost unknown he had gone all out for small animal work – never looked at farm stock – and had set a new standard by the modern procedures in his animal hospital which was run as nearly as possible on human lines. It was, in fact, fashionable for veterinary surgeons of that era to belittle dog and cat work; a lot of the older men who had spent their lives among the teeming thousands of draught horses in city and agriculture would sneer, 'Oh I've no time to bother with those damn things.' Bennett had gone dead in the opposite direction.

I had never met him but I knew he was a young man in his early thirties. I had heard a lot about his skill, his business acumen, and about his reputation as a *bon viveur*. He was, they said, a dedicated devotee of the work-hard-play-hard school.

The Veterinary Hospital was a long low building near the top of a busy street. I drove into a yard and knocked at a door in the corner. I was looking with some awe at a gleaming Bentley dwarfing my own battered little Austin when the door was opened by a pretty receptionist.

'Good evening,' she murmured with a dazzling smile which I thought must be worth another half crown on the bill for a start. 'Do come in, Mr Bennett is expecting you.'

I was shown into a waiting room with magazines and flowers on a corner table and many impressive photographs of dogs and cats on the walls – taken, I learned later, by the principal himself. I was looking closely at a superb study of two white poodles when I heard a footstep behind me. I turned and had my first view of Granville Bennett.

He seemed to fill the room. Not over tall but of tremendous bulk. Fat, I thought at first, but as he came nearer it seemed to me that the tissue of which he was composed wasn't distributed like fat. He wasn't flabby, he didn't stick out in any particular place, he was just a big, wide, solid, hard-looking man. From the middle of a pleasant blunt-featured face the most magnificent pipe I had ever seen stuck forth shining and glorious, giving out delicious wisps of expensive smoke. It was an enormous pipe, in fact it would have looked downright silly with a smaller man, but on him it was a thing of beauty. I had a final impression of a beautifully cut dark suit and sparkling shirt cuffs as he held out a hand.

'James Herriot!' He said it as somebody else might have said 'Winston Churchill', or 'Stanley Matthews'.

'That's right.'

'Well, this is grand. Jim, is it?'

'Well yes, usually.'

'Lovely. We've got everything laid on for you, Jim. The girls are waiting in the theatre.'

'That's very kind of you, Mr Bennett.'

'Granville, Granville please!' He put his arm through mine and led me to the operating room.

46

Dinah was already there, looking very woebegone. She had had a sedative injection and her head nodded wearily. Bennett went over to her and gave her a swift examination.

'Mm, yes, let's get on, then.'

The two girls went into action like cogs in a smooth machine. Bennett kept a large lay staff and these animal nurses, both attractive, clearly knew what they were about. While one of them pulled up the anaesthetic and instrument trolleys the other seized Dinah's foreleg expertly above the elbow, raised the radial vein by pressure and quickly clipped and disinfected the area.

The big man strolled up with a loaded needle and effortlessly slipped the needle into the vein.

'Pentothal,' he said as Dinah slowly collapsed and lay unconscious on the table. It was one of the new short-acting anaesthetics which I had never seen used.

While Bennett scrubbed up and donned sterilised gown and cap the girls rolled Dinah on her back and secured her there with ties to loops on the operating table. They applied the ether and oxygen mask to her face then shaved and swabbed the operation site. The big man returned in time to have a scalpel placed in his hand.

With almost casual speed he incised skin and muscle layers and when he went through the peritoneum the horns of the uterus which in normal health would have been two slim pink ribbons now welled into the wound like twin balloons, swollen and turgid with pus. No wonder Dinah had felt ill, carrying that lot around with her.

The stubby fingers tenderly worked round the mass, ligated the ovarian vessels and uterine body then removed the whole thing and dropped it into an enamel bowl. It wasn't till he had begun to stitch that I realised that the operation was nearly over though he had been at the table for only a few minutes. It would all have looked childishly easy except that his total involvement showed in occasional explosive commands to the nurses.

And as I watched him working under the shadowless lamp with the white tiled walls around him and the rows of instruments gleaming by his side it came to me with a rush of mixed emotions that this was what I had always wanted to do myself. My dreams when I had first decided on veterinary work had been precisely of this. Yet here I was, a somewhat shaggy cow doctor; or perhaps more correctly a farm physician, but certainly something very different. The scene before me was a far cry from my routine of kicks and buffets, of muck and sweat. And yet I had no regrets; the life which had been forced on me by circumstances had turned out to be a thing of magical fulfilment. It came to me with a flooding certainty that I would rather spend my days driving over the unfenced roads of the high country than stooping over that operating table.

And anyway I couldn't have been a Bennett. I don't think I could have matched his technique and this whole set up was eloquent of a lot of things like business sense, foresight and driving ambition which I just didn't possess.

My colleague was finished now and was fitting up an intravenous saline drip. He taped the needle down in the vein then turned to me.

'That's it, then, Jim. It's up to the old girl now.' He began to lead me from the room and it struck me how very pleasant it must be to finish your job and walk away from it like this. In Darrowby I'd have been starting now to wash the instruments, scrub the table, and the final scene would have been of Herriot the great surgeon swilling the floor with mop and bucket. This was a better way.

Back in the waiting room Bennett pulled on his jacket and extracted from a side pocket the immense pipe which he inspected with a touch of anxiety as if he feared mice had been nibbling at it in his absence. He wasn't satisfied with his examination because he brought forth a soft yellow cloth and began to polish the briar with intense absorption. Then he held the pipe high, moving it s ightly from side to side, his eyes softening at the play of the light on the exquisite grain. Finally he produced a pouch of mammoth proportions, filled the bowl, applied a match with a touch of reverence and closed his eyes as a fragrant mist drifted from his lips.

'That baccy smells marvellous,' I said. 'What is it?'

'Navy Cut De Luxe.' He closed his eyes again. 'You know, I could eat the smoke.'

I laughed. 'I use the ordinary Navy Cut myself.'

He gazed at me like a sorrowing Buddha, 'Oh you mustn't, laddie, you mustn't. This is the only stuff. Rich . . . fruity . . .' His hand made languid motions in the air. 'Here, you can take some away with you.'

He pulled open a drawer. I had a brief view of a stock which wouldn't have disgraced a fair-sized tobacconist's shop; innumerable tins, pipes, cleaners, reamers, cloths.

'Try this,' he said, 'and tell me if I'm not right.'

I looked down at the first container in my hand. 'Oh but I can't take all this. It's a four ounce tin!'

'Rubbish, my boy. Put it in your pocket.' He became suddenly brisk. 'Now I expect you'll want to hang around till old Dinah comes out of the anaesthetic so why don't we have a quick beer? I'm a member of a nice little club just across the road.'

'Well fine, sounds great.'

He moved lightly and swiftly for a big man and I had to hurry to keep up with him as he left the surgery and crossed to a building on the other side of the street.

# 7

Inside the club was masculine comfort, hails of welcome from some prosperous looking members and a friendly greeting from the man behind the bar.

'Two pints, Fred,' murmured Bennett absently, and the drinks appeared with amazing speed. My colleague poured his down apparently without swallowing and turned to me.

'Another, Jim?'

I had just tried a sip at mine and began to gulp anxiously at the bitter ale. 'Right, but let me get this one.'

'No can do, laddie.' He glanced at me with mild severity. 'Only members can buy drinks. Same again, Fred.'

I found I had two glasses at my elbow and with a tremendous effort I got the first one down. Gasping slightly I was surveying the second one timidly when I noticed that Bennett was three-quarters down his. As I watched he drained it effortlessly.

'You're slow, Jim,' he said, smiling indulgently. 'Just set them up again will you, Fred.'

In some alarm I watched the barman ply his handle and attacked my second pint resolutely. I surprised myself by forcing it over my tonsils then, breathing heavily, I got hold of the third one just as Bennett spoke again.

'We'll just have one for the road, Jim,' he said pleasantly. 'Would you be so kind, Fred?'

This was ridiculous but I didn't want to appear a piker at our first meeting. With something akin to desperation I raised the third and began to suck feebly at it. When my glass was empty I almost collapsed against the counter. My stomach was agonisingly distended and a light perspiration had broken out on my brow. As I almost lay there I saw my colleague moving across the carpet towards the door.

'Time we were off, Jim,' he said. 'Drink up.'

It's wonderful what the human frame can tolerate when put to the test. I would have taken bets that it was impossible for me to drink that fourth pint without at least half an hour's rest, preferably in the prone position, but as Bennett's shoe tapped impatiently I tipped the beer a little at a time into my mouth, feeling it wash around my back teeth before incredibly disappearing down my gullet. I believe the water torture was a favourite with the Spanish Inquisition and as the pressure inside me increased I knew just how their victims felt.

When I at last blindly replaced my glass and splashed my way from the bar the big man was holding the door open. Outside in the street he placed an arm across my shoulder.

'The old Spaniel won't be out of it yet,' he said. 'We'll just slip to my house and have a bite – I'm a little peckish.'

Sunk in the deep upholstery of the Bentley, cradling my swollen abdomen in my arms I watched the shop fronts flicker past the windows and give way to the darkness of the open countryside. We drew up outside a fine grey stone house in a typical Yorkshire village and Bennett ushered me inside.

He pushed me towards a leather armchair. 'Make yourself at home, laddie. Zoe's out at the moment but I'll get some grub.' He bustled through to the kitchen and reappeared in seconds with a deep bowl which he placed on a table by my side.

'You know, Jim,' he said, rubbing his hands. 'There's nothing better after beer than a few pickled onions.'

I cast a timorous glance into the bowl. Everything in this man's life seemed to be larger than life, even the onions. They were bigger than golf balls, brownish-white, glistening.

'Well thanks Mr Ben . . . Granville.' I took one of them, held it between finger and thumb and stared at it helplessly. The beer hadn't even begun to sort itself out inside me; the idea of starting on this potent-looking vegetable was unthinkable.

Granville reached into the bowl, popped an onion into his mouth, crunched it quickly, swallowed and sank his teeth into a second. 'By God, that's good. You know, my little wife's a marvellous cook. She even makes pickled onions better than anyone.'

Munching happily he moved over to the sideboard and clinked around for a few moments before placing in my hand a heavy cut glass tumbler about two thirds full of neat whisky. I couldn't say anything because I had taken the plunge and put the onion in my mouth; and as I bit boldly into it the fumes rolled in a volatile wave into my nasal passages, making me splutter. I took a gulp at the whisky and looked up at Granville with watering eyes.

He was holding out the onion bowl again and when I declined he regarded it for a moment with hurt in his eyes. 'It's funny you don't like them, I always thought Zoe did them marvellously.'

'Oh you're wrong, Granville, they're delicious. I just haven't finished this one.'

He didn't reply but continued to look at the bowl with gentle sorrow. I realised there was nothing else for it; I took another onion.

Immensely gratified, Granville hurried through to the kitchen again. This time when he came back he bore a tray with an enormous cold roast, a loaf of bread, butter and mustard.

'I think a beef sandwich would go down rather nicely, Jim,' he murmured, as he stropped his carving knife on a steel. Then he noticed my glass of whisky still half full.

'C'mon, c'mon, c'mon!' he said with some asperity. 'You're not touching your drink.' He watched me benevolently as I drained the glass then he refilled it to its old level. 'That's better. And have another onion.'

I stretched my legs out and rested my head on the back of the chair in an attempt to ease my internal turmoil. My stomach was a lake of volcanic lava bubbling and popping fiercely in its crater with each additional piece of onion, every sip of whisky setting up a fresh violent reaction. Watching Granville at work, a great wave of nausea swept over me. He was sawing busily at the roast, carving off slices which looked to be an inch thick, slapping mustard on them and enclosing them in the bread. He hummed with contentment as the pile grew. Every now and then he had another onion.

'Now then, laddie,' he cried at length, putting a heaped plate at my elbow. 'Get yourself round that lot.' He took his own supply and collapsed with a sigh into another chair.

He took a gargantuan bite and spoke as he chewed. 'You know, Jim, this is something I enjoy – a nice little snack. Zoe always leaves me plenty to go at when she pops out.' He engulfed a further few inches of sandwich. 'And I'll tell you something, though I say it myself, these are bloody good, don't you think so?'

'Yes indeed.' Squaring my shoulders I bit, swallowed and held my breath as another unwanted foreign body slid down to the ferment below.

Just then I heard the front door open.

'Ah, that'll be Zoe,' Granville said, and was about to rise when a disgracefully fat Staffordshire Bull Terrier burst into the room, waddled across the carpet and leapt into his lap.

'Phoebles, my dear, come to daddykins!' he shouted. 'Have you had nice walkies with mummy?'

The Staffordshire was closely followed by a Yorkshire Terrier which was also enthusiastically greeted by Granville.

'Yoo-hoo, Victoria, yoo-hoo!'

The Yorkie, an obvious smiler, did not jump up but contented herself with sitting at her master's feet, baring her teeth ingratiatingly every few seconds.

I smiled through my pain. Another myth exploded; the one about these specialist small animal vets not being fond of dogs themselves. The big man crooned over the two little animals. The fact that he called Phoebe 'Phoebles' was symptomatic.

I heard light footsteps in the hall and looked up expectantly. I had Granville's wife taped neatly in my mind; domesticated, devoted, homely; many of these dynamic types had wives like that, willing slaves content to lurk in the background. I waited confidently for the entrance of a plain little hausfrau.

When the door opened I almost let my vast sandwich fall. Zoe Bennett was a glowing warm beauty who would make any man alive stop for another look. A lot of soft brown hair, large grey-green friendly eyes, a tweed suit sitting sweetly on a slim but not too slim figure; and something else, a wholesomeness, an inner light which made me wish suddenly that I was a better man or at least that I looked better than I did.

In an instant I was acutely conscious of the fact that my shoes were dirty, that my old jacket and corduroy trousers were out of place here. I hadn't troubled to change but had rushed straight out in my working clothes, and they were different from Granville's because I couldn't go round the farms in a suit like his.

'My love, my love!' he carolled joyously as his wife bent over and kissed him fondly. 'Let me introduce Jim Herriot from Darrowby.'

The beautiful eyes turned on me.

'How d'you do, Mr Herroit!' She looked as pleased to see me as her husband had done and again I had the desperate wish that I was more presentable; that my hair was combed, that I didn't have this mounting conviction that I was going to explode into a thousand pieces at any moment.

'I'm going to have a cup of tea, Mr Herroit. Would you like one?'

'No-no, no no, thank you very much but no, no, not at the moment.' I backed away slightly.

'Ah well, I see you've got one of Granville's little sandwiches.' She giggled and went to get her tea.

When she came back she handed a parcel to her husband. 'I've been shopping today, darling. Picked up some of those shirts you like so much.'

'My sweet! How kind of you!' He began to tear at the brown paper like a schoolboy and produced three elegant shirts in cellophane covers. 'They're marvellous, my pet, you spoil me.' He looked up at me. 'Jim! These are the most wonderful shirts, you must have one.' He flicked a shining package across the room on to my lap.

I looked down at it in amazement. 'No, really I can't . . .'

'Of course you can. You keep it.'

'But Granville, not a shirt . . . it's too . . .'

'It's a very good shirt.' He was beginning to look hurt again. I subsided.

They were both so kind. Zoe sat right by me with her tea cup, chatting pleasantly, while Granville beamed at me from his chair as he finished the last of the sandwiches and started again on the onions.

The proximity of the attractive woman was agreeable but embarrassing. My corduroys in the warmth of the room had begun to give off the unmistakable bouquet of the farmyard where they spent most of their time. And though it was one of my favourite scents there was no doubt it didn't go with these elegant surroundings.

And worse still, I had started a series of internal rumblings and musical tinklings which resounded only too audibly during every lull in the conversation. The only other time I have heard such sounds was in a cow with an advanced case of displacement of the abomasum. My companions delicately feigned deafness even when I produced a shameful, explosive belch which made the little fat dog start up in alarm, but when another of these mighty borborygmi escaped me and almost made the windows rattle I thought it time to go.

In any case I wasn't contributing much else. The alcohol had taken hold and I was increasingly conscious that I was just sitting there with a stupid leer on my face. In striking contrast to Granville who looked just the same as when I first met him back at the surgery. He was cool and possessed, his massive urbanity unimpaired. It was a little hard.

So, with the tin of tobacco bumping against my hip and the shirt tucked under my arm I took my leave.

Back at the hospital I looked down at Dinah. The old dog had come through wonderfully well and she lifted her head and gazed at me sleepily. Her colour was good and her pulse strong. The operative shock had been dramatically minimised by my colleague's skilful speedy technique and by the intravenous drip.

I knelt down and stroked her ears. 'You know, I'm sure she's going to make it, Granville.'

Above me the great pipe nodded with majestic confidence.

'Of course, laddie, of course.'

And he was right. Dinah was rejuvenated by her hysterectomy and lived to delight her mistress for many more years.

On the way home that night she lay by my side on the passenger seat, her nose poking from a blanket. Now and then she rested her chin on my hand as it gripped the gear lever and occasionally she licked me lazily.

I could see she felt better than I did.

# 8

As I looked at the group of sick young cattle on the hillside a mixture of apprehension and disbelief flooded through me. Surely not more trouble for the Dalbys.

The old saw 'It never rains but it pours' seems to apply with particular force to farming. The husk outbreak last year and now this. It had all started with the death of Billy Dalby; big, slow-smiling, slow-talking Billy. He was as strong and tough as any of the shaggy beasts which ranged his fields but he had just melted away in a few weeks. Cancer of the pancreas they said it was and Billy was gone before anybody could realise it and there was only his picture smiling down from the kitchen mantelpiece on his wife and three young children.

The general opinion was that Mrs Dalby should sell up and get out. You needed a man to run this place and anyway Prospect House was a bad farm. Neighbouring farmers would stick out their lower lips and shake their heads when they looked at the boggy pastures on the low side of the house with the tufts of spiky grass sticking from the sour soil or at the rocky outcrops and scattered stones on the hillside fields. No, it was a poor place and a woman would never make a go of it.

Everybody thought the same thing except Mrs Dalby herself. There wasn't much of her, in fact she must have been one of the smallest women I have ever seen – around five feet high – but there was a core of steel in her. She had her own mind and her own way of doing things.

I remember when Billy was still alive I had been injecting some sheep up there and Mrs Dalby called me into the house.

'You'll have a cup of tea, Mr Herriot?' She said it in a gracious way, not casually, her head slightly on one side and a dignified little smile on her face.

And when I went into the kitchen I knew what I would find; the inevitable tray. It was always a tray with Mrs Dalby. The hospitable Dales people were continually asking me in for some kind of refreshment – a 'bit o' dinner' perhaps, but if it wasn't midday there was usually a mug of tea and a scone or a hunk of thick-crusted apple pie – but Mrs Dalby invariably set out a special tray. And there it was today with a clean cloth and the best china cup and saucer and side plates with sliced buttered scones and iced cakes and malt bread and biscuits. It was on its own table away from the big kitchen table.

'Do sit down, Mr Herriot,' she said in her precise manner. 'I hope that tea isn't too strong for you.'

Her speech was what the farmers would call 'very proper' but it went with her personality which to me embodied a determination to do everything as correctly as possible.

'Looks perfect to me, Mrs Dalby.' I sat down, feeling somewhat exposed, in the middle of the kitchen with Billy smiling comfortably from an old armchair by the fire and his wife standing by my side.

She never sat down with us but stood there, very erect, hands clasped in front of her, head inclined, ceremoniously attending to my every wish. 'Let me fill your cup, Mr Herriot,' or 'Won't you try some of this custard tart?'

She wasn't what you would call pretty; it was a rough-skinned red little face with tiny, very dark eyes but there was a sweet expression and a quiet dignity. And as I say, there was strength.

Billy died in the spring and as everybody waited for Mrs Dalby to make arrangement for the sale she went right on with the running of the farm. She did it with the help of a big farm worker called Charlie who had helped Billy occasionally but now came full time. During the summer I was called out a few times for trivial ailments among the cattle and I could see that Mrs Dalby was managing to hang on; she looked a bit haggard because she was now helping in the fields and buildings as well as coping with her housework and young family, but she was still fighting.

It was half way through September when she asked me to call to see some young cattle – stirks of around nine months – which were coughing.

'They were really fit when they were turned out in May,' she said, as we walked across the grass to the gate in the corner. 'But they've gone down badly this last week or two.'

I held the gate open, we walked through, and as I approached the group of animals I grew progressively uneasy. Even at this distance I could see that something was far wrong; they were not moving around or grazing as they should have been but were curiously immobile. There would be about thirty of them and many had their necks extended forward as if seeking air. And from the bunch a barking cough was carried to us on the soft breeze of late summer.

By the time we reached the cattle my uneasiness had been replaced by a dry-mouthed dread. They didn't seem to care as I moved in among them and I had to shout and wave my arms to get them moving; and they had barely begun to stir before the coughing broke out throughout the group; not just an occasional bark but a hacking chorus which seemed almost to be tearing the little animals apart. And they weren't just coughing; most of them were panting, standing straddle-legged, ribs heaving in a desperate fight for breath. A few showed bubbles of saliva at their lips and from here and there among the pack groans of agony sounded as the lungs laboured.

I turned as in a dream to Mrs Dalby.

'They've got husk.' Even as I said it it sounded a grimly inadequate description of the tragedy I was witnessing. Because this was neglected husk, a terrible doom-laden thing.

'Husk?' the little woman said brightly. 'What causes it?'

I looked at her for a moment then tried to make my voice casual.

'Well it's a parasite. A tiny worm which infests the bronchial tubes and sets up bronchitis – in fact that's the proper name, parasitic bronchitis. The larvae climb up the blades of grass and the cattle eat them as they graze. Some pastures are badly affected with it.' I broke off. A lecture was out of place at a time like this.

What I felt like saying was why in God's name hadn't I been called in weeks ago. Because this wasn't only bronchitis now; it was pneumonia, pleurisy, emphysema and any other lung condition you cared to name with not merely a few of the hair-like worms irritating the tubes, but great seething masses of them crawling everywhere, balling up and blocking the vital air passages. I had opened up a lot of calves like these and I knew how it looked.

I took a deep breath. 'They're pretty bad, Mrs Dalby. A mild attack isn't so bad if you can get them off the grass right away, but this has gone a long way beyond that. You can see for yourself, can't you – they're like a lot of little skeletons. I wish I'd seen them sooner.'

She looked up at me apprehensively and I decided not to belabour the point. It would be like rubbing it in; saying what her neighbours had said all along, that her inexperience would land her in trouble sooner or later. If Billy had been here he probably would never have turned his young cattle on to this marshy field; or he would have spotted the trouble right at the start and brought them inside. Charlie would be no help in a situation like this; he was a good willing chap but lived up to the Yorkshire saying, 'Strong in t'arm and thick in t'head.' Farming is a skilful business and Billy, the planner, the stocks-man, the experienced agriculturist who knew his own farm inside out, just wasn't there.

Mrs Dalby drew herself up with that familiar gesture.

'Well what can we do about it, Mr Herriot?'

An honest reply in those days would have been, 'Medicinally nothing.' But I didn't say that.

'We've got to get them all inside immediately. Every mouthful of this grass is adding to the worm burden. Is Charlie around to give us a hand?'

'Yes, he's in the next field, mending a wall.' She trotted across the turf and in a minute or two returned with the big man ambling by her side.

'Aye, ah thought it were a touch of husk,' he said amiably, then with a hint of eagerness, 'Are ye goin' to give them the throat injection?'

'Yes . . . yes . . . but let's get them up to the buildings.' As we drove the cattle slowly up the green slope I marvelled ruefully at this further example of faith in the intratracheal injection for husk. There was really no treatment for the condition and it would be another twenty years before one appeared in the shape of diethylcarbamazine, but the accepted procedure was to inject a mixture of chloroform, turpentine and creosote into the wind-pipe. Modern vets may raise their eyebrows at the idea of intro-ducing this barbaric concoction directly into the delicate lung tissue and we old ones didn't think much of it either. But the farmers loved it.

When we had finally got the stirks into the fold yard I looked round with something like despair. The short journey had exacerbated their symptoms tremendously and I stood in the middle of a symphony of coughs, grunts and groans while the cattle, tongues protruding, ribs pumping, gasped for breath.

I got a bottle of the wonderful injection from the car, and with Charlie holding the head and little Mrs Dalby hanging on to the tail I began to go through the motions. Seizing the trachea in my left hand I inserted the needle between the car-tilaginous rings and squirted a few c.c.'s into the lumen and, as always, the stirk gave a reflex cough, sending up the distinctive aroma of the medicaments into our faces.

'By gaw, you can smell it straight off, guvnor,' Charlie said with deep satisfaction. 'Ye can tell it's gettin' right to t'spot.'

Most of the farmers said something like that. And they had faith. The books spoke comfortably about the chloroform stupefying the worms, the turpentine killing them and the creosote causing increased coughing which expelled them. But I didn't believe a word of it. The good results which followed were in my opinion due entirely to bringing the animals in from the infected pasture.

But I knew I had to do it and we injected every animal in the yard. There were thirty-two of them and Mrs Dalby's tiny figure was involved in the catching of all of them; clutching vainly at their necks, grabbing their tails, pushing them up against the wall. William, the eldest son, aged eight, came in from school and plunged into the fray by his mother's side.

My repeated 'Be careful, Mrs Dalby!' or Charlie's gruff

'Watch thissen, Missis, or you'll get lamed!' had no effect. During the mêlée both she and the little boy were kicked, trodden on and knocked down but they never showed the slightest sign of being discouraged.

At the end, the little woman turned to me, her face flushed to an even deeper hue. Panting, she looked up. 'Is there anything else we can do, Mr Herriot?'

'Yes there is.' In fact the two things I was going to tell her were the only things which ever did any good. 'First, I'm going to leave you some medicine for the worms which are in the stomach. We can get at them there, so Charlie must give every stirk a dose. Secondly, you'll have to start giving them the best possible food – good hay and high protein cake.'

Her eyes widened. 'Cake? That's expensive stuff. And hay...'

I knew what she was thinking. The precious hay safely garnered for next winter's feed; to have to start using it now was a cruel blow, especially with all that beautiful grass out there; grass, the most natural, most perfect food for cattle but every blade carrying its own load of death.

'Can't they go out again . . . ever?' she asked in a small voice.

'No, I'm sorry. If they had just had a mild attack you could have kept them in at nights and turned them out after the dew had left the grass in the mornings. The larvae climb up the grass mainly when it's wet. But your cattle have got too far. We daren't risk them picking up any more worms.'

'Right . . . thank you, Mr Herriot. We know where we are, anyway.' She paused. 'Do you think we'll lose any of them?'

My stomach contracted into a tight ball. I had already told her to buy cake she couldn't afford and it was a certainty she would have to lay out more precious cash for hay in the winter. How was I going to tell her that nothing in the world was going to stop this batch of beasts dying like flies? When animals with husk started blowing bubbles it was nearly hopeless and the ones which were groaning with every breath were quite simply doomed. Nearly half of them were in these two categories and what about the rest? The pathetic barking other half? Well, they had a chance.

'Mrs Dalby,' I said, 'it would be wrong of me to make light of this. Some of them are going to die, in fact unless there's a miracle you are going to lose quite a few of them.' At the sight of her stricken face I made an attempt to be encouraging. 'However, where there's life there's hope and sometimes you get pleasant surprises at this job.' I held up a finger. 'Worm them and get some good grub into them! That's your hope – to help them fight it off themselves.'

'I see.' She lifted her chin in her characteristic way. 'And now you must come in for a wash.'

And of course there it was in its usual place in the kitchen; the tray with all the trimmings.

'Really, Mrs Dalby. You shouldn't have bothered. You have enough to do without this.'

'Nonsense,' she said, the smile back on her face. 'You take one spoonful of sugar don't you?'

As I sat there she stood in her habitual position, hands clasped in front of her, watching me while the middle boy, Dennis, who was five, looked up at me solemnly and Michael, a mere toddler of two, fell over the coal scuttle and started to bawl lustily.

The usual procedure was to repeat the intratracheal injection in four days so I had to go through with it. Anyway, it gave me a chance to see how the cattle were faring.

When I drew up in the yard my first sight was of a long sack-covered mound on the cobbles. A row of hooves protruded from beneath the sacks. I had expected something of the sort but the reality was still like a blow in the face. It was still quite early in the morning and perhaps I wasn't feeling quite strong enough to have the evidence of my failure thrust before my eyes. Because failure it undoubtedly was; even though I had been in a hopeless position from the start there was something damning in those motionless hooves jutting from their rough blanket.

I made a quick count. There were four dead cattle under there. Wearily I made my way into the fold yard; I had no cheerful expectation of what I would find inside. Two of the stirks were down and unable to rise from the deep straw, the rest were still panting, but I noticed with a faint lifting of my gloom that several of them were doggedly munching at the cubes of cake in the troughs and other were pulling an occasional wisp of hay from the racks. It was incredible how animals with advanced respiratory symptoms would still eat; and it provided the only gleam of hope.

I walked over to the house. Mrs Dalby greeted me cheerfully as though those carcases outside didn't exist.

'It's time for the second injection,' I said, and then after some hesitation, 'I see you've lost four of them . . . I'm sorry.'

'Well you told me, Mr Herriot.' She smiled through the tired lines on her face. 'You said I had to expect it so it wasn't as big a shock as it might have been.' She finished washing the youngest child's face, seized a towel in her work-roughened hands and rubbed him briskly, then she straightened up. It was Saturday and William was at home and I noticed not for the first time that there was something about the little boy which suggested that even at his age he had decided he was going to be the man about the house. He pulled on his little wellingtons and marched resolutely with us across the yard to do his bit as he saw it. I rested my hand on his shoulder as he walked beside me; he would have to grow up a lot more rapidly than most youngsters but I had the feeling that the realities of life wouldn't bowl him over very easily.

We gave the animals their second injection with the two little Dalbys again throwing themselves fearlessly into the rough and tumble and that was about the last practical thing I did in the husk outbreak.

Looking back, there is a macabre fascination in recalling situations like this when we veterinary surgeons were utterly helpless in the face of inevitable diaster. Nowadays, thank heavens, the young members of the profession do not have to stand among a group of gasping, groaning creatures with the sick knowledge that they can't do a thing about it; they have an excellent oral vaccine to prevent husk and efficient therapeutic agents to treat it.

But with the Dalbys who needed my help so desperately I had nothing to offer; my memories are of repeated comfortless visits, of death, and of an all-pervading reek of chloroform, creosote and turpentine. When the business had finally come to an end a dozen of the stirks had died, about five were alive but blowing hard and would probably be stunted and unthrifty for the rest of their lives. The rest, thanks to the good feeding and not to my treatment, had recovered.

It was a crushing blow for any farmer to take but for a widow struggling to survive it could have been fatal. But on my last visit little Mrs Dalby, hovering as usual, hands clasped, above the tea tray, was undefeated.

'Only them as has them can lose them,' she said firmly, her head tilted as always.

I had heard that said many times and they were brave Yorkshire words. But I wondered . . . did she have enough to be able to lose so many?

She went on, 'I know you've told me not to turn the young beasts on to that field next year but isn't there anything we can give them to stop them getting husk?'

'No, Mrs Dalby, I'm sorry.' I put down my cup. 'I don't think there's anything country vets need and want more than a husk vaccine. People keep asking us that question and we have to keep on saying no.'

We had to keep on saying no for another twenty years as we watched disasters like I had just seen at the Dalbys', and the strange thing is that now we have a first rate vaccine it is taken completely for granted.

Driving away I stopped to open the gate at the end of the track and looked back at the old stone farmhouse crouching against the lower slopes. It was a perfect autumn day with mellow golden sunshine softening the harsh sweep of fell and moor with their striding walls and the air so still and windless that the whirring of a pigeon's wings overhead was loud in the silence. Across the valley on the hilltop a frieze of sparse trees stood as motionless as though they had been painted across the blue canvas of sky.

It seemed wrong that in the midst of this beauty was worry and anxiety, grinding struggle and the threat of ruin. I closed the gate and got back into the car. That little woman over there may have weathered this calamity but as I started the engine the thought was strong in my mind that another such thing would finish her.

# 9

I was vastly relieved when winter came and spring followed and I saw virtually nothing of Mrs Dalby. It was one market day in mid-summer that she came to the surgery. I was just going to open the door when Siegfried beat me to it. More than most people he appreciated the hospitality we were shown on the farms and he had sampled Mrs Dalby's tray as often as I had. On top of that he had the deepest admiration for her indomitable battle to keep the farm going for her children, so that whenever she appeared at Skeldale House he received her like royalty. His manners, always impeccable, became those of a Spanish grandee.

I watched him now as he threw the door wide and hurried to the top step.

'Why, Mrs Dalby! How very nice to see you! Do come inside.' He extended his hand towards the house.

The little woman, dignified as ever, inclined her head, smiled and walked past him while Siegfried hastened to her side; and as they negotiated the passage he kept up a running fire of enquiries. 'And how is William . . . and Dennis . . . and little Michael? Good, good, splendid.'

At the sitting-room door there was the same ceremonious opening and courteous gestures and once inside a tremendous scraping of armchairs as he hauled them around to make sure she was comfortable and in the right position.

Next he galloped through to the kitchen to organise some refreshment and when Mrs Hall appeared with the tray he raked it with an anxious glance as though he feared it might fall below the standard of Mrs Dalby's. Apparently reassured, he poured the tea, hovered around solicitously for a moment or two then sat down opposite, the very picture of rapt attention.

The little woman thanked him and sipped at her cup.

'Mr Farnon, I have called to see you about some young beasts. I turned a batch of thirty-five out this spring and they looked in good condition but now they're losing ground fast – all of them.'

My heart gave a great thump and something must have shown in my face because she smiled across at me.

'Oh don't worry, Mr Herriot, it's not husk again. There's not a cough among the lot of them. But they are going thin and they're badly scoured.'

'I think I know what that will be,' Siegfried said, leaning across to push a plate of Mrs Hall's flapjack towards her. 'They'll have picked up a few worms. Not lungworms but the stomach and intestinal kind. They probably just need a good dose of medicine to clear them out.'

She nodded and took a piece of the flapjack. 'Yes, that's what Charlie thought and we've dosed the lot of them. But it doesn't seem to have made any difference.'

'That's funny.' Siegfried rubbed his chin. 'Mind you they sometimes need a repeat but you should have seen some improvement. Perhaps we'd better have a look at them.'

'That's what I would like,' she said. 'It would set my mind at rest.'

Siegfried opened the appointment book. 'Right, and the sooner the better. Tomorrow morning all right? Splendid.' He made a quick note then looked up at her. 'By the way I'm going off for a week's holiday starting this evening so Mr Herriot will be coming.'

'That will be fine,' she replied, turning to me and smiling without a trace of doubt or misgiving. If she was thinking 'This is the fellow who supervised the deaths of nearly half of my young stock last year' she certainly didn't show it. In fact when

66

she finally finished her tea and left she waved and smiled again as though she could hardly wait to see me again.

And when I walked across the fields with Mrs Dalby next day it was like turning the clock back to last year, except that we were going in the other direction; not down towards the marshy ground below the house but up to the stony pastures which climbed in an uneven checkerboard between their stone walls over the lower slopes of the hill.

The similarity persisted as we approached, too. These young beasts – roans, reds, red and whites – were an almost exact counterpart of last year's batch; shaggy little creatures, little more than calves, they stood spindly-legged and knock-kneed regarding us apathetically as we came up the rise. And though their symptoms were entirely different from the previous lot there was one thing I could say for sure; they were very ill.

As I watched I could see the dark watery diarrhoea flowing from them without any lifting of the tails as though there was nothing they could do to control it. And every one of them was painfully thin, the skin stretched over the jutting pelvic bones and the protruding rows of ribs.

'I haven't neglected them this time,' Mrs Dalby said.

'I know they look dreadful but this seems to have happened within a few days.'

'Yes . . . yes . . . I see . . .' My eyes were hunting desperately among the little animals trying to find some sort of clue. I had seen unthriftiness from parasitism but nothing like this.

'Have you kept a lot of cattle in these fields over the last year or two?' I asked.

She paused in thought for a moment. 'No . . . no . . . I don't think so. Billy used to let the milk cows graze up here now and then but that's all.'

The grass wouldn't be likely to be 'sick' with worms, then. In any case it didn't look like that. What it did look like was Johne's disease, but how in God's name could thirty-five young things like this get Johne's at the same time? Salmonella . . .? Coccidiosis . . .? Some form of poisoning, perhaps . . . this was the time of year when cattle ate strange plants. I walked slowly round the field, but there was nothing unusual to be seen; it took even the grass all its time to grow on these wind-blown hillsides and there was no great range of other herbage. I could see bracken higher up the fell but none down here; Billy would have cleared it years ago.

'Mrs Dalby,' I said. 'I think you'd better give these stirks another dose of the worm medicine just to be sure and in the meantime I'm going to take some samples of the manure for examination at the laboratory.'

I brought up some sterile jars from the car and went painstakingly round the pasture scooping up as wide a range as possible from the pools of faeces.

I took them to the lab myself and asked them to phone the results through. The call came within twenty-four hours; negative for everything. I resisted the impulse to dash out to the farm immediately; there was nothing I could think of doing and it wouldn't look so good for me to stand there gawping at the beasts and scratching my head. Better to wait till tomorrow to see if the second dose of worm medicine did any good. There was no reason why it should, because none of the samples showed a pathogenic worm burden.

In these cases I always hope that inspiration will come to me as I am driving around or even when I am examining other animals but this time as I climbed from the car outside Prospect House I was barren of ideas.

The young beasts were slightly worse. I had decided that if I still couldn't think of anything I would give the worst ones vitamin injections more or less for the sake of doing something; so with Charlie holding the heads I inserted the hypodermic under the taut skins of ten of the little creatures, trying at the same time to put away the feeling of utter futility. We didn't have to drive them inside; they were easily caught in the open field and that was a bad sign in itself.

'Well you'll let me know, Mrs Dalby,' I said hoarsely as I got back into the car. 'If that injection improves them I'll do the lot.' I gave what I hoped was a confident wave and drove off.

I felt so bad that it had a numbing effect on me and over the next few days my mind seemed to shy away from the subject of the Dalby stirks as though by not thinking about them they would just go away. I was reminded that they were still very much there by a phone call from Mrs Dalby.

'I'm afraid my cattle aren't doing any good, Mr Herriot.' Her voice was strained.

I grimaced into the receiver. 'And the ones I injected . . .?'

'Just the same as the others.'

I had to face up to reality now and drove out to Prospect House immediately; but the feeling of cold emptiness, of having nothing to offer, made the journey a misery. I hadn't the courage to go to the farmhouse and face Mrs Dalby but hurried straight up through the fields to where the young beasts were gathered.

And when I walked among them and studied them at close range the apprehension I had felt on the journey was nothing to the sick horror which rushed through me now. Another catastrophe was imminent here. The big follow-up blow which was all that was needed to knock the Dalby family out once and for all was on its way. These animals were going to die. Not just half of them like last year but all of them, because there was hardly any variation in their symptoms; there didn't seem to be a single one of them which was fighting off the disease.

But what disease? God almighty, I was a veterinary surgeon! Maybe not steeped in experience but I wasn't a new beginner any more. I should surely have some small inkling why a whole great batch of young beasts was sinking towards the knacker yard in front of my eyes.

I could see Mrs Dalby coming up the field with little William, striding in his tough, arm-swinging way by her side, and Charlie following behind.

What the hell was I going to say to them? Shrug my shoulders with a light laugh and say I hadn't a single clue in my head and that it would probably be best to phone Mallock now and ask them to shoot the lot of them straight away for dog meat? They wouldn't have any cattle to bring on for next year but that wouldn't matter because they would no longer be farming.

Stumbling among the stricken creatures I gazed at them in turn, almost choking as I looked at the drooping, sunken-eyed heads, the gaunt little bodies, the eternal trickle of that deadly scour. There was a curious immobility about the group, probably because they were too weak to walk about; in fact as I watched, one of them took a few steps, swayed and almost fell.

Charlie was pushing open the gate into the field just a hundred yards away. I turned and stared at the nearest animal, almost beseeching it to tell me what was wrong with it, where it felt the pain, how this thing had all started. But I got no response. The stirk, one of the smallest, only calf-size, with a very dark roan-coloured head showed not the slightest interest but gazed back at me incuriously through its spectacles. What was that . . . what was I thinking about . . . spectacles? Was my reason toppling . . . ? But yes, by God, he did have spectacles . . . a ring of lighter hair surrounding each eye. And that other beast over there . . . he was the same. Oh glory be, now I knew! At last I knew!

Mrs Dalby, panting slightly, had reached me.

'Good morning, Mr Herriot,' she said, trying to smile. 'What do you think, then?' She looked around the cattle with anxious eyes.

'Ah, good morning to you, Mrs Dalby,' I replied expansively, fighting down the impulse to leap in the air and laugh and shout and perhaps do a few cartwheels. 'Yes, I've had a look at them and it is pretty clear now what the trouble is.'

'Really? Then what . . . ?'

'It's copper deficiency.' I said it casually as though I had been turning such a thing over in my mind right from the beginning. 'You can tell by the loss of the pigment in the coat, especially around the eyes. In fact when you look at them you can see that a lot of them are a bit paler than normal.' I waved an airy hand in the general direction of the stirks.

Charlie nodded. 'Aye, by gaw, you're right. Ah thowt they'd gone a funny colour.'

'Can we cure it?' Mrs Dalby asked the inevitable question.

'Oh yes, I'm going straight back to the surgery now to make up a copper mixture and we'll dose the lot. And you'll have to repeat that every fortnight while they are out at grass. It's a bit of a nuisance, I'm afraid, but there's no other way. Can you do it?'

'Oh aye, we'll do it,' Charlie said.

And 'Oh aye, we'll do it,' little William echoed, sticking out his chest and strutting around aggressively as though he wanted to start catching the beasts right away.

The treatment had a spectacular effect. I didn't have the modern long-lasting copper injections at my disposal but the solution of copper sulphate which I concocted under the surgery tap at Skeldale House worked like magic. Within a few weeks that batch of stirks was capering, lively and fully fleshed, over those hillside fields. Not a single death, no lingering unthriftiness. It was as though the whole thing had never happened, as though the hand of doom had never hovered over not only the cattle but the little family of humans.

It had been a close thing and, I realised, only a respite. That little woman had a long hard fight ahead of her still.

I have always abhorred change of any kind but it pleases me to come forward twenty years and spectate at another morning in the kitchen at Prospect House. I was seated at the same little table picking a buttered scone from the same tray and wondering whether I should follow it with a piece of malt bread or one of the jam tarts.

Billy still smiled down from the mantelpiece and Mrs Dalby, hands clasped in front of her, was watching me, her head a little on one side, the same half smile curving her lips. The years had not altered her much; there was some grey in her hair but the little red, weathered face and the bright eyes were as I had always known them.

I sipped my tea and looked across at the vast bulk of William sprawled in his father's old chair, smiling his father's smile at me. There were about fifteen stones of William and I had just been watching him in action as he held a fully grown bullock's hind foot while I examined it. The animal had made a few attempts to kick but the discouragement on its face had been obvious as William's great hands effortlessly engulfed its fetlock and a corner of his wide shoulder span dug into its abdomen.

No, I couldn't expect William to be the same, nor Dennis and Michael clattering into the kitchen now in their heavy boots and moving over to the sink to wash their hands. They were six footers too with their father's high-shouldered easy slouching walk but without William's sheer bulk.

Their tiny mother glanced at them then up at the picture on the mantelpiece.

'It would have been our thirtieth anniversary today,' she said conversationally.

I looked up at her, surprised. She never spoke of such things and I didn't know how to answer. I couldn't very well say 'congratulations' when she had spent twenty of those years alone. She had never said a word about her long fight; and it had been a winning fight. She had bought the neighbouring farm lower down the Dale when old Mr Mason retired; it was a good farm with better land and William had lived there after his marriage and they ran the two places as one. Things were pretty good now with her three expert stocksmen sons eliminating the need for outside labour except old Charlie who still pottered around doing odd jobs.

'Yes, thirty years,' Mrs Dalby said, looking slowly round the room as though she was seeing it for the first time. Then she turned back and bent over me, her face serious.

'Mr Herriot,' she said, and I was sure that at last, on this special day, she was going to say something about the years of struggle, the nights of worry and tears, the grinding toil.

For a moment she rested her hand lightly on my shoulder and her eyes looked into mine.

'Mr Herriot, are you quite sure that tea is to your liking?'

# 10

Every professional visit has its beginning in a call, a summons from the client which can take varying forms. ...

'This is Joe Bentley speaking,' said the figure on the surgery doorstep. It was an odd manner of address, made stranger by the fact that Joe was holding his clenched fist up by his jaw and staring vacantly past me.

''ello, 'ello,' Joe continued as though into space, and suddenly everything became clear. That was an imaginary telephone he was holding and he was doing his best to communicate with the vet; and not doing badly considering the innumerable pints of beer that were washing around inside him.

On market days the pubs stayed open from ten o'clock till five and Joe was one of the now extinct breed who took their chance to drink themselves almost insensible. The modern farmer may have a few drinks on market day but the old reckless intake is rare now.

In Darrowby it was confined to a group of hard-bitten characters, all of them elderly, so even then the custom was on the wane. But it wasn't uncommon to see them when they came to pay their bills, leaning helplessly against the surgery wall and pushing their cheque books wordlessly at us. Some of them still used a pony and trap and the old joke about the horse taking them home was illustrated regularly. One old chap kept an enormously powerful ancient car simply for the purpose of getting him home; even if he engaged top gear by mistake when he collapsed into the driver's seat the vehicle would still take off. Some didn't go home at all on market day but spent the night carousing and playing cards till dawn.

As I looked at Joe Bentley swaying on the step I wondered what his programme might be for the rest of the evening. He closed his eyes, held his fist close to his face, and spoke again.

'Hellow, who's there?' he asked in an affected telephone voice.

'Herriot speaking,' I replied. Clearly Joe wasn't trying to be funny. He was just a little confused. It was only right to co-operate with him. 'How are you, Mr Bentley?'

'Nicely, thank ye,' Joe answered solemnly, eyes still tightly closed. 'Are you very well?'

'I'm fine, thanks. Now what can I do for you?'

This seemed to floor him temporarily because he remained silent for several seconds, opening his eyes occasionally and squinting somewhere over my left shoulder with intense concentration. Then something seemed to click; he closed his eyes again, cleared his throat and recommenced.

'Will you come up to ma place? I've a cow wants cleansin'.'

'Do you want me to come tonight?'

Joe gave this serious thought, pursing his lips and scratching his ear with his free hand before answering.

'Nay, morning'll do. Goodbye and thank ye.' He replaced the phantom telephone carefully in its rest, swung round and made his way down the street with great dignity. He hardly staggered at all and there was something purposeful in his bearing which convinced me that he was heading back to the Red Bear. For a moment I thought he would fall outside Johnson's the iron-mongers but by the time he rounded the corner into the market place he was going so well that I felt sure he'd make it.

And I can remember Mr Biggins standing by the desk in our office, hands deep in his pockets, chin thrust forward stubbornly.

'I 'ave a cow gruntin' a bit.'

'Oh, right, we'll have a look at her.' I reached for a pen to write the visit in the book.

He shuffled his feet. 'Well ah don't know. She's maybe not as bad as all that.'

'Well, whatever you say . . .'

'No,' he said. 'It's what you say – you're t'vet.'

'It's a bit difficult,' I replied. 'After all, I haven't seen her. Maybe I'd better pay you a visit.'

'Aye, that's all very fine, but it's a big expense. It's ten bob every time you fellers walk on to ma place and that's before you start. There's all t'medicines and everything on top.'

'Yes, I understand, Mr Biggins. Well, would you like to take something away with you ? A tin of stomach powder, perhaps ?'

'How do you know it's t'stomach ?'

'Well I don't actually . . .'

'It might be summat else.'

'That's very true, but . . .'

'She's a right good cow, this,' he said with a touch of aggression. 'Paid fifty pun for her at Scarburn Market.'

'Yes, I'm sure she is. And consequently I really think she'd be worth a visit. I could come out this afternoon.'

There was a long silence. 'Aye, but it wouldn't be just one visit, would it ? You'd be comin' again next day and maybe the one after that and before we knew we'd 'ave a clonkin' great bill.'

'Yes, I'm sorry, Mr Biggins, everything is so expensive these days.'

'Yes, by gaw!' He nodded vigorously. 'Sometimes it ud be cheaper to give you t'cow at t'end of it.'

'Well now, hardly that . . . but I do see your point.'

I spent a few moments in thought. 'How about taking a fever drink as well as the stomach powder ? That would be safer.'

He gave me a long blank stare. 'But you still wouldn't be sure, would you ?'

'No, not quite sure, not absolutely . . .'

'She could even 'ave a wire in 'er.'

'True, very true.'

'Well then, shoving medicines down her neck isn't goin' to do no good is it ?'

'It isn't, you're right.'

'Ah don't want to lose this cow, tha knows!' he burst out truculently. 'Ah can't afford to lose 'er!'

'I realise that, Mr Biggins. That's why I feel I should see her – I did suggest that if you remember.'

He did not reply immediately and only the strain in his eyes and a faint twitching of a cheek muscle betrayed the inner struggle which was raging. When he finally spoke it was in a hoarse croak.

'Aye, well, it might be best . . . but . . . er we could mebbes leave 'er till mornin' and see how she is then.'

'That's a good idea.' I smiled in relief. 'You have a look at her first thing in the morning and give me a ring before nine if she's no better.'

My words seemed to deepen his gloom. 'But what if she doesn't last till mornin' ?'

'Well of course there is that risk.'

'Not much good ringin' you if she's dead, is it ?'

'That's true, of course.'

'Ah'd be ringin' Mallock the knacker man, wouldn't I ?'

'Afraid so, yes . . .'

'Well that's no bloody use to me, gettin' five quid from Mallock for a good cow!'

'Mm, no . . . I can see how you feel.'

'Ah think a lot about this cow!'

'I'm sure you do.'

'It ud be a big loss for me.'

'Quite.'

Mr Biggins hunched his shoulders and glared at me belligerently. 'Well then what are you goin' to do about 'er ?'

'Let's see.' I ran my fingers through my hair. 'Perhaps you could wait till tonight and see if she recovers and if she isn't right by say, eight o'clock you could let me know and I'd come out.'

'You'd come out then, would you ?' he said slowly, narrowing his eyes.

I gave him a bright smile. 'That's right.'

'Aye, but last time you came out at night you charged extra, ah'm sure you did.'

'Well, probably,' I said, spreading my hands. 'That's usual in veterinary practices.'

'So we're worse off than afore, aren't we ?'

'When you look at it like that . . . I suppose so . . .'

'Ah'm not a rich man, tha knows.'

'I realise that.'

'Takes me all ma time to pay t'ordinary bill without extras.'

'Oh I'm sure . . .'

'So that idea's a bad egg, ain't it?'

'Seems like it . . . yes . . .' I lay back in my chair, feeling suddenly tired.

Mr Biggins glowered at me morosely but I wasn't going to be tempted into any further gambits. I gave him what I fancied was a neutral stare and I hoped it conveyed the message that I was open to suggestions but wasn't going to make any myself.

The silence which now blanketed the room seemed to be of a durable nature. Down at the end of the street the church clock tolled the quarter hour, far off in the market place a dog barked, Miss Dobson, the grocer's daughter, glided past the window on her bicycle but no word was uttered.

Mr Biggins, biting his lower lip, darting his eyes desperately from his feet to me and back again, was clearly at the end of his resources, and it came to me at last that I had to take a firm initiative.

'Mr Biggins,' I said. 'I've got to be on my way. I have a lot of calls and one of them is within a mile of your farm, so I shall see your cow around three o'clock.' I stood up to indicate that the interview was over.

The farmer gave me a hunted look. I had the feeling that he had been resigned to a long period of stalemate and this sudden attack had taken him out of his stride. He opened his mouth as though to speak then appeared to change his mind and turned to go. At the door he paused, raised his hand and looked at me beseechingly for a moment, then he sank his chin on his chest and left the room.

I watched him through the window and as he crossed the road he stopped half way in the street in the same indeterminate way, muttering to himself and glancing back at the surgery; and as he lingered there I grew anxious that he might be struck by a passing car, but at length he squared his shoulders and trailed slowly out of sight.

* * *

And sometimes it isn't easy to get a clear picture over the telephone ...

'This is Bob Fryer.'

'Good morning, Herriot here.'

'Now then, one of me sows is bad.'

'Oh right, what's the trouble?'

A throaty chuckle. 'Ah, that's what ah want *you* to tell *me*!'

'Oh, I see.'

'Aye, ah wouldn't be ringin' you up if I knew what the trouble was, would I? Heh, heh, heh, heh!'

The fact that I had heard this joke about two thousand times interfered with my full participation in the merriment but I managed a cracked laugh in return.

'That's perfectly true, Mr Fryer. Well, why have you rung me?'

'Damn, I've told ye – to find out what the trouble is.'

'Yes, I understand that, but I'd like some details. What do you mean when you say she's bad?'

'Well, she's just a bit off it.'

'Quite, but could you tell me a little more?'

A pause. 'She's dowly, like.'

'Anything else?'

'No ... no ... she's a right poorly pig, though.'

I spent a few moments in thought. 'Is she doing anything funny?'

'Funny? Funny? Nay, there's nowt funny about t'job, I'll tell tha! It's no laughin' matter.'

'Well ... er ... let me put it this way. Why are you calling me out?'

'I'm calling ye out because you're a vet. That's your job, isn't it?'

I tried again. 'It would help if I knew what to bring with me. What are her symptoms?'

'Symptoms? Well, she's just off colour, like.'

'Yes, but what is she doing?'

'She's doin' nowt. That's what bothers me.'

'Let's see.' I scratched my head. 'Is she very ill?'

'I reckon hes's in bad fettle.'

'But would you say it was an urgent matter?'

Another long pause. 'Well, she's nobbut middlin'. She's not framin' at all.'

'Yes ... yes ... and how long has she been like this?'

'Oh, for a bit.'

'But how long exactly?'

'For a good bit.'

'But Mr Fryer, I want to know when she started these symptoms. How long has she been affected?'

'Oh ... ever since we got 'er.'

'Ah, and when was that?'

'Well, she came wi' the others ...'

# 11

It was going to take a definite effort of will to get out of the car. I had driven about ten miles from Darrowby, thinking all the time that the Dales always looked their coldest, not when they were covered with snow, but as now, when the first sprinkling streaked the bare flanks of the fells in bars of black and white like the ribs of a crouching beast. And now in front of me was the farm gate rattling on its hinges as the wind shook it.

The car, heaterless and draughty as it was, seemed like a haven in an uncharitable world and I gripped the wheel tightly with my woollen-gloved hands for a few moments before opening the door. The wind almost tore the handle from my fingers as I got out but I managed to crash the door shut before stumbling over the frozen mud to the gate. Muffled as I was in heavy coat and scarf pulled up to my ears I could feel the icy gusts biting at my face, whipping up my nose and hammering painfully into the air spaces in my head.

I had driven through and, streaming-eyed, was about to get back into the car when I noticed something unusual. There was a frozen pond just off the path and among the rime-covered rushes which fringed the dead opacity of the surface a small object stood out, shiny black.

I went over and looked closer. It was a tiny kitten, probably about six weeks old, huddled and immobile, eyes tightly closed. Bending down, I poked gently at the furry body. It must be dead; a morsel like this couldn't possibly survive in such cold ... but no, there was a spark of life because the mouth opened soundlessly for a second then closed.

Quickly I lifted the little creature and tucked it inside my coat. As I drove into the farmyard I called to the farmer who was carrying two buckets out of the calf house. 'I've got one of your kittens here, Mr Butler. It must have strayed outside.'

Mr Butler put down his buckets and looked blank. 'Kitten? We haven't got no kittens at present.'

I showed him my find and he looked more puzzled.

'Well that's a rum 'un, there's no black cats on this spot. We've all sorts o' colours but no black 'uns.'

'Well he must have come from somewhere else,' I said. 'Though I can't imagine anything so small travelling very far. It's rather mysterious.'

I held the kitten out and he engulfed it with his big, work-roughened hand.

'Poor little beggar, he's only just alive. I'll take him into t'house and see if the missus can do owt for him.'

In the farm kitchen Mrs Butler was all concern. 'Oh what a shame!' She smoothed back the bedraggled hair with one finger. 'And it's got such a pretty face.' She looked up at me. 'What is it, anyway, a him or a her?'

I took a quick look behind the hind legs. 'It's a Tom.'

'Right,' she said. 'I'll get some warm milk into him but first of all we'll give him the old cure.'

She went over to the fireside oven on the big black kitchen range, opened the door and popped him inside.

I smiled. It was the classical procedure when new-born lambs were found suffering from cold and exposure; into the oven they went and the results were often dramatic. Mrs Butler left the door partly open and I could just see the little black figure inside; he didn't seem to care much what was happening to him.

The next hour I spent in the byre wrestling with the hind feet of a cow. The cleats were overgrown and grossly misshapen and upturned, causing the animal to hobble along on her heels. My job was to pare and hack away the excess horn and my long held opinion that the hind feet of a cow were never meant to be handled by man was thoroughly confirmed. We had a rope round the hock and the leg pulled up over a beam in the roof but the leg still pistoned back and forth while I hung on till my teeth rattled. By the time I had finished the sweat was running into my eyes and I had quite forgotten the cold day outside.

Still, I thought, as I eased the kinks from my spine when I had finished, there were compensations. There was a satisfaction in the sight of the cow standing comfortably on two almost normal looking feet.

'Well that's summat like,' Mr Butler grunted. 'Come in the house and wash your hands.'

In the kitchen as I bent over the brown earthenware sink I kept glancing across at the oven.

Mrs Butler laughed. 'Oh he's still with us. Come and have a look.'

It was difficult to see the kitten in the dark interior but when I spotted him I put out my hand and touched him and he turned his head towards me.

'He's coming round,' I said. 'That hour in there has worked wonders.'

'Doesn't often fail.' The farmer's wife lifted him out. 'I think he's a little tough 'un.' She began to spoon warm milk into the tiny mouth. 'I reckon we'll have him lappin' in a day or two.'

'You're going to keep him, then?'

'Too true we are. I'm going to call him Moses.'

'Moses?'

'Aye, you found him among the rushes, didn't you?'

I laughed. 'That's right. It's a good name.'

*  *  *  81

I was on the Butler farm about a fortnight later for the ever-recurring job of 'cleansing' a cow and I kept looking around for Moses. Farmers rarely have their cats indoors and I thought that if the black kitten had survived he would have joined the feline colony around the buildings.

Farm cats have a pretty good time. They may not be petted or cosseted but it has always seemed to me that they lead a free, natural life. They are expected to catch mice but if they are not so inclined there is abundant food at hand; bowls of milk here and there and the dogs' dishes to be raided if anything interesting is left over. I had seen plenty of cats around today, some flitting nervously away, others friendly and purring. There was a tabby loping gracefully across the cobbles and a big tortoise-shell was curled on a bed of straw at the warm end of the byre; cats are connoisseurs of comfort. When Mr Butler went to fetch the hot water I had a quick look in the bullock house and a white Tom regarded me placidly from between the bars of a hay rack where he had been taking a siesta. But there was no sign of Moses.

I finished drying my arms and was about to make a casual reference to the kitten when Mr Butler handed me my jacket.

'Come round here with me if you've got a minute,' he said. 'I've got summat to show you.'

I followed him through the door at the end and across a passage into the long, low-roofed piggery. He stopped at a pen about half way down and pointed inside.

'Look 'ere,' he said.

I leaned over the wall and my face must have shown my astonishment because the farmer burst into a shout of laughter.

'That's summat new for you, isn't it?'

I stared unbelievingly down at a large sow stretched comfortably on her side, suckling a litter of about twelve piglets and right in the middle of the long pink row, furry black and incongruous, was Moses. He had a teat in his mouth and was absorbing his nourishment with the same rapt enjoyment as his smooth-skinned fellows on either side.

'What the devil . . . ?' I gasped.

Mr Butler was still laughing. 'I thought you'd never have seen anything like that before, I never have, any road.'

'But how did it happen?' I still couldn't drag my eyes away.

'It was the Missus's idea,' he replied. 'When she'd got the little youth lappin' milk she took him out to find a right warm spot for him in the buildings. She settled on this pen because the sow, Bertha, had just had a litter and I had a heater in and it was grand and cosy.'

I nodded. 'Sounds just right.'

'Well she put Moses and a bowl of milk in here,' the farmer went on, 'but the little feller didn't stay by the heater very long – next time I looked in he was round at t'milk bar.'

I shrugged my shoulders. 'They say you see something new every day at this game, but this is something I've never even heard of. Anyway, he looks well on it – does he actually live on the sow's milk or does he still drink from his bowl?'

'A bit of both, I reckon. It's hard to say.'

Anyway, whatever mixture Moses was getting he grew rapidly into a sleek, handsome animal with an unusually high gloss to his coat which may or may not have been due to the porcine element of his diet. I never went to the Butlers' without having a look in the pig pen. Bertha, his foster mother, seemed to find nothing unusual in this hairy intruder and pushed him around casually with pleased grunts just as she did with the rest of her brood.

Moses for his part appeared to find the society of the pigs very congenial. When the piglets curled up together and settled down for a sleep Moses would be somewhere in the heap and when his young colleagues were weaned at eight weeks he showed his attachment to Bertha by spending most of his time with her.

And it stayed that way over the years. Often he would be right inside the pen, rubbing himself happily along the comforting bulk of the sow, but I remember him best in his favourite place; crouching on the wall looking down perhaps meditatively on what had been his first warm home.

# 12

I was beginning to learn a few tricks of my own.

In my bachelor days those early morning rings at the door-bell used to start me galloping downstairs into the freezing passage in my pyjamas full of enthusiasm, in fact almost bursting with impatience to learn what the immediate future held for me. But marriage had maybe softened me. At any rate, a long run of sessions in my bare feet on the doorstep with the bracing Yorkshire air whistling round my ankles had persuaded me that this was an overrated pastime.

The trouble was that in those days there were very few telephones on the farms and many of the farmers used to cycle in to the surgery when they wanted the vet; and of course farmers are inclined to rise rather early; a lot of them seemed to think that around 7 a.m. was a good time.

I just had to alter my system and now when I heard that long jangling downstairs I crawled out from beside Helen, tiptoed over to the window and opened it. Our bed-sitter being at the front of the house I was able to push my head through a few inches of space and carry on long conversations while most of me stayed warmly inside.

But on this Sunday morning something was wrong. I had heard the ring, taken up my kneeling position on the floor and got my head through the window. But I couldn't see anybody.

'Hello!' I called.

''ellow!' came back the reply immediately. But there was nobody on the step.

'Hello!' I shouted.

''ellow!' a hearty bellow responded.

'Hello!' I bawled at the top of my voice. I still couldn't see a soul.

''ellow, 'ellow, 'ellow!' echoed a full-throated yell with just a touch of asperity in it.

This was ridiculous. I didn't feel up to another effort – my head was beginning to throb – so I pushed the sash up a few inches more and leaned further out into the street.

And as I gazed down over the long stretch of ivy-covered brick it became clear why I had been unable to see anybody on the step. A man with very bandy legs encased in brown leggings was leaning against the wall of the house; he was bent double and apparently hollering straight down at the ground. I was baffled at first then I realised that he was directing his cries down through the small iron grating which led to the cellar. There was a chute there where the coalman used to tip his bags.

From my new vantage point I was able to attract the man's attention and when he looked up I saw it was Mr Dawson of Highstones.

He grinned cheerfully, quite unabashed. 'Oh, you're there are you? I have a cow with a touch o' felon. Give us a call some time this morning will you?' He waved and was gone.

I returned thoughtfully to Helen's side. And as I tried to drop off to sleep again the strong impression kept pushing into my consciousness that Mr Dawson wouldn't have been at all surprised if I had popped my head up through the grating instead of the window. It seemed to me that he had accepted the fact that I dwelt somewhere in the grimy darkness at the bottom of that cleft. It lent weight to an idea that had been growing in my mind for some time; that farmers looked on vets as different beings. We weren't really people at all.

There was Mr Coates last week. He had got me out of bed at 3 a.m. to a farrowing and when I stumbled, eyes half closed, from the car he was standing outside the piggery holding a lamp.

'Well now, Mr Herriot,' he said brightly, 'were you in bed when ah phoned?'

I stared at the man. 'In bed? Where the heck do you think I'd be at three o'clock in the morning?'

'Well ah don't know.' Mr Coates looked a little confused. 'Ah thought you might be up studyin'.'

There it was again. Up studyin'! Did they really think a vet was a creature apart – a kind of troglodyte who lived in a cell with only his text books and instruments for company? He didn't have a social life, he required no sleep, he didn't even have to eat. This last point was a very real one; I have often noticed a certain puzzlement in a farmer's face when I said I'd be as quick as I could but I'd have to finish my dinner first; or a pregnant silence at the end of the phone when I said I was just starting my breakfast.

But the man who most blatantly ignored my nutritional requirements and actually seemed to be trying to sabotage them was Mr Grainger of Beckton. He was a fierce man in his sixties and he called to see me every Saturday evening at six o'clock. What made this particularly wearing was that Helen chose each Saturday to put on a sumptuous high tea. Maybe she wanted to remind me of my Scottish upbringing but she used to set before me things like herrings in oatmeal with mustard sauce or sole and chips or ham and eggs and fill in the spaces on the table with new-baked scones, pancakes, curd tarts, cherry cakes.

It was usually when I was half way through the first course that the bell rang and there, sure enough, was Mr Grainger glaring belligerently through the glass door. He would never come into the house. All he wanted was a ten minutes' discussion on the doorstep. At first I used to say, 'I'm just at my tea,' or something like that, or I'd go on chewing in an exaggerated manner and keep wiping my lips on a napkin until I realised I was wasting my time. Mr Grainger was only interested in me as an object to talk at.

I said he wanted a discussion but that was the wrong word; he just wanted to air his views. An insight into his character could be gained from the remarks of one of his neighbours who told me that the Beckton Farmers' Discussion Group had folded up because whenever Mr Grainger got up to speak all the other farmers walked out.

In any case it seemed to enliven his Saturday evening to hold me trapped there while he described the symptoms displayed by his livestock during the previous week. He never asked me for advice; he made it quite clear that he knew a lot better than me how to treat his animals, but he did want to tell me about it.

And he told me at great length, his hands clasped over his stick in front of him, his eyes fixed on mine in a hostile stare.

But nothing is wholly bad and I did reap some small recompense from observing his antics as he tried to illustrate his case histories with actions.

I can recall one Saturday when he was complaining bitterly that he had been swindled over a carthorse he had just purchased. He was a particularly stiff-jointed man and not cut out for portraying the lameness of horses, but he managed to give an astounding impression of stringhalt. I diagnosed it instantly as he strutted up and down the pavement in front of Skeldale House, jerking one leg up behind him at every step. Then he stopped abruptly and held the offending limb out, quivering, behind him ... good heavens, maybe he was a shiverer, too! The farmer kept his eyes on me and seemed oblivious of the interest of the passers-by. There were quite a few people in the street, probably bound for the early show at the cinema, but for the moment they appeared to find Mr Grainger more entertaining.

'And that's not all,' he cried. 'There's summat wrang with his watterworks.'

'Really? How do you mean?'

'Why 'e can't stale properly. Has a 'ell of a job. Gets himself all wraxed up like this.'

Mr Grainger went into another of his impersonations – that of a horse having difficulty in passing urine – and I had to admit it was probably his best yet. He planted his stick firmly on the pavement and holding the top with both hands he backed away from it till his body was parallel with the ground. Then he began to straddle his legs further and further apart. The knot of people on the other side of the road had increased to a fair-sized crowd and they stared, fascinated, at the extraordinary sight. Mr Grainger was indeed the very picture of equine suffering and as he hollowed his back and paddled his wide-spaced feet I could almost share the desperate battle for release. When he finally raised his head and groaned the effect was harrowing.

When all was finished Mr Grainger did as he always did –

gave me a cold nod and stumped off without a word. There was no need for him to say, 'See you next Saturday'. I knew he'd be back.

Then there was Mr Grimsdale. His attitude towards me was something I couldn't quite make out, but I did know that he always had a depressing effect on me. He did this by the simple expedient of telling me that I didn't look very well.

I thought back to the visit to his farm yesterday when he had called me to a cow with a cut teat. He was a tall cadaverous man with sunken cheeks and a mournful expression – he would have made a wonderful undertaker – and he looked at me in his own particular way as I got out of the car.

I wondered what it would be today. My own conviction is that you should never tell anybody they don't look well, no matter what you think. And Mr Grimsdale's little sallies bit especially deeply because he always referred to me in agricultural terms as though I were one of his bullocks.

'You've lost a bit o' ground lately, young man,' he would say, directing a piercing glance from my face down to my feet and down again. 'Aye, you're losin' ground fast – it's plain to see.'

Or another time it might be, 'You've run off a bit, Mr Herriot. There's no doubt you've run off.' And his stick would twitch in his hand as if he would have liked to give me an exploratory poke.

But today he didn't say anything until I had finished stitching the teat and was washing my hands in a bucket of water. Then as I straightened up he adopted his usual stance; throwing up his head and jutting his chin he appraised me gloomily.

'You've failed since ah last saw you, young man. Soon as you walked across t'yard this morning ah thought to meself, aye that lad's failed over t'last week or two.'

And as the sharp eyes bored into me from behind the long pointed nose his viewpoint was plain. He, at any rate, could contemplate the prospect of my early demise with some compassion but without going to pieces.

I worked up a sickly smile as I always did.

'Oh, I'm fine, Mr Grimsdale, never felt better.' But the voice had an uncertain quaver and I knew by my sinking stomach that his shaft had gone home again. And then there was the usual humiliating business when I had driven away. I always stopped the car just round the corner where a high curve of wall hid me from the farm.

Staring into the car mirror I put out my tongue, pulled down my eyelids to have a look at my mucous membranes and muttered desperately as though Mr Grimsdale was still there.

'I feel fine, really I do ... fine ... fine ...'

Talking of farmers' attitudes to their vets, I think it is fair to say that in Robert Hewison's cheerful household, though Siegfried's prowess as an animal doctor was highly regarded, his main claim to fame was as a judge of Christmas cake.

Mrs Hewison was a baker of great repute and when she started long before the festive season to stir up vast quantities of fruit and candied peel and butter and all the other things that went into her peerless cakes it was a very serious business. Not that there was any question of a failure – her cakes varied from excellent to superb – but once the long process had been completed and the last piece of marzipan and icing applied she dearly loved to have the accolade from an expert. And in her eyes Siegfried was number one.

Robert Hewison confided in me once: 'Tha knows, my missus is never content till your guvnor's had a taste.'

I was privileged to be present on one of these occasions. It was a few days before Christmas and Siegfried and I had gone together to Robert's farm to lift a horse which had got cast in its stall. We did the job successfully with the aid of slings and a block and tackle and Robert, as always, asked us into the house.

The farmer's wife, her dark, rather solemn face illumined by friendly eyes, ushered us to the two tall wooden chairs by the fireside.

'Come and get warmed up, gentlemen,' she said. 'And you'll have a drink and a bit o' cake, won't you?'

'You're very kind, Mrs Hewison,' replied Siegfried. 'That would be lovely.'

He sat down, but I went through to the offshoot of the kitchen to wash my hands at the sink. The farmer's wife was cutting at a large cake on a table nearby. She nudged me and whispered conspiratorially.

'This isn't me own cake. It's one me sister baked, but I'm not telling Mr Farnon that. We'll just see what he says.'

I stared at her. 'But is that quite fair? Hadn't you better tell him?'

'No, I want to have his true judgement, so I'm not sayin' a word.'

I went back to the kitchen with some misgiving. It was unlike this lady to play jokes, but maybe after years of unqualified approbation she wanted to put my colleague's sincerity to the test. Anyway, I hoped nothing unfortunate would happen.

As I took my place by the fire Robert and his three sons came in and sat around in a circle. I was given a piece of cake, too, but nobody paid any attention to me; all eyes were on Siegfried.

'I'd like to know what you think of t'cake this year, Mr Farnon,' our hostess said.

My colleague toasted the family gracefully, sipped at his whisky then lifted the plate with its slice of cake. Silence fell upon the company. Holding the plate in the palm of his hand he studied the cake carefully from various angles before breaking off a fair-sized piece. This he massaged gently between thumb and forefinger for a few moments, his eyes half closed. Then after sniffing at it a couple of times he put it in his mouth.

I could feel the tension building in the room as he chewed gravely, his face quite expressionless. When he had finally swallowed the portion he smacked his lips once or twice meditatively then turned his head and looked full at Mrs Hewison. Amid a deathly hush they gazed into each other's eyes for several long seconds but Siegfried still didn't say anything. Instead he reached for his glass again and took another drink of whisky which he seemed to wash around his mouth before breaking off another portion of cake.

He took a long time over this piece, chewing in a slow motion, his eyes, deadly serious, staring sightlessly in front of him. Robert, the boys, all of us, leaned a little forward in our chairs, as he finally swallowed the last crumb, wiped his lips and sat immobile, apparently wrapped in thought. Then as he clearly came to a decision he sat upright in his chair, straightened his shoulders and turned resolutely towards the lady of the house once more.

Siegfried was and is a man of the highest principle. Over the years I have known him he has always given his opinions truthfully, fearlessly and with a total disregard of the consequences; and though this trait ruffled the stream of his life on occasion, there were times, as now, when it stood him in good stead.

'Mrs Hewison,' he said, his eyes steady and unwavering. 'This is a good cake.' He paused. 'A very good cake indeed.' He hesitated again and I could see the real iron in the man coming out. 'But if you will permit me, I'm bound to say that it is not up to your usual standard.'

Mrs Hewison, usually an undemonstrative person, burst into a loud cry of delight and Robert and his sons, who were obviously in on the joke, roared and clapped their hands.

Siegfried looked around in some surprise at the sudden tumult which went on and on as though somebody had scored a goal in the cup final. He was obviously puzzled and of course there was no way he could know that his previous exalted position in the household was now utterly impregnable.

# 13

I was back at Granville Bennett's again. Back in the tiled operating theatre with the great lamp pouring its harsh light over my colleague's bowed head, over the animal nurses, the rows of instruments, the little animal stretched on the table.

Until late this afternoon I had no idea that another visit to Hartington was in store for me; not until the doorbell rang as I was finishing a cup of tea and I went along the passage and opened the door and saw Colonel Bosworth on the step. He was holding a wicker cat basket.

'Can I trouble you for a moment, Mr Herriot?' he said.

His voice sounded different and I looked up at him questioningly. Most people had to look up at Colonel Bosworth with his lean six feet three inches and his tough soldier's face which matched the D.S.O. and M.C. which he had brought out of the war. I saw quite a lot of him, not only when he came to the surgery but out in the country where he spent most of his time hacking along the quiet roads around Darrowby on a big hunter with two Cairn terriers trotting behind. I liked him. He was a formidable man but he was unfailingly courteous and there was a gentleness in him which showed in his attitude to his animals.

'No trouble,' I replied. 'Please come inside.'

In the waiting room he held out the basket. His eyes were strained and there was shock and hurt in his face.

'It's little Maudie,' he said.

'Maudie . . . your black cat?' When I had been to his house the little creature had usually been in evidence, rubbing down the colonel's ankles, jumping on his knee competing assiduously with the terriers for his attention.

'What's the matter, is she ill?'

'No . . . no . . .' He swallowed and spoke carefully. 'She's had an accident, I'm afraid.'

'What kind of accident?'

'A car struck her. She never goes out into the road in front of the house but for some reason she did this afternoon.'

'I see.' I took the basket from him. 'Did the wheel go over her?'

'No, I don't think it can have done that because she ran back into the house afterwards.'

'Oh well,' I said. 'That sounds hopeful. It probably isn't anything very much.'

The colonel paused for a moment. 'Mr Herriot, I wish you were right but its . . . rather frightful. It's her face you see. Must have been a glancing blow but I . . . really don't see how she can live.'

'Oh . . . as bad as that . . . I'm sorry. Anyway come through with me and I'll have a look.'

He shook his head. 'No, I'll stay here if you don't mind. And there's just one thing.' He laid his hand briefly on the basket. 'If you think, as I do, that it's hopeless, please put her to sleep immediately. She must not suffer any more.'

I stared at him uncomprehendingly for a moment then hurried along the passage to the operating room. I put the basket on the table, slid the wooden rod from its loops and opened the lid. I could see the sleek little black form crouched in the depths and as I stretched my hand out gingerly towards it the head rose slowly and turned towards me with a long, open-mouthed wail of agony.

And it wasn't just an open mouth. The whole lower jaw was dangling uselessly, the mandible shattered and splintered, and as another chilling cry issued from the basket I had a horrific glimpse of jagged ends of bone gleaming from the froth of blood and saliva.

I closed the basket quickly and leaned on the lid.

'Christ!' I gasped. 'Oh Christ!'

I closed my eyes but couldn't dispel the memory of the grotesque face, the terrible sound of pain and worst of all the eyes filled with the terrified bewilderment which makes animal suffering so unbearable.

With trembling haste I reached behind me to the trolley for the bottle of Nembutal. This was the one thing vets could do, at any rate; cut short this agony with merciful speed. I pulled 5 c.c.'s into the syringe; more than enough – she'd drift into sleep and never wake up again. Opening the basket I reached down and underneath the cat and slipped the needle through the abdominal skin; an intraperitoneal injection would have to do. But as I depressed the plunger it was as though a calmer and less involved person was tapping me on the shoulder and saying, 'Just a minute, Herriot, take it easy. Why don't you think about this for a bit?'

I stopped after injecting 1 c.c. That would be enough to anaesthetise Maudie. In a few minutes she would feel nothing. Then I closed the lid and began to walk about the room. I had repaired a lot of cats' broken jaws in my time; they seemed to be prone to this trouble and I had gained much satisfaction from wiring up symphyseal fractures and watching their uneventful healing. But this was different.

After five minutes I opened the basket and lifted the little cat, sound asleep and as limp as a rag doll, on to the table.

I swabbed out the mouth and explored with careful fingers, trying to piece the grisly jigsaw together. The symphysis had separated right enough and that could be fastened together with wire, but how about those mandibular rami, smashed clean through on both sides – in fact there were two fractures on the left. And some of the teeth had been knocked out and others slackened; there was nothing to get hold of. Could they be held together by metal plates screwed into the bone? Maybe... and was there a man with the skill and equipment to do such a job ...? I thought I just might know one.

I went over the sleeping animal carefully; there wasn't a thing amiss except that pathetic drooping jaw. Meditatively I stroked the smooth, shining fur. She was only a young cat with years of life in front of her and as I stood there the decision came to me with a surge of relief and I trotted back along the passage to ask the colonel if I could take Maudie through to Granville Bennett.

It had started to snow heavily when I set out and I was glad it was downhill all the way to Hartington; many of the roads higher up the Dale would soon be impassable on a night like this.

In the Veterinary Hospital I watched the big man drilling, screwing, stitching. It wasn't the sort of job which could be hurried but it was remarkable how quickly those stubby fingers could work. Even so, we had been in the theatre for nearly an hour and Granville's complete absorption showed in the long silences broken only by the tinkling of instruments, occasional barking commands and now and then a sudden flare of exasperation. And it wasn't only the nurses who suffered; I had scrubbed up and had been pressed into service and when I failed to hold the jaw exactly as my colleague desired he exploded in my face.

'Not that bloody way, Jim! ... What the hell are you playing at? ... No, no, no, no, *no*! ..... Oh God Almighty!'

But at last all was finished and Granville threw off his cap and turned away from the table with the air of finality which had made me envy him the first time. He was sweating. In his office he washed his hands, towelled his brow, and pulled on an elegant grey jacket from the pocket of which he produced a pipe. It was a different pipe from last time; I learned in time that all Granville's pipes were not only beautiful but big and this one had a bowl like a fair-sized coffee cup. He rubbed it gently along the side of his nose, gave it a polish with the yellow cloth he always seemed to carry and held it lovingly against the light.

'Straight grain, Jim. Superb, isn't it?'

He contentedly scooped tobacco from his vast pouch, ignited it and puffed a cloud of delectable smoke at me before taking me by the arm. 'Come on, laddie. I'll show you round while they're clearing up in there.'

We did a tour of the hospital, taking in the waiting and consulting rooms, X-ray room, dispensary and, of course, the office with its impressive card index system with case histories of all patients, but the bit I enjoyed most was walking along the row of heated cubicles where an assortment of animals were recovering from their operations.

Granville stabbed his pipe at them as we went along. 'Spay, enterotomy, aural haematoma, entropion.' Then he bent suddenly, put a finger through the wire front and adopted a wheedling tone. 'Come now, George, come on little fellow, don't be frightened, it's only Uncle Granville.'

A small West Highland with a leg in a cast hobbled to the front and my colleague tickled his nose through the wire.

'That's George Wills-Fentham,' he said in explanation. 'Old Lady Wills-Fentham's pride and joy. Nasty compound fracture but he's doing very nicely. He's a bit shy is George but a nice little chap when you get to know him, aren't you, old lad?' He continued his tickling and in the dim light I could see the short white tail wagging furiously.

Maudie was lying in the very last of the recovery pens, a tiny, trembling figure. That trembling meant she was coming out of the anaesthetic and I opened the door and stretched my hand out to her. She still couldn't raise her head but she was looking at me and as I gently stroked her side, her mouth opened in a faint rusty miaow. And with a thrill of deep pleasure I saw that her lower jaw belonged to her again; she could open and close it; that hideous dangling tatter of flesh and bone was only a bad memory.

'Marvellous, Granville,' I murmured. 'Absolutely bloody marvellous.'

Smoke plumed in quiet triumph from the noble pipe. 'Yes, it's not bad, is it laddie. A week or two on fluids and she'll be as good as new. No problems there.'

I stood up. 'Great! I can't wait to tell Colonel Bosworth. Can I take her home tonight?'

'No, Jim, no. Not this time. I just want to keep an eye on her for a couple of days then maybe the colonel can collect her himself.' He led me back into the brightly lit office where he eyed me for a moment.

'You must come and have a word with Zoe while you're here,' he said. 'But first, just a suggestion. I wonder if you'd care to slip over with me to . . .'

I took a rapid step backward. 'Well . . . er . . . really. I don't think so,' I gabbled. 'I enjoyed my visit to the club that other night but . . . er . . . perhaps not this evening.'

'Hold on, laddie, hold on,' Granville said soothingly. 'Who said anything about the club? No, I just wondered if you'd like to come to a meeting with me?'

'Meeting?'

'Yes, Professor Milligan's come through from Edinburgh to speak to the Northern Veterinary Society about metabolic diseases. I think you'd enjoy it.'

'You mean milk fever, acetonaemia and all that?'

'Correct. Right up your street, old son.'

'Well it is, isn't it? I wonder . . .' I stood for a few moments deep in thought, and one of the thoughts was why an exclusively small animal man like Granville wanted to hear about cow complaints. But I was maybe doing him an injustice; he probably wanted to maintain a broad, liberal view of veterinary knowledge.

It must have been obvious that I was dithering because he prodded me a little further.

'I'd like to have your company, Jim, and anyway I see you're all dressed and ready for anything. Matter of fact when you walked in tonight I couldn't help thinking what a smart lad you looked.'

He was right there. I hadn't dashed through in my farm clothes this time. With the memory of my last visit still painfully fresh in my mind I was determined that if I was going to meet the charming Zoe again I was going to be: (a) Properly dressed, (b) Sober, (c) in a normal state of health and not bloated and belching like an impacted bullock. Helen, agreeing that my image needed refurbishing, had rigged me out in my best suit.

Granville ran his hand along my lapel. 'Fine piece of serge if I may say so.'

I made up my mind. 'Right, I'd like to come with you. Just let me ring Helen to say I won't be straight back and then I'm your man.'

# 14

Outside it was still snowing; city snow drifting down in a wet curtain which soon lost itself in the dirty churned-up slush in the streets. I pulled my coat higher round my neck and huddled deeper in the Bentley's leather luxury. As we swept past dark buildings and shops I kept expecting Granville to turn up some side street and stop, but within a few minutes we were speeding through the suburbs up towards the North Road. This meeting, I thought, must be out in one of the country institutes, and I didn't say anything until we had reached Scotch Corner and the big car had turned on to the old Roman Road at Bowes.

I stretched and yawned. 'By the way, Granville, where are they holding this meeting?'

'Appleby,' my colleague replied calmly.

I came bolt upright in my seat then I began to laugh.

'What's the joke, old son?' Granville enquired.

'Well ... Appleby ... ha-ha-ha! Come on, where are we really heading?'

'I've told you, laddie, the Pemberton Arms, Appleby, to be exact.'

'Do you mean it?'

'Of course.'

'But hell, Granville, that's on the other side of the Pennines.'

'Quite right. Always has been, laddie.'

I ran a hand through my hair. 'Wait a minute. Surely it isn't worth going about forty miles in weather like this. We'll never get over Bowes Moor you know – in fact I heard yesterday it was blocked. Anyway, it's nearly eight o'clock – we'd be too late.'

The big man reached across and patted my knee.

'Stop worrying, Jim. We'll get there and we'll be in plenty of time. You've got to remember you're sitting in a proper motor car now. A drop of snow is nothing.'

As if determined to prove his word he put his foot down and the great car hurtled along the dead straight stretch of road. We skidded a bit on the corner at Greta Bridge then roared through Bowes and up to the highest country. I couldn't see much. In fact on the moor top I couldn't see anything, because up there it was the real country snow; big dry flakes driving straight into the headlights and settling comfortably with millions of their neighbours on the already deep white carpet on the road. I just didn't know how Granville was able to see, never mind drive fast; and I had no idea how we were going to get back over here in a few hours' time when the wind had drifted the snow across the road. But I kept my mouth shut. It was becoming increasingly obvious that I emerged as a sort of maiden aunt in Granville's company, so I held my peace and prayed.

I followed this policy through Brough and along the lower road where the going was easier until I climbed out with a feeling of disbelief in the yard of the Pemberton Arms. It was nine o'clock.

We slipped into the back of the room and I settled into my chair, prepared to improve my mind a little. There was a man on the platform holding forth and at first I had difficulty in picking up the substance of his words; he wasn't mentioning anything about animal diseases but suddenly everything clicked into place.

'We are indeed grateful,' the man was saying, 'to Professor Milligan for coming all this way and for giving us a most interesting and instructive talk. I know I speak for the entire audience when I say we have enjoyed it thoroughly, so may I ask you to show your appreciation in the usual manner.' There was a long round of applause then an outburst of talk and a pushing back of chairs.

I turned to Granville in some dismay. 'That was the vote of thanks. It's finished.'

'So it is, laddie.' My colleague didn't seem unduly disappointed or even surprised. 'But come with me – there are compensations.'

We joined the throng of vets and moved across the richly carpeted hall to another room where bright lights shone down on a row of tables laden with food. Then I recognised Bill Warrington the Burroughs Wellcome representative and all became clear.

This was a commercially sponsored evening and the real action, in Granville's estimation, began right here. I remembered then that Siegfried had once told me that Granville hated to miss any of these occasions. Though the most generous of men there was some piquancy in the gratis food and drink which attracted him irresistibly.

Even now he was guiding me purposefully towards the bar. But our progress was slow due to a phenomenon peculiar to Granville; everybody seemed to know him. Since those days I have been with him to restaurants, pubs, dances and it has been just the same. In fact I have often thought that if I took him to visit some lost tribe in the jungles of the Amazon one of them would jump and say, 'Well hello, Granville old boy!' and slap him on the back.

Finally however he fought his way through his fellow vets and we reached the bar where two dark little men in white coats were already under pressure; they were working with the impersonal concentration of people who knew that the whisky always took a hammering on veterinary evenings, but they paused and smiled as my colleague's massive presence hovered at the counter.

'Now then, Mr Bennett. How are you, Mr Bennett?'

'Good evening, Bob. Nice to see you, Reg.' Granville responded majestically.

I noticed that Bob put down his bottle of ordinary whisky and reached down for a bottle of Glenlivet Malt to charge Granville's glass. The big man sniffed the fine spirit appreciatively.

'And one for my friend, Mr Herriot,' he said.

The barmen's respectful expressions made me feel suddenly important and I found myself in possession of my own vast measure of Glenlivet. I had to get it down quickly followed by a few speedy refills since the barmen took their cue from my companion's consumption.

Then I followed in Granville's regal wake as he made his way among the tables with the air of a man in his natural environment. Messrs Burroughs Wellcome had done us proud and we worked our way through a variety of canapes, savouries and cold meats. Now and again we revisited the bar for more of the Glenlivet then back to the tables.

I knew I had drunk too much and now I was eating too much.

But the difficulty with Granville was that if I ever declined anything he took it as a personal insult.

'Try one of those prawn things,' he would say, sinking his teeth into a mushroom vol au vent and if I hesitated a wounded look would come into his eyes.

But I was enjoying myself. Veterinary surgeons are my favourite people and I revelled as I always did in their tales of successes and failures. Especially the failures; they were particularly soothing. Whenever the thought of how we were going to get home stole into my mind I banished it quickly.

Granville seemed to have no qualms because he showed no signs of moving when the company began to thin out; in fact we were the last to leave, our departure being accorded a touch of ceremony by a final substantial stirrup cup from Bob and Reg.

As we left the hotel I felt fine; a little light-headed perhaps and with the merest hint of regret at being pressed to a second helping of trifle and cream, but otherwise in excellent shape. As we settled once more into the Bentley Granville was at his most expansive.

'Excellent meeting that, Jim. I told you it would be worth the journey.'

We were the only members of the company who were headed eastward and were alone on the road. In fact it occurred to me that we hadn't seen a single car on the road to Appleby and now there was something uncomfortable in our total isolation. The snow had stopped and the brilliant moon flooded its cold light over a white empty world. Empty, that is, except for us, and our solitary state was stressed by the smooth, virgin state of the glistening carpet ahead.

I was conscious of an increasing disquiet as the great gaunt spine of the Pennines bulked before us and as we drew nearer it reared up like an angry white monster.

Past the snow-burdened roofs of Brough then the long climb with the big car slipping from side to side as it fought its way up the bending, twisting hill, engine bellowing. I thought I'd feel better when we reached the top but the first glimpse of the

Bowes Moor road sent my stomach into a lurch of apprehension; miles and miles of it coiling its way across the most desolate stretch of country in all England. And even from this distance you could see the drifts, satin smooth and beautiful, pushing their deadly way across our path.

On either side of the road a vast white desert rolled and dipped endlessly toward the black horizon; there was not a light, not a movement, not a sign of life anywhere.

The pipe jutted aggressively as Granville roared forward to do battle. We hit the first drift, slewed sideways for a tense few seconds then we were on the other side, speeding into the unbroken surface. Then the next drift and the next and the next. Often I thought we were stuck but always, wheels churning, engine screaming we emerged. I had had plenty of experience of snow driving and I could appreciate Granville's expertise as, without slackening speed he picked out the shallowest, narrowest part of each obstruction for his attack. He had this heavy powerful car to help him but he could drive all right.

However, my trepidation at being stranded in this waste land was gradually being overshadowed by another uneasiness. When I had left the hotel I was pretty well topped up with food and drink and if I had been handled gently for the next few hours I'd have been all right. But on the bumpy journey to Brough I had been increasingly aware of a rising queasiness; my mind kept flitting back unhappily to that exotic cocktail, Reg's speciality, which Granville had said I must try; he had prevailed on me too, to wash down the whiskies with occasional beers which, he said, were essential to maintain a balanced intake of fluids and solids. And that final trifle – it had been a mistake.

And now I wasn't just being bumped, I was being thrown around like a pea in a drum as the Bentley lurched and skidded and occasionally took off altogether. Soon I began to feel very ill indeed. And like a seasick man who didn't care if the ship foundered I lost all interest in our progress; I closed my eyes, braced my feet on the floor and shrunk into an inner misery.

I hardly noticed as, after an age of violent motion, we finally began to go downhill and thundered through Bowes. After that there was little danger of having to spend the night in the car but Granville kept his foot down and we rocked over the frozen ground while I felt steadily worse.

I would dearly have loved to ask my colleague to stop and allow me to be quietly sick by the roadside but how do you say such a thing to a man who never seemed to be in the least affected by over-indulgence and who, even at that moment was chatting gaily as he refilled his pipe with his free hand. The internal pounding seemed to have forced extra alcohol into my bloodstream because on top of my other discomforts my vision was blurred, I was dizzy and had the strong conviction that if I tried to stand up I would fall flat on my face.

I was busy with these preoccupations when the car stopped.

'We'll just pop in and say hello to Zoe,' Granville said.

'Wha's that?' I slurred.

'We'll go inside for a few minutes.'

I looked around. 'Where are we?'

Granville laughed. 'Home, old son. I can see a light, so Zoe's still up. You must come and have a quick cup of coffee.'

I crawled laboriously from the seat and stood leaning on the car. My colleague tripped lightly to the door and rang the bell. He was as fit as a fiddle I thought bitterly as I reeled after him. I was slumped against the porch breathing heavily when the door opened and there was Zoe Bennett, bright eyed, glowing, beautiful as ever.

'Why Mr Herriot!' she cried. 'How nice to see you again!'

Slack-jawed, green-faced, rumple-suited, I stared into her eyes, gave a gentle hiccup and staggered past her into the house.

Next morning Granville rang to say all was going to be well because Maudie had been able to lap a little milk. It was kind of him to let me know and I didn't want to sound churlish by saying that was all I had managed to do, too.

It happened that morning by a coincidence that I had a far outlying visit and had to pass the Scotch Corner turning on the North Road. I stopped the car and sat gazing at the long snow-covered road stretching towards the Pennines. I was starting my engine when an A.A. man came over and spoke at my window.

'You're not thinking of trying the Bowes Moor road, are you?' he said.

'No, no. I was just looking.'

He nodded in satisfaction.

'I'm glad to hear that. It's blocked you know. There hasn't been a car over there for two days.'

# 15

One of the things Helen and I had to do was furnish our bedsitter and kitchen. And when I say 'furnish' I use the word in its most austere sense. We had no high-flown ideas about luxury; it was, after all, a temporary arrangement and anyway we had no money to throw around.

My present to Helen at the time of our marriage was a modest gold watch and this had depleted my capital to the extent that a bank statement at the commencement of our married life revealed the sum of twenty-five shillings standing to my credit. Admittedly I was a partner now but when you start from scratch it takes a long time to get your head above water.

But we did need the essentials like a table, chairs, cutlery, crockery, the odd rug and carpet, and Helen and I decided that it would be most sensible to pick up these things at house sales. Since I was constantly going round the district I was able to drop in at these events and the duty of acquiring our necessities had been delegated to me. But after a few weeks it was clear that I was falling down on the job.

I had never realised it before but I had a blind spot in these matters. I would go to a sale and come away with a pair of brass candlesticks and a stuffed owl. On another occasion I acquired an ornate inkwell with a carved metal figure of a dog on it together with a polished wooden box with innumerable fascinating little drawers and compartments for keeping homeopathic prescriptions. I could go on for a long time about the things I bought but they were nearly all useless.

Helen was very nice about it.

'Jim,' she said one day when I was proudly showing her a model of a fully rigged sailing ship in a bottle which I had been lucky enough to pick up, 'it's lovely, but I don't think we need it right now.'

I must have been a big disappointment to the poor girl and also to the local auctioneers who ran the sales. These gentlemen, when they saw me hovering around the back of the crowd would cheer up visibly. They, in common with most country folk, thought all vets were rich and that I would be bidding for some of the more expensive items. When a nice baby grand piano came up they would look over the heads at me with an expectant smile and their disappointment was evident when I finally went away with a cracked-faced barometer or a glove stretcher.

A sense of my failure began to seep through to me and when I had to take a sample through to the Leeds laboratory I saw a chance to atone.

'Helen,' I said, 'there's a huge saleroom right in the city centre. I'll take an hour off and go in there. I'm bound to see something we need.'

'Oh good!' my wife replied. 'That's a great idea! There'll be lots to choose from there. You haven't had much chance to find anything at those country sales.' Helen was always kind.

After my visit to the Leeds lab I asked the way to the salerooms.

'Leave your car here,' one of the locals advised me. 'You'll never park in the main street and you can get a tram right to the door.'

I was glad I listened to him because when I arrived the traffic was surging both ways in a nonstop stream. The saleroom was at the top of an extraordinarily long flight of smooth stone steps leading right to the top of the building. When I arrived, slightly out of breath, I thought immediately I had come to the right place, a vast enclosure strewn with furniture, cookers, gramophones, carpets – everything you could possibly want in a house.

I wandered around fascinated for quite a long time then my attention centred on two tall piles of books quite near to where the auctioneer was selling. I lifted one of them. It was *The Geography of the World*. I had never seen such beautiful books; as big as encyclopaedias and with thick embossed covers and gold lettering. The pages, too, were edged with gold and the paper was of a delightfully smooth texture. Quite enthralled I turned the pages, marvelling at the handsome illustrations, the coloured pictures each with its covering transparent sheet. They were a little old-fashioned, no doubt, and when I looked at the front I saw they were printed in 1858; but they were things of beauty.

Looking back, I feel that fate took a hand here because I had just reluctantly turned away when I heard the auctioneer's voice.

'Now then, here's a lovely set of books. *The Geography of the World in Twenty Four Volumes*. Just look at them. You don't find books like them today. Who'll give me a bid ?'

I agreed with him. They were unique. But they must be worth pounds. I looked round the company but nobody said a word.

'Come on, ladies and gentlemen, surely somebody wants this wonderful addition to their library. Now what do I hear ?'

Again the silence than a seedy looking man in a soiled mackintosh spoke up.

'Arf a crown,' he said morosely.

I looked around expecting a burst of laughter at this sally, but nobody was amused. In fact the auctioneer didn't seem surprised.

'I have a half a crown bid.' He glanced about him and raised his hammer. With a thudding of the heart I realised he was going to sell.

I heard my own voice, slightly breathless. 'Three shillings.'

'I have a bid of three shillings for *The Geography of the World in Twenty Four Volumes.* Are you all done?' Bang went the hammer. 'Sold to the gentleman over there.'

They were mine! I couldn't believe my luck. This surely was the bargain to end all bargains. I paid my three shillings while one of the men tied a length of rough string round each pile. The first pause in my elation came when I tried to lift my purchases. Books are heavy things and these were massive specimens; and there were twenty-four of them.

With a hand under each string I heaved like a weight-lifter and, pop-eyed, veins standing out on my forehead, I managed to get them off the ground and began to stagger shakily to the exit.

The first string broke on the top step and twelve of my volumes cascaded downwards over the smooth stone. After the first moment of panic I decided that the best way was to transport the intact set down to the bottom and come back for the others. I did this but it took me some time and I began to perspire before I was all tied up again and poised on the kerb ready to cross the road.

The second string broke right in the middle of the tramlines as I attempted a stiff-legged dash through a break in the traffic. For about a year I scrabbled there in the middle of the road while horns hooted, tram bells clanged and an interested crowd watched from the sidewalks. I had just got the escaped volumes in a column and was reknotting the string when the other lot burst from their binding and slithered gently along the metal rails; and it was when I was retrieving them that I noticed a large policeman, attracted by the din and the long line of vehicles, walking with measured strides in my direction.

In my mental turmoil I saw myself for the first time in the hands of the law. I could be done on several charges – Breach of the Peace, Obstructing Traffic to name only two – but I perceived that the officer was approaching very slowly and rightly or wrongly I feel that when a policeman strolls towards you like that he is a decent chap and is giving you a chance to get away. I took my chance. He was still several yards off when I had my two piles reassembled and I thrust my hands under the strings, tottered to the far kerb and lost myself in the crowd.

When I finally decided there was no longer any fear of feeling the dread grip on my shoulder I stopped in my headlong flight and rested in a shop doorway. I was puffing like a broken-winded horse and my hands hurt abominably. The saleroom string was coarse, hairy and abrasive and already it threatened to take the skin off my fingers.

Anyway, I thought, the worst was over. The tram stop was just at the end of the block there. I joined the queue and when the tram arrived, shuffled forward with the others. I had one foot on the step when a large hand was thrust before my eyes.

'Just a minute, brother, just a minute! Where d'you think you're goin'?' The face under the conductor's hat was the meaty, heavy jowled, pop-eyed kind which seems to take a mournful pleasure in imparting bad news.

'You're not bringin' that bloody lot on 'ere, brother, I'll tell tha now!'

I looked up at him in dismay. 'But ... it's just a few books ...'

'Few books! You want a bloody delivery van for that lot. You're not usin' my tram – passengers couldn't stir inside!' His mouth turned down aggressively.

'Oh but really,' I said with a ghastly attempt at an ingratiating smile, 'I'm just going as far as ...'

'You're not goin' anywhere in 'ere, brother! Ah've no time to argue – move your foot, ah'm off!'

The bell ding-dinged and the tram began to move. As I hopped off backwards one of the strings broke again.

After I had got myself sorted out I surveyed my situation and it appeared fairly desperate. My car must be over a mile away, mostly uphill, and I would defy the most stalwart Nepalese Sherpa to transport these books that far. I could of course just abandon the things; lean them against this wall and take to my heels ... But no, that would be anti-social and anyway they were beautiful. If only I could get them home all would be well.

Another tram rumbled up to the stop and again I hefted my

burden and joined the in-going passengers, hoping nobody would notice.

It was a female voice this time.

'Sorry, you can't come on, luv.' She was middle-aged, motherly and her plump figure bulged her uniform tightly.

'We don't 'ave delivery men on our trams. It's against t'rules.'

I repressed a scream. 'But I'm not a . . . these are my own books. I've just bought them.'

'Bought 'em ?' Her eyebrows went up as she stared at the dusty columns.

'Yes . . . and I've got to get them home somehow.'

'Well somebody'll tek 'em home for you luv. Hasta got far to go ?'

'Darrowby.'

'Eee, by gum, that's a long way. Right out in t'country.' She peered into the tram's interior. 'But there isn't no room in there, luv.'

The passengers had all filed in and I was left alone standing between my twin edifices; and the conductress must have seen a desperate light in my eyes because she made a sudden gesture.

'Come on then, luv! You stand out 'ere on the platform wi' me. I'm not supposed to, but ah can't see you stuck there.'

I didn't know whether to kiss her or burst into tears. In the end I did neither but stacked the books in a corner of the platform and stood swaying over them till we arrived at the park where I had left my car.

The relief at my deliverance was such that I laughed off the few extra contretemps on my way to the car. There were in fact several more spills before I had the books tucked away on the back seat but when I finally drove away I felt like singing.

It was when I was threading my way through the traffic that I began to rejoice that I lived in the country, because the car was filled with an acrid reek which I thought could only come from the conglomeration of petrol fumes and industrial smoke. But even when the city had been left behind and I was climbing into the swelling green of the Pennines the aroma was still with me.

I wound down the window and gulped greedily as the sweet grassy air flowed in but when I closed it the strange pungency returned immediately. I stopped, leaned over and sniffed at the region of the back seat. And there was no doubt about it; it was the books.

Ah well, they must have been kept in a damp place or something like that. I was sure it would soon pass off. But in the meantime it certainly was powerful; it nearly made my eyes water.

I had never really noticed the long climb to our eyrie on top of Skeldale House but it was different today. I suppose my arms and shoulders were finally beginning to feel the strain and that string, bristly but fragile, was digging into my hands harder than ever, but it was true that every step was an effort and when I at last gained the top landing I almost collapsed against the door of our bed-sitter.

When, perspiring and dishevelled, I entered, Helen was on her knees, dusting the hearth. She looked up at me expectantly.

'Any luck, Jim?'

'Yes, I think so,' I replied with a trace of smugness. 'I think I got a bargain.'

Helen rose and looked at me eagerly. 'Really?'

'Yes.' I decided to play my trump card. 'I only had to spend three shillings!'

'Three shillings! What ... where ...?'

'Wait there a minute.' I went out to the landing and put my hand under those strings. This, thank heaven, would be the last time I would have to do this. A lunge and a heave and I had my prizes through the doorway and displayed for my wife's inspection.

She stared at the two piles. 'What have you got there?'

'*The Geography of the World in Twenty Four Volumes,*' I replied triumphantly.

'The Geography of the ... and is that all?'

'Yes, couldn't manage anything else, I'm afraid. But look — aren't they magnificent books!'

My wife's level gaze had something of disbelief, a little of wonder. For a moment one corner of her mouth turned up then she coughed and became suddenly brisk.

'Ah well, we'll have to see about getting some shelves for them. Anyway, leave them there for now.' She went over and kneeled again by the hearth. But after a minute or two she paused in her dusting.

'Can you smell anything funny?'

'Well, er . . . I think it's the books, Helen. They're just a bit musty . . . I don't think it'll last long.'

But the peculiar exhalation was very pervasive and it was redolent of extreme age. Very soon the atmosphere in our room was that of a freshly opened mausoleum.

I could see Helen didn't want to hurt my feelings but she kept darting looks of growing alarm at my purchases. I decided to say it for her.

'Maybe I'd better take them downstairs just for now.'

She nodded gratefully.

The descent was torture, made worse by the fact that I had thought I was finished with such things. I finally staggered into the office and parked the books behind the desk. I was panting and rubbing my hands when Siegfried came in.

'Ah, James, had a nice run through to Leeds?'

'Yes, they said at the lab that they'd give us a ring about those sheep as soon as they've cultured the organisms.'

'Splendid!' My colleague opened the door of the cupboard and put some forms inside then he paused and began to sniff the air.

'James, there's a bloody awful stink in here.'

I cleared my throat. 'Well yes, Siegfried, I bought a few books while I was in Leeds. They seem a little damp.' I pointed behind the desk.

Siegfried's eyes widened as he looked at the twin edifices. 'What the devil are they?'

I hesitated. '*The Geography of the World in Twenty Four Volumes.*'

He didn't say anything but looked from me to the books and back again. And he kept sniffing. There was no doubt that only his innate good manners were preventing him from telling me to get the damn things out of here.

'I'll find a place for them,' I said, and with a great weariness pushed my hands yet again under the strings. My mind was in a ferment as I shuffled along the passage. What in heaven's name was I going to do with them? But as I passed the cellar door on my right it seemed to provide the answer.

There were great vaulted chambers oeneath Skeldale House, a proper wine cellar in the grand days. The man who went down there to read the gas meter always described them as 'The Cattycombs' and as I descended into the murky, dank-smelling depths I thought sadly that it was a fitting resting place for my books. We kept only coal and wood down here now and from the muffled thuds I judged that Tristan was chopping logs.

He was a great log chopper and when I rounded the corner he was whirling his axe expertly round his head. He stopped when he saw me with my burden and asked the inevitable question.

I answered for, I hoped, the last time. '*The Geography of the World in Twenty Four Volumes*.' And I followed with a blow by blow account of my story.

As he listened he opened one tome after another, sniffed at it and replaced it hurriedly. And he didn't have to tell me, I knew already. My cherished books were down here to stay.

But the compassion which has always been and still is uppermost among the many facets of Tristan's character came to the fore now.

'Tell you what, Jim,' he said. 'We can put them in there.' He pointed to a dusty wine bin just visible in the dim light which filtered through the iron grating at the top of the coal chute which led from the street.

'It's just like a proper book shelf.'

He began to lift the volumes into the bin and when he had arranged them in a long row he ran his finger along the faded opulence of the bindings.

'There now, they look a treat in there, Jim.' He paused and rubbed his chin. 'Now all you want is somewhere to sit. Let's

112

see now . . . ah, yes!' He retreated into the gloom and reappeared with an armful of the biggest logs. He made a few more journeys and in no time had rigged up a seat for me within arm's reach of the books.

'That'll do fine,' he said with deep satisfaction. 'You can come down here and have a read whenever you feel like it.'

And that is how it turned out. The books never came up those steps again but quite frequently when I had a few minutes to spare and wanted to improve my mind I went down and sat on Tristan's seat in the twilight under the grating and renewed my acquaintance with *The Geography of the World in Twenty Four Volumes*.

# 16

I was sitting at the desk in the office at Skeldale House, writing up tuberculin testing forms when a young woman tapped on the door and walked in.

'I think I'm pregnant,' she murmured shyly.

I looked up at her in some surprise. It was an unusual opening to a conversation and I didn't quite know how to reply. She was about my own age and her demure attractiveness and rather prim style of dress didn't seem to belong to one so outspoken.

A furtive glance at her left hand did not help. She was wearing gloves so I was unable to use the presence or absence of a wedding ring to say either 'Congratulations' or 'Bad luck'.

'Really?' I replied lamely and followed it up with what I hoped was a non-committal smile.

'Yes, I think so.' She looked down and smoothed a finger along the strap of her handbag. Then she faced me again with an expectant expression as though she was waiting for me to make a move or say something helpful.

I dredged my mind desperately. There ought to be a fitting rejoinder somewhere but at the moment it escaped me. The silence was becoming embarrassing when the girl spoke again.

'Will you be able to examine me tonight?'

My face must have registered extreme emotion because she continued hastily.

'If it isn't suitable . . . I could come tomorrow night, doctor.'

Suddenly all was clear and I began to relax. The fact that our surgery was right next door to that of the local medicos gave rise to various contretemps but this was something new. Usually it was somebody wandering aimlessly along the passage, 'Looking for t'doctor', and they invariably left hastily when they discovered our identity. People often say to me, 'Vets must know just as much as doctors' but when it comes to the crunch they are never very keen to let me treat them.

There were notable exceptions to this rule among the older breed of farmers. Quite a few of these tough old men came to consult us about their rheumatism or their indigestion because 'them fellers next door never do me any bloody good.'

But usually it was just the accidental visitor and the doctors in their turn occasionally had their surgery hour enlivened by a lady marching in with a shaggy creature on a lead and asking them to squeeze out its anal glands.

I stood up and gave the girl a reassuring smile, while my mind ticked over busily. It seemed to me that in her delicate condition the sudden revelation that she was in the presence of a veterinary surgeon might have disastrous effects. So I took her gently by the arm, steered her from the room and along the passage to the front door. Still preserving a discreet silence I escorted her over the few yards of pavement to where our medical colleagues' plates hung by their entrance. I opened the door, led her inside, ushered her into the waiting room among the patient rows of country folk sitting there, gave her a final smile and nod, and fled.

There was another night when Tristan and I were tidying up after a cat spay. The sound of heavy boots echoed on the passage tiles then the door burst open and a stocky man in a cloth cap and collarless shirt strode in.

'I'm not goin' to be waitin' along there!' he said belligerently in the rich tones of Erin.

'Is that so?' I replied.

'Yiss, it is so. I haven't the time to be sittin' waitin'!'

'I see. Well what can we do for you?'

He grabbed a chair, pulled it up to the table, sat down, leaned his elbow on the freshly washed surface and looked up at me with a truculent eye.

'It's me ear!' He cocked the offending organ in my direction.

I realised he was one of the many Irish labourers who came to the district every year to help with the turnip hoeing. I could understand his entering the wrong door but was surprised at his aggressiveness; most of his compatriots were noted for their charm.

I was about to redirect him when Tristan, loth as always to pass up the slightest chance of a giggle, broke in.

'Your ear, eh?' he murmured sympathetically. 'Is it very painful?'

'Oh aye, it hurts bad. I think I've got a little bile startin' in there.'

Tristan tut-tutted. 'Too bad, too bad, let's have a look at it.' He moved over to the instrument cupboard and produced the auroscope which we used for examining dogs with ear canker. Taking it from its case he switched on the light and bent over the man.

'Just bend your head over a little, will you? Fine, fine.' He sounded very professional.

He inserted the auroscope and peered into the depths of the ear. 'Hmm . . . hmm . . . yes, yes, I see. Oh that's rather nasty.' At last he nodded gently. 'You are quite right. You have a little infected spot in there.'

'That's what I thought,' the man grunted. 'What are you going to do, then?'

Tristan rested his chin on his hands for a moment.

'I really think I ought to give you an injection. It would be the quickest way of clearing the thing up.' He spoke seriously but confidently with the hint of a grave smile at the corner of his lips. Like me he was wearing a white coat and would have passed without a quibble as a Harley Street specialist.

The man seemed similarly impressed. He squared his shoulders and nodded. 'Right then, let's be havin' it. You ought to know.'

As I watched wonderingly Tristan laid our white enamel tray on the table and on it he deposited a roll of cotton wool, a bottle of iodine and a row of enormous needles. They were the big, wide-bored needles for running calcium under a cow's skin and lying there they looked like items from a plumber's kit.

Next he rummaged in a cupboard for some time then emerged bearing the only 100 c.c. syringe in the practice. This was very rarely used – occasionally for giving sodium iodide injections to bullocks – and it was a fearsome object. Unlike its modern plastic counterparts it was made of glass and with its massive mounting of stainless steel and great metal plunger it looked much bigger.

The Irishman had been shifting uneasily in his seat as Tristan set out his stall but as the syringe clattered down on the enamel his eyes widened and he swallowed a couple of times.

My colleague, however, was wonderfully composed. He whistled softly as he fitted one of the huge needles to the nozzle of the syringe, then hummed a light tune while he hoisted a jar of acrivlavine solution on to the table. Carefully, almost lovingly, he drew up the full 100 c.c.'s then stood with the syringe poised against the light, giving off iridescent gleams as he rocked it gently to and fro.

The man had lost a lot of his bluster. His mouth hung slightly open.

'Just a minute,' he said a trifle breathlessly. 'Phwhaat doctors are you?'

'I beg your pardon,' enquired Tristan, still juggling with his dreadful instrument.

'Phwhaat's your names? Phwhaat do you call you doctors?'

Tristan gave a light laugh. 'Oh we're not doctors. We're vets.'

116

'Vits!' the chair grated on the floor as the man pushed back from the table.

'Yes, that's right,' Tristan said innocently, advancing with the loaded syringe. 'But you needn't worry. I assure you . . .'

I don't think I have ever seen anybody leave a room as quickly as that man. His chair overturned, there was a scurry, a scraping of hobnails, the clattering of fleeing feet in the passage then the banging of the outside door.

He was gone, never to return . . .

I don't think there is much doubt that we held an earthy fascination for our medical colleagues. They were constantly drifting in to watch us at work, particularly my own doctor, Harry Allinson, whose bald head often hovered over me as I operated on the small animals.

'I've got to hand it to you boys,' he used to say. 'When we come up against a surgical case we write a note to the hospital but you just switch on the steriliser.'

He was interested, too, in our work with the microscope. It intrigued him that we should spend so much time peering down at skin scrapings for mange, blood films for anthrax milk and sputum smears for tuberculosis.

'Sometimes I think you are a really scientific chap, Jim,' he would laugh. 'Then I see you with your instruments.'

He was referring to the occasions when he met me coming out of the surgery in the morning carrying my kit for the round; the grisly docking knives, firing tools, tooth forceps and dehorning shears which are now mercifully consigned to the museum. He would lift them from my arms and examine them wonderingly. 'You put the horse's tail in there, do you? And you bring the blade down like this . . . bang . . . just like a guillotine . . . my God!'

I felt the same way myself.

Harry Allinson's towering, wide-shouldered frame was part of the scenery of Darrowby. He was a Scot, like so many of the doctors in Yorkshire, a great athlete in his youth, a scratch golfer and an ebullient personality. One of his main characteristics was sheer noisiness and it was his habit to march into his patients' homes shouting and banging about. He was to deliver both my children and years later when one or the other was ill I have heard him come hollering into the house . . . 'Anybody in? Who's there? Come on, let's be having you!' And it was wonderful how the little measles-ridden form revived and began to shout back at him.

It was rewarding, too, to discover the gentleness and understanding behind the uproar. Those qualities were always there when people needed them.

Although he saw so much of my own work I was unable, naturally enough, to see him in action apart from when he was attending my own family. There was one time, however, when I did have a peep behind the curtain.

I was called to see a lame cart horse and as I walked on to the farm I was surprised to see the vast form of Gobber Newhouse almost obscuring the view. The entire twenty stones of him was leaning on a shovel and he appeared to be part of a gang of building workers putting up a new barn.

'Nah then, Herriot,' he said affably, 'what've ye been killin' this mornin'?' He followed this typical sally with a throaty chuckle and looked round at his colleagues for applause.

I gave him a nod and passed by. Fortunately I didn't often see Gobber but when I did he always addressed me as 'Herriot' and he invariably got in some little dig. And incidentally this was the first time I had ever observed him going through the motions of work; the Labour Exchange must have put some pressure on him because normally his life consisted of drinking, gambling, fighting and knocking his long-suffering little wife about.

I spent some time with the horse's hind foot resting on my knee as I pared away at the sole. But there was no sign of pus and the only abnormality was a smelly disintegration of the horn around the frog.

'He's got thrush,' I said to the farmer. 'This doesn't often make them lame but he has shed quite a lot of horn and some of the sensitive tissues are exposed. I'll leave you some lotion for him.'

I was walking back to get the bottle from the car when I saw there was some kind of commotion among the builder's men. They were standing in a group around Gobber who was seated on an upturned milk pail. He had his boot off and was anxiously examining his foot.

The foreman called over to me. 'Are you going straight back to Darrowby, Mr Herriot?'

'Yes, I am.'

'Well maybe you wouldn't mind givin' this feller a lift. He's stood on a nail – went clean through his boot. Could you take him to a doctor?'

'Yes, of course.' I went over and viewed the fat man whose mates seemed to be enjoying the situation.

'Here's the vet come to see ye, Gobber,' one of them cried. 'He'll soon fix you up. He's been doctorin' t'oss's foot, now he can do yours. Will we haud 'im down for ye, Mr Herriot?'

Another peered gloomily at the punctured wound on the foot. 'By Gaw, this is a 'ell of a farm for lockjaw, Gobber. Ah'm afraid ye'll die a 'orrible death.'

The big man was not amused. His face was a tragic mask and the effort of hauling his foot into view above his enormous belly made him shake uncontrollably.

I opened the car door and, supported by a man on either side, he limped with many facial contortions across the farmyard. At first I thought we'd never be able to get him into the little vehicle and he groaned piteously as we pushed, pulled and finally wedged him into the passenger seat.

As we headed along the road to Darrowby he cleared his throat nervously.

'Mr Herriot,' he said. It was the first time he had ever accorded me a 'Mister'. 'Is it true that where there's a lot of 'osses there's more lockjaw?'

'Yes, I should say so,' I replied.

He swallowed. 'There's allus been a lot of 'osses at that farm, hasn't there?'

'There has indeed.'

'And what . . .' He passed a hand across his forehead. 'What kind of . . . er . . . cuts gets lockjaw in them?'

I saw no reason to be merciful. 'Oh, deep punctured wounds like you have. Especially in the feet.'

'Oh bloody 'ell!' moaned Gobber. Like many bullies he was a big baby when his own hide was in danger.

Watching him sweating there I relented a little.

'Don't worry,' I said. 'The doctor will give you a little shot and you'll have nothing to worry about.'

The big man squirmed and wrung his hands. 'Ah but I don't like t'needle.'

'It's nothing, really,' I said, with only the slightest touch of sadism. 'Just a quick jab.'

'Oh bloody 'ell!'

At the surgery Harry Allinson gave us a cold look as we staggered in. He had attended a few of Mrs Newhouse's black eyes and he didn't approve of Gobber.

'Right, Jim,' he grunted. 'Leave him to me.'

I was about to go when Gobber caught at my sleeve.

'Stay with me, Mr Herriot!' he whimpered. The man was in a pitiable state of fright and I looked questioningly at the doctor.

Harry shrugged. 'OK, you can stay and hold his hand if that's what he wants.'

He produced a phial of tetanus antitoxin and a syringe.

'Drop your trousers and bend over, Newhouse,' he ordered curtly.

Gobber complied, exposing flaccid acres of the biggest backside, horses included, which I had ever seen.

'You know, Newhouse,' Harry said conversationally as he filled the syringe before the big man's terrified eyes. 'Your wife tells me you have no feelings.' He laughed gently. 'Yes, that's what she says . . . you have absolutely no feelings.'

He stepped quickly to the rear, rammed the needle deep into the quivering buttock, then, as a shrill howl shook the windows, he looked into Gobber's face with a wolfish grin.

'But you bloody well felt that, didn't you!'

# 17

You often see dogs running along a road but there was something about this one which made me slow down and take a second look.

It was a small brown animal and it was approaching on the other side; and it wasn't just ambling by the grass verge but galloping all out on its short legs, head extended forward as though in desperate pursuit of something unseen beyond the long empty curve of tarmac ahead. As the dog passed I had a brief glimpse of two staring eyes and a lolling tongue, then he was gone.

My car stalled and lurched to a halt but I sat unheeding, still gazing into the mirror at the small form receding rapidly until it was almost invisible against the browns and greens of the surrounding moor. As I switched on the engine I had difficulty in dragging my thoughts back to the job in hand; because I had seen something chilling there, a momentary but vivid impression of frantic effort, despair, blind terror. And driving away, the image stayed with me. Where had that dog come from? There were no roadside farms on this high, lonely by-way, not a parked car anywhere. And in any case he wasn't just casually going somewhere; there was a frenzied urgency in his every movement.

It was no good, I had to find out. I backed off the unfenced road among the sparse tufts of heather and turned back in the direction I had come. I had to drive a surprisingly long way before I saw the little animal, still beating his solitary way, and at the sound of the approaching car he halted, stared for a moment then trotted on again. But his labouring limbs told me he was near exhaustion and I pulled up twenty yards ahead of him, got out and waited.

He made no protest as I knelt on the roadside turf and caught him gently as he came up to me. He was a Border terrier and after another quick glance at the car his eyes took on their terrified light as he looked again at the empty road ahead.

He wasn't wearing a collar but there was a ring of flattened hair on his neck as though one had recently been removed. I opened his mouth and looked at his teeth; he wasn't very old – probably around two or three. There were rolls of fat along his ribs so he hadn't been starved. I was examining his skin when suddenly the wide panting mouth closed and the whole body stiffened as another car approached. For a moment he stared at it with fierce hope but when the vehicle flashed by he sagged and began to pant again.

So that was it. He had been dumped. Some time ago the humans he had loved and trusted had opened their car door, hurled him out into an unknown world and driven merrily away. I began to feel sick – physically sick – and a murderous rage flowed through me. Had they laughed, I wondered, these people, at the idea of the bewildered little creature toiling vainly behind them?

I passed my hand over the rough hairs of the head. I could forgive anybody for robbing a bank but never for this. 'Come on, fella,' I said, lifting him gently, 'you're coming home with me.'

Sam was used to strange dogs in the car and he sniffed incuriously at the newcomer. The terrier huddled on the passenger seat trembling violently and I kept my hand on him as I drove.

Back in our bed-sitter Helen pushed a bowl of meat and biscuit under his nose but the little animal showed no interest.

'How could anybody do this?' she murmured. 'And anyway, why? What reason could they have?'

I stroked the head again. 'Oh, you'd be surprised at some of the reasons. Sometimes they do it because a dog turns savage, but that can't be so in this case.' I had seen enough of dogs to interpret the warm friendly light behind the fear in those eyes. And the way the terrier had submitted unquestioningly as I had prised his mouth open, lifted him, handled him, all pointed to one thing; he was a docile little creature.

'Or sometimes,' I continued, 'they dump dogs just because

they're tired of them. They got them when they were charming puppies and have no interest in them when they grow up. Or maybe the licence is due to be paid – that's a good enough reason for some people to take a drive into the country and push their pets out into the unknown.'

I didn't say any more. There was quite a long list and why should I depress Helen with tales of the other times when I had seen it happen? People moving to another house where they couldn't keep a dog. A baby arriving and claiming all the attention and affection. And dogs were occasionally abandoned when a more glamorous pet superseded them.

I looked at the little terrier. This was the sort of thing which could have happened to him. A big dashing Alsatian, an eye-catching Saluki – anything like that would take over effortlessly from a rather roly-poly Border terrier with some people. I had seen it in the past. The little fellow was definitely running to fat despite his comparative youth; in fact when he had been running back there his legs had splayed out from his shoulders. That was another clue; it was possible he had spent most of his time indoors without exercise.

Anyway I was only guessing. I rang the police. No reports of a lost dog in the district. I hadn't really expected any.

During the evening we did our best to comfort the terrier but he lay trembling, his head on his paws, his eyes closed. The only time he showed interest was when a car passed along the street outside, then he would raise his head and listen, ears pricked, for a few seconds till the sound died away. Helen hoisted him on to her lap and held him there for over an hour, but he was too deeply sunk in his misery to respond to her caresses and soft words.

I finally decided it would be the best thing to sedate him and gave him a shot of morphine. When we went to bed he was stretched out sound asleep in Sam's basket with Sam himself curled up philosophically on the rug by his side.

Next morning he was still unhappy but sufficiently recovered to look around him and take stock. When I went up and spoke to him he rolled over on his back, not playfully but almost automatically as though it was a normal mannerism. I bent and rubbed his chest while he looked up at me non-committally. I liked dogs which rolled over like this; they were usually good-natured and it was a gesture of trust.

'That's better, old lad,' I said. 'Come on, cheer up!'

For a moment his mouth opened wide. He had a comical little monkey face and briefly it seemed to be split in two by a huge grin, making him look extraordinarily attractive.

Helen spoke over my shoulder. 'He's a lovely little dog, Jim! He's so appealing – I could get really fond of him.'

Yes, that was the trouble. So could I. I could get too fond of all the unwanted animals which passed through our hands; not just the abandoned ones but the dogs which came in for eutha-nasia with the traumatic addendum 'unless you can find him a home'. That put the pressure on me. Putting an animal to sleep when he was incurably ill, in pain, or so old that life had lost its savour was something I could tolerate. In fact often it seemed as though I were doing the suffering creature a favour. But when a young, healthy, charming animal was involved then it was a harrowing business.

What does a vet do in these circumstances. Refuse and send the owners away with the lurking knowledge that the man might go round to the chemist and buy a dose of poison? That was far worse than our humane, painless barbiturate. One thing a vet can't do is take in all those animals himself. If I had given way to all my impulses I would have accumulated a positive menagerie by now.

It was a hell of a problem which had always troubled me and now I had a soft hearted wife which made the pull twice as strong.

I turned to her now and voiced my thoughts.

'Helen, we can't keep him, you know. One dog in a bed-sitter is enough.' I didn't add that we ourselves probably would not be in the bed-sitter much longer; that was another thing I didn't want to bring up.

She nodded. 'I suppose so. But I have the feeling that this is one of the sweetest little dogs I've seen for a long time. When he gets over his fear, I mean. What on earth can we do with him?'

'Well, he's a stray.' I bent again and rubbed the rough hair over the chest. 'So he should really go to the kennels at the police station. But if he isn't claimed in ten days we are back where we started.' I put my hand under the terrier's body and lifted him, limp and unresisting, into the crook of my arm. He liked people, this one; liked and trusted them. 'I could ask around the practice, of course, but nobody seems to want a dog when there's one going spare.' I thought for a moment or two. 'Maybe an advert in the local paper.'

'Wait a minute,' Helen said. 'Talking about the paper – didn't I read something about an animal shelter last week?'

I looked at her uncomprehendingly then I remembered.

'That's right. Sister Rose from the Topley Banks hospital. They were interviewing her about the stray animals she had taken in. It would be worth a try.' I replaced the terrier in Sam's basket. 'We'll keep this little chap today and I'll ring Sister Rose when I finish work tonight.'

At teatime I could see that things were getting out of hand. When I came in the little dog was on Helen's knee and it looked as though he had been there for a long time. She was stroking his head and looking definitely broody.

Not only that, but as I looked down at him I could feel myself weakening. Little phrases were creeping unbidden into my mind . . . 'I wonder if we could find room for him . . .' . . . 'Not much extra trouble . . .' . . . 'Perhaps if we . . .'

I had to act quickly or I was sunk. Reaching for the phone I dialled the hospital number. They soon found Sister Rose and I listened to a cheerful, businesslike voice. She didn't seem to find anything unusual in the situation and the matter-of-fact way she asked questions about the terrier's age, appearance, temperament etc. gave the impression that she had seen a lot of unwanted animals through her hands.

I could hear the firm pencilling sounds as she took notes then, 'Well now that sounds fine. He's the sort we can usually find a home for. When can you bring him along?'

'Now,' I replied.

The misty look in Helen's eyes as I marched out with the dog under my arm told me I was only just in time. And as I drove along the road I couldn't put away the thought that if things had been different – the future settled and a proper home – this little brown creature rolling on his back on the passenger seat with his wide mouth half open and the friendly eyes fixed questioningly on mine would never have got away from me. Only when the occasional car flashed by did he spring upright and look from the window with the old despairing expression. Would he ever forget?

Sister Louisa Rose was a rather handsome woman in her late forties with the sort of healthy smiling face I had imagined at the other end of the phone. She reached out and took the terrier from me with the eager gesture of the animal lover.

'Oh, he looks rather a dear, doesn't he?' she murmured.

Behind her house, a modern bungalow in the open country near the hospital, she led me to a row of kennels with outside runs. Some of them housed single dogs but there was one large one with an assortment of mixed breeds playing happily together on the grass.

'I think we'll put him in here,' she said. 'It'll cheer him up quicker than anything and I'm sure he'll mix in well.' She opened a door in the wire netting surround and pushed the little animal in. The other dogs surrounded him and there was the usual ceremonious sniffing and leg-cocking.

Sister Rose cupped her chin with her hand and looked down thoughtfully through the wire. 'A name, we must have a name . . . let me see . . . no . . . no . . . yes . . . Pip! We'll call him Pip!'

She looked at me with raised eyebrows and I nodded vigorously. 'Yes, definitely – just right. He looks like a Pip.'

She smiled impishly. 'I think so, too, but I've had a lot of practice, you know. I've become rather good at it.'

'I'll bet you have. I suppose you've named all this lot?'

'Of course.' She began to point them out one by one. 'There's Bingo – he was a badly neglected puppy. And Fergus – just lost. That bigger retriever is Griff – he was the survivor of a car crash

126

where his owners were killed. And Tessa, badly injured when she was thrown from a fast-moving vehicle. Behind her over there is Sally Anne who really started me in the business of Animal Sheltering. She was found heavily pregnant with her paws bleeding so she must have run for many miles. I took her in and managed to find homes for all her puppies and she's still here. Placing those pups got me into contact with a lot of pet owners and before I knew what was happening everybody had the idea that I regularly took in stray animals. So I started and you can see the result. I shall have to expand these premises soon.'

Pip didn't look so lonely now and after the preliminary courtesies he joined a group watching interestedly a fierce tug-of-war on a stick between a Collie and a crossed Labrador.

I laughed. 'You know I had no idea you had all these dogs. How long do you keep them?'

'Till I can find a home for them. Some are only here a day, others stay for weeks or months. And there are one or two like Sally Anne who seem to be permanent boarders now.'

'But how on earth do you feed them all? It must be an expensive business.'

She nodded and smiled. 'Oh I run little dog shows, coffee mornings, raffles, jumble sales, anything, but whatever my efforts I'm afraid the strays keep munching their way into the red. But I manage.'

She managed, I guessed, by dipping deeply into her own pocket. Around me the abandoned and rejected dogs barked and ran around happily. I had often thought when I encountered cruelty and neglect that there was a whole army of people who did these unspeakable things, a great unheeding horde who never spared a thought for the feelings of the helpless creatures who depended on them. It was frightening in a way, but thank heavens there was another army ranged on the other side, an army who fought for the animals with everything they had – with their energy, their time, their money.

I looked at Sister Rose, at the steady eyes in the clear-skinned, scrubbed, nurse's face. I would have thought her profession of dedication to the human race would have filled her life utterly with no room for anything else, but it was not so.

'Well, I'm very grateful to you, Sister,' I said. 'I hope somebody will take Pip off your hands soon and if there's anything else I can do, please let me know.'

She smiled. 'Oh don't worry, I have a feeling this little chap won't be here very long.'

Before leaving I leaned on the wire and took another look at the Border terrier. He seemed to be settling all right but every now and then he stopped and looked up at me with those questioning eyes which pulled so hard. I had the nasty feeling that I, too, was letting him down. His owners, then me, then Sister Rose, all in a couple of days . . . I hoped it would work out for him.

# 18

I found it difficult to get that dog out of my mind and I lasted only a week before dropping in at the Animal Shelter. Sister Rose in an old mackintosh and wellingtons was filling the feeding bowls in one of the kennels.

'You've come about Pip, I expect,' she said, putting down her bucket. 'Well he went yesterday. I thought I'd have no trouble. A very nice couple called round. They wanted to give a home to a stray and they picked him out straight away.' She pushed the hair back from her forehead. 'In fact I've had a good week. I've found excellent homes for Griff and Fergus too.'

'Fine, fine. That's great.' I paused for a moment. 'I was wondering . . . er . . . about Pip. Has he gone out of the district ?'

'Oh, no, he's right here in Darrowby. The people are called Plenderleith – he's a retired civil servant, quite high up I believe and he gave a generous donation to the centre though I didn't expect one. They've bought one of those nice little houses on the Houlton Road and there's a lovely garden for Pip to play. I gave them your name, by the way, so no doubt they'll be coming round to see you.'

A wave of totally irrational pleasure swept over me.

'Ah well, I'm glad to hear that. I'll be able to see how he's getting on.'

I didn't have long to wait. It was less than a week later that I opened the waiting-room door and saw an elderly couple sitting there with Pip on the end of a very new lead. He adopted his usual gambit of rolling on to his back as soon as he saw me, but this time there was no helpless appeal in his expression but sheer joyous abandon with the comical little face split across by a wide panting grin. As I went through the ritual of chest rubbing I noticed he was wearing a new collar, too; expensive looking, with a shining medallion bearing his name, address and telephone number. I lifted him and we all went through to the consulting room.

'Well now, what's the trouble?' I asked.

'No trouble, really,' the man replied. He was plump, and the pink face, grave eyes and immaculate dark suit accorded perfectly with my idea of a top civil servant.

'I have recently acquired this small animal and should be grateful for your advice about him. By the way, my name is Plenderleith and may I introduce my wife.'

Mrs Plenderleith was plump too, but it was a giggly plumpness. She didn't look such a solid citizen as her husband.

'Firstly,' he continued, 'I should like you to give him a thorough check-up.'

I had already done this, but went through it again, though Pip made things difficult by rolling over every time I got the stethoscope on his chest. And as I took his temperature I noticed that Mr Plenderleith ran his hand repeatedly over the brown hair of the back while his wife, looking over his shoulder, made encouraging noises and nodded reassuringly at the little dog.

'Absolutely sound in wind and limb,' I pronounced as I finished.

'Splendid,' the man said. 'Er . . . there was this little brown mark on his abdomen . . .' A touch of anxiety showed in his eyes.

'Just a patch of pigment. Nothing, I assure you.'

'Ah yes, good, good.' Mr Plenderleith cleared his throat. 'I have to confess, Mr Herriot, that my wife and I have never owned an animal before. Now I believe in doing things thoroughly, so in order to give him proper care and attention I have decided to study the matter. With this in view I have purchased some books on the subject.' He produced some shiny volumes from under his arm. *Care of the Dog*, *The Dog in Sickness and Health*, and finally *The Border Terrier*.

'Good idea,' I replied. Normally I would have shied away from this imposing battery but in this case I liked the way things were going. I had the growing conviction that Pip was on a good wicket here.

'I have already gleaned a considerable amount from my reading,' Mr Plenderleith went on, 'and I believe it is desirable that he be inoculated against distemper. As you know, he is a stray so there is no means of ascertaining whether or not this has been done.'

I nodded. 'Quite right. In fact I was going to suggest that.' I produced a phial of the vaccine and began to fill a syringe.

Pip was much less concerned than his owners as I gently injected the contents under his skin. Mr Plenderleith, his face rigid with apprehension, kept patting the dog's head while his wife at the other end stroked the hind limbs and adjured her pet to be brave.

After I had put the syringe away, Mr Plenderleith, visibly relieved, recommenced his investigations. 'Let me see now.' He put on his spectacles, produced a gold pencil and snapped open a leather bound pad where I could see a long list of neatly written notes. 'I have one or two queries here.'

And he had indeed. He grilled me at length on feeding, housing, exercise, the relative values of wicker dog baskets and metal frame beds, the salient features of the common ailments, often referring to his shiny books. 'I have a note here concerning page 143, line 9. It says . . .'

130

I answered him patiently, leaning across the table. I had a waiting list of farm visits including several fairly urgent jobs but I listened with growing contentment. I had hoped for concerned and responsible persons to take this little animal over and these people were right out of the blueprint.

When at length Mr Plenderleith had finished he put away his notebook and pencil and removed his spectacles with the firm precise movements which seemed part of him.

'One of the reasons I desired a dog, Mr Herriot,' he went on, 'was to provide myself with exercise. Don't you think that is a good idea?'

'It certainly is. One of the surest ways to keep fit is to own an active little animal like this. You simply *have* to take him out and just think of all the lovely grassy tracks over the hills around here. On Sunday afternoons when other people are lying asleep in their chairs under their newspapers you'll be out there striding the fells, rain, hail or snow.'

Mr Plenderleith squared his shoulders and his jaw jutted as though he already saw himself battling through a blizzard.

'And another thing,' his wife giggled, 'it'll take some of this off.' She thumped him irreverently on his bulging waistline.

'Now now, my dear,' he admonished her gravely, but I had seen the makings of a sheepish grin which completely belied his stuffed shirt image. Mr Plenderleith, I felt, was all right.

He put his books under his arm and reached out for the little dog. 'Come, Pip, we mustn't delay Mr Herriot any longer.' But his wife was too quick for him. She gathered the terrier into her arms and as we walked along the passage she held the rough face against her own.

Outside the surgery door I saw them installed in a spotless little family saloon and as they drove away Mr Plenderleith inclined his head gravely, his wife gave a gay wave, but Pip, his hind legs on her knee, feet on the dashboard, gazing eagerly through the windscreen was too busy and interested to look at me.

As they rounded the corner I had the impression of a little cycle coming to a happy end. And of course the main cog in the sequence of events had been Sister Rose. This was just one of the helpless creatures she had salvaged. Her Animal Shelter would grow and expand and daily she would work harder without gain to herself. There were other people like her all over the country, other Shelters; and I felt I had been given a privileged glimpse of that selfless army which battled ceaselessly and untiringly on the side of the great throng of dependent animals.

But right now I was concerned only with one thing. Pip had come home for good.

# 19

'Double Bezique!' Helen said, laying out the two queens of spades and the jacks of diamonds. And she looked across at me with a grin of triumph.

She had the right kind of mouth, wide and generous, for such a grin and there was no doubt she had cause for jubilation.

'Well that's torn it,' I grunted moodily. 'I've been wondering where those cards were and now I know. But why didn't you declare them separately ?'

'It's better fun this way,' my wife replied with a callous laugh. 'I wanted to see your face when I put them all out at once.'

'OK, OK,' I said. 'Gloat all you want. I didn't realise I had married a sadist.'

With a sinking heart I saw her move her little peg five hundred points up the board. It was a body blow and one from which I knew I would never recover. She had already won two games tonight – I was being thrashed.

Still, there were compensations. There was a subdued excitement in just sitting there by our fireside on a black winter's night like this and listening to the wind buffeting the tall old house. I think it was the nearness of the wild that made the coals burn brighter and the room seem cosier, the awareness of the towering bare hills close by and the night wind shrieking over the high tops and over the vast white emptiness of the moors where it was cold, cold, and a man could quite easily lose himself and die.

I dealt the next hand and looked with disgust at the rubbish I had given myself. I stole a glance at Helen. The faintest trace of smugness showed in her face as she viewed her hand. This wasn't going to be my night.

We played a lot of Bezique on those dark evenings. There wasn't much to do in Darrowby but boredom was never a problem. At the beginning, in the summer days, we walked every day along the grassy tracks in the hills which make Yorkshire the finest walking country in England. We started to cultivate a piece of the long garden behind the house for our own use and I discovered an undreamed-of fascination in peas and broad beans. We picked mushrooms which may not sound very exciting but I have warm memories of the two of us wandering around sunlit fields with carrier bags and stopping now and then to look at the beauty nearby. In those days before the old permanent pastures were ploughed up and artificial fertilisers were scarcely used mushrooms grew abundantly; and they were marvellous to eat. There was tennis, too, and at weekends Helen came with me on my rounds.

But when the winter closed in Bezique was the thing. I studied my cards again and listened to the wind. It made a soft whistling noise down in the tiled passage far below. It was always as cold as the street in that passage and not much warmer in the graceful sitting room where the wind would tug at the heavy curtains over the french windows and perhaps send fugitive gusts up the stairs to Siegfried's and Tristan's rooms and then up to us on the top.

And the wind would push its fingers up under the tiles into the two empty silent rooms which lay even higher than us. Rooms where the dust lay thick beneath their tiny windows and the wind would stir the cobwebs among the rafters and pull at the little bell hanging from the great coiled spring. I could hear

133

the faint tinkling which in the days of the old house's glory would summon a little maidservant from her high nest.

But now the bell went unheeded in the empty darkness. There was nobody to answer it. The six servants who used to look after the Georgian elegance of Skeldale House were only a memory among the older folk of Darrowby and there was only Mrs Hall the housekeeper in her room at the end of the offshoot.

'Royal marriage,' I said stiffly, putting out the king and queen of trumps and advancing my peg a paltry forty points.

Helen nodded and I could see she was trying not to look condescending. She hadn't declared anything for some time now and I had a nasty feeling she was building up to something big. She bent over and poked the fire. There was too much coal on it because I had laid the fire this evening.

We had a system that whoever was first home did that job. We had to arrange something like this because Helen was a working girl now. There wasn't much to do in our two rooms and our finances were at a low ebb so she had taken a job as secretary to the local millers. The mill was on the roadside down by the river and passers-by could see the big mill wheel turning in the water and hear the great stones grinding the corn in the room upstairs with the opening on to the road where the lorries came to collect the loaded bags.

Helen's office was behind the mill shop, a floury, dusty, mealy place stacked tightly with sacks of cow cake, sheep nuts, hen pellets and drums of black treacle and when I slowed down outside I could often catch a glimpse of her red-sweatered back as she bent over her books.

Tonight I had been first home and Helen had come in as I was lighting my pile of sticks and coal. Girls used to wear things called 'pixie hoods' in those days and I can see her now in a blue pixie hood, her face flushed with the long climb up the stairs looking round that door at me busy with my chores.

But tonight my worst fears were being realised. My wife gave a long contented sigh and laid out one by one the dread ace, king, queen, jack and ten.

'Sequence,' she murmured in a matter of fact tone and moved her peg up another two hundred and fifty.

It wasn't a defeat, it was a massacre. It was obvious I hadn't long to live. But as I scanned the board anxiously the front door bell echoed along the passage downstairs.

Maybe I was going to be saved. I leapt to my feet and began the familiar descent.

A bulky figure loomed beyond the glass door at the end of the passage and as I turned the handle a waft of beer fumes blew in.

'Ah want a cleansing drink,' the figure said.

I opened the door wide. 'Come inside for a minute, it's a cold night.'

It was Reg Mallaby, a member of the large body of farmers who liked to drop in at the surgery on the way home after a night in the pub or the cinema, just to pick up some medicaments for the livestock.

We went into the office and he stood leaning on the desk, breathing heavily.

'A cleansing drink, eh?' I said. 'Right, I'll bring one through.'

Of course there was no such thing as a cleansing drink – there never has been – and when I first came to Darrowby and didn't know any better I used to waste a lot of time telling the farmers so. I went out of my way to explain as lucidly as I could that nothing you poured down a cow's throat could possibly influence the separation of the afterbirth and that they shouldn't throw their money away on something which was useless. The farmers listened with growing disbelief then left, offended, to purchase a cleansing drink at the chemist's shop.

I took a more practical view now and went through to the stock-room. There was quite a pile of the square packets there. They were wrapped in bright red paper with lettering in confident black capitals and we did a brisk trade in them at half a crown a time. We bought them by the gross from a wholesaler and though I never had them analysed I had a strong suspicion that they consisted of a pound of Epsom salts flavoured with aromatic powder.

'Here you are, Mr Mallaby,' I said. 'That's what you want, isn't it?'

'Aye, that's it, young man.' The farmer handled the packet almost lovingly. 'They're champion things, these, tha knows. Ah've never known 'em fail. Must have some wonderful stuff in 'em.'

He handed over his half crown then looked at me benevolently. 'I 'ope I haven't disturbed you, lad. Maybe you were doing summat important like?'

'No, that's quite all right, Mr Mallaby.' I looked at him with mingled surprise and gratitude. He was the first of the nocturnal callers who had shown any interest or concern. It had always been another symptom of the general opinion that vets have no private life. 'No, you needn't worry about that. I was just playing cards with my wife.'

The farmer nodded and a slow seraphic smile crept over his face. There was no doubt he had been indulging to the full. Then he narrowed his eyes suddenly.

'Is your Missus t'lass that works at t'mill?'

'Yes, that's right. She's in the office there.'

His face became very solemn. 'Aye well, I 'ave a complaint to make.'

'A complaint? What do you mean?'

I must have looked astonished because he held up a placatory hand.

'Now then, young man, she's a grand lass, I'm not sayin' nowt about that. But she sent me a wrong bill.'

'A wrong bill? In what way?'

'There was a mistake in it. She charged me for a lot o' things I never 'ad.'

'Well that's very strange. Are you absolutely sure?' I could easily imagine myself making clerical errors but in my experience Helen was a model of efficiency in that line.

'Aye, ah'm sure,' he replied. 'Hau'd on a minute and I'll show you. I 'ave it in my pocket here.'

He put his cleansing drink on the desk and began a laborious search of his pockets. He tracked down the offending account

136

among a huge wad of envelopes which he extracted from inside his coat.

'There y'are, young man,' he said importantly. 'Just have a look at that.'

I studied the paper carefully. Opposite a date at the top there was an entry. 'Two bags pig meal' and underneath on dates when the order had obviously been repeated Helen had put dittos by writing 'do . . . do . . . do . . . do'.

'Well what's wrong with it, Mr Mallaby ?'

The farmer pursed his lips. 'Ah'll tell ye. Ye see that about pig meal ?'

I nodded.

'Well,' he went on, 'ah've had a few bags o' that, I'm not denyin' and I expect to pay for't. But . . .' and here he raised a portentous forefinger, 'there's one thing I'm certain of. Ah've never 'ad none o' them bloody doo-doo's.'

# 20

No vet likes to have his job made more difficult and as I worked inside the ewe I fought a rising tide of irritation.

'You know, Mr Kitson,' I said testily, 'you should have got me out sooner. How long have you been trying to lamb this ewe ?'

The big man grunted and shrugged his shoulders. 'Oh, for a bit – not ower long.'

'Half an hour – an hour ?'

'Nay, nay, nobbut a few minutes.' Mr Kitson regarded me gloomily along his pointed nose. It was his habitual expression; in fact I had never seen him smile and the idea of a laugh ever disturbing those pendulous cheeks was unthinkable.

I gritted my teeth and decided to say no more about it, but I knew it had taken more than a few minutes to cause the swelling of the vaginal wall, this sandpaper dryness of the little creatures inside. And it was a simple enough presentation – biggish twins, one anterior the other posterior, but of course as often happens the hind legs of one were laid alongside the head of the other giving the illusion that they belonged to the same lamb. I'd like to bet that Mr Kitson had been guddling for ages inside her with his big rough hands in a dogged attempt to bring that head and those legs out together.

If I had been there at the start it would have been the work of a few moments but instead here I was without an inch of space, trying to push things around with one finger instead of my full hand and getting nowhere.

Fortunately the present day farmer doesn't often play this trick on us. The usual thing I hear at a lambing is, 'Nay, I just had a quick feel and I knew it wasn't a job for me,' or something I heard from a farmer the other day, 'Two men at one ewe's no good,' and I think that says it very well.

But Mr Kitson was of the old school. He didn't believe in getting the vet out until every other avenue had been explored and when he did finally have to fall back on our services he was usually dissatisfied with the result.

'This is no good,' I said, withdrawing my hand and swilling it quickly in the bucket. 'I'll have to do something about this dryness.'

I walked the length of the old stable which had been converted into temporary lambing pens and lifted a tube of lubricating cream from the car boot. Coming in again I heard a faint sound from my left. The stable was dimly lit and an ancient door had been placed across the darkest corner to make a small enclosure. I looked inside and in the gloom could just discern a ewe lying on her chest, head outstretched. Her ribs rose and fell with the typical quick distressed respirations of a sheep in pain. Occasionally she moaned softly.

'What's the trouble here?' I asked.

Mr Kitson regarded me impassively from the other end of the building. 'She 'ad a roughish time lambin' yesterday.'

'How do you mean, roughish?'

'Well . . . a big single lamb wi' a leg back and I couldn't fetch it round.'

'So you just pulled it out as it was . . . with the leg back?'

'Aye, nowt else ah could do.'

I leaned over the door and lifted the ewe's tail, filthy with faeces and discharge. I winced as I saw the tumefied, discoloured vulva and perineum.

'She could do with a bit of attention, Mr Kitson.'

The farmer looked startled. 'Nay, nay, I don't want none o' that. It's over with her – there's nowt you can do.'

'You mean she's dying?'

'That's right.'

I put my hand on the sheep's head, feeling the coldness of the ears and lips. He could be right.

'Well have you rung Mallock to come and pick her up? She really should be put out of her pain as soon as possible.'

'Aye . . . ah'll do that.' Mr Kitson shuffled his feet and looked away.

I knew what the situation was. He was going to let the ewe 'take her chance'. The lambing season was always a rewarding and fulfilling time for me but this was the other side of the coin. It was a hectic time in the farming year, a sudden onslaught of extra work on top of the routine jobs and in some ways it overwhelmed the resources of farmers and vets alike. The flood of new life left a pathetic debris behind it; a flotsam and jetsam of broken creatures; ewes too old to stand a further pregnancy, some debilitated by diseases like liver fluke and toxaemia, others with infected arthritic joints and others who had just had a 'roughish time'. You were inclined to find them lying half forgotten in dark corners like the one in this stable. They had been left there to 'take their chance'.

I returned in silence to my original patient. My lubricating cream made a great difference and I was able to use more than one finger to explore. I had to make up my mind whether to repel the posterior or anterior presentation and since the head was well into the vagina I decided to bring out the anterior first.

139

With the farmer's help I raised the ewe's hindquarters till they were resting on a straw bale. I could work downhill now and gently pushed the two hind limbs away into the depths of the uterus. In the space which this left I was able to hook a finger round the fore limbs which were laid back along the ribs of the anterior lamb and bring them into the passage. I only needed another application of the cream and a few moments' careful traction and the lamb was delivered.

But it was all too late. The tiny creature was quite dead and the knell of disappointment sounded in me as it always did at the sight of the perfectly formed body which lacked only the spark of life.

Hurriedly I greased my arm again and felt inside for the re-pelled lamb. There was plenty of room now and I was able to loop my hand round the hocks and draw the lamb out without effort. This time I had little hope of life and my efforts were solely to relieve the ewe's discomfort but as the lamb came into the cold outside air I felt the convulsive jerk and wriggle of the woolly little form in my hands which told me all was well.

It was funny how often this happened; you got a dead lamb – sometimes even a decomposed one – with a live one lurking behind it. Anyway it was a bonus and with a surge of pleasure I wiped the mucus from its mouth and pushed it forward for its mother to lick. A further exploration of the uterus revealed nothing more and I got to my feet.

'Well she's come to no harm, and I think she'll be all right now,' I said. 'And could I have some fresh water, Mr Kitson, please?'

The big man wordlessly emptied the bucket on to the stable floor and went off towards the house. In the silence I could faintly hear the panting of the ewe in the far corner. I tried not to think of what lay in front of her. Soon I would drive off and see other cases, then I would have lunch and start my afternoon round while hidden in this cheerless place a helpless animal was gasping her life away. How long would it take her to die? A day? Two days?

It was no good. I had to do something about it. I ran out to my car, grabbed the bottle of nembutal and my big 50 c.c. syringe and hurried back into the stable. I vaulted over the rotting timbers of the door, drew out 40 c.c.'s from the bottle and plunged the whole dose into the sheep's peritoneal cavity. Then I leapt back, galloped the length of the stable and when Mr Kitson returned I was standing innocently where he had left me.

I towelled myself, put on my jacket and gathered up my bottle of antiseptic and the tube of cream which had served me so well.

Mr Kitson preceded me along the stable and on the way out he glanced over the door in the corner.

'By gaw, she's goin' fast,' he grunted.

I looked over his shoulder into the gloom. The panting had stopped and was replaced by slow, even respirations. The eyes were closed. The sheep was anaesthetised. She would die in peace.

'Yes,' I said. 'She's definitely sinking. I don't think it will be very long now.' I couldn't resist a parting shaft. 'You've lost this ewe and that lamb back there. I think I could have saved both of them for you if you'd given me a chance.'

Maybe my words got through to Mr Kitson, because I was surprised to be called back to the farm a few days later to a ewe which had obviously suffered very little interference.

The animal was in a field close to the house and she was clearly bursting with lambs; so round and fat she could hardly waddle. But she looked bright and healthy.

'There's a bloody mix-up in there,' Mr Kitson said morosely. 'Ah could feel two heads and God only knows how many feet. Didn't know where the 'ell I was.'

'But you didn't try very hard?'

'Nay, never tried at all.'

Well, we were making progress. As the farmer gripped the sheep round the neck I knelt behind her and dipped my hands in the bucket. For once it was a warm morning. Looking back, my memories of lambing times have been of bitter winds searing the grass of the hill pastures, of chapped hands, chafed arms, gloves, scarves and cold-nipped ears. For years after I left Glasgow I kept waiting for the balmy early springs of western Scotland. After thirty years I am still waiting and it has begun to dawn on me that it doesn't happen that way in Yorkshire.

But this morning was one of the exceptions. The sun blazed from a sky of soft blue, there was no wind but a gentle movement of the air rolled the fragrance of the moorland flowers and warm grass over and around me as I knelt there.

And I had my favourite job in front of me. I almost chuckled as I fished around inside the ewe. There was all the room in the world, everything was moist and fresh and unspoiled, and it was child's play to fit the various jigsaws together. In about thirty seconds I had a lamb wriggling on the grass, in a few moments more a second, then a third and finally to my delight I reached away forward and found another little cloven foot and whisked it out into the world.

'Quadruplets!' I cried happily, but the farmer didn't share my enthusiasm.

'Nowt but a bloody nuisance,' he muttered. 'She'd be far better wi' just two.' He paused and gave me a sour look. 'Any road, ah reckon there wasn't no need to call ye. I could've done that job meself.'

I looked at him sadly from my squatting position. Sometimes in our job you feel you just can't win. If you take too long you're no good, if you're too quick the visit wasn't necessary. I have never quite subscribed to the views of a cynical old colleague who once adjured me: 'Never make a lambing look easy. Hold the buggers in for a few minutes if necessary.' But at times I felt he had a point.

Anyway, I had my own satisfaction in watching the four lambs. So often I had pitied these tiny creatures in their entry into an uncharitable world, sometimes even of snow and ice, but today it was a joy to see them trying to struggle to their feet under the friendly sun, their woolly coats already drying rapidly. Their mother, magically deflated, was moving among them in a

142

bemused manner as though she couldn't quite believe what she saw. As she nosed and licked them her deep-throated chuckles were answered by the first treble quaverings of her family. I was listening, enchanted, to this conversation when Mr Kitson spoke up.

'There's t'ewe you lambed t'other day.'

I looked up and there indeed she was, trotting proudly past, her lamb close at her flank.

'Ah yes, she looks fine,' I said. That was good to see but my attention was caught by something else. I pointed across the grass.

'That ewe away over there . . .' As a rule all sheep look alike to me but there was something about this one I recognised . . . a loss of wool from her back, a bare strip of skin stretched over the jutting ridge of her spinal column . . . surely I couldn't be mistaken.

The farmer followed my pointing finger. 'Aye, that's t'awd lass that was laid in the stable last time you were here.' He turned an expressionless gaze on me. 'The one you told me to get Mallock to fetch.'

'But . . . but . . . she was dying!' I blurted out.

The corner of Mr Kitson's mouth twitched upwards in what must have been the nearest possible approach to a smile. 'Well, that's what you tellt me, young feller.' He hunched his shoulders. 'Said she 'adn't long to go, didn't you?'

I had no words to offer. I just gaped at him. I must have been the picture of bewilderment and it seemed the farmer was puzzled too because he went on.

'But I'll tell tha summat. Ah've been among sheep all me life but ah've never seen owt like it. That ewe just went to sleep.'

'Is that so?'

'Aye, went to sleep, ah tell you and she stayed sleepin' for two days!'

'She slept for two days?'

'She did, ah'm not jokin', nor jestin'. Ah kept goin' into t'stable but she never altered. Lay there peaceful as you like all t'first day, then all t'second, then when I went in on t'third morning she was standin' there lookin' at me and ready for some grub.'

'Amazing!' I got to my feet. 'I must have a look at her.'

I really wanted to see what had become of that mass of inflammation and tumefaction under her tail and I approached her carefully, jockeying her bit by bit into the bottom corner of the field. There we faced each other for a few tense moments as I tried a few feints and she responded with nimble side-steps; then as I made my final swoop to catch her fleece she eluded me effortlessly and shot past me with a thundering of hooves. I gave chase for twenty yards but it was too hot and wellingtons aren't the ideal gear for running In any case I have long held the notion that if a vet can't catch his patient there's nothing much to worry about.

And as I walked back up the field a message was tapping in my brain. I had discovered something discovered something by accident. That ewe's life had been saved not by medicinal therapy but simply by stopping her pain and allowing nature to do its own job of healing. It was a lesso I have never forgotten; that animals confronted with severe continuous pain and the terror and shock that goes with it will often retreat even into death, and if you can remove that pain amazing things can happen. It is difficult to explain rationally but I know that it is so.

By the time I had got back to Mr Kitson the sun was scorching the back of my neck and I could feel a trickle of sweat under my shirt. The big man was still watching the ewe which had finished its gallop and was cropping the grass contentedly.

'Ah can't get over it,' he murmured, scratching the thin bristle on his jaw. 'Two whole days and never a move.' He turned to me and his eyes widened.

'Ah'll tell tha, young man, you'd just think she'd been drugged!'

# 21

I found it difficult to get Mr Kitson's ewe out of my mind but I had to make the effort because while all the sheep work was going on the rest of the practice problems rolled along unabated. One of these concerned the Flaxtons' Poodle, Penny.

Penny's first visit to the surgery was made notable by the attractiveness of her mistress. When I stuck my head round the waiting-room door and said, 'Next please,' Mrs Flaxton's little round face with its shining tight cap of blue-black hair seemed to illuminate the place like a beacon. It is possible that the effect was heightened by the fact that she was sitting between fifteen stone Mrs Barmby, who had brought her canary to have its claws clipped, and old Mr Spence who was nearly ninety and had called round for some flea powder for his cat, but there was no doubt she was good to look at.

And it wasn't just that she was pretty; there was a round-eyed, innocent appeal about her and she smiled all the time. Penny, sitting on her knee, seemed to be smiling from under the mound of brown curls on her forehead.

In the consulting room I lifted the little dog on to the table. 'Well now, what's the trouble ?'

'She has a touch of sickness and diarrhoea,' Mrs Flaxton replied. 'It started yesterday.'

'I see.' I turned and lifted the thermometer from the trolley. 'Has she had a change of food ?'

'No, nothing like that.'

'Is she inclined to eat rubbish when she's out ?'

Mrs Flaxton shook her head. 'No, not as a rule. But I suppose even the nicest dog will have a nibble at a dead bird or something horrid like that now and then.' She laughed and Penny laughed back at her.

'Well, she has a slightly raised temperature but she seems bright enough.' I put my hand round the dog's middle. 'Let's have a feel at your tummy, Penny.'

The little animal winced as I gently palpated the abdomen, and there was a tenderness throughout the stomach and intestines.

'She has gastroenteritis,' I said. 'But it seems fairly mild and I think it should clear up quite soon. I'll give you some medicine for her and you'd better keep her on a light diet for a few days.'

'Yes, I'll do that. Thank you very much.' Mrs Flaxton's smile deepened as she patted her dog's head. She was about twenty-three and she and her young husband had only recently come to Darrowby. He was a representative of one of the big agricultural firms which supplied meal and cattle cake to the farms and I saw him occasionally on my rounds. Like his wife, and indeed his dog, he gave off an ambience of eager friendliness.

I sent Mrs Flaxton off with a bottle of bismuth, kaolin and chlorodyne mixture which was one of our cherished treatments. The little dog trotted down the surgery steps, tail wagging, and I really didn't expect any more trouble.

Three days later, however, Penny was in the surgery again. She was still vomiting and the diarrhoea had not taken up in the least.

I got the dog on the table again and carried out a further examination but there was nothing significant to see. She had now had five days of this weakening condition but though she had lost a bit of her perkiness she still looked remarkably bright. The Toy Poodle is small but tough and very game and this one wasn't going to let anything get her down easily.

But I still didn't like it. She couldn't go on like this. I decided to alter the treatment to a mixture of carbon and astringents which had served me well in the past.

'This stuff looks a bit messy,' I said, as I gave Mrs Flaxton a powder box full of the black granules. 'But I have had good results with it. She's still eating, isn't she, so I should mix it in her food.'

'Oh thank you.' She gave me one of her marvellous smiles as she put the box in her bag and I walked along the passage with her to the door. She had left her pram at the foot of the steps and I knew before I looked under the hood what kind of baby

I would find. Sure enough the chubby face on the pillow gazed at me with round friendly eyes and then split into a delightful grin.

They were the kind of people I liked to see but as they moved off down the street I hoped for Penny's sake that I wouldn't be seeing them for a long time. However, it was not to be. A couple of days later they were back and this time the Poodle was showing signs of strain. As I examined her she stood motionless and dead-eyed with only the occasional twitch of her tail as I stroked her head and spoke to her.

'I'm afraid she's just the same, Mr Herriot,' her mistress said. 'She's not eating much now and whatever she does goes straight through her. And she has a terrific thirst – always at her water bowl and then she brings it back.'

I nodded. 'I know. This inflammation inside her gives her a raging desire for water and of course the more she drinks the more she vomits. And this is terribly weakening.'

Again I changed the treatment. In fact over the next few days I ran through just about the entire range of available drugs. I look back with a wry smile at the things I gave that little dog, powdered epicacuanha and opium, sodium salicylate and tincture of camphor, even way-out exotics like decoction of haematoxylin and infusion of caryophyllum which thank heavens have been long forgotten. I might have done a bit of good if I had had access to a gut-active antibiotic like neomycin but as it was I got nowhere.

I was visiting Penny daily as she was unfit to bring to the surgery. I had her on a diet of arrowroot and boiled milk but that, like my medical treatment, achieved nothing. And all the time the little dog was slipping away.

The climax came about three o'clock one morning. As I lifted the bedside phone Mr Flaxton's voice, with a tremor in it, came over the line.

'I'm terribly sorry to get you out of your bed at this hour, Mr Herriot, but I wish you'd come round to see Penny.'

'Why, is she worse?'

'Yes, and she's . . . well . . . she's suffering now, I'm afraid.

**147**

You saw her this afternoon, didn't you? Well since then she's been drinking and vomiting and this diarrhoea running away from her all the time till she's about at the far end. She's just lying in her basket crying. I'm sure she's in great pain.'

'Right, I'll be there in a few minutes.'

'Oh thank you.' He paused for a moment. 'And Mr Herriot ... you'll come prepared to put her down, won't you?'

My spirits, never very high at that time in the morning, plummeted to the depths. 'As bad as that, is it?'

'Well honestly we can't bear to see her. My wife is so upset ... I don't think she can stand any more.'

'I see.' I hung up the phone and threw the bedclothes back with a violence which brought Helen wide awake. Being disturbed in the small hours was one of the crosses a vet's wife has to bear, but normally I crept out as quietly as I could. This time, however, I stamped about the bedroom, dragging on my clothes and muttering to myself; and though she must have wondered what this latest crisis meant she wisely watched me in silence until I turned out the light and left.

I had not far to go. The Flaxtons lived in one of the new bungalows on the Brawton Road less than a mile away. The young couple, in their dressing gowns, led me into the kitchen and before I reached the dog basket in the corner I could hear Penny's whimperings. She was not lying comfortably curled up, but on her chest, head forward, obviously acutely distressed. I put my hands under her and lifted her and she was almost weightless. A Toy Poodle in its prime is fairly insubstantial but after her long illness Penny was like a bedraggled little piece of thistledown, her curly brown coat wet and soiled by vomit and diarrhoea.

Mrs Flaxton's smile for once was absent. I could see she was keeping back the tears as she spoke.

'It really would be the kindest thing ...'

'Yes ... yes ...' I replaced the tiny animal in her basket and crouched over her, chin in hand. 'Yes, I suppose you're right.'

But still I didn't move but stayed, squatting there, staring down in disbelief at the evidence of my failure. This dog was only two years old – a lifetime of running and jumping and barking in front of her; all she was suffering from was gastro-enteritis and now I was going to extinguish the final spark in her. It was a bitter thought that this would be just about the only positive thing I had done right from the start.

A weariness swept over me that was not just due to the fact that I had been snatched from sleep. I got to my feet with the slow stiff movements of an old man and was about to turn away when I noticed something about the little animal. She was on her chest again, head extended, mouth open, tongue lolling as she panted. There was something there I had seen before some-where . . . that posture . . . and the exhaustion, pain and shock . . . it slid almost imperceptibly into my sleepy brain that she looked exactly like Mr Kitson's ewe in its dark corner. A dif-ferent species, yes, but all the other things were there.

'Mrs Flaxton,' I said, 'I want to put Penny to sleep. Not the way you think, but to anaesthetise her. Maybe if she has a rest from this nonstop drinking and vomiting and straining it will give nature a chance.'

The young couple looked at me doubtfully for a few moments then it was the husband who spoke.

'Don't you think she has been through enough, Mr Herriot?'

'She has, yes she has.' I ran a hand through my rumpled un-combed hair. 'But this won't cause her any more distress. She won't know a thing about it.'

When they still hesitated I went on. 'I would very much like to try it – it's just an idea I've got.'

They looked at each other, then Mrs Flaxton nodded. 'All right, go ahead, but this will be the last, won't it?'

Out into the night air to my car for the same bottle of nem-butal and a very small dose for the little creature. I went back to my bed with the same feeling I had had about the ewe; come what may there would be no more suffering.

Next morning Penny was still stretched peacefully on her side and when, about four o'clock in the afternoon, she showed signs of awakening I repeated the injection.

Like the ewe she slept for forty-eight hours and when she

finally did stagger to her feet she did not head immediately for her water bowl as she had done for so many days. Instead she made her feeble way outside and had a walk round the garden.

From then on, recovery, as they say in the case histories, was uneventful. Or as I would rather write it, she wonderfully and miraculously just got better and never ailed another thing throughout her long life.

Helen and I used to play tennis on the grass courts near the Darrowby cricket ground. So did the Flaxtons and they always brought Penny along with them. I used to look through the wire at her romping with other dogs and later with the Flaxtons' fast growing young son and I marvelled.

I do not wish to give the impression that I advocate wholesale anaesthesia for all animal ailments but I do know that sedation has a definite place. Nowadays we have a sophisticated range of sedatives and tranquillisers to choose from and when I come up against an acute case of gastroenteritis in dogs I use one of them as an adjunct to the normal treatment; because it puts a brake on the deadly exhausting cycle and blots out the pain and fear which go with it.

And over the years, whenever I saw Penny running around, barking, bright-eyed, full of the devil, I felt a renewed welling of thankfulness for the cure which I discovered in a dark corner of a stable by accident.

# 22

The name was on the garden gate – Lilac Cottage. I pulled out my list of visits and checked the entry again. 'Cook, Lilac Cottage, Marston Hall. Bitch overdue for whelping.' This was the place all right, standing in the grounds of the Hall, a nineteenth-century mansion house whose rounded turrets reared above the fringe of pine trees less than half a mile away.

The door was opened by a heavy featured dark woman of about sixty who regarded me unsmilingly.

'Good morning, Mrs Cook,' I said. 'I've come to see your bitch.'

She still didn't smile. 'Oh, very well. You'd better come in.'

She led me into the small living room and as a little Yorkshire Terrier jumped down from an armchair her manner changed.

'Come here, Cindy my darlin',' she cooed. 'This gentleman's come to make you better.' She bent down and stroked the little animal, her face radiant with affection.

I sat down in another armchair. 'Well what's the trouble, Mrs Cook?'

'Oh, I'm worried to death.' She clasped her hands anxiously. 'She should have had her pups yesterday and there's nothing happenin'. Ah couldn't sleep all night – I'd die if anything happened to this dog.'

I looked at the terrier, tail wagging, gazing up, bright-eyed under her mistress's caress. 'She doesn't seem distressed at all. Has she shown any signs of labour?'

'What d'you mean?'

'Well, has she been panting or uneasy in any way? Is there any discharge?'

'No, nothing like that.'

I beckoned to Cindy and spoke to her and she came timidly across the lino till I was able to lift her on to my lap. I palpated the distended abdomen; there were a lot of pups in there but everything appeared normal. I took her temperature – normal again.

'Bring me some warm water and soap, Mrs Cook, will you please?' I said. The terrier was so small that I had to use my little finger, soaped and disinfected, to examine her, and as I felt carefully forward the walls of the vagina were dry and clinging and the cervix, when I reached it, tightly closed.

I washed and dried my hands. 'This little bitch isn't any-

151

where near whelping, Mrs Cook. Are you sure you haven't got your dates wrong?'

'No, I 'aven't, it was sixty-three days yesterday.' She paused in thought for a moment. 'Now ah'd better tell you this, young man. Cindy's had pups before and she did self and same thing – wouldn't get on with t'job. That was two years ago when I was livin' over in Listondale. I got Mr Broomfield the vet to her and he just gave her an injection. It was wonderful – she had the pups half an hour after it.'

I smiled. 'Yes, that would be pituitrin. She must have been actually whelping when Mr Broomfield saw her.'

'Well whatever it was, young man, I wish you'd give her some now. Ah can't stand all this suspense.'

'I'm sorry.' I lifted Cindy from my lap and stood up. 'I can't do that. It would be very harmful at this stage.'

She stared at me and it struck me that that dark face could look very forbidding. 'So you're not goin' to do anything at all?'

'Well...' There are times when it is a soothing procedure to give a client something to do even if it is unnecessary. 'Yes, I've got some tablets in the car. They'll help to keep the little dog fit until she whelps.'

'But I'd far rather have that injection. It was just a little prick. Didn't take Mr Broomfield more than a second to do.'

'I assure you, Mrs Cook, it can't be done at the moment. I'll get the tablets from the car.'

Her mouth tightened. I could see she was grievously disappointed in me. 'Oh well if you won't you won't, so you'd better get them things.' She paused: 'And me name isn't Cook!'

'It isn't?'

'No it isn't, young man.' She didn't seem disposed to offer further information so I left in some bewilderment.

Out in the road, a few yards from my car, a farm man was trying to start a tractor. I called over to him.

'Hey, the lady in there says her name isn't Cook.'

'She's right an' all. She's the cook over at the Hall. You've gotten a bit mixed up.' He laughed heartily.

It all became suddenly clear; the entry in the day book, everything. 'What's her right name, then?'

'Booby,' he shouted just as the tractor roared into life.

Funny name, I thought, as I produced my harmless vitamin tablets from the boot and returned to the cottage. Once inside I did my best to put things right with plenty of 'Yes, Mrs Booby' and 'No, Mrs Booby' but the lady didn't thaw. I told her not to worry and that I was sure nothing would happen for several days but I could tell I wasn't impressing her.

I waved cheerfully as I went down the path.

'Goodbye, Mrs Booby,' I cried. 'Don't hesitate to ring me if you're in doubt about anything.'

She didn't appear to have heard.

'Oh I wish you'd do as I say,' she wailed. 'It was just a little prick.'

The good lady certainly didn't hesitate to ring. She was at me again the next day and I had to rush out to her cottage. Her message was the same as before; she wanted the wonderful injection which would make those pups pop out and she wanted it right away. Mr Broomfield hadn't messed about and wasted time like I had. And on the third and fourth and fifth mornings she had me out at Marston examining the little bitch and reciting the same explanations. Things came to a head on the sixth day.

In the room at Lilac Cottage the dark eyes held a desperate light as they stared into mine. 'I'm about at the end of my tether, young man. I tell you I'll die if anything happens to this dog. I'll die. Don't you understand?'

'Of course I know how you feel about her, Mrs Booby. Believe me, I fully understand.'

'Then why don't you do something?' she snapped.

I dug my nails into my palms. 'Look, I've told you. A pituitrin injection works by contracting the muscular walls of the uterus, so it can only be given when labour has started and the cervix is open. If I find it is indicated I will do it, but if I give this injection now it could cause rupture of the uterus. It could

153

cause death.' I stopped because I fancied little bubbles were beginning to collect at the corners of my mouth.

But I don't think she had listened to a word. She sunk her head in her hands. 'All this time, I can't stand it.'

I was wondering if I could stand more of it myself. Bulging Yorkshire Terriers had begun to prance through my dreams at night and I greeted each new day with a silent prayer that the pups had arrived. I held out my hand to Cindy and she crept reluctantly towards me. She was heartily sick of this strange man who came every day and squeezed her and stuck fingers into her and she submitted again with trembling limbs and frightened eyes to the indignity.

'Mrs Booby,' I said, 'are you absolutely sure that dog didn't have access to Cindy after the service date you gave me?'

She sniffed. 'You keep askin' me that and ah've been thinking about it. Maybe he did come a week after, now I think on.'

'Well, that's it, then!' I spread my hands. 'She's held to the second mating, so she should be due tomorrow.'

'Ah would still far rather you would get it over with today like Mr Broomfield did . . . it was just a little prick.'

'But Mrs Booby . . .!'

'And let me tell you another thing, me name's not Booby!'

I clutched at the back of the chair. 'It's not?'

'Naw!'

'Well . . . what is it, then?'

'It's Dooley . . . Dooley!' She looked very cross.

'Right . . . right . . .' I stumbled down the garden path and drove away. It was not a happy departure.

Next morning I could hardly believe it when there was no call from Marston. Maybe all was well at last. But I turned cold when an urgent call to go to Lilac Cottage was passed on to one of the farms on my round. I was right at the far end of the practice area and was in the middle of a tough calving and it was well over three hours before I got out at the now familiar garden gate. The cottage door was open and as I ventured up the path a little brown missile hurtled out at me. It was Cindy, but a transformed Cindy, a snarling, barking little bundle of ferocity; and though I recoiled she fastened her teeth in my trouser cuff and hung on grimly.

I was hopping around on one leg trying to shake off the growling little creature when a peal of almost girlish laughter made me look round.

Mrs Dooley, vastly amused, was watching me from the doorway. 'My word, she's different since she had them pups. Just shows what a good little mother she is, guarding them like that.' She gazed fondly at the tiny animal dangling from my ankle.

'Had the pups . . . ?'

'Aye, when they said you'd be a long time I rang Mr Farnon. He came right away and d'you know he gave Cindy that injection I've wanted all along. And I tell you 'e wasn't right out of t'garden gate before the pups started. She's had seven – beauties they are.'

'Ah well that's fine, Mrs Dooley . . . splendid.' Siegfried had obviously felt a pup in the passage. I finally managed to rid myself of Cindy and when her mistress lifted her up I went into the kitchen to inspect the family.

They certainly were grand pups and I lifted the squawking little morsels one by one from their basket while their mother snarled from Mrs Dooley's arms like a starving wolfhound.

'They're lovely, Mrs Dooley,' I murmured.

She looked at me pityingly. 'I told you what to do, didn't I, but you wouldn't 'ave it. It only needed a little prick. Ooo, that Mr Farnon's a lovely man – just like Mr Broomfield.'

This was a bit much. 'But you must realise, Mrs Dooley, he just happened to arrive at the right time. If I had come . . .'

'Now, now, young man, be fair. Ah'm not blamin' you, but some people have had more experience. We all 'ave to learn.' She sighed reminiscently. 'It was just a little prick – Mr Farnon'll have to show you how to do it. I tell you he wasn't right out of t'garden gate . . .'

Enough is enough. I drew myself up to my full height. 'Mrs Dooley, madam,' I said frigidly, 'let me repeat once and for all . . .'

'Oh, hoity toity, hoity toity, don't get on your high horse wi' me!' she exclaimed. 'We've managed very nicely without you, so don't complain.' Her expression became very severe. 'And one more thing – me name's not Mrs Dooley.'

My brain reeled for a moment. The world seemed to be crumbling about me. 'What did you say?'

'I said me name's not Mrs Dooley.'

'It isn't?'

'Naw!' She lifted her left hand and as I gazed at it dully I realised it must have been all the mental stress which had prevented me from noticing the total absence of rings.

'Naw!' she said. 'It's Miss!'

# 23

I had never been married before so there was nothing in my past experience to go by but it was beginning to dawn on me that I was very nicely fixed.

I am talking, of course, of material things. It would have been enough for me or anybody else to be paired with a beautiful girl whom I loved and who loved me. I hadn't reckoned on the other aspects.

This business of studying my comfort, for instance. I thought such things had gone out of fashion, but not so with Helen. It was brought home to me again as I walked in to breakfast this morning. We had at last acquired a table – I had bought it at a farm sale and brought it home in triumph tied to the roof of my car – and now Helen had vacated the chair on which she used to sit at the bench and had taken over the high stool. She was perched away up there now, transporting her food from far below, while I was expected to sit comfortably in the chair. I don't think I am a selfish swine by nature but there was nothing I could do about it.

And there were other little things. The neat pile of clothing laid out for me each morning; the clean, folded shirt and handkerchief and socks so different from the jumble of my bachelor days. And when I was late for meals, which was often, she served me with my food but instead of going off and doing something else she would down tools and sit watching me while I ate. It made me feel like a sultan.

It was this last trait which gave me a clue to her behaviour. I suddenly remembered that I had seen her sitting by Mr Alderson while he had a late meal; sitting in the same pose, one arm on the table, quietly watching him. And I realised I was reaping the benefit of her lifetime attitude to her father. Mild little man though he was she had catered gladly to his every wish in the happy acceptance that the man of the house was number one; and the whole pattern was rubbing off on me now.

In fact it set me thinking about the big question of how girls might be expected to behave after marriage. One old farmer giving me advice about choosing a wife once said; 'Have a bloody good look at the mother first, lad', and I am sure he had a point. But if I may throw in my own little word of counsel it would be to have a passing glance at how she acts towards her father.

Watching her now as she got down and started to serve my breakfast the warm knowledge flowed through me as it did so often that my wife was the sort who just liked looking after a man and that I was so very lucky.

And I was certainly blooming under the treatment. A bit too much, in fact, and I was aware I shouldn't be attacking this plateful of porridge and cream; especially with all that material sizzling in the frying pan. Helen had brought with her to Skeldale House a delicious dowry in the shape of half a pig and there hung from the beams of the topmost attic a side of bacon and a majestic ham; a constant temptation. Some samples were in the pan now and though I had never been one for large breakfasts I did not demur when she threw in a couple of big brown eggs to keep them company. And I put up only feeble resistance when she added some particularly tasty smoked sausage which she used to buy in a shop in the market place.

When I had got through it all I rose rather deliberately from the table and as I put on my coat I noticed it wasn't so easy to button as it used to be.

'Here are your sandwiches, Jim,' Helen said, putting a parcel in my hand. I was spending a day in the Scarburn district, tuberculin testing for Ewan Ross, and my wife was always concerned lest I grow faint from lack of nourishment on the long journey.

I kissed her, made a somewhat ponderous descent of the long flights of stairs and went out the side door. Half way up the garden I stopped as always and looked up at the window under the tiles. An arm appeared and brandished a dishcloth vigorously. I waved back and continued my walk to the yard. I found I was puffing a little as I got the car out and I laid my parcel almost guiltily on the back seat. I knew what it would contain; not just sandwiches but meat and onion pie, buttered scones, ginger cake to lead me into further indiscretions.

There is no doubt that in those early days I would have grown exceedingly gross under Helen's treatment. But my job saved me; the endless walking between the stone barns scattered along the hillsides, the climbing in and out of calf pens, pushing cows around, and regular outbursts of hard physical effort in calving and foaling. So I escaped with only a slight tightening of my collar and the occasional farmer's remark, 'By gaw, you've been on a good pasture, young man!'

Driving away, I marvelled at the way she indulged my little whims, too. I have always had a pathological loathing of fat, so Helen carefully trimmed every morsel from my meat. This feeling about fat, which almost amounted to terror, had been intensified since coming to Yorkshire, because back in the thirties the farmers seemed to live on the stuff. One old man, noticing my pop-eyed expression as I viewed him relishing his lunch of roast fat bacon, told me he had never touched lean meat in his life.

'Ah like to feel t'grease runnin' down ma chin!' he chuckled. He pronounced it 'grayus' which made it sound even worse. But he was a ruddy-faced octogenarian, so it hadn't done him any harm; and this held good for hundreds of others just like him. I used to think that the day in day out hard labour of farming burned it up in their systems but if I had to eat the stuff it would kill me very rapidly.

The latter was, of course, a fanciful notion as was proved to me one day.

It was when I was torn from my bed one morning at 6 a.m. to attend a calving heifer at old Mr Horner's small farm and when I got there I found there was no malpresentation of the calf but that it was simply too big. I don't like a lot of pulling but the heifer, lying on her bed of straw, was obviously in need of assistance. Every few seconds she strained to the utmost and a pair of feet came into view momentarily then disappeared as she relaxed.

'Is she getting those feet out any further?' I asked.

'Nay, there's been no change for over an hour,' the old man replied.

'And when did the water bag burst?'

'Two hours since.'

There was no doubt the calf was well and truly stuck and getting drier all the time, and if the labouring mother had been able to speak I think she would have said: 'For Pete's sake get this thing away from me!'

I could have done with a big strong man to help me but Mr Horner, apart from his advanced age, was a rather shaky light-weight. And since the farm was perched on a lonely eminence miles from the nearest village there was no chance of calling in a neighbour. I would have to do the job myself.

It took me nearly an hour. With a thin rope behind the calf's ears and through his mouth to stop the neck from telescoping I eased the little creature inch by inch into the world. Not so much pulling but rather leaning back and helping the heifer as she strained. She was a rather undersized little animal and she lay patiently on her side, accepting the situation with the resigna-tion of her kind. She could never have calved without help and all the time I had the warm conviction that I was doing what she wanted and needed. I felt I should be as patient as she was so I didn't hurry but let things come in their normal sequence; the little nose with the nostrils twitching reassuringly, then the eyes wearing a preoccupied light during the tight squeeze, then the ears and with a final rush the rest of the calf.

The young mother was obviously none the worse because she rolled on to her chest almost immediately and began to sniff with the utmost interest at the new arrival. She was in better shape than myself because I discovered with some surprise that I was sweating and breathless and my arms and shoulders were aching.

The farmer, highly pleased, rubbed my back briskly with the towel as I bent over the bucket, then he helped me on with my shirt.

'Well that's champion, lad. You'll come in and have a cup of tea now, won't you?'

In the kitchen Mrs Horner placed a steaming mug on the table and smiled across at me.

'Will you sit down along o' my husband and have a bit o' breakfast?' she asked.

There is nothing like an early calving to whet the appetite and I nodded readily. 'That's very kind of you, I'd love to.'

It is always a good feeling after a successful delivery and I sighed contentedly as I sank into a chair and watched the old lady set out bread, butter and jam in front of me. I sipped my tea and as I exchanged a word with the farmer I didn't see what she was doing next. Then my toes curled into a tight ball as I found two huge slices of pure white fat lying on my plate.

Shrinking back in my seat I saw Mrs Horner sawing at a great hunk of cold boiled bacon. But it wasn't ordinary bacon, it was one hundred per cent fat without a strip of lean anywhere. Even in my shocked state I could see it was a work of art; cooked to a turn, beautifully encrusted with golden crumbs and resting on a spotless serving dish . . . but fat.

She dropped two similar slices on her husband's plate and looked at me expectantly.

My position was desperate. I could not possibly offend this

sweet old person but on the other hand I knew beyond all doubt that there was no way I could eat what lay in front of me. Maybe I could have managed a tiny piece if it had been hot and fried crisp, but cold, boiled and clammy . . . never. And there was an enormous quantity; two slices about six inches by four and at least half an inch thick with the golden border of crumbs down one side. The thing was impossible.

Mrs Horner sat down opposite me. She was wearing a flowered mob cap over her white hair and for a moment she reached out, bent her head to one side and turned the dish with the slab of bacon a little to the left to show it off better. Then she turned to me and smiled. It was a kind, proud smile.

There have been times in my life when, confronted by black and hopeless circumstances, I have discovered in myself un-dreamed-of resources of courage and resolution. I took a deep breath, seized knife and fork and made a bold incision in one of the slices, but as I began to transport the greasy white seg-ment to my mouth I began to shudder and my hand stayed frozen in space. It was at that moment I spotted the jar of piccalilli.

Feverishly I scooped a mound of it on to my plate. It seemed to contain just about everything; onions, apples, cucumber and other assorted vegetables jostling each other in a powerful mustard-vinegar sauce. It was the work of a moment to smother my loaded fork with the mass, then I popped it into my mouth, gave a couple of quick chews and swallowed. It was a start and I hadn't tasted a thing except the piccalilli.

'Nice bit of bacon,' Mr Horner murmured.

'Delicious!' I replied, munching desperately at the second forkful. 'Absolutely delicious!'

'And you like ma piccalilli too!' The old lady beamed at me. 'Ah can tell by the way you're slappin' it on!' She gave a peal of delighted laughter.

'Yes, indeed.' I looked at her with streaming eyes. 'Some of the best I've ever tasted.'

Looking back, I realise it was one of the bravest things I have ever done. I stuck to my task unwaveringly, dipping again and again into the jar, keeping my mind a blank, refusing grimly to think of the horrible thing that was happening to me. There was only one bad moment, when the piccalilli, which packed a tremendous punch and was never meant to be consumed in large mouthfuls, completely took my breath away and I went into a long coughing spasm. But at last I came to the end. A final heroic crunch and swallow, a long gulp at my tea and the plate was empty. The thing was accomplished.

And there was no doubt it had been worth it. I had been a tremendous success with the old folks. Mr Horner slapped my shoulder.

'By gaw, it's good to see a young feller enjoyin' his food! When I were a lad I used to put it away sharpish, like that, but ah can't do it now.' Chuckling to himself, he continued with his breakfast.

His wife showed me the door. 'Aye, it was a real compliment to me.' She looked at the table and giggled. 'You've nearly finished the jar!'

'Yes, I'm sorry, Mrs Horner,' I said, smiling through my tears and trying to ignore the churning in my stomach. 'But I just couldn't resist it.'

Contrary to my expectations I didn't drop down dead soon afterwards but for a week I was oppressed by a feeling of nausea which I am prepared to believe was purely psychosomatic.

At any rate, since that little episode I have never knowingly eaten fat again. My hatred was transformed into something like an obsession from then on.

And I haven't been all that crazy about piccalilli either.

# 24

I wondered how long this feeling of novelty at being a married man would last. Maybe it went on for years and years. At any rate I did feel an entirely different person from the old Herriot as I paced with my wife among the stalls at the garden fête.

It was an annual affair in aid of the Society for the Prevention of Cruelty to Children and it was held on the big lawn behind the Darrowby vicarage with the weathered brick of the old house showing mellow red beyond the trees. The hot June sunshine bathed the typically English scene; the women in their flowered dresses, the men perspiring in their best suits, laughing children running from the tombola to the coconut shy or the ice-cream kiosk. In a little tent at one end, Mrs Newbould, the butcher's wife, thinly disguised as Madame Claire the fortune teller, was doing a brisk trade. It all seemed a long way from Glasgow.

And the solid citizen feeling was heightened by the pressure of Helen's hand on my arm and the friendly nods of the passers-by. One of these was the curate, Mr Blenkinsopp. He came up to us, exuding, as always, a charm that was completely unworldly.

'Ah, James,' he murmured. 'And Helen!' He beamed on us with the benevolence he felt for the entire human race. 'How nice to see you here!'

He walked along with us as the scent from the flower beds and the trodden grass rose in the warm air.

'You know, James, I was just thinking about you the other day. I was in Rainby – you know I take the service there every second week – and they were telling me they were having great difficulty in finding young men for the cricket team. I wondered if you would care to turn out for them.'

'Me? Play cricket?'

'Yes, of course.'

I laughed. 'I'm afraid I'm no cricketer. I'm interested in the game and I like to watch it, but where I come from they don't play it very much.'

'Oh, but surely you must have played at some time or other.'

'A bit at school, but they go more for tennis in Scotland. And anyway it was a long time ago.'

'Oh well, there you are.' Mr Blenkinsopp spread his hands. 'It will come back to you easily.'

'I don't know about that,' I said. 'But another thing, I don't live in Rainby, doesn't that matter?'

'Not really,' the curate replied. 'It is such a problem finding eleven players in these tiny villages that they often call on outsiders. Nobody minds.'

I stopped my stroll over the grass and turned to Helen. She was giving me an encouraging smile and I began to think, well ... why not? It looked as though I had settled in Yorkshire. I had married a Yorkshire girl. I might as well start doing the Yorkshire things, like playing cricket – there wasn't anything more Yorkshire than that.

'All right then, Mr Blenkinsopp,' I said. 'You're not getting any bargain but I don't mind having a go.'

'Splendid! The next match is on Tuesday evening – against Hedwick. I am playing so I'll pick you up at six o'clock.' His face radiated happiness as though I had done him the greatest favour.

'Well, thanks,' I replied. 'I'll have to fix it with my partner to be off that night, but I'm sure it will be O.K.'

The weather was still fine on Tuesday and, going round my visits, I found it difficult to assimilate the fact that for the first time in my life I was going to perform in a real genuine cricket match.

It was funny the way I felt about cricket. All my experience of the game was based on the long-range impressions I had gained during my Glasgow boyhood. Gleaned from newspapers, from boys' magazines, from occasional glimpses of Hobbs and Sutcliffe and Woolley on the cinema newsreels, they had built up a strangely glamorous picture in my mind. The whole thing, it seemed to me, was so deeply and completely English; the gentle clunk of bat on ball, the white-clad figures on the wide sweep of smooth turf; there was a softness, a graciousness about cricket which you found nowhere else; nobody ever got excited or upset at this leisurely pursuit. There was no doubt at all that I looked on cricket with a romanticism and nostalgia which would have been incomprehensible to people who had played the game all their lives.

Promptly at six Mr Blenkinsopp tooted the horn of his little car outside the surgery. Helen had advised me to dress ready for action and she had clearly been right because the curate, too, was resplendent in white flannels and blazer. The three young farmers crammed in the back were, however, wearing open-necked shirts with their ordinary clothes.

'Hello, James!' said Mr Blenkinsopp.

'Now then, Jim,' said two of the young men in the back. But 'Good afternoon, Mr Herriot,' said the one in the middle.

He was Tom Willis, the captain of the Rainby team and in my opinion, one of nature's gentlemen. He was about my own age and he and his father ran the kind of impoverished small-holding which just about kept them alive. But there was a sensitivity and refinement about him and a courtesy which never varied. I never cared how people addressed me and a lot of the farmers used my first name, but to Tom and his father I was always Mr Herriot. They considered it was the correct way to address the vet and that was that.

Tom leaned from the back seat now, his lean face set in its usual serious expression.

'It's good of you to give up your time, Mr Herriot. I know you're a busy man but we're allus short o' players at Rainby.'

'I'm looking forward to it, Tom, but I'm no cricketer, I'll tell you now.'

He gazed at me with gentle disbelief and I had an uncomfortable feeling that everybody had the impression that because I had been to college I was bound to have a blue.

Hedwick was at the top end of Allerdale, a smaller offshoot of the main Dale, and as we drove up the deep ever-narrowing cleft in the moorland I wound down the window. It was the sort of country I saw every day but I wasn't used to being a passenger and there was no doubt you could see more this way. From the overlapping fringe of heather far above, the walls ran in spidery lines down the bare green flanks to the softness of the valley floor where grey farmhouses crouched; and the heavy scent of the new cut hay lying in golden swathes in the meadows drifted into the car. There were trees, too, down here, not the stunted dwarfs of the high country above us, but giants in the exultant foliage of high summer.

We stopped at Hedwick because we could go no further. This was the head of the Dale, a cluster of cottages, a farm and a pub. Where the road curved a few cars were drawn up by the side of a solid-looking wall on which leaned a long row of cloth-capped men, a few women and chattering groups of children.

'Ah,' said Mr Blenkinsopp. 'A good turn-out of spectators. Hedwick always support their team well. They must have come from all over the Dale.'

I looked around in surprise. 'Spectators?'

'Yes, of course. They've come to see the match.'

Again I gazed about me. 'But I can't see the pitch.'

'It's there,' Tom said. 'Just over t'wall.'

I leaned across the rough stones and stared in some bewilderment at a wildly undulating field almost knee deep in rough grass among which a cow, some sheep and a few hens wandered contentedly. 'Is this it?'

'Aye, that's it. If you stand on t'wall you can see the square.'

I did as he said and could just discern a five foot wide strip of bright green cut from the crowding herbage. The stumps stood expectantly at either end. A massive oak tree sprouted from somewhere around mid-on.

The strip stood on the only level part of the field, and that was a small part. Within twenty yards it swept up steeply to a thick wood which climbed over the lower slopes of the fell. On the other side it fell away to a sort of ravine where the rank grass ended only in a rocky stream. The wall bordering the near side ran up to a group of farm buildings.

There was no clubhouse but the visiting team were seated on a form on the grass while nearby, a little metal score board about four feet high stood near its pile of hooked number plates.

The rest of our team had arrived, too, and with a pang of alarm I noticed that there was not a single pair of white flannels among them. Only the curate and I were properly attired and the immediate and obvious snag was that he could play and I couldn't.

Tom and the home captain tossed a coin. Hedwick won and elected to bat. The umpires, two tousle-haired, sunburnt young fellows in grubby white coats strolled to the wicket, our team followed and the Hedwick batsmen appeared. Under their pads they wore navy blue serge trousers (a popular colour among both teams) and one of them sported a bright yellow sweater.

Tom Willis with the air of authority and responsibility which was natural to him began to dispose the field. No doubt convinced that I was a lynx-eyed catcher he stationed me quite close to the bat on the off side then after a grave consultation with Mr Blenkinsopp he gave him the ball and the game was on.

And Mr Blenkinsopp was a revelation. In his university sweater, gleaming flannels and brightly coloured cap he really looked good. And indeed it was soon very clear that he was good. He handed his cap to the umpire, retreated about twenty yards into the undergrowth, then turned and, ploughing his way back at ever increasing speed, delivered the ball with remarkable velocity bang on the wicket. The chap in yellow met it respectfully with a dead bat and did the same with the next but then he uncoiled himself and belted the third one high over the fielders on to the slope beneath the wood. As one of our men galloped after it the row of heads above the wall broke into a babel of noise.

They cheered every hit, not with the decorous ripple of applause I had always imagined, but with raucous yells. And they had plenty to shout about. The Hedwick lads, obviously accustomed to the peculiarities of their pitch wasted no time on classical strokes; they just gave a great hoick at the ball and when they connected it travelled immense distances. Occasionally they missed and Mr Blenkinsopp or one of our other bowlers shattered their stumps but the next man started cheerfully where they left off.

It was exhilarating stuff but I was unable to enjoy it. Everything I did, in fact my every movement proclaimed my ignorance to the knowledgeable people around me. I threw the ball in to the wrong end, I left the ball when I should have chased it and sped after it when I should have stayed in my place. I couldn't understand half the jargon which was being bandied around. No, there was not a shadow of a doubt about it; here in this cricket mad corner of a cricket mad county I was a foreigner.

Five wickets had gone down when a very fat lad came out to bat. His appearance of almost perfect rotundity was accentuated by the Fair Isle sweater stretched tightly over his bulging abdomen and judging by the barrage of witticisms which came from the heads along the wall it seemed he was a local character. He made a violent cross-batted swish at the first delivery, missed, and the ball sank with a thud into his midriff. Howls of laughter arose from players, spectators and umpires alike as he collapsed slowly at the crease and massaged himself ruefully. He slashed at the next one and it flew off the edge of his bat like a bullet, struck my shinbone a fearful crack and dropped into the grass. Resisting the impulse to scream and hop around in my agony I gritted my teeth, grabbed the ball and threw it in.

'Oh well stopped, Mr Herriot,' Tom Willis called from his position at mid-on. He clapped his hands a few times in encouragement.

Despite his girth the fat lad smote lustily and was finally caught in the outfield for fifteen.

The next batsman seemed to be taking a long time to reach the wicket. He was shuffling, bent-kneed, through the clover like a very old man, trailing his bat wearily behind him, and when he finally arrived at the crease I saw that he was indeed fairly advanced in years. He wore only one pad, strapped over baggy grey trousers which came almost up to his armpits and were suspended by braces. A cloth cap surmounted a face shrunken like a sour apple. From one corner of the downturned mouth a cigarette dangled.

He took guard and looked at the umpire.

'Middle and leg,' he grunted.

'Aye, that's about it, Len,' the umpire replied.

Len pursed his little mouth.

'About it . . . about it . . . ? Well is it or bloody isn't it ?' he enquired peevishly.

The young man in white grinned indulgently. 'Aye it is, Len, that's it.'

The old man removed his cigarette, flicked it on to the grass and took up his guard again. His appearance suggested that he might be out first ball or in fact that he had no right to be there at all, but as the delivery came down he stepped forward and with a scything sweep thumped the ball past the bowler and just a few inches above the rear end of the cow which had wandered into the line of fire. The animal looked round in some surprise as the ball whizzed along its backbone and the old man's crabbed features relaxed into the semblance of a smile.

'By gaw, vitnery,' he said, looking at me, 'ah damn near made a bit of work for tha there.' He eyed me impassively for a moment. 'Ah reckon tha's never took a cricket ball out of a cow's arse afore, eh ?'

Len returned to the job in hand and proved a difficult man to dislodge. But it was the batsman at the other end who was worrying Tom Willis. He had come in first wicket down, a ruddy faced lad of about nineteen wearing a blue shirt and he was still there piling on the runs.

At the end of the over, Tom came up to me. 'Fancy turning your arm over, Mr Herriot ?' he enquired gravely.

'Huh ?'

'Would you like a bowl ? A fresh man might just unsettle this feller.'

'Well . . . er . . .' I didn't know what to say. The idea of me bowling in a real match was unthinkable. Tom made up my mind by throwing me the ball.

Clasping it in a clammy hand I trotted up to the wicket while the lad in the blue shirt crouched intently over his bat. All the other bowlers had hurled their missiles down at top speed but as I ambled forward it burst on me that if I tried that I would be miles off my target. Accuracy, I decided, must be my watchword and I sent a gentle lob in the direction of the wicket. The batsman, obviously convinced that such a slow ball must be laden with hidden malice followed its course with deep suspicion and smothered it as soon as it arrived. He did the same with the second but that was enough for him to divine that I wasn't bowling off breaks, leg breaks or googlies but simply little dollies and he struck the third ball smartly into the ravine.

There was a universal cry of '*Maurice!*' from our team because Maurice Briggs, the Rainby blacksmith, was fielding down there and since he couldn't see the wicket he had to be warned. In due course the ball soared back from the depths, propelled no doubt by Maurice's strong right arm, and I recommenced my attack. The lad in blue thumped my remaining three deliveries effortlessly for six. The first flew straight over the wall and the row of cars into the adjoining field, the next landed in the farmyard and the third climbed in a tremendous arc away above the ravine and I heard it splash into the beck whence it was retrieved with a certain amount of profanity by the invisible Maurice.

An old farm man once said to me when describing a moment of embarrassment, 'Ah could've got down a mouse 'ole.' And as I returned to my place in the field I knew just what he meant. In fact the bowler at the other end got through his over almost without my noticing it and I was still shrunk in my cocoon of shame when I saw Tom Willis signalling to me.

I couldn't believe it. He was throwing me the ball again. It was a typically magnanimous gesture, a generous attempt to assure me that I had done well enough to have another go.

Again I shambled forward and the blue-shirted lad awaited me, almost licking his lips. He had never come across anyone like me before and it seemed too good to be true that I should be given another over; but there I was, and he climbed gratefully into each ball I sent down and laid into it in a kind of ecstasy with the full meat of the bat.

I would rather not go into details. Sufficient to say that I have a vivid memory of his red face and blue shirt and of the ball whistling back over my head after each delivery and of the almost berserk yells of the spectators. But he didn't hit every ball for six. In fact there were two moments of light relief in my torment; one when the ball smashed into the oak tree, ricocheted and almost decapitated old Len at the other end; the other when a ball snicked off the edge of the bat and ploughed through a very large cow pat, sending up a noisome spray along its course. It finished at the feet of Mr Blenkinsopp and the poor man was clearly in a dilemma. For the last hour he had been swooping on everything that came near him with the grace of the born cricketer.

But now he hovered over the unclean object, gingerly extending a hand then withdrawing it as his earthier colleagues in the team watched in wonder. The batsmen were galloping up and down, the crowd was roaring but the curate made no move. Finally he picked the thing up with the utmost daintiness in two fingers, regarded it distastefully for a few moments and carried it to the wicketkeeper who was ready with a handful of grass in his big gloves.

At the end of the over Tom came up to me. 'Thank ye, Mr Herriot, but I'm afraid I'll have to take you off now. This wicket's not suited to your type of bowling – not takin' spin at all.' He shook his head in his solemn way.

I nodded thankfully and Tom went on. 'Tell ye what, go down and relieve that man in the outfield. We could do wi' a safe pair of hands down there.'

# 25

I obeyed my skipper's orders and descended to the ravine and when Maurice had clambered up the small grassy cliff which separated me from the rest of the field I felt strangely alone. It was a dank, garlic-smelling region, perceptively colder than the land above and silent except for the gurgle of the beck behind me. There was a little hen house down here with several hens pecking around and some sheep who obviously felt it was safer than the higher ground.

I could see nothing of the pitch, only occasional glimpses of the heads of players so I had no idea of what was going on. In fact it was difficult to believe I was still taking part in a cricket match but for the spectators. From their position along the wall they had a grandstand view of everything and in fact were looking down at me from short range. They appeared to find me quite interesting, too, because a lot of them kept their eyes on me, puffing their pipes and making remarks which I couldn't hear but which caused considerable hilarity.

It was a pity about the spectators because it was rather peaceful in the ravine. It took a very big hit to get down there and I was more or less left to ruminate. Occasionally the warning cries would ring out from above and a ball would come bounding over the top. Once a skied drive landed with a thud in a patch of deep grass and with an enraged squawking a Rhode Island cockerel emerged at top speed and legged it irascibly to a safer haven.

Now and then I clawed my way up the bank and had a look at the progress of the game. Len had gone but the lad in blue was still there. After another dismissal I was surprised to see one of the umpires give his coat to the outgoing batsman, seize the bat and start laying about him. Both umpires were in fact members of the team.

It was after a long spell of inaction and when I was admiring the long splash of gold which the declining sun was throwing

down the side of the fell when I heard the frantic yells. *'Jim !
James ! Mr Herriot !'* The whole team was giving tongue and,
as I learned later, the lad in the blue shirt had made a catchable
shot.

But I knew anyway. Nobody but he could have struck the
blow which sent that little speck climbing higher and higher into
the pale evening sky above me; and as it began with terrifying
slowness to fall in my direction time came to a halt. I was aware
of several of my team mates breasting the cliff and watching me
breathlessly, of the long row of heads above the wall, and suddenly I was gripped by a cold resolve. I was going to catch this
fellow out. He had humiliated me up there but it was my turn
now.

The speck was coming down faster now as I stumbled about
in the tangled vegetation trying to get into position. I nearly fell
over a ewe with two big fat lambs sucking at her then I was right
under the ball, hands cupped, waiting.

It fell, at the end, like a cannon ball, heavy and unyielding,
on the end of my right thumb, bounded over my shoulder and
thumped mournfully on the turf.

A storm of derision broke from the heads, peals of delighted
laughter, volleys of candid comment.

'Get a basket!' advised one worthy.

'Fetch 'im a bucket!' suggested another.

As I scrabbled for the ball among the herbage I didn't know
which was worse – the physical pain which was excruciating, or
the mental anguish. After I had finally hurled the thing up the
cliff I cradled the throbbing thumb in my other hand and rocked
back and forth on my heels, moaning softly.

My team mates returned sadly to their tasks but Tom Willis,
I noticed, lingered on, looking down at me.

'Hard luck, Mr Herriot. Very easy to lose t'ball against them
trees.' He nodded encouragingly then was gone.

I was not troubled further in the innings. We never did get
blue-shirt out and he had an unbeaten sixty-two at the close.
The Hedwick score was a hundred and fifty-four, a very useful
total in village cricket.

There was a ten minute interval while two of our players donned the umpires' coats and our openers strapped on their pads. Tom Willis showed me the batting list he had drawn up and I saw without surprise that I was last man in.

'Our team's packed with batting, Mr Herriot,' he said seriously. 'I couldn't find a place for you higher up the order.'

Mr Blenkinsopp, preparing to receive the first ball, really looked the part, gay cap pulled well down, college colours bright on the broad V of his sweater. But in this particular situation he had one big disadvantage; he was too good.

All the coaching he had received had been aimed at keeping the ball down. An 'uppish' stroke was to be deplored. But everything had to be uppish on this pitch.

As I watched from my place on the form he stepped out and executed a flawless cover drive. At Headingley the ball would have rattled against the boards for four but here it travelled approximately two and a half feet and the fat lad stooped carelessly, lifted it from the dense vegetation and threw it back to the bowler. The next one the curate picked beautifully off his toes and flicked it to square leg for what would certainly have been another four anywhere else. This one went for about a yard before the jungle claimed it.

It saddened me to watch him having to resort to swiping tactics which were clearly foreign to him. He did manage to get in a few telling blows but was caught on the boundary for twelve.

It was a bad start for Rainby with that large total facing them and the two Hedwick fast bowlers looked very formidable. One of them in particular, a gangling youth with great long arms and a shock of red hair seemed to fire his missiles with the speed of light, making the batsmen duck and dodge as the ball flew around their ears.

'That's Tagger Hird,' explained my nearest team mate on the bench. 'By gaw 'e does chuck 'em down. It's a bugger facin' him when the light's getting bad.'

I nodded in silence. I wasn't looking forward to facing him at all, in any kind of light. In fact I was dreading any further display of my shortcomings and I had the feeling that walking out

174

there to the middle was going to be the worst part of all.

But meanwhile I couldn't help responding to the gallant fight Rainby were putting up. As the match went on I found we had some stalwarts in our ranks. Bert Chapman the council roadman and an old acquaintance of mine strode out with his ever present wide grin splitting his brick-red face and began to hoist the ball all over the field. At the other end Maurice Briggs the blacksmith, sleeves rolled high over his mighty biceps and the bat looking like a Woolworths toy in his huge hands, clouted six after six, showing a marked preference for the ravine where there now lurked some hapless member of the other team. I felt for him, whoever it was down there; the sun had gone behind the hills and the light was fading and it must have been desperately gloomy in those humid depths.

And then when Tom came in he showed the true strategical sense of a captain. When Hedwick were batting it had not escaped his notice that they aimed a lot of their shots at a broad patch of particularly impenetrable vegetation, a mato grosso of rank verdure containing not only tangled grasses but nettles, thistles and an abundance of nameless flora. The memory of the Hedwick batsmen running up and down while his fielders thrashed about in there was fresh in his mind as he batted, and at every opportunity he popped one with the greatest accuracy into the jungle himself.

It was the kind of innings you would expect from him; not spectacular, but thoughtful and methodical. After one well-placed drive he ran seventeen while the fielders clawed at the undergrowth and the yells from the wall took on a frantic note.

And all the time we were creeping nearer to the total. When eight wickets had fallen we had reached a hundred and forty and our batsmen were running whether they hit the ball or not. It was too dark by now, to see, in any case, with great black banks of cloud driving over the fell top and the beginnings of a faint drizzle in the air.

In the gathering gloom I watched as the batsman swung, but only managed to push the ball a few yards up the pitch. Nevertheless he broke into a full gallop and collided with his partner who was roaring up from the other end. They fell in a heap with the ball underneath and the wicketkeeper, in an attempt at a run-out, dived among the bodies and scrabbled desperately for the ball. Animal cries broke out from the heads on the wall, the players were all bellowing at each other and at that moment I think the last of my romantic illusions about cricket slipped quietly away.

But soon I had no more time to think about such things. There was an eldritch scream from the bowler and our man was out L.B.W. It was my turn to bat.

Our score was a hundred and forty-five and as, dry-mouthed, I buckled on my pads, the lines of the poem came back to me. 'Ten to win and the last man in.' But I had never dreamed that my first innings in a cricket match would be like this, with the rain pattering steadily on the grass and the oil lamps on the farm winking through the darkness.

Pacing my way to the wicket I passed close by Tagger Hird who eyed me expressionlessly, tossing the ball from one meaty hand to another and whistling softly to himself. As I took guard he began his pounding run up and I braced myself. He had already dropped two of our batsmen in groaning heaps and I realised I had small hope of even seeing the ball.

But I had decided on one thing! I wasn't going to just stand there and take it. I wasn't a cricketer but I was going to try to hit the ball. And as Tagger arrived at full gallop and brought his arm over I stepped out and aimed a violent lunge at where I thought the thing might be. Nothing happened. I heard the smack on the sodden turf and the thud into the wicketkeeper's gloves, that was all.

The same thing happened with the next two deliveries. Great flailing blows which nearly swung me off my feet but nothing besides the smack and the thud. As Tagger ran up the fourth time I was breathless and my heart was thumping. I was playing a whirlwind innings except that I hadn't managed to make contact so far.

Again the arm came over and again I leapt out. And this time there was a sharp crack. I had got a touch but I had no idea where the ball had gone. I was standing gazing stupidly around me when I heard a bellowed '*Come on!*' and saw my partner thundering towards me. At the same time I spotted a couple of fielders running after something away down on my left and then the umpire made a signal. I had scored a four.

With the fifth ball I did the same thing and heard another crack, but this time, as I glared wildly about me I saw there was activity somewhere behind me on my right. We ran three and I had made seven.

There had been a no-ball somewhere and with the extra delivery Tagger scattered my partner's stumps and the match was over. We had lost by two runs.

'A merry knock, Mr Herriot,' Tom said, as I marched from the arena. 'Just for a minute I was beginnin' to think you were goin' to pull it off for us there.'

There was a pie and pea supper for both teams in the pub and as I settled down with a frothing pint of beer the thought kept coming back to me. Seven not out! After the humiliations of the evening it was an ultimate respectability. I had not at any time seen the ball during my innings and I had no idea how it had arrived in those two places but I had made seven not out. And as the meal arrived in front of me – delicious home-made steak and kidney pie with mounds of mushy peas – and I looked around at the roomful of laughing sunburnt men I began to feel good.

Tom sat on one side of me and Mr Blenkinsopp on the other. I had been interested to see that the curate could sink a pint with the best of them and he smiled as he put down his glass.

'Well done indeed, James. Nearly a story book ending. And you know, I'm quite sure you'd have clinched it if your partner had been able to keep going.'

I felt myself blushing. 'Well it's very kind of you, but I was a bit lucky.'

'Lucky? Not a bit of it!' said Mr Blenkinsopp. 'You played two beautiful strokes – I don't know how you did it in the conditions.'

'Beautiful strokes ?'

'Most certainly. A delightful leg glance followed by a late cut of the greatest delicacy. Don't you agree, Tom ?'

Tom sprinkled a little salt on his peas and turned to me. 'Ah do agree. And the best bit was how you got 'em up in the air to clear t'long grass. That was clever that was.' He conveyed a forkful of pie to his mouth and began to munch stolidly.

I looked at him narrowly. Tom was always serious so there was nothing to be learned from his expression. He was always kind, too, he had been kind all evening.

But I really think he meant it this time.

# 26

'Is this the thing you've been telling me about ?' I asked.

Mr Wilkin nodded. 'Aye, that's it, it's always like that.'

I looked down at the helpless convulsions of the big dog lying at my feet; at the staring eyes, the wildly pedalling limbs. The farmer had told me about the periodic attacks which had begun to affect his sheepdog, Gyp, but it was coincidence that one should occur when I was on the farm for another reason.

'And he's all right afterwards, you say ?'

'Right as a bobbin. Seems a bit dazed, maybe, for about an hour then he's back to normal.' The farmer shrugged. 'I've had lots o' dogs through my hands as you know and I've seen plenty of dogs with fits. I thought I knew all the causes – worms, wrong feeding, distemper – but this has me beat. I've tried everything.'

'Well you can stop trying, Mr Wilkin,' I said. 'You won't be able to do much for Gyp. He's got epilepsy.'

'Epilepsy ? But he's a grand, normal dog most of t'time.'

'Yes, I know. That's how it goes. There's nothing actually wrong with his brain – it's a mysterious condition. The cause is unknown but it's almost certainly hereditary.'

Mr Wilkin raised his eyebrows. 'Well that's a rum 'un. If it's hereditary why hasn't it shown up before now? He's nearly two years old and he didn't start this till a few weeks ago.'

'That's typical,' I replied. 'Eighteen months to two years is about the time it usually appears.'

Gyp interrupted us by getting up and staggering towards his master, wagging his tail. He seemed untroubled by his experience. In fact the whole thing had lasted less than two minutes.

Mr Wilkin bent and stroked the rough head briefly. His craggy features were set in a thoughtful cast. He was a big powerful man in his forties and now as the eyes narrowed in that face which rarely smiled he looked almost menacing. I had heard more than one man say he wouldn't like to get on the wrong side of Sep Wilkin and I could see what they meant. But he had always treated me right and since he farmed nearly a thousand acres I saw quite a lot of him.

His passion was sheepdogs. A lot of farmers liked to run dogs at the trials but Mr Wilkin was one of the top men. He bred and trained dogs which regularly won at the local events and occasionally at the national trials. And what was troubling me was that Gyp was his main hope.

He had picked out the two best pups from a litter – Gyp and Sweep – and had trained them with the dedication that had made him a winner. I don't think I have ever seen two dogs enjoy each other quite as much; whenever I was on the farm I would see them together, sometimes peeping nose by nose over the half door of the loose box where they slept, occasionally slinking devotedly round the feet of their master but usually just playing together. They must have spent hours rolling about in ecstatic wrestling matches, growling and panting, gnawing gently at each other's limbs.

A few months ago George Crossley, one of Mr Wilkin's oldest friends and a keen trial man, had lost his best dog with nephritis and Mr Wilkin had let him have Sweep. I was surprised at the time because Sweep was shaping better than Gyp in his training and looked like turning out a real champion. But it was Gyp who remained. He must have missed his friend but there were other dogs on the farm and if they didn't quite make up for Sweep he was never really lonely.

As I watched, I could see the dog recovering rapidly. It was extraordinary how soon normality was restored after that frightening convulsion. And I waited with some apprehension to hear what his master would say.

The cold, logical decision for him to make would be to have Gyp put down and, looking at the friendly, tail-wagging animal I didn't like the idea at all. There was something very attractive about him. The big-boned, well-marked body was handsome but his most distinctive feature was his head where one ear somehow contrived to stick up while the other lay flat, giving him a lop-sided, comic appeal. Gyp, in fact, looked a bit of a clown. But a clown who radiated goodwill and camaraderie.

Mr Wilkin spoke at last. 'Will he get any better as he grows older?'

'Almost certainly not,' I replied.

'Then he'll always 'ave these fits?'

'I'm afraid so. You say he has them every two or three weeks – well it will probably carry on more or less like that with occasional variations.'

'But he could have one any time?'

'Yes.'

'In the middle of a trial, like.' The farmer sunk his head on his chest and his voice rumbled deep. 'That's it, then.'

In the long silence which followed, the fateful words became more and more inevitable. Sep Wilkin wasn't the man to hesitate in a matter which concerned his ruling passion. Ruthless culling of any animal which didn't come up to standard would be his policy. When he finally cleared his throat I had a sinking premonition of what he was going to say.

But I was wrong.

'If I kept him, could you do anything for him?' he asked.

'Well I could give you some pills for him. They might decrease the frequency of the fits.' I tried to keep the eagerness out of my voice.

'Right . . . right . . . I'll come into t'surgery and get some,' he muttered.

'Fine. But . . . er . . . you won't ever breed from him, will you you ?' I said.

'Naw, naw, naw,' the farmer grunted with a touch of irritability as though he didn't want to pursue the matter further.

And I held my peace because I felt intuitively that he did not want to be detected in a weakness; that he was prepared to keep the dog simply as a pet. It was funny how events began to slot into place and suddenly make sense. That was why he had let Sweep, the superior trial dog, go. He just liked Gyp. In fact Sep Wilkin, hard man though he may be, had succumbed to that off-beat charm.

So I shifted to some light chatter about the weather as I walked back to the car, but when I was about to drive off the farmer returned to the main subject.

'There's one thing about Gyp I never mentioned,' he said, bending to the window. 'I don't know whether it has owt to do with the job or not. He has never barked in his life.'

I looked at him in surprise. 'You mean never, ever ?'

'That's right. Not a single bark. T'other dogs make a noise when strangers come on the farm but I've never heard Gyp utter a sound since he was born.'

'Well that's very strange,' I said. 'But I can't see that it is connected with his condition in any way.'

And as I switched on the engine I noticed for the first time that while a bitch and two half grown pups gave tongue to see me on my way Gyp merely regarded me in his comradely way, mouth open, tongue lolling, but made no noise. A silent dog.

The thing intrigued me. So much so that whenever I was on the farm over the next few months I made a point of watching the big sheepdog at whatever he was doing. But there was never any change. Between the convulsions which had settled down to around three week intervals he was a normal active happy animal. But soundless.

I saw him, too, in Darrowby when his master came in to market. Gyp was often seated comfortably in the back of the car, but if I happened to speak to Mr Wilkin on these occasions I kept off the subject because, as I said, I had the feeling that he more than most farmers would hate to be exposed in keeping a dog for other than working purposes.

And yet I have always entertained a suspicion that most farm dogs were more or less pets. The dogs on sheep farms were of course indispensable working animals and on other establishments they no doubt performed a function in helping to bring in the cows. But watching them on my daily rounds I often wondered. I saw them rocking along on carts at haytime, chasing rats among the stooks at harvest, pottering around the buildings or roaming the fields at the side of the farmer; and I wondered . . . what did they really do?

My suspicions were strengthened at other times – as when I was trying to round up some cattle into a corner and the dog tried to get into the act by nipping at a hock or tail. There was invariably a hoarse yell of 'Siddown, dog!' or 'Gerrout, dog!'

So right up to the present day I still stick to my theory; most farm dogs are pets and they are there mainly because the farmer just likes to have them around. You would have to put a farmer on the rack to get him to admit it but I think I am right. And in the process those dogs have a wonderful time. They don't have to beg for walks, they are out all day long, and in the company of their masters. If I want to find a man on a farm I look for his dog, knowing the man won't be far away. I try to give my own dogs a good life but it cannot compare with the life of the average farm dog.

There was a long spell when Sep Wilkin's stock stayed healthy and I didn't see either him or Gyp, then I came across them both by accident at a sheepdog trial. It was a local event run in conjunction with the Mellerton Agricultural Show and since I was in the district I decided to steal an hour off.

I took Helen with me, too, because these trials have always fascinated us. The wonderful control of the owners over their animals, the intense involvement of the dogs themselves, the sheer skill of the whole operation always held us spellbound.

She put her arm through mine as we went in at the entrance gate to where a crescent of cars was drawn up at one end of a long field. The field was on the river's edge and through a fringe of trees the afternoon sunshine glinted on the tumbling water of the shallows and turned the long beach of bleached stones to a dazzling white. Groups of men, mainly competitors, stood around chatting as they watched. They were quiet, easy, bronzed men and as they seemed to be drawn from all social strata from prosperous farmers to working men their garb was varied; cloth caps, trilbies, deerstalkers or no hat at all; tweed jackets, stiff best suits, open-necked shirts, fancy ties, sometimes neither collar nor tie. Nearly all of them leaned on long crooks with the handles fashioned from rams' horns.

Snatches of talk reached us as we walked among them.

'You got 'ere, then, Fred.' 'That's a good gather.' 'Nay, 'e's missed one, 'e'll get nowt for that.' 'Them sheep's a bit flighty.' 'Aye they're buggers.' And above it all the whistles of the man running a dog; every conceivable level and pitch of whistle with now and then a shout. 'Sit!' 'Get by!' Every man had his own way with his dog.

The dogs waiting their turn were tied up to a fence with a hedge growing over it. There were about seventy of them and it was rather wonderful to see that long row of waving tails and friendly expressions. They were mostly strangers to each other but there wasn't even the semblance of disagreement, never mind a fight. It seemed that the natural obedience of these little creatures was linked to an amicable disposition.

This appeared to be common to their owners, too. There was no animosity, no resentment at defeat, no unseemly display of triumph in victory. If a man overran his time he ushered his group of sheep quietly in the corner and returned with a philosophical grin to his colleagues. There was a little quiet leg-pulling but that was all.

We came across Sep Wilkin leaning against his car at the best vantage point about thirty yards away from the final pen. Gyp, tied to the bumper, turned and gave me his crooked grin while

Mrs Wilkin on a camp stool by his side rested a hand on his shoulder. Gyp, it seemed, had got under her skin too.

Helen went over to speak to her and I turned to her husband. 'Are you running a dog today, Mr Wilkin?'

'No, not this time, just come to watch. I know a lot o' the dogs.'

I stood near him for a while watching the competitors in action, breathing in the clean smell of trampled grass and plug tobacco. In front of us next to the pen the judge stood by his post.

I had been there for about ten minutes when Mr Wilkin lifted a pointing finger. 'Look who's there!'

George Crossley with Sweep trotting at his heels was making his way unhurriedly to the post. Gyp suddenly stiffened and sat up very straight, his cocked ears accentuating the lop-sided look. It was many months since he had seen his brother and companion; it seemed unlikely I thought, that he would remember him. But his interest was clearly intense, and as the judge waved his white handkerchief and the three sheep were released from the far corner he rose slowly to his feet.

A gesture from Mr Crossley sent Sweep winging round the perimeter of the field in a wide, joyous gallop and as he neared the sheep a whistle dropped him on his belly. From then on it was an object lesson in the cooperation of man and dog. Sep Wilkin had always said Sweep would be a champion and he looked the part, darting and falling at his master's commands. Short piercing whistles, shrill plaintive whistles; he was in tune with them all.

No dog all day had brought his sheep through the three lots of gates as effortlessly as Sweep did now and as he approached the pen near us it was obvious that he would win the cup unless some disaster struck. But this was the touchy bit; more than once with other dogs the sheep had broken free and gone bounding away within feet of the wooden rails.

George Crossley held the gate wide and extended his crook. You could see now why they all carried those long sticks. His commands to Sweep, huddled flat along the turf, were now almost inaudible but the quiet words brought the dog inching first one way then the other. The sheep were in the entrance to the pen now but they still looked around them irresolutely and the game was not over yet. But as Sweep wriggled towards them almost imperceptibly they turned and entered and Mr Crossley crashed the gate behind them.

As he did so he turned to Sweep with a happy cry of '*Good lad!*' and the dog responded with a quick jerking wag of his tail.

At that, Gyp, who had been standing very tall, watching every move with the most intense concentration raised his head and emitted a single resounding bark.

'*Woof!*' went Gyp as we all stared at him in astonishment.

'Did you hear that?' gasped Mrs Wilkin.

'Well, by gaw!' her husband burst out, looking open-mouthed at his dog.

Gyp didn't seem to be aware that he had done anything unusual. He was too preoccupied by the reunion with his brother and within seconds the two dogs were rolling around, chewing playfully at each other as of old.

I suppose the Wilkins as well as myself had the feeling that this event might start Gyp barking like any other dog, but it was not to be.

Six years later I was on the farm and went to the house to get some hot water. As Mrs Wilkin handed me the bucket she looked down at Gyp who was basking in the sunshine outside the kitchen window.

'There you are, then, funny fellow,' she said to the dog.

I laughed. 'Has he ever barked since that day?'

Mrs Wilkin shook her head. 'No he hasn't, not a sound. I waited a long time but I know he's not going to do it now.'

'Ah well, it's not important. But still, I'll never forget that afternoon at the trial,' I said.

'Nor will I!' She looked at Gyp again and her eyes softened in reminiscence. 'Poor old lad, eight years old and only one woof!'

# 27

A full surgery! But the ripple of satisfaction as I surveyed the packed rows of heads waned quickly as realisation dawned. It was only the Dimmocks again.

I first encountered the Dimmocks one evening when I had a call to a dog which had been knocked down by a car. The address was down in the old part of the town and I was cruising slowly along the row of decaying cottages looking for the number when a door burst open and three shock-headed little children ran into the street and waved me down frantically.

'He's in 'ere, Mister!' they gasped in unison as I got out, and then began immediately to put me in the picture.

'It's Bonzo!' 'Aye, a car 'it 'im!' 'We 'ad to carry 'im in, Mister!' They all got their words in as I opened the garden gate and struggled up the path with the three of them hanging on to my arms and tugging at my coat; and en route I gazed in wonder at the window of the house where a mass of other young faces mouthed at me and a tangle of arms gesticulated.

Once through the door which opened directly into the living room I was swamped by a rush of bodies and borne over to the corner where I saw my patient.

Bonzo was sitting upright on a ragged blanket. He was a large shaggy animal of indeterminate breed and though at a glance there didn't seem to be much ailing him he wore a pathetic expression of self pity. Since everybody was talking at once I decided to ignore them and carry out my examination. I worked my way over legs, pelvis, ribs and spine; no fractures. His mucous membranes were a good colour, there was no evidence of internal injury. In fact the only thing I could find was slight bruising over the left shoulder. Bonzo had sat like a statue as I felt over him, but as I finished he toppled over on to his side and lay looking up at me apologetically, his tail thumping on the blanket.

'You're a big soft dog, that's what you are,' I said and the tail thumped faster.

I turned and viewed the throng and after a moment or two managed to pick out the parents. Mum was fighting her way to the front while at the rear, Dad, a diminutive figure, was beaming at me over the heads. I did a bit of shushing and when the babel died down I addressed myself to Mrs Dimmock.

'I think he's been lucky,' I said. 'I can't find any serious injury. I think the car must have bowled him over and knocked the wind out of him for a minute, or he may have been suffering from shock.'

The uproar broke out again. 'Will 'e die, Mister?' 'What's the matter with 'im?' 'What are you going to do?'

I gave Bonzo an injection of a mild sedative while he lay rigid, a picture of canine suffering, with the tousled heads looking down at him with deep concern and innumerable little hands poking out and caressing him.

Mrs Dimmock produced a basin of hot water and while I washed my hands I was able to make a rough assessment of the household. I counted eleven little Dimmocks from a boy in his early teens down to a grubby faced infant crawling around the floor; and judging by the significant bulge in Mum's midriff the number was soon to be augmented. They were clad in a motley selection of hand-me-downs; darned pullovers, patched trousers, tattered dresses, yet the general atmosphere in the house was of unconfined *joie de vivre*.

Bonzo wasn't the only animal and I stared in disbelief as another biggish dog and a cat with two half grown kittens appeared from among the crowding legs and feet. I would have thought that the problem of filling the human mouths would have been difficult enough without importing several animals.

But the Dimmocks didn't worry about such things; they did what they wanted to do, and they got by. Dad, I learned later, had never done any work within living memory. He had a 'bad back' and lived what seemed to me a reasonably gracious life, roaming interestedly around the town by day and enjoying a quiet beer and a game of dominoes in a corner of the Four Horse Shoes by night.

I saw him quite often; he was easy to pick out because he invariably carried a walking stick which gave him an air of dignity and he always walked briskly and purposefully as though he were going somewhere important.

I took a final look at Bonzo, still stretched on the blanket, looking up at me with soulful eyes then I struggled towards the door.

'I don't think there's anything to worry about,' I shouted above the chattering which had speedily broken out again, 'but I'll look in tomorrow and make sure.'

When I drew up outside the house next morning I could see Bonzo lolloping around the garden with several of the children. They were passing a ball from one to the other and he was leaping ecstatically high in the air to try to intercept it.

He was clearly none the worse for his accident but when he saw me opening the gate his tail went down and he dropped almost to his knees and slunk into the house. The children received me rapturously.

'You've made 'im better, Mister!' 'He's all right now, isn't he?' 'He's 'ad a right big breakfast this mornin', Mister!'

I went inside with little hands clutching at my coat. Bonzo was sitting bolt upright on his blanket in the same attitude as the previous evening, but as I approached he slowly collapsed on to his side and lay looking up at me with a martyred expression.

I laughed as I knelt by him. 'You're the original old soldier, Bonzo, but you can't fool me. I saw you out there.'

I gently touched the bruised shoulder and the big dog tremblingly closed his eyes as he resigned himself to his fate. Then when I stood up and he realised he wasn't going to have another injection he leapt to his feet and bounded away into the garden.

There was a chorus of delighted cries from the Dimmocks and they turned and looked at me with undisguised admiration. Clearly they considered that I had plucked Bonzo from the jaws of death. Mr Dimmock stepped forward from the mass.

188

'You'll send me a bill, won't you,' he said, with the dignity that was peculiar to him.

My first glance last night had decided me that this was a no-charging job and I hadn't even written it in the book, but I nodded solemnly.

'Very well, Mr Dimmock, I'll do that.'

And throughout our long association, though no money ever changed hands, he always said the same thing – 'You'll send me a bill, won't you.'

This was the beginning of my close relationship with the Dimmocks. Obviously they had taken a fancy to me and wanted to see as much as possible of me. Over the succeeding weeks and months they brought in a varied selection of dogs, cats, budgies, rabbits at frequent intervals, and when they found that my services were free they stepped up the number of visits; and when one came they all came. I was anxiously trying to expand the small animal side of the practice and increasingly my hopes were raised momentarily then dashed when I opened the door and saw a packed waiting room.

And it increased the congestion when they started bringing their auntie, Mrs Pounder, from down the road with them to see what a nice chap I was. Mrs Pounder, a fat lady who always wore a greasy velour hat perched on an untidy mound of hair, evidently shared the family tendency to fertility and usually brought a few of her own ample brood with her.

That is how it was this particular morning. I swept the assembled company with my eye but could discern only beaming Dimmocks and Pounders; and this time I couldn't even pick out my patient. Then the assembly parted and spread out as though by prearranged signal and I saw little Nellie Dimmock with a tiny puppy on her knee.

Nellie was my favourite. Mind you, I liked all the family; in fact they were such nice people that I always enjoyed their visits after that first disappointment. Mum and Dad were always courteous and cheerful and the children, though boisterous, were never ill-mannered; they were happy and friendly and if they saw me in the street they would wave madly and go on waving till I was out of sight. And I saw them often because they were continually scurrying around the town doing odd jobs – delivering milk or papers. Best of all, they loved their animals and were kind to them.

But as I say, Nellie was my favourite. She was about nine and had suffered an attack of 'infantile paralysis', as it used to be called, when very young. It had left her with a pronounced limp and a frailty which set her apart from her robust brothers and sisters. Her painfully thin legs seemed almost too fragile to carry her around but above the pinched face her hair, the colour of ripe corn, flowed to her shoulders and her eyes, though slightly crossed, gazed out calm and limpid blue through steel-rimmed spectacles.

'What's that you've got, Nellie ?' I asked.

'It's a little dog,' she almost whispered. ''e's mine.'

'You mean he's your very own ?'

She nodded proudly. 'Aye, 'e's mine.'

'He doesn't belong to your brothers and sisters, too ?'

'Naw, 'e's mine.'

Rows of Dimmock and Pounder heads nodded in eager acquiescence as Nellie lifted the puppy to her cheek and looked up at me with a smile of a strange sweetness. It was a smile that always tugged at my heart; full of a child's artless happiness and trust but with something else which was poignant and maybe had to do with the way Nellie was.

'Well, he looks a fine dog to me,' I said. 'He's a Spaniel, isn't he ?'

She ran a hand over the little head. 'Aye, a Cocker. Mr Brown said 'e was a Cocker.'

There was a slight disturbance at the back and Mr Dimmock appeared from the crush. He gave a respectful cough.

'He's a proper pure bred, Mr Herriot,' he said. 'Mr Brown from the bank's bitch had a litter and 'e gave this 'un to Nellie.' He tucked his stick under his arm and pulled a long envelope from an inside pocket. He handed it to me with a flourish. 'That's 'is pedigree.'

190

I read it through and whistled softly. 'He's a real blue-blooded hound, all right, and I see he's got a big long name. Darrowby Tobias the third. My word, that sounds great.'

I looked down at the little girl again. 'And what do *you* call him, Nellie?'

'Toby,' she said softly. 'I calls 'im Toby.'

I laughed. 'All right, then. What's the matter with Toby anyway. Why have you brought him?'

'He's been sick, Mr Herriot.' Mrs Dimmock spoke from somewhere among the heads. 'He can't keep nothin' down.'

'Well I know what that'll be. Has he been wormed?'

'No, don't think so.'

'I should think he just needs a pill,' I said. 'But bring him through and I'll have a look at him.'

Other clients were usually content to send one representative through with their animals but the Dimmocks all had to come. I marched along with the crowd behind me filling the passage from wall to wall. Our consulting-cum-operating room was quite small and I watched with some apprehension as the procession filed in after me. But they all got in, Mrs Pounder, her velour hat slightly askew, squeezing herself in with some difficulty at the rear.

My examination of the puppy took longer than usual as I had to fight my way to the thermometer on the trolley then struggle in the other direction to get the stethoscope from its hook on the wall. But I finished at last.

'Well I can't find anything wrong with him,' I said. 'So I'm pretty sure he just has a tummy full of worms. I'll give you a pill now and you must give it to him first thing tomorrow morning.'

Like a football match turning out, the mass of people surged along the passage and into the street and another Dimmock visit had come to an end.

I forgot the incident immediately because there was nothing unusual about it. The pot-bellied appearance of the puppy made my diagnosis a formality; I didn't expect to see him again.

But I was wrong. A week later my surgery was once more overflowing and I had another squashed-in session with Toby in the little back room. My pill had evacuated a few worms but he was still vomiting, still distended.

'Are you giving him five very small meals a day as I told you?' I asked.

I received emphatic affirmative and I believed them. The Dimmocks really took care of their animals. There was something else here, yet I couldn't find it. Temperature normal, lungs clear, abdomen negative on palpation; I couldn't make it out. I dispensed a bottle of our antacid mixture with a feeling of defeat. A young puppy like this shouldn't need such a thing.

This was the beginning of a frustrating period. There would be a span of two or three weeks when I would think the trouble had righted itself then without warning the place would be full of Dimmocks and Pounders and I'd be back where I started.

And all the time Toby was growing thinner.

I tried everything; gastric sedatives, variations of diet, quack remedies. I interrogated the Dimmocks repeatedly about the character of the vomiting – how long after eating, what were the intervals between, and I received varying replies. Sometimes he brought his food straight back, at others he retained it for several hours. I got nowhere.

It must have been over eight weeks later – Toby would be about four months old – when I again viewed the assembled Dimmocks with a sinking heart. Their visits had become depressing affairs and I could not foresee anything better today as I opened the waiting-room door and allowed myself to be almost carried along the passage. This time it was Dad who was the last to wedge himself into the consulting room then Nellie placed the little dog on the table.

I felt an inward lurch of sheer misery. Toby had grown despite his disability and was now a grim caricature of a Cocker Spaniel, the long silky ears drooping from an almost fleshless skull, the spindly legs pathetically feathered. I had thought Nellie was thin but her pet had outdone her. And he wasn't just thin, he was trembling slightly as he stood arch-backed on the smooth surface, and his face had the dull inward look of an animal which has lost interest.

The little girl ran her hand along the jutting ribs and the pale, squinting eyes looked up at me through the steel spectacles with that smile which pulled at me more painfully than ever before. She didn't seem worried. Probably she had no idea how things were, but whether she had or not I knew I'd never be able to tell her that her dog was slowly dying.

I rubbed my eyes wearily. 'What has he had to eat today ?'

Nellie answered herself. 'He's 'ad some bread and milk.'

'How long ago was that ?' I asked, but before anybody could reply the little dog vomited, sending the half digested stomach contents soaring in a graceful arc to land two feet away on the table.

I swung round on Mrs Dimmock. 'Does he always do it like that ?'

'Aye he mostly does – sends it flying out, like.'

'But why didn't you tell me ?'

The poor lady looked flustered. 'Well ... I don't know ... I ...'

I held up a hand. 'That's all right, Mrs Dimmock, never mind.' It occurred to me that all the way through my totally ineffectual treatment of this dog not a single Dimmock or Pounder had uttered a word of criticism so why should I start to complain now ?

But I knew what Toby's trouble was now. At last, at long last I knew.

And in case my present day colleagues reading this may think I had been more than usually thick-headed in my handling of the case I would like to offer in my defence that such limited text books as there were in those days made only a cursory reference to pyloric stenosis (narrowing of the exit of the stomach where it joins the small intestine) and if they did they said nothing about treatment.

But surely, I thought, somebody in England was ahead of the books. There must be people who were actually doing this operation ... and if there were I had a feeling one might not be too far away ...

I worked my way through the crush and trotted along the

passage to the phone.

'Is that you, Granville?'

'*Jim!*' A bellow of pure unalloyed joy. 'How are you, laddie?'

'Very well, how are you?'

'Ab-so-lutely tip top, old son! Never better!'

'Granville, I've got a four-month-old spaniel pup I'd like to bring through to you. It's got pyloric stenosis.'

'Oh lovely!'

'I'm afraid the little thing's just about on its last legs – a bag of bones.'

'Splendid, splendid!'

'This is because I've been mucking about for four weeks in ignorance.'

'Fine, just fine!'

'And the owners are a very poor family. They can't pay anything I'm afraid.'

'Wonderful!'

I hesitated a moment. 'Granville, you do ... er ... you have ... operated on these cases before?'

'Did five yesterday.'

'What!'

A deep rumble of laughter. 'I do but jest, old son, but you needn't worry, I've done a few. And it isn't such a bad job.'

'Well that's great.' I looked at my watch. 'It's half past nine now, I'll get Siegfried to take over my morning round and I'll see you before eleven.'

# 28

Granville had been called out when I arrived and I hung around his surgery till I heard the expensive sound of the Bentley purring into the yard. Through the window I saw yet another magnificent pipe glinting behind the wheel then my colleague, in an impeccable pin-striped suit which made him look like the Director of the Bank of England, paced majestically towards the side door.

'Good to see you, Jim!' he exclaimed, wringing my hand warmly. Then before removing his jacket he took his pipe from his mouth and regarded it with a trace of anxiety for a second before giving it a polish with his yellow cloth and placing it tenderly in a drawer.

It wasn't long before I was under the lamp in the operating room bending over Toby's small outstretched form while Granville – the other Granville Bennett – worked with fierce concentration inside the abdomen of the little animal.

'You see the gross gastric dilatation,' he murmured. 'Classical lesion.' He gripped the pylorus and poised his scalpel. 'Now I'm going through the serous coat.' A quick deft incision. 'A bit of blunt dissection here for the muscle fibres . . . down . . . down . . . a little more . . . ah, there it is, can you see it – the mucosa bulging into the cleft. Yes . . . yes . . . just right. That's what you've got to arrive at.'

I peered down at the tiny tube which had been the site of all Toby's troubles. 'Is that all, then?'

'That's all, laddie.' He stepped back with a grin. 'The obstruction is relieved now and you can take bets that this little chap will start to put weight on now.'

'That's wonderful, Granville. I'm really grateful.'

'Nonsense, Jim, it was a pleasure. You can do the next one yourself now, eh?' He laughed, seized needle and sutures and sewed up the abdominal muscles and skin at an impossible pace.

A few minutes later he was in his office pulling on his jacket, then as he filled his pipe he turned to me.

'I've got a little plan for the rest of the morning, laddie.'

I shrank away from him and threw up a protective hand. 'Well now, er . . . it's kind of you, Granville, but I really . . . I honestly must get back . . . we're very busy, you know . . . can't leave Siegfried too long . . . work'll be piling up . . .' I stopped because I felt I was beginning to gibber.

My colleague looked wounded. 'All I meant, old son, was that we want you to come to lunch. Zoe is expecting you.'

'Oh . . . oh, I see. Well that's very kind. We're not going . . . anywhere else, then ?'

'Anywhere else ?' He blew out his cheeks and spread his arms wide. 'Of course not. I just have to call in at my branch surgery on the way.'

'Branch surgery ? I didn't know you had one.'

'Oh yes, just a stone's throw from my house.' He put an arm round my shoulders. 'Well let's go, shall we ?'

As I lay back, cradled in the Bentley's luxury, I dwelt happily on the thought that at last I was going to meet Zoe Bennett when I was my normal self. She would learn this time that I wasn't a perpetually drunken oaf. In fact the next hour or two seemed full of rosy promise; an excellent lunch illumined by my witty conversation and polished manners, then back with Toby, magically resuscitated, to Darrowby.

I smiled to myself when I thought of Nellie's face when I told her her pet was going to be able to eat and grow strong and playful like any other pup. I was still smiling when the car pulled up on the outskirts of Granville's home village. I glanced idly through the window at a low stone building with leaded panes and a wooden sign dangling over the entrance. It read 'Old Oak Tree Inn'. I turned quickly to my companion.

'I thought we were going to your branch surgery ?'

Granville gave me a smile of childish innocence. 'Oh that's what I call this place. It's so near home and I transact quite a lot of business here.' He patted my knee. 'We'll just pop in for an appetiser, eh ?'

'Now wait a minute,' I stammered, gripping the sides of my seat tightly. 'I just can't be late today. I'd much rather . . .'

Granville raised a hand. 'Jim, laddie, we won't be in for long.' He looked at his watch. 'It's exactly twelve thirty and I promised Zoe we'd be home by one o'clock. She's cooking roast beef and Yorkshire pudding and it would take a braver man than me to let her pudding go flat. I guarantee we'll be in that house at one o'clock on the dot – O.K. ?'

I hesitated. I couldn't come to much harm in half an hour. I climbed out of the car.

As we went into the pub a large man, who had been leaning on the counter, turned and exchanged enthusiastic greetings with my colleague.

'Albert!' cried Granville. 'Meet Jim Herriot from Darrowby. Jim, this is Albert Wainright, the landlord of the Wagon and Horses over in Matherley. In fact he's the president of the Licensed Victuallers' Association this year, aren't you, Albert ?'

The big man grinned and nodded and for a moment I felt overwhelmed by the two figures on either side of me. It was difficult to describe the hard, bulky tissue of Granville's construction but Mr Wainright was unequivocally fat. A checked jacket hung open to display an enormous expanse of striped shirted abdomen overflowing the waistband of his trousers. Above a gay bow tie cheerful eyes twinkled at me from a red face and when he spoke his tone was rich and fruity. He embodied the rich ambience of the term 'Licensed Victualler'.

I began to sip the half pint of beer I had ordered but when another appeared in two minutes I saw I was going to fall hopelessly behind and switched to the whiskies and sodas which the others were drinking. And my undoing was that both my companions appeared to have a standing account here; they downed their drinks, tapped softly on the counter and said, 'Yes please, Jack,' whereupon three more glasses appeared with magical speed. I never had a chance to buy a round. In fact no money ever changed hands.

It was a quiet, friendly little session with Albert and Granville carrying on a conversation of the utmost good humour punctuated by the almost soundless taps on the bar. And as I fought to keep up with the two virtuosos the taps came more and more frequently till I seemed to hear them every few seconds.

Granville was as good as his word. When it was nearly one o'clock he looked at his watch.

'Got to be off now, Albert. Zoe's expecting us right now.'

And as the car rolled to a stop outside the house dead on time I realised with a dull despair that it had happened to me again. Within me a witch's brew was beginning to bubble, sending choking fumes into my brain. I felt terrible and I knew for sure I would get rapidly worse.

Granville, fresh and debonair as ever, leaped out and led me into the house.

'Zoe, my love!' he warbled, embracing his wife as she came through from the kitchen.

When she disengaged herself she came over to me. She was wearing a flowered apron which made her look if possible even more attractive.

'Hel-_lo_!' she cried and gave me that look which she shared with her husband as though meeting James Herriot was an unbelievable boon. 'Lovely to see you again. I'll get lunch now.' I replied with a foolish grin and she skipped away.

Flopping into an armchair I listened to Granville pouring steadily over at the sideboard. He put a glass in my hand and sat in another chair. Immediately the obese Staffordshire Terrier bounded on to his lap.

'Phoebles, my little pet!' he sang joyfully. 'Daddykins is home again.' And he pointed playfully at the tiny Yorkie who was sitting at his feet, baring her teeth repeatedly in a series of ecstatic smiles. 'And I see you, my little Victoria, I see you!'

By the time I was ushered to the table I was like a man in a dream, moving sluggishly, speaking with slurred deliberation. Granville poised himself over a vast sirloin, stropped his knife briskly then began to hack away ruthlessly. He was a prodigal server and piled about two pounds of meat on my plate then he started on the Yorkshire puddings. Instead of a single big one, Zoe had made a large number of little round ones as the farmers' wives often did, delicious golden cups, crisply brown round the sides. Granville heaped about six of these by the side of the meat as I watched stupidly. Then Zoe passed me the gravy boat.

With an effort I took a careful grip on the handle, closed one eye and began to pour. For some reason I felt I had to fill up each of the little puddings with gravy and owlishly directed the stream into one then another till they were all overflowing. Once I missed and spilled a few drops of the fragrant liquid on the tablecloth. I looked up guiltily at Zoe and giggled.

Zoe giggled back, and I had the impression that she felt that though I was a peculiar individual there was no harm in me. I just had this terrible weakness that I was never sober day or night, but I wasn't such a bad fellow at heart.

It usually took me a few days to recover from a visit to Granville and by the following Saturday I was convalescing nicely. It happened that I was in the market place and saw a large concourse of people crossing the cobbles. At first I thought from the mixture of children and adults that it must be a school outing but on closer inspection I realised it was only the Dimmocks and Pounders going shopping.

When they saw me they diverted their course and I was engulfed by a human wave.

'Look at 'im now, Mister!' 'He's eatin' like a 'oss now!' 'He's goin' to get fat soon, Mister!' The delighted cries rang around me.

Nellie had Toby on a lead and as I bent over the little animal I could hardly believe how a few days had altered him. He was still skinny but the hopeless look had gone; he was perky, ready to play. It was just a matter of time now.

His little mistress ran her hand again and again over the smooth brown coat.

'You are proud of your little dog, aren't you Nellie,' I said, and the gentle squinting eyes turned on me.

'Yes, I am.' She smiled that smile again. 'Because 'e's mine.'

# 29

There is plenty of time for thinking during the long hours of driving and now as I headed home from a late call my mind was idly assessing my abilities as a planner.

I had to admit that planning was not one of my strong points. Shortly after we were married I told Helen that I didn't think we should have children just at present. I pointed out that I would soon be going away, we did not have a proper home, our financial state was precarious and it would be far better to wait till after the war.

I had propounded my opinions weightily, sitting back in my chair and puffing my pipe like a sage, but I don't think I was really surprised when Helen's pregnancy was positively confirmed.

From the warm darkness the grass smell of the Dales stole through the open window and as I drove through a silent village it was mingled briefly with the mysterious sweetness of wood smoke. Beyond the houses the road curved smooth and empty between the black enclosing fells. No . . . I hadn't organised things very well. Leaving Darrowby and maybe England for an indefinite period, no home, no money and a pregnant wife. It was an untidy situation. But I was beginning to realise that life was not a tidy little parcel at any time.

The clock tower showed 11 p.m. as I rolled through the market place and, turning into Trengate, I saw that the light had been turned off in our room. Helen had gone to bed. I drove round to the yard at the back, put away the car and walked down the long garden. It was the end to every day, this walk; sometimes stumbling over frozen snow but tonight moving easily through the summer darkness under the branches of the apple trees to where the house stood tall and silent against the stars.

In the passage I almost bumped into Siegfried.

'Just getting back from Allenby's, James ?' he asked. 'I saw on the book that you had a colic.'

I nodded. 'Yes, but it wasn't a bad one. Just a bit of spasm. Their grey horse had been feasting on some of the hard pears lying around the orchard.'

Siegfried laughed. 'Well I've just beaten you in by a few minutes. I've been round at old Mrs Dewar's for the last hour holding her cat's paw while it had kittens.'

We reached the corner of the passage and he hesitated. 'Care for a nightcap, James?'

'I would, thanks,' I replied, and we went into the sitting room. But there was a constraint between us because Siegfried was off to London early next morning to enter the Air Force – he'd be gone before I got up – and we both knew that this was a farewell drink.

I dropped into my usual armchair while Siegfried reached into the glass-fronted cupboard above the mantelpiece and fished out the whisky bottle and glasses. He carelessly tipped out two prodigal measures and sat down opposite.

We had done a lot of this over the years, often yarning till dawn, but naturally enough it had faded since my marriage. It was like turning back the clock to sip the whisky and look at him on the other side of the fireplace and to feel, as though it were a living presence, the charm of the beautiful room with its high ceiling, graceful alcoves and french window.

We didn't talk about his departure but about the things we had always talked about and still do; the miraculous recovery of that cow, what old Mr Jenks said yesterday, the patient that knocked us flat, leapt the fence and disappeared for good. Then Siegfried raised a finger.

'Oh, James, I nearly forgot. I was tidying up the books and I find I owe you some money.'

'You do?'

'Yes, and I feel rather bad about it. It goes back to your pre-partnership days when you used to get a cut from Ewan Ross's testing. There was a slip-up somewhere and you were underpaid. Anyway, you've got fifty pounds to come.'

'Fifty pounds! Are you sure?'

'Quite sure, James, and I do apologise.'

'No need to apologise, Siegfried. It'll come in very handy right now.'

'Good, good . . . anyway, the cheque's in the top drawer of the desk if you'll have a look tomorrow.' He waved a languid hand and started to talk about some sheep he had seen that afternoon.

But for a few minutes I hardly heard him. Fifty pounds! It was a lot of money in those days, especially when I would soon be earning three shillings a day as an A.C.2 during my initial training. It didn't solve my financial problem but it would be a nice little cushion to fall back on.

My nearest and dearest are pretty unanimous that I am a bit slow on the uptake and maybe they are right because it was many years later before it got through to me that there never was any fifty pounds owing. Siegfried knew I needed a bit of help at that time and when it all became clear long afterwards I realised that this was exactly how he would do it. No embarrassment to me. He hadn't even handed me the cheque. . . .

As the level in the bottle went down the conversation became more and more effortless. At one point some hours later my mind seemed to have taken on an uncanny clarity and it was as if I was disembodied and looking down at the pair of us. We had slid very low in our chairs, our heads well down the backs, legs extended far across the rug. My partner's face seemed to stand out in relief and it struck me that though he was only in his early thirties he looked a lot older. It was an attractive face, lean, strong-boned with steady humorous eyes, but not young. In fact, Siegfried, in the time I had known him, had never looked young, but he has the last laugh now because he has hardly altered with the years and is one of those who will never look old.

At that moment of the night when everything was warm and easy and I felt omniscient it seemed a pity that Tristan wasn't there to make up the familiar threesome. As we talked, the memories marched through the room like a strip of bright pictures; of November days on the hillsides with the icy rain driving into our faces, of digging the cars out of snow drifts, of the spring sunshine warming the hard countryside. And the thought recurred that Tristan had been part of it all and that I was going to miss him as much as I would miss his brother.

I could hardly believe it when Siegfried rose, threw back the curtains, and the grey light of morning streamed in. I got up and stood beside him as he looked at his watch.

'Five o'clock, James,' he said, and smiled. 'We've done it again.'

He opened the french window and we stepped into the hushed stillness of the garden. I was taking grateful gulps of the sweet air when a single bird call broke the silence.

'Did you hear that blackbird?' I said.

He nodded and I wondered if he was thinking the same thing as myself; that it sounded just like the same blackbird which had greeted the early daylight when we talked over my first case those years ago.

We went up the stairs together in silence. Siegfried stopped at his door.

'Well, James . . .' he held out his hand and his mouth twitched up at the corner.

I gripped the hand for a moment then he turned and went into his room. And as I trailed dumbly up the next flight it seemed strange that we had never said goodbye. We didn't know when, if ever, we would see each other again yet neither of us said a word. I don't know if Siegfried wanted to say anything but there was a lot trying to burst from me.

I wanted to thank him for being a friend as well as a boss, for teaching me so much, for never letting me down. There were other things, too, but I never said them.

Come to think of it, I've never even thanked him for that fifty pounds . . . until now.

# 30

'Look, Jim,' Helen said, 'this is one engagement we can't be late for. Old Mrs Hodgson is an absolute pet – she'd be terribly hurt if we let her supper spoil.'

I nodded. 'You're right, my girl, that mustn't happen. But I've got only three calls this afternoon and Tristan's doing the evening. I can't see anything going wrong.'

This nervousness about a simple action like going out for a meal might be incomprehensible to the layman but to vets and their wives it was very real, particularly in those days of one or two-man practices. The idea of somebody preparing a meal for me then waiting in vain for me to turn up was singularly horrifying but it happened to all of us occasionally.

It remained a gnawing worry whenever Helen and I were asked out; especially to somebody like the Hodgsons. Mr Hodgson was a particularly likeable old farmer, short-sighted to the point of semi-blindness, but the eyes which peered through the thick glasses were always friendly. His wife was just as kind and she had looked at me quizzically when I had visited the farm two days ago.

'Does it make you feel hungry, Mr Herriot?'

'It does indeed, Mrs Hodgson. It's a marvellous sight.'

I was washing my hands in the farm kitchen and stealing a glance at a nearby table where all the paraphernalia of the family pig-killing lay in their full glory. Golden rows of pork pies, spareribs, a mound of newly made sausages, jars of brawn. Great pots were being filled with lard, newly rendered in the fireside oven.

She looked at me thoughtfully. 'Why don't you bring Mrs Herriot round one night and help us eat it?'

'Well that's most kind of you and I'd love to, but . . .'

'Now then, no buts!' She laughed. 'You know there's far too much stuff here – we have to give so much away.'

This was quite true. In the days when every farmer and many

of the townsfolk of Darrowby kept pigs for home consumption, killing time was an occasion for feasting. The hams and sides were cured and hung up but the masses of offal and miscellaneous pieces had to be eaten at the time; and though farmers with big families could tackle it, others usually passed delicious parcels round their friends in the happy knowledge that there would be a reciprocation in due course.

'Well, thanks, Mrs Hodgson,' I said. 'Tuesday evening, then, seven o'clock.'

And here I was on Tuesday afternoon heading confidently into the country with the image of Mrs Hodgson's supper hanging before me like a vision of the promised land. I knew what it would be; a glorious mixed grill of spareribs, onions, liver and pork fillet garlanded with those divine farm sausages which are seen no more. It was something to dream about.

In fact I was still thinking about it when I drew into Edward Wiggin's farmyard. I walked over to the covered barn and looked in at my patients – a dozen half grown bullocks resting on the deep straw. I had to inject these fellows with Blackleg vaccine. If I didn't it was a fair bet that one or more of them would be found dead due to infection with the deadly Clostridium which dwelt in the pastures of that particular farm.

It was a common enough disease and stockholders had recognised it for generations and had resorted to some strange practices to prevent it; such as running a seton – a piece of twine or bandage – through the dewlap of the animal. But now we had an efficient vaccine.

I was thinking I'd be here for only a few minutes because Mr Wiggin's man, Wilf, was an expert beast catcher; then I saw the farmer coming across the yard and my spirits sank. He was carrying his lassoo. Wilf, by his side, rolled his eyes briefly heavenwards when he saw me. He too clearly feared the worst.

We went into the barn and Mr Wiggin began the painstaking process of arranging his long, white rope, while we watched him gloomily. He was a frail little man in his sixties and had spent some years of his youth in America. He didn't talk a lot about it but everybody in time gained the impression that he had been a sort of cowboy over there and indeed he talked in a soft Texan drawl and seemed obsessed with the mystique of the ranch and the open range. Anything to do with the Wild West was near to his heart and nearest of all was his lassoo.

You could insult Mr Wiggin with many things and he wouldn't turn a hair but question his ability to snare the wildest bovine with a single twirl of his rope and the mild little man could explode into anger. And the unfortunate thing was that he was no good at it.

Mr Wiggin had now got a long loop dangling from his hand and he began to whirl it round his head as he crept towards the nearest bullock. When he finally made his cast the result was as expected; the rope fell limply half way along the animal's back and dropped on to the straw.

'Tarnation!' said Mr Wiggin and started again. He was a man of deliberate movements and there was something maddening in the way he methodically assembled his rope again. It seemed an age before he once more advanced on a bullock with the rope whirring round his head.

'Bugger it!' Wilf grunted as the loop end lashed him across the face.

His boss turned on him. 'Keep out of the dadblasted road, Wilf,' he said querulously. 'I gotta start again now.'

This time he didn't even make contact with the animal and as he retrieved his lassoo from the straw Wilf and I leaned wearily against the wall of the barn.

Yet again the whizz of the rope and a particularly ambitious throw which sent it high into the criss-cross of beams in the roof where it stuck. The farmer tugged at it several times in vain.

'Goldurn it, it's got round a nail up there. Slip across the yard and fetch a ladder, Wilf.'

As I waited for the ladder then watched Wilf climbing into the shadowy heights of the barn I pondered on Mr Wiggin. The way he spoke, the expressions he used were familiar to most Yorkshire folk since they filtered continually across the Atlantic in films and books. In fact there were dark mutterings that Mr

Wiggin had learned them that way and had never been near a ranch in his life. There was no way of knowing.

At last the rope was retrieved, the ladder put away, and the little man went into action once more. He missed again but one of the bullocks got its foot in the loop and for a few moments the farmer hung on with fierce determination as the animal produced a series of piston-like kicks to rid itself of the distraction. And as I watched the man's lined face set grimly, the thin shoulders jerking, it came to me that Mr Wiggin wasn't just catching a beast for injection; he was roping a steer, the smell of the prairie was in his nostrils, the cry of the coyote in his ears.

It didn't take long for the bullock to free itself and with a grunt of 'Ornery crittur!' Mr Wiggin started again. And as he kept on throwing his rope ineffectually I was uncomfortably aware that time was passing and that our chances of doing our job were rapidly diminishing. When you have to handle a bunch of young beasts the main thing is not to upset them. If Mr Wiggin hadn't been there we would have penned them quietly in a corner and Wilf would have moved among them and caught their noses in his powerful fingers.

They were thoroughly upset. They had been peacefully chewing the cud or having a mouthful of hay from the rack but now, goaded by the teasing rope, were charging around like racehorses. Wilf and I watched in growing despair as Mr Wiggin for once managed to get a loop round one of them, but it was too wide and slipped down and round the body. The bullock shook it off with an angry bellow then went off at full gallop, bucking and kicking. I looked at the throng of frenzied creatures milling past; it was getting more like a rodeo every minute.

And it was a disastrous start to the afternoon. I had seen a couple of dogs at the surgery after lunch and it had been nearly two thirty when I set out. It was now nearly four o'clock and I hadn't done a thing.

And I don't think I ever would have if fate hadn't stepped in. By an amazing fluke Mr Wiggin cast his loop squarely over the horns of a shaggy projectile as it thundered past him, the rope tightened on the neck and Mr Wiggin on the other end flew gracefully through the air for about twenty feet till he crashed into a wooden feeding trough.

We rushed to him and helped him to his feet. Badly shaken but uninjured he looked at us.

'Doggone, I jest couldn't hold the blame thing,' he murmured. 'Reckon I'd better sit down in the house for a while. You'll have to catch that pesky lot yourselves.'

Back in the barn, Wilf whispered to me, 'By gaw it's an ill wind, guvnor. We can get on now. And maybe it'll make 'im forget that bloody lassoo for a bit.'

The bullocks were too excited to be caught by the nose but instead Wilf treated me to an exhibition of roping, Yorkshire style. Like many of the local stocksmen he was an expert with a halter and it fascinated me to see him dropping it on the head of a moving animal so that one loop fell behind the ears and the other snared the nose.

With a gush of relief I pulled the syringe and bottle of vaccine from my pocket and had the whole batch inoculated within twenty minutes.

Driving off I glanced at my watch and my pulse quickened as I saw it was a quarter to five. The afternoon had almost slipped away and there were still two more calls. But I had till seven o'clock and surely I wouldn't come across any more Mr Wiggins. And as the stone walls flipped past I ruminated again on that mysterious little man. Had he once been a genuine cowboy or was the whole thing fantasy?

I recalled that one Thursday evening Helen and I were leaving the Brawton cinema where we usually finished our half day; the picture had been a Western and just before leaving the dark interior I glanced along the back row and right at the far end I saw Mr Wiggin all on his own, huddled in the corner and looking strangely furtive.

Ever since then I have wondered. . . .


Five o'clock saw me hurrying into the smallholding belonging to the Misses Dunn. Their pig had cut its neck on a nail and my previous experience of this establishment suggested that it wouldn't be anything very serious.

These two maiden ladies farmed a few acres just outside Dollingsford village. They were objects of interest because they did most of the work themselves and in the process they lavished such affection on their livestock that they had become like domestic pets. The little byre held four cows and whenever I had to examine one of them I could feel the rough tongue of her neighbour licking at my back; their few sheep ran up to people in the fields and sniffed round their legs like dogs; calves sucked at your fingers, an ancient pony wandered around wearing a benign expression and nuzzling anyone within reach. The only exception among the amiable colony was the pig, Prudence, who was thoroughly spoiled.

I looked at her now as she nosed around the straw in her pen. She was a vast sow and the four-inch laceration in her neck muscles was obviously posing no threat to her life; but it was gaping and couldn't be left like that.

'I'll have to put a few stitches in there,' I said, and the big Miss Dunn gasped and put a hand to her mouth.

'Oh dear! Will it hurt her? I shan't be able to look, I'm afraid.'

She was a tall muscular lady in her fifties with a bright red face and often as I looked at her wide shoulders and the great arms with their bulging biceps I had the feeling that she could flatten me effortlessly with one blow if she so desired. But strangely she was nervous and squeamish about the realities of animal doctoring and it was always her little wisp of a sister who helped at lambings, calvings and the rest.

'Oh you needn't worry, Miss Dunn,' I replied. 'It'll be all over before she knows what's happening.' I climbed into the pen, went up to Prudence, and touched her gently on the neck.

Immediately the sow unleashed a petulant scream as though she had been stabbed with a hot iron and when I tried to give her back a friendly scratch the huge mouth opened again and the deafening sound blasted out. And this time she advanced on me threateningly. I stood my ground till the yawning cavern with its yellowed teeth was almost touching my leg then I put a hand on the rail and vaulted out of the pen.

'We'll have to get her into a smaller space,' I said. 'I'll never be able to stitch her in that big pen  She has too much room to move around and she's too big to hold.'

Little Miss Dunn held up her hand. 'We have the very place. In the calf house across the yard. If we got her into one of those narrow stalls she wouldn't be able to turn round.'

'Fine!' I rubbed my hands. 'And I'll be able to do the stitching over the top from the passage. Let's get her over there.'

I opened the door and after a bit of poking and pushing Prudence ambled majestically out on to the cobbles of the yard. But there she stood, grunting sulkily, a stubborn glint in her little eyes, and when I leaned my weight against her back end it was like trying to move an elephant. She had no intention of moving any further; and that calf house was twenty yards away.

I stole a look at my watch. Five fifteen, and I didn't seem to be getting anywhere.

The little Miss Dunn broke into my thoughts. 'Mr Herriot, I know how we can get her across the yard.'

'You do?'

'Oh yes, Prudence has been naughty before and we have found a way of persuading her to move.'

I managed a smile. 'Great! How do you do it?'

'Well now,' and both sisters giggled, 'she is very fond of digestive biscuits '

'What's that?'

'She simply loves digestive biscuits.'

'She does?'

'Adores them!'

'Well, that's very nice,' I said  'But I don't quite see . . .'

The big Miss Dunn laughed. 'Just you wait and I'll show you.'

She began to stroll towards the house and it seemed to me that though those ladies were by no means typical Dales' farmers they did share the general attitude that time was of no consequence. The door closed behind her and I waited . . . and as the minutes ticked away I began to think she was brewing herself a cup of tea. In my mounting tension I turned away and gazed down over the hillside fields to where the grey roofs and old church tower of Dollingsford showed above the riverside trees. The quiet of the scene was in direct contrast to my mental state.

Just when I was giving up hope, big Miss Dunn reappeared carrying a long round paper container. She gave me a roguish smile as she held it up to me.

'These are what she likes. Now just watch.'

She produced a biscuit and threw it down on the cobbles a few feet in front of the sow. Prudence eyed it impassively for a few moments then without haste strolled forward, examined it carefully, and began to eat it.

When she had finished, big Miss Dunn glanced at me conspiratorially and threw another biscuit in front of her. The pig again moved on unhurriedly and started on the second course. This was gradually leading her towards the buildings across the yard but it was going to take a long time. I reckoned that each biscuit was advancing her about ten feet and the calf house would be all of twenty yards away, so allowing three minutes a biscuit it was going to take nearly twenty minutes to get there.

I broke out in a sweat at the thought, and my fears were justified because nobody was in the slightest hurry. Especially Prudence who slowly munched each titbit then snuffled around picking up every crumb while the ladies smiled down at her fondly.

'Look,' I stammered. 'Do you think you could throw the biscuits a bit further ahead of her . . . just to save time, I mean ?'

Little Miss Dunn laughed gaily. 'Oh we've tried that, but she's such a clever old darling. She knows she'll get less that way.'

To demonstrate she threw the next biscuit about fifteen feet away from the pig but the massive animal surveyed it with a cynical expression and didn't budge until it was kicked back to the required spot. Miss Dunn was right; Prudence wasn't so daft.

So I just had to wait, gritting my teeth as I watched the

211

agonising progress. I was almost at screaming point at the end though the others were thoroughly enjoying themselves. But at last the final biscuit was cast into the calf pen, the pig made her leisurely way inside and the ladies, with triumphant giggles, closed the door behind her.

I leapt forward with my needle and suture silk and of course as soon as I laid a finger on her skin Prudence set up an almost unbearable nonstop squeal of rage. Big Miss Dunn put her hands over her ears and fled in terror but her little sister stayed with me bravely and passed me my scissors and dusting powder whenever I asked in sign language above the din.

My head was still ringing as I drove away, but that didn't worry me as much as the time. It was six o'clock.

# 31

Tensely I assessed my position. The next and final visit was only a couple of miles away – I could make it in ten minutes. Then say twenty minutes on the farm, fifteen minutes back to Darrowby, a lightning wash and change and I could still be pushing my knees under Mrs Hodgson's table by seven o'clock.

And the next job wasn't a long one; just a bull to ring. Nowadays, since the advent of Artificial Insemination, there aren't many bulls about – only the big dairy men and pedigree breeders keep them – but in the thirties nearly every farmer had one, and inserting rings in their noses was a regular job. The rings were put in when they were about a year old and were necessary to restrain the big animals when they had to be led around.

I was immensely relieved when I arrived to find the gaunt figure of old Ted Buckle the farmer and his two men waiting for me in the yard. A classical way for a vet to waste time is to go hollering around the empty buildings then do more of the same out in the empty fields, waving madly, trying to catch the eye of a dot on the far horizon.

'Now then, young man,' Ted said, and even that short phrase took a fair time to come out. To me, the old man was a constant delight; speaking the real old Yorkshire – which you seldom hear now and which I won't try to reproduce here – with slow deliberation as though he were savouring every syllable as much as I was enjoying listening to him. 'You've come, then.'

'Yes, Mr Buckle, and I'm glad to see you're ready and waiting for me.'

'Aye, ah doan't like keepin' you fellers hangin' about.' He turned to his men. 'Now then, lads, go into that box and get haud'n that big lubber for Mr Herriot.'

The 'lads', Ernest and Herbert, who were both in their sixties, shuffled into the bull's loose box and closed the door after them. There were a few seconds of muffled banging against the wood, a couple of bellows and the occasional Anglo-Saxon expression from the men, then silence.

'Ah think they have 'im now,' Ted murmured and, not for the first time, I looked wonderingly at his wearing apparel. I had never seen him in anything else but that hat and coat in the time I had known him. With regard to the coat, which countless years ago must have been some kind of mackintosh, two things puzzled me: why he put it on and how he put it on. The long tatter of unrelated ribbons tied round the middle with binder twine could not possibly afford him any protection from the elements and how on earth did he know which were the sleeve holes among all the other apertures? And the hat, an almost crownless trilby from the early days of the century whose brim drooped vertically in sad folds over ears and eyebrows; it seemed incredible that he actually hung the thing up on a peg each night and donned it again in the morning.

Maybe the answer was to be found in the utterly serene humorous eyes which looked out from the skeleton-thin face. Nothing changed for Ted and the passage of a decade was a fleeting thing. I remember him showing me the old-fashioned 'reckon' which held the pans and kettles over the fire on his farm kitchen. He pointed out the row of holes where you could adjust it for large pans or small as though it were some modern invention.

'Aye, it's a wonderful thing, and t'lad that put it in for me made a grand job!'

'When was that, Mr Buckle?'

'It was eighteen ninety-seven. Ah remember it well. He was a right good workman was t'lad.'

But the men had reappeared with the young bull on a halter and they soon had him held in the accepted position for ringing.

There was a ritual about this job, a set pattern as unvarying as a classical ballet. Ernest and Herbert pulled the bull's head over the half door and held it there by pulling on a shank on either side of the halter. The portable crush had not yet been invented and this arrangement with the bull inside the box and the men outside was adopted for safety's sake. The next step was to make a hole through the tough tissue at the extremity of the nasal septum with the special punch which I had ready in its box.

But first there was a little refinement which I had introduced myself. Though it was the general custom to punch the hole without any preliminaries I always had the feeling that the bull might not like it very much; so I used to inject a couple of c.c.'s of local anaesthetic into the nose before I started. I poised my syringe now and Ernest, holding the left shank, huddled back apprehensively against the door.

'Tha's standin' middlin' to t'side, Ernest,' Ted drawled. 'Doesta think he's goin' to jump on top o' tha?'

'Naw, naw.' The man grinned sheepishly and took a shorter hold of the rope.

But he jumped back to his former position when I pushed the needle into the gristle just inside the nostril because the bull let loose a sudden deep-throated bellow of anger and reared up above the door. Ted had delayed ringing this animal; he was nearly eighteen months and very big.

'Haud 'im, lads,' Ted murmured as the two men clung to the

ropes. 'That's right – he'll settle down shortly.'

And he did. With his chin resting on the top of the door, held by the ropes on either side, he was ready for the next act. I pushed my punch into the nose, gripped the handles and squeezed. I never felt much like a professional gentleman when I did this, but at least my local had worked and the big animal didn't stir as the jaws of the instrument clicked together, puncturing a small round hole in the hard tissue.

The next stage in the solemn rite was unfolded as I unwrapped the bronze ring from its paper covering, took out the screw and opened the ring wide on its hinge. I waited for the inevitable words.

Ted supplied them. 'Take tha' cap off, Herbert. Tha woan't catch caud just for a minute.'

It was always a cap. A big bucket, a basin would have been more practical to hold that stupid, tiny screw and equally foolish little screwdriver, but it was always a cap. And a greasy old cap such as Herbert now removed from his polished pate.

My next step would be to slip the ring through the hole I had made, close it, insert the screw and tighten it up. That was where the cap came in; it was held under the ring to guard against sudden movements, because if the screw fell and was lost in the dirt and straw then all was lost. Then Ted would hand me the long rasp or file which every farmer had around somewhere and I would carefully smooth off the rim of the screw whether it needed it or not.

But this time there was to be a modification of the stereotyped little drama. As I stepped forward with my ring the young bull and I stood face to face and for a moment the wide set eyes under the stubby horns looked into mine. And as I reached out he must have moved slightly because the sharp end of the ring pricked him a little on the muzzle; the merest touch, but he seemed to take it as a personal insult because his mouth opened in an exasperated bawl and again he reared on his hind legs.

He was a well grown animal and in that position he looked very large indeed; and when his fore feet clumped down on the half door and the great rib cage loomed above us he was definitely formidable.

215

'The bugger's comin' over!' Ernest gasped and released his hold on the halter shank. He had never had much enthusiasm for the job and he abandoned it now without regret. Herbert was made of sterner stuff and he hung on grimly to his end as the bull thrashed above him, but after a cloven hoof had whizzed past his ear and another whistled just over his gleaming dome he too let go and fled.

Ted, untroubled as always, was well out of range and there remained only myself dancing in front of the door and gesticulating frantically at the bull in the vain hope that I might frighten him back whence he came; and the only thing that kept me there was the knowledge that every inch he scrambled out was taking me further from Mrs Hodgson's glorious supper.

I stood my ground until the snorting, bellowing creature was two thirds over, hanging grotesquely with the top of the door digging deep into his abdomen, then with a final plunge he was into the yard and I ran for cover. But the bull was not bent on mischief; he took one look at the open gate into the field and thundered through it like an express train.

From behind a stack of milk churns I watched sadly as he curveted joyously over the grass, revelling in his new found freedom. Bucking and kicking, tail in the air he headed for the far horizon where the wide pasture dipped to a beck which wandered along the floor of a shallow depression. And as he disappeared over the brow of the hill the last hope of my spareribs went with him.

'It'll tek us an hour to catch that bugger,' grunted Ernest gloomily.

I looked at my watch. Half past six. The bitter injustice of the whole thing overwhelmed me and I set up a wail of lamentation.

'Yes, dammit, and I've got an appointment in Darrowby at seven o'clock!' I stamped over the cobbles for a moment or two then swung round on old Ted. 'I'll never make it now . . . I'll have to ring my wife . . . have you got a phone?'

Ted's drawl was lazier than ever. 'Nay, we 'aven't got no phone. Ah don't believe in them things.' He fished out a tobacco tin from his pocket, unscrewed the lid and produced a battered timepiece which he scrutinised without haste. 'Any road, there's nowt to stop ye bein' back i' Darrowby by seven.'

'But . . . but . . . that's impossible . . . and I can't keep these people waiting . . . I must get to a phone.'

'Doan't get s'flustered, young man.' The old man's long face creased into a soothing smile. 'Ah tell ye you won't be late.'

I waved my arms around. 'But he's just said it'll take an hour to catch that bull!'

'Fiddlesticks! Ernest allus talks like that . . . 'e's never 'appy unless 'e's miserable. Ah'll get bull in i' five minutes.'

'Five minutes! That's ridiculous! I'll . . . I'll drive down the road to the nearest phone box while you're catching him.'

'You'll do nowt of t'sort, lad.' Ted pointed to a stone water trough against the wall. 'Go and sit thissen down and think of summat else . . . ah'll only be five minutes.'

Wearily I sank on to the rough surface and buried my face in my hands. When I looked up the old man was coming out of the byre and in front of him ambled a venerable cow. By the number of rings on the long curving horns she must have been well into her teens; the gaunt pelvic bones stood out like a hatstand and underneath her a pendulous udder almost touched the ground.

'Get out there awd lass,' Ted said and the old cow trotted into the field, her udder swinging gently at each step. I watched her until she had disappeared over the hill, then turned to see Ted throwing cattle cake into a bucket.

He strolled through the gate and as I gazed uncomprehendingly he began to beat the bucket with a stick. At the same time he raised his voice in a reedy tenor and called out across the long stretch of green.

'Cush, cush!' he cried. 'Cush, pet, cush!'

Almost immediately the cow reappeared over the brow and just behind her the bull. I looked with wonder as Ted banged on his bucket and the cow broke into a stiff gallop with my patient close by her side. When she reached the old man she plunged her head in among the cake while the bull, though he was as big as she, pushed his nose underneath her and seized

217

one of her teats in his great mouth. It was an absurd sight but she didn't seem to mind as the big animal, almost on his knees, sucked away placidly.

In fact it was like a soothing potion because when the cow was led inside he followed; and he made no complaint as I slipped the ring in his nose and fastened it in with the screw which mercifully had survived inside Herbert's cap.

'Quarter to seven!' I panted happily as I jumped into the driving seat. 'I'll get there in time now.' I could see Helen and me standing on the Hodgson's step and the door opening and the heavenly scent of the spareribs and onions drifting out from the kitchen.

I looked again at the scarecrow figure with the hat brim drooping over the calm eyes. 'You did a wonderful job there, Mr Buckle. I wouldn't have believed it if I hadn't seen it. It was amazing how that bull followed the cow like that.'

The old man smiled and I had a sudden surging impression of the wisdom in that quiet mind.

'There's nowt amazin' about it, lad, it's most nat'ral thing in t'world. That's 'is mother.'

# 32

I slowed down and gazed along the farm lane. That was Tristan's car parked against the byre and inside, behind that green door, he was calving a cow. Because Tristan's student days were over. He was a fully fledged veterinary surgeon now and the great world of animal doctoring with all its realities stretched ahead.

Not for long, though, because like many others he was bound for the army and would leave soon after myself. But it wouldn't be so bad for Tristan because at least he would be doing his own job. When Siegfried and I had volunteered for service there had been no need for our profession in the army so we had gone into R.A.F. aircrew which was the only branch open to our 'reserved occupation'. But when it came to Tristan's turn the fighting had escalated in the far east and they were crying out for vets to doctor the horses, mules, cattle, camels.

The timing suggested that the Gods were looking after him as usual. In fact I think the Gods love people like Tristan who sway effortlessly before the winds of fate and spring back with a smile, looking on life always with blithe optimism. Anyway it seemed natural and inevitable that whereas Siegfried and I as second class aircraftmen pounded the parade ground for weary hours Captain Tristan Farnon sailed off to the war in style.

But in the meantime I was glad of his help. After my departure he would run things with the aid of an assistant, then, when he left, the practice would be in the hands of two strangers till we returned. It seemed strange but everything was impermanent at that time.

I drew up and looked thoughtfully at the car. This was Mark Dowson's place and when I had rung the surgery from out in the country Helen told me about this calving. I didn't want to butt in and fuss but I couldn't help wondering how Tristan was getting on, because Mr Dowson was a dour, taciturn character who wouldn't hesitate to come down on the young man if things went wrong.

Still, I hadn't anything to worry about because since he qualified Tristan was doing fine. The farmers had always liked him during his sporadic visits as a student but now that he was on the job regularly the good reports were coming in thick and fast.

'I'll tell tha, that young feller does work! Doesn't spare 'imself,' or 'Ah've never seen a lad put his 'eart and soul into his job like this 'un.' And one man drew me to one side and muttered, 'He meks some queer noises but he does try. I think he'd kill 'isself afore he'd give up.'

That last remark made me think. Tristan's forte was certainly not brute effort and I had been a bit bewildered at some of the comments till I began to remember some of my experiences with him in his student days. He had always applied his acute intelligence to any situation in his own particular way and the way he reacted to the little accidents of country practice led me to believe he was operating a system.

The first time I saw this in action was when he was standing by the side of a cow watching me pulling milk from a teat. Without warning the animal swung round and brought an un-yielding cloven hoof down on his foot. This is a common and fairly agonising experience and before the days of steel-tipped wellingtons I have frequently had the skin removed from my toes in neat parchment-like rolls. When it happened to me I was inclined to hop around and swear a bit and my performance was usually greeted with appreciative laughter from the farmers. Tristan, however, handled it differently.

He gasped, leaned with bowed head against the cow's pelvic bone for a moment then opened his mouth wide and emitted a long groan. Then, as the cowman and I stared at him, he reeled over the cobbles dragging the damaged limb uselessly behind him. Arrived at the far wall he collapsed against it, face on the stone, still moaning pitifully.

Thoroughly alarmed, I rushed to his aid. This must be a fracture and already my mind was busy with plans to get him to hospital with all possible speed. But he revived rapidly and when we left the byre ten minutes later he was tripping along with no trace of a limp. And I did notice one thing; nobody had laughed at him, he had received only sympathy and commiseration.

This sort of thing happened in other places. He sustained a few mild kicks, he was crushed between cows, he met with many of the discomforts which are part of our life and he reacted in the same histrionic way. And how it paid off! To a man, the farmers exhibited the deepest concern when he went into his act and there was something more; it actually improved his image. I was pleased about that because impressing Yorkshire farmers isn't the easiest task and if Tristan's method worked it was all right with me.

But I smiled to myself as I sat outside the farm. I couldn't see Mr Dowson being affected by any sign of suffering. I had had my knocks there in the past and he obviously hadn't cared a damn.

On an impulse I drove down the lane and walked into the byre. Tristan, stripped off and soaped, was just inserting an arm into a large red cow while the farmer, pipe in hand, was holding the tail. My colleague greeted me with a pleasant smile but Mr Dowson just nodded curtly.

'What have you got, Triss?' I asked.

'Both legs back,' he replied. 'And they're a long way in. Look at the length of her pelvis.'

I knew what he meant. It wasn't a difficult presentation but it could be uncomfortable in these long cows. I leaned back against the wall; I might as well see how he fared.

He braced himself and reached as far forward as he could, and just then the cow's flanks bulged as she strained hard against him. This is never very nice; the powerful contractions of the uterus squeeze the arm relentlessly between calf and pelvis and you have to grit your teeth till it passes off.

Tristan, however, went a little further.

'Ooh! Aah! Ouch!' he cried. Then as the animal still kept up the pressure he went into a gasping groan. When she finally relaxed he stood there quite motionless for a few seconds, his head hanging down as though the experience had drained him of all his strength.

The farmer drew on his pipe and regarded him impassively. Throughout the years I had known Mr Dowson I had never seen any particular emotion portrayed in those hard eyes and craggy features. In fact it had always seemed to me that I could have dropped down dead in front of him and he wouldn't even blink.

My colleague continued his struggle and the cow, entering into the spirit of the game, fought back with a will. Some animals will stand quietly and submit to all kinds of internal interference but this was a strainer; every movement of the arm within her was answered by a violent expulsive effort. I had

221

been through it a hundred times and I could almost feel the grinding pressure on the wrist, the helpless numbing of the fingers.

Tristan showed what he thought about it all by a series of heart-rending sounds. His repertoire was truly astounding and he ranged from long harrowing moans through shrill squeals to an almost tearful whimpering.

At first Mr Dowson appeared oblivious to the whole business, puffing smoke, glancing occasionally through the byre door, scratching at the bristle on his chin. But as the minutes passed his eyes were dragged more and more to the suffering creature before him until his whole attention was riveted on the young man.

And in truth he was worth watching because Tristan added to his vocal performance an extraordinary display of facial contortions. He sucked in his cheeks, rolled his eyes, twisted his lips, did everything in fact but wiggle his ears. And there was no doubt he was getting through to Mr Dowson. As the noises and grimaces became more extravagant the farmer showed signs of growing uneasiness; he darted anxious glances at my colleague and occasionally his pipe trembled violently. Like me, he clearly thought some dreadful climax was at hand.

As if trying to bring matters to a head the cow started to build up a supreme effort. She straddled her legs wide, grunted deeply and went into a prolonged heave. As her back arched Tristan opened his mouth wide in a soundless protest then little panting cries began to escape him. This, I thought, was his most effective ploy yet; a long drawn 'Aah . . . aah . . . aah . . .' creeping gradually up the scale and building increasing tension in his audience. My toes were curling with apprehension when, with superb timing, he released a sudden piercing scream.

That was when Mr Dowson cracked. His pipe had almost wobbled from his mouth but now he stuffed it into his pocket and rushed to Tristan's side.

'Ista all right, young man ?' he enquired hoarsely.

My colleague, his face a mask of anguish, did not reply.

The farmer tried again. 'Will ah get you a cup o' tea ?'

For a moment Tristan made no response, then, eyes closed, he nodded dumbly.

Mr Dowson scampered eagerly from the byre and within minutes returned with a steaming mug. After that I had to shake my head to dispel the feeling of unreality. It couldn't be true, this vision of the hard-bitten farmer feeding the tea to the young man in sips, cradling the lolling head in a horny hand. Tristan was still inside the cow, still apparently semi-conscious with pain but submitting helplessly to the farmer's ministrations.

With a sudden lunge he produced one of the calf's legs and as he flopped against the cow's rump he was rewarded with another long gulp of tea. After the first leg the rest wasn't so bad and the second leg and the calf itself soon followed.

As the little creature landed wriggling on the floor, Tristan collapsed on his knees beside it and extended a trembling hand towards a pile of hay, prepared to give the new arrival a rub down.

Mr Dowson would have none of it.

'George!' he bellowed to one of his men in the yard. 'Get in 'ere and wisp this calf!' Then solicitously to Tristan, 'You maun come into t'house, lad, and have a drop o' brandy. You're about all in.'

The dream continued in the farm kitchen and I watched disbelievingly as my colleague fought his way back to health and strength with the aid of several stiff measures of Martell Three Star. I had never had treatment like this and a wave of envy swept over me as I wondered whether it was worth adopting Tristan's system.

But I still have never found the courage to try it.

# 33

It was strange, but somehow the labels on the calves' backs made them look even more pathetic; the auction mart labels stuck roughly with paste on the hairy rumps, stressing the little creatures' role as helpless merchandise.

As I lifted one sodden tail and inserted the thermometer a thin whitish diarrhoea trickled from the rectum and streamed down the thighs and hocks.

'It's the old story, I'm afraid, Mr Clark,' I said.

The farmer shrugged and dug his thumbs under his braces. In the blue overalls and peaked porter's cap he always wore he didn't look much like a farmer and for that matter this place did not greatly resemble a farm; the calves were in a converted railway wagon and all around lay a weird conglomeration of rusting agricultural implements, pieces of derelict cars, broken chairs. 'Aye, it's a beggar isn't it? I wish I didn't have to buy calves in markets but you can't always find 'em on t'farms when you want them. This lot looked all right when I got them two days since.'

'I'm sure they did.' I looked at the five calves, arch-backed, trembling, miserable. 'But they've had a tough time and it's showing now. Taken from their mothers at a week old, carted for miles in a draughty wagon, standing for most of the day at the mart then the final journey here on a cold afternoon. They didn't have a chance.'

'Well ah gave them a good bellyful of milk as soon as they came. They looked a bit starved and ah thought it would warm them up.'

'Yes, you'd think it would, Mr Clark, but really their stomachs weren't in a fit state to accept rich food like that when they were cold and tired. Next time if I were you I'd just give them a drink of warm water with maybe a little glucose and make them comfortable till next day.'

'White scour' they called it. It killed countless thousands of calves every year and the name always sent a chill through me because the mortality rate was depressingly high.

I gave each of them a shot of E coli antiserum. Most authorities said it did no good and I was inclined to agree with them. Then I rummaged in my car boot and produced a packet of our astringent powders of chalk, opium and catechu.

'Here, give them one of these three times a day, Mr Clark,' I said. I tried to sound cheerful but I'm sure my tone lacked conviction. Whiskered veterinary surgeons in top hats and tail coats had been prescribing chalk opium and catechu a hundred years ago and though it might have been helpful in mild diarrhoea it was almost useless against the lethal bacterial enteritis of white scour. It was a waste of time just trying to dry up the diarrhoea; what was wanted was a drug which would knock out the vicious bugs which caused it, but there wasn't such a thing around.

However there was one thing which we vets of those days used to do which is sometimes neglected since the arrival of the modern drugs; we attended to the comfort and nursing of the animals. The farmer and I wrapped each calf in a big sack which went right round its body and was fastened with binder twine round the ribs, in front of the brisket and under the tail. Then I fussed round the shed, plugging up draught holes, putting up a screen of straw bales between the calves and the door.

Before I left I took a last look at them; there was no doubt they were warm and sheltered now. They would need every bit of help with only my astringent powders fighting for them.

I didn't see them again until the following afternoon. Mr Clark was nowhere around so I went over to the railway wagon and opened the half door.

This, to me, is the thing that lies at the very heart of veterinary practice; the wondering and worrying about how your patient is progressing then the long moment when you open that door and find out. I rested my elbows on the timbers and looked inside. The calves were lying quite motionless on their sides, in fact I had to look closely to make sure they were not dead. I banged the door behind me with deliberate force but not a head was raised.

Walking through the deep straw and looking down at the outstretched animals, each in his rough sacking jacket, I swore to myself. It looked as though the whole lot was going to perish. Great, great, I thought as I kicked among the straw – not just one or two but a hundred per cent death rate this time.

'Well you don't look very 'opeful, young man.' Mr Clark's head and shoulders loomed over the half door.

I dug my hands into my pockets. 'No, damn it, I'm not. They've gone down really fast, haven't they?'

'Aye, it's ower wi' them all right. I've just been in t'house ringing Mallock.'

The knacker man's name was like the pealing of a mournful bell. 'But they're not dead yet,' I said.

'No, but it won't be long. Mallock allus gives a bob or two more if he can get a beast alive. Makes fresher dog meat, he says.'

I didn't say anything and I must have looked despondent because the farmer gave a wry smile and came over to me.

'It isn't your fault, lad. I know all about this dang white scour. If you get the right bad sort there's nothing anybody can do. And you can't blame me for tryin' to get a bit back – I've got to make the best of a bad job.'

'Oh I know,' I said. 'I'm just disappointed I can't have a go at them with this new medicine.'

'What's that, then?'

I took the tin from my pocket and read the label. 'It's called M and B 693, or sulphapyridine, to give it its scientific name. Just came in the post this morning. It's one of a completely new range of drugs – they're called the sulphonamides and we've never had anything like them before. They're supposed to actually kill certain germs, such as the organisms which cause scour.'

Mr Clark took the tin from me and removed the lid. 'A lot of little blue tablets, eh? Well ah've seen a few wonder cures for this ailment but none of 'em's much good – this'll be another, I'll bet.'

'Could be,' I said. 'But there's been a lot of discussion about these sulphonamides in our veterinary journals. They're not quack remedies, they're a completely fresh field. I wish I could have tried them on your calves.'

'Well look at them.' The farmer gazed gloomily over the five still bodies. 'Their eyes are goin' back in their heads. Have you ever seen calves like that get better ?'

'No, I haven't, but I'd still like to have a go.'

As I spoke a tall-sided wagon rumbled into the yard. A sprightly, stocky man descended from the driver's seat and came over to us.

'By gaw, Jeff,' said Mr Clark. 'You 'aven't been long.'

'Naw, they got me on t'phone at Jenkinson's, just down t' road.' He gave me a smile of peculiar sweetness.

I studied Jeff Mallock as I always did with a kind of wonder. He had spent the greater part of his forty odd years delving in decomposing carcases, slashing nonchalantly with his knife at tuberculous abscesses, wallowing in infected blood and filthy uterine exudates yet he remained a model of health and fitness. He had the clear eyes and the smooth pink skin of a twenty-year-old and the effect was heightened by the untroubled serenity of his expression. To the best of my knowledge Jeff never took any hygienic precautions such as washing his hands and I have seen him enjoying a snack on his premises, seated on a heap of bones and gripping a cheese and onion sandwich with greasy fingers.

He peered over the door at the calves. 'Yes, yes, a clear case of stagnation of t'lungs. There's a lot of it about right now.'

Mr Clark looked at me narrowly. 'Lungs ? You never said owt about lungs, young man.' Like all farmers he had complete faith in Jeff's instant diagnosis.

I mumbled something. I had found it useless to argue this point. The knacker man's amazing ability to tell at a glance the cause of an animal's illness or death was a frequent source of embarrassment to me. No examination was necessary – he just knew, and of all his weird catalogue of diseases stagnation of t'lungs was the favourite.

He turned to the farmer. 'Well, ah'd better shift 'em now, Willie. Reckon they won't last much longer.'

I bent down and lifted the head of the nearest calf. They were all shorthorns, three roans, a red and this one which was pure white. I passed my fingers over the hard little skull, feeling the tiny horn buds under the rough hair. When I withdrew my hand the head dropped limply on to the straw and it seemed to me that there was something of finality and resignation in the movement.

My thoughts were interrupted by the roar of Jeff's engine. He was backing his wagon round to the door of the calf house and as the high unpainted boards darkened the entrance the atmosphere of gloom deepened. These little animals had suffered two traumatic journeys in their short lives. This was to be the last, the most fateful and the most sordid.

When the knacker man came in he stood by the farmer, looking at me as I squatted in the straw among the prostrate creatures. They were both waiting for me to quit the place, leaving my failure behind me.

'You know, Mr Clark,' I said, 'even if we could save one of them it would help to reduce your loss.'

The farmer regarded me expressionlessly. 'But they're all dyin', lad. You said so yourself.'

'Yes, I did, I know, but the circumstances could be a bit different today.'

'Ah know what it is.' He laughed suddenly. 'You've got your heart set on havin' a go with them little tablets, haven't you?'

I didn't answer but looked up at him with a mute appeal.

He was silent for a few moments then he put a hand on Mallock's shoulder. 'Jeff, if this young feller is that concerned about ma stock I'll 'ave to humour 'im. You're not bothered, are you?'

'Nay, Willie, nay,' replied Jeff, completely unruffled, 'I can pick 'em up tomorrow, just as easy.'

'Right,' I said. 'Let's have a look at the instructions.' I fished out the pamphlet from the tin and read rapidly, working out the dose for the weight of the calves. 'We'll have to give them a loading dose first. I think twelve tablets per calf then six every eight hours after that.'

'How do you get 'em down their necks?' the farmer asked.

'We'll have to crush them and shake them up in water. Can we go into the house to do that?'

In the farm kitchen we borrowed Mrs Clark's potato masher and pounded the tablets until we had five initial doses measured out. Then we returned to the shed and began to administer them to the calves. We had to go carefully as the little creatures were so weak they had difficulty in swallowing, but the farmer held each head while I trickled the medicine into the side of the mouth.

Jeff enjoyed every minute of it. He showed no desire to leave but produced a pipe richly decorated with nameless tissues, leaned on the top of the half door and, puffing happily, watched us with tranquil eyes. He was quite unperturbed by his wasted journey and when we had finished he climbed into his wagon and waved to us cordially.

'I'll be back to pick 'em up in t'mornin', Willie,' he cried, quite without malice I'm sure. 'There's no cure for stagnation of t'lungs.'

I thought of his words next day as I drove back to the farm. He was just stating the fact; his supply of dog meat was merely being postponed for another twenty-four hours. But at least, I told myself, I had the satisfaction of having tried, and since I expected nothing I wasn't going to be disappointed.

As I pulled up in the yard Mr Clark walked over and spoke through the window. 'There's no need for you to get out of the car.' His face was a grim mask.

'Oh,' I said, the sudden lurch in my stomach belying my calm facade. 'Like that, is it?'

'Aye, come and look 'ere.' He turned and I followed him over to the shed. By the time the door creaked open a slow misery had begun to seep into me.

Unwillingly I gazed into the interior.

Four of the calves were standing in a row looking up at us with interest. Four shaggy, rough-jacketed figures, bright-eyed and alert. The fifth was resting on the straw, chewing absently at one of the strings which held his sack.

The farmer's weathered face split into a delighted grin. 'Well ah told you there was no need to get out of your car, didn't I? They don't need no vitnery, they're back to normal.'

I didn't say anything. This was something which my mind, as yet, could not comprehend. As I stared unbelievingly the fifth calf rose from the straw and stretched luxuriously.

'He's wraxin', d'you see?' cried Mr Clark. 'There's nowt much wrong wi' them when they do that.'

We went inside and I began to examine the little animals. Temperatures were normal, the diarrhoea had dried up, it was uncanny. As if in celebration the white calf which had been all but dead yesterday began to caper about the shed, kicking up his legs like a mustang.

'Look at that little bugger!' burst out the farmer. 'By gaw I wish I was as fit meself!'

I put the thermometer back in its tube and dropped it into my side pocket. 'Well, Mr Clark,' I said slowly, 'I've never seen anything like this. I still feel stunned.'

'Beats hen-racin', doesn't it,' the farmer said, wide-eyed, then he turned towards the gate as a wagon appeared from the lane. It was the familiar doom-burdened vehicle of Jeff Mallock.

The knacker man showed no emotion as he looked into the shed. In fact it was difficult to imagine anything disturbing those pink cheeks and placid eyes, but I fancied the puffs of blue smoke from his pipe came a little faster as he took in the scene. The pipe itself showed some fresh deposits on its bowl – some fragments of liver, I fancied, since yesterday.

When he had looked his fill he turned and strolled towards his wagon. On the way he gazed expansively around him and then at the dark clouds piling in the western sky.

'Ah think it'll turn to rain afore t'day's out, Willie,' he murmured.

I didn't know it at the time but I had witnessed the beginning of the revolution. It was my first glimpse of the tremendous therapeutic breakthrough which was to sweep the old remedies into oblivion. The long rows of ornate glass bottles with their carved stoppers and Latin inscriptions would not stand on the dispensary shelves much longer and their names, dearly familiar for many generations – Sweet Spirits of Nitre, Sal ammoniac, Tincture of Camphor – would be lost and vanish for ever.

This was the beginning and just around the corner a new wonder was waiting – Penicillin and the other antibiotics. At last we had something to work with, at last we could use drugs which we knew were going to do something.

All over the country, probably all over the world at that time, vets were having these first spectacular results, going through the same experience as myself; some with cows, some with dogs and cats, others with valuable racehorses, sheep, pigs in all kinds of environments. But for me it happened in that old converted railway wagon among the jumble of rusting junk on Willie Clark's farm.

Of course it didn't last – not the miraculous part of it anyway. What I had seen at Willie Clark's was the impact of something new on an entirely unsophisticated bacterial population, but it didn't go on like that. In time the organisms developed a certain amount of resistance and new and stronger sulphonamides and antibiotics had to be produced. And so the battle has continued. We have good results now but no miracles, and I feel I was lucky to be one of the generation which was in at the beginning when the wonderful things did happen.

Those five calves never looked behind them and the memory of them gives me a warm glow even now. Willie, of course, was overjoyed and even Jeff Mallock gave the occasion his particular accolade. As he drove away he called back to us:

'Them little blue tablets must have good stuff in 'em. They're fust things I've ever seen could cure stagnation of t'lungs.'

# 34

There was one marvellous thing about the set-up in Darrowby. I had the inestimable advantage of being a large animal practitioner with a passion for dogs and cats. So that although I spent most of my time in the wide outdoors of Yorkshire there was always the captivating background of the household pets to make a contrast.

I treated some of them every day and it made an extra interest in my life; interest of a different kind, based on sentiment instead of commerce and because of the way things were it was something I could linger over and enjoy. I suppose with a very intensive small animal practice it would be easy to regard the thing as a huge sausage machine, an endless procession of hairy forms to prod with hypodermic needles. But in Darrowby we got to know them all as individual entities.

Driving through the town I was able to identify my ex-patients without difficulty; Rover Johnson, recovered from his ear canker, coming out of the ironmongers with his mistress; Patch Walker, whose broken leg had healed beautifully, balanced happily on the back of his owner's coal wagon, or Spot Briggs who was a bit of a rake anyway and would soon be tearing himself again on barbed wire, ambling all alone across the market place cobbles in search of adventure. I got quite a kick out of recalling their ailments and mulling over their characteristics. Because they all had their own personalities and they were manifested in different ways.

One of these was their personal reaction to me and my treatment. Most dogs and cats appeared to bear me not the slightest ill will despite the fact that I usually had to do something disagreeable to them.

But there were exceptions and one of these was Magnus, the Miniature Dachshund from the Drovers' Arms.

He was in my mind now as I leaned across the bar counter.

'A pint of Smiths, please, Danny,' I whispered.

The barman grinned. 'Coming up, Mr Herriot.' He pulled at the lever and the beer hissed gently into the glass and as he passed it over the froth stood high and firm on the surface.

'That ale looks really fit tonight,' I breathed almost inaudibly.

'Fit ? It's beautiful!' Danny looked fondly at the brimming glass. 'In fact it's a shame to sell it.'

I laughed, but pianissimo. 'Well it's nice of you to spare me a drop.' I took a deep pull and turned to old Mr Fairburn who was as always sitting at the far corner of the bar with his own fancy flower-painted glass in his hand.

'It's been a grand day, Mr Fairburn,' I murmured *sotto voce*. The old man put his hand to his ear. 'What's that you say ?'

'Nice warm day it's been.' My voice was like a soft breeze sighing over the marshes.

I felt a violent dig at my back. 'What the heck's the matter with you, Jim ? Have you got laryngitis ?'

I turned and saw the tall bald-headed figure of Dr Allinson, my medical adviser and friend. 'Hello, Harry,' I cried. 'Nice to see you.' Then I put my hand to my mouth.

But it was too late. A furious yapping issued from the manager's office. It was loud and penetrating and it went on and on.

'Damn, I forgot,' I said wearily. 'There goes Magnus again.'

'Magnus ? What are you talking about ?'

'Well, it's a long story.' I took another sip at my beer as the din continued from the office. It really shattered the peace of the comfortable bar and I could see the regulars fidgeting and looking out into the hallway.

Would that little dog ever forget ? It seemed a long time now since Mr Beckwith, the new young manager at the Drovers, had brought Magnus in to the surgery. He had looked a little apprehensive.

'You'll have to watch him, Mr Herriot.'

'What do you mean ?'

'Well, be careful. He's very vicious.'

I looked at the sleek little form, a mere brown dot on the table. He would probably turn the scale at around six pounds. And I couldn't help laughing.

'Vicious? He's not big enough, surely.'

'Don't you worry!' Mr Beckwith raised a warning finger. 'I took him to the vet in Bradford where I used to manage the White Swan and he sank his teeth into the poor chap's finger.'

'He did?'

'He certainly did! Right down to the bone! By God I've never heard such language but I couldn't blame the man. There was blood all over the place. I had to help him to put a bandage on.'

'Mm, I see.' It was nice to be told before you had been bitten and not after. 'And what was he trying to do to the dog? Must have been something pretty major.'

'It wasn't you know. All I wanted was his nails clipping.'

'Is that all? And why have you brought him today?'

'Same thing.'

'Well honestly, Mr Beckwith,' I said, 'I think we can manage to cut his nails without bloodshed. If he'd been a Bull Mastiff or an Alsatian we might have had a problem, but I think that you and I between us can control a Miniature Dachshund.'

The manager shook his head. 'Don't bring me into it. I'm sorry, but I'd rather not hold him, if you don't mind.'

'Why not?'

'Well, he'd never forgive me. He's a funny little dog.'

I rubbed my chin. 'But if he's as difficult as you say and you can't hold him, what do you expect me to do?'

'I don't know, really . . . maybe you could sort of dope him . . . knock him out?'

'You mean a general anaesthetic? To cut his claws . . . ?'

'It'll be the only way, I'm afraid.' Mr Beckwith stared gloomily at the tiny animal. 'You don't know him.'

It was difficult to believe but it seemed pretty obvious that this canine morsel was the boss in the Beckwith home. In my experience many dogs had occupied this position but none as small as this one. Anyway, I had no more time to waste on this nonsense.

'Look,' I said. 'I'll put a tape muzzle on his nose and I'll have this job done in a couple of minutes.' I reached behind me for the nail clippers and laid them on the table, then I unrolled a length of bandage and tied it in a loop.

'Good boy, Magnus,' I said ingratiatingly as I advanced towards him.

The little dog eyed the bandage unwinkingly until it was almost touching his nose then, with a surprising outburst of ferocity, he made a snarling leap at my hand. I felt the draught on my fingers as a row of sparkling teeth snapped shut half an inch away, but as he turned to have another go my free hand clamped on the scruff of his neck.

'Right, Mr Beckwith,' I said calmly, 'I have him now. Just pass me that bandage again and I won't be long.'

But the young man had had enough. 'Not me!' he gasped. 'I'm off!' He turned the door handle and I heard his feet scurrying along the passage.

Ah well, I thought, it was probably best. With boss dogs my primary move was usually to get the owner out of the way. It was surprising how quickly these tough guys calmed down when they found themselves alone with a no-nonsense stranger who knew how to handle them. I could recite a list who were raving tearaways in their own homes but apologetic tail-waggers once they crossed the surgery threshold. And they were all bigger than Magnus.

Retaining my firm grip on his neck I unwound another foot of bandage and as he fought furiously, mouth gaping, lips retracted like a scaled-down Siberian wolf, I slipped the loop over his nose, tightened it and tied the knot behind his ears. His mouth was now clamped shut and just to make sure, I applied a second bandage so that he was well and truly trussed.

This was when they usually packed in and I looked confidently at the dog for signs of submission. But above the encircling white coils the eyes glared furiously and from within the little frame an enraged growling issued, rising and falling like the distant droning of a thousand bees.

Sometimes a stern word or two had the effect of showing them who was boss.

'Magnus!' I barked at him. 'That's enough! Behave yourself!' I gave his neck a shake to make it clear that I wasn't kidding but the only response was a sidelong squint of pure defiance from the slightly bulging eyes.

I lifted the clippers. 'All right,' I said wearily, 'if you won't have it one way you'll have it the other.' And I tucked him under one arm, seized a paw and began to clip.

He couldn't do a thing about it. He fought and wriggled but I had him as in a vice. And as I methodically trimmed the overgrown nails, wrathful bubbles escaped on either side of the bandage along with his splutterings. If dogs could swear I was getting the biggest cursing in history.

I did my job with particular care, taking pains to keep well away from the sensitive core of the claw so that he felt nothing, but it made no difference. The indignity of being mastered for once in his life was insupportable.

Towards the conclusion of the operation I began to change my tone. I had found in the past that once dominance has been established it is quite easy to work up a friendly relationship, so I started to introduce a wheedling note.

'Good little chap,' I cooed. 'That wasn't so bad, was it?'

I laid down the clippers and stroked his head as a few more resentful bubbles forced their way round the bandage. 'All right, Magnus, we'll take your muzzle off now.' I began to loosen the knot. 'You'll feel a lot better then, won't you?'

So often it happened that when I finally removed the restraint the dog would apparently decide to let bygones be bygones and in some cases would even lick my hand. But not so with Magnus. As the last turn of bandage fell from his nose he made another very creditable attempt to bite me.

'All right, Mr Beckwith,' I called along the passage, 'you can come and get him now.'

My final memory of the visit was of the little dog turning at the top of the surgery steps and giving me a last dirty look before his master led him down the street.

It said very clearly, 'Right, mate, I won't forget you.'

\*       \*       \*

That had been weeks ago but ever since that day the very sound of my voice was enough to set Magnus yapping his disapproval. At first the regulars treated it as a big joke but now they had started to look at me strangely. Maybe they thought I had been cruel to the animal or something. It was all very embarrassing because I didn't want to abandon the Drovers; the bar was always cosy even on the coldest night and the beer very consistent.

Anyway if I had gone to another pub I would probably have started to do my talking in whispers and people would have looked at me even more strangely then.

How different it was with Mrs Hammond's Irish Setter. This started with an urgent phone call one night when I was in the bath. Helen knocked on the bathroom door and I dried off quickly and threw on my dressing gown. I ran upstairs and as soon as I lifted the receiver an anxious voice burst in my ear.

'Mr Herriot, it's Rock! He's been missing for two days and a man has just brought him back now. He found him in a wood with his foot in a gin trap. He must . . .' I heard a half sob at the end of the line. 'He must have been caught there all this time.'

'Oh, I'm sorry! Is it very bad?'

'Yes it is.' Mrs Hammond was the wife of one of the local bank managers and a capable, sensible woman. There was a pause and I imagined her determinedly gaining control of herself. When she spoke her voice was calm.

'Yes, I'm afraid it looks as though he'll have to have his foot amputated.'

'Oh, I'm terribly sorry to hear that.' But I wasn't really surprised. A limb compressed in one of those barbarous instruments for forty-eight hours would be in a critical state. These traps are now mercifully illegal but in those days they often provided me with the kind of jobs I didn't want and the kind of decisions I hated to make. Did you take a limb from an uncomprehending animal to keep it alive or did you bring down the merciful but final curtain of euthanasia? I was responsible for the fact that there were several three-legged dogs and cats running around Darrowby and though they seemed happy enough and their owners still had the pleasure of their pets, the thing, for me, was clouded with sorrow.

Anyway, I would do what had to be done.

'Bring him straight round, Mrs Hammond,' I said.

Rock was a big dog but he was the lean type of Setter and seemed very light as I lifted him on to the surgery table. As my arms encircled the unresisting body I could feel the rib cage sharply ridged under the skin.

'He's lost a lot of weight,' I said.

His mistress nodded. 'It's a long time to go without food. He ate ravenously when he came in, despite his pain.'

I put a hand beneath the dog's elbow and gently lifted the leg. The vicious teeth of the trap had been clamped on the radius and ulna but what worried me was the grossly swollen state of the foot. It was at least twice its normal size.

'What do you think, Mr Herriot?' Mrs Hammond's hands twisted anxiously at the handbag which every woman seemed to bring to the surgery irrespective of the circumstances.

I stroked the dog's head. Under the light, the rich sheen of the coat glowed red and gold. 'This terrific swelling of the foot. It's partly due to inflammation but also to the fact that the circulation was pretty well cut off for the time he was in the trap. The danger is gangrene – that's when the tissue dies and decomposes.'

'I know,' she replied. 'I did a bit of nursing before I married.'

Carefully I lifted the enormous foot. Rock gazed calmly in front of him as I felt around the metacarpals and phalanges, working my way up to the dreadful wound.

'Well, it's a mess,' I said, 'but there are two good things. First, the leg isn't broken. The trap has gone right down to the bone but there is no fracture. And second and more important, the foot is still warm.'

'That's a good sign?'

'Oh yes. It means there's still some circulation. If the foot had been cold and clammy the thing would have been hopeless. I would have had to amputate.'

'You think you can save his foot, then?'

I held up my hand. 'I don't know, Mrs Hammond. As I say, he still has some circulation but the question is how much. Some of this tissue is bound to slough off and things could look very nasty in a few days. But I'd like to try.'

I flushed out the wound with a mild antiseptic in warm water and gingerly explored the grisly depths. As I snipped away the pieces of damaged muscle and cut off the shreds and flaps of dead skin the thought was uppermost that it must be extremely unpleasant for the dog; but Rock held his head high and scarcely flinched. Once or twice he turned his head towards me enquiringly as I probed deeply and at times I felt his moist nose softly brushing my face as I bent over the foot, but that was all.

The injury seemed a desecration. There are few more beautiful dogs than an Irish Setter and Rock was a picture; sleek coated and graceful with silky feathers on legs and tail and a noble, gentle-eyed head. As the thought of how he would look without a foot drove into my mind I shook my head and turned quickly to lift the sulphanilamide powder from the trolley behind me. Thank heavens this was now available, one of the new revolutionary drugs, and I packed it deep into the wound with the confidence that it would really do something to keep down the infection. I applied a layer of gauze then a light bandage with a feeling of fatalism. There was nothing else I could do.

Rock was brought in to me every day. And every day he endured the same procedure; the removal of the dressing which was usually adhering to the wound to some degree, then the inevitable trimming of the dying tissues and the rebandaging. Yet, incredibly, he never showed any reluctance to come. Most of my patients came in very slowly and left at top speed, dragging their owners on the end of the leads; in fact some turned tail at the door, slipping their collar and sped down Trengate with their owners in hot pursuit. Dogs aren't so daft and there is doubtless a dentist's chair type of association about a vet's surgery.

Rock, however, always marched in happily with a gentle waving of his tail. In fact when I went into the waiting room and saw him sitting there he usually offered me his paw. This had always been a characteristic gesture of his but there seemed something uncanny about it when I bent over him and saw the white-swathed limb outstretched towards me.

After a week the outlook was grim. All the time the dead tissue had been sloughing and one night when I removed the dressing Mrs Hammond gasped and turned away. With her nursing training she had been very helpful, holding the foot this way and that intuitively as I worked, but tonight she didn't want to look.

I couldn't blame her. In places the white bones of the metacarpals could be seen like the fingers of a human hand with only random strands of skin covering them.

'Is it hopeless, do you think?' she whispered, still looking away.

I didn't answer for a moment as I felt my way underneath the foot. 'It does look awful, but do you know, I think we have reached the end of the road and are going to turn the corner soon.'

'How do you mean?'

'Well, all the under surface is sound and warm. His pads are perfectly intact. And do you notice, there's no smell tonight? That's because there is no more dead stuff to cut away. I really think this foot is going to start granulating.'

She stole a look. 'And do you think those ... bones ... will be covered over?'

'Yes, I do.' I dusted on the faithful sulphanilamide. 'It won't be exactly the same foot as before but it will do.'

And it turned out just that way. It took a long time but the new healthy tissue worked its way upwards as though determined to prove me right and when, many months later, Rock came into the surgery with a mild attack of conjunctivitis he proffered a courteous paw as was his wont. I accepted the civility and as we shook hands I looked at the upper surface of the foot. It was hairless, smooth and shining, but it was completely healed.

'You'd hardly notice it, would you?' Mrs Hammond said.

'That's right, it's marvellous. Just this little bare patch. And he walked in without a limp.'

Mrs Hammond laughed. 'Oh, he's quite sound on that leg now. And do you know, I really think he's grateful to you – look at him.'

I suppose the animal psychologists would say it was ridiculous even to think that the big dog realised I had done him a bit of good; that lolling-tongued open mouth, warm eyes and outstretched paw didn't mean anything like that.

Maybe they are right, but what I do know and cherish is the certainty that after all the discomforts I had put him through Rock didn't hold a thing against me.

I have to turn to the other side of the coin to discuss Timmy Butterworth. He was a wire-haired Fox Terrier who resided in Gimber's yard, one of the little cobbled alleys off Trengate, and the only time I had to treat him was one lunch time.

I had just got out of the car and was climbing the surgery steps when I saw a little girl running along the street, waving frantically as she approached. I waited for her and when she panted up to me her eyes were wide with fright.

'Ah'm Wendy Butterworth,' she gasped. 'Me mam sent me. Will you come to our dog?'

'What's wrong with him?'

'Me mam says he's et summat!'

'Poison?'

'Ah think so.'

It was less than a hundred yards away, not worth taking the car. I broke into a trot with Wendy by my side and within seconds we were turning into the narrow archway of the 'yard'. Our feet clattered along the tunnel-like passage then we emerged into one of the unlikely scenes which had surprised me so much when I first came to Darrowby; the miniature street with its tiny crowded houses, strips of garden, bow windows looking into each other across a few feet of cobbles. But I had no time to gaze around me today because Mrs Butterworth, stout, red-faced and very flustered was waiting for me.

'He's in 'ere, Mr Herriot!' she cried and threw wide the door of one of the cottages. It opened straight into the living room and I saw my patient sitting on the hearth rug looking somewhat thoughtful.

'What's happened, then?' I asked.

The lady clasped and unclasped her hands. 'I saw a big rat run down across t'yard yesterday and I got some poison to put down for 'im.' She gulped agitatedly. 'I mixed it in a saucer full o' porridge then somebody came to t'door and when ah came back, Timmy was just finishin' it off!'

The terrier's thoughtful expression had deepened and he ran his tongue slowly round his lips with the obvious reflection that that was the strangest porridge he had ever tasted.

I turned to Mrs Butterworth. 'Have you got the poison tin there?'

'Yes, here it is.' With a violently trembling hand she passed it to me.

I read the label. It was a well known name and the very look of it sounded a knell in my mind recalling the many dead and dying animals with which it was associated. Its active ingredient was zinc phosphide and even today with our modern drugs we are usually helpless once a dog has absorbed it.

I thumped the tin down on the table. 'We've got to make him vomit immediately! I don't want to waste time going back to the surgery – have you got any washing soda? If I push a few crystals down it'll do the trick.'

'Oh dear!' Mrs Butterworth bit her lip. 'We 'aven't such a thing in the house . . . is there anything else we could . . .'

'Wait a minute!' I looked across the table, past the piece of cold mutton, the tureen of potatoes and a jar of pickles. 'Is there any mustard in that pot?'

'Aye, it's full.'

Quickly I grabbed the pot, ran to the tap and diluted the mustard to the consistency of milk.

'Come on!' I shouted. 'Let's have him outside.'

I seized the astonished Timmy, whisked him from the rug, shot through the door and dumped him on the cobbles. Holding his body clamped tightly between my knees and his jaws close together with my left hand I poured the liquid mustard into the side of his mouth whence it trickled down to the back of his throat. There was nothing he could do about it, he had swallowed the disgusting stuff, and when about a tablespoon had gone down I released him.

After a single affronted glare at me the terrier began to retch then to lurch across the smooth stones. Within seconds he had deposited his stolen meal in a quiet corner.

'Do you think that's the lot?' I asked.

'That's it,' Mrs Butterworth replied firmly. 'I'll fetch a brush and shovel.'

Timmy, his short tail tucked down, slunk back into the house and I watched him as he took up his favourite position on the hearthrug. He coughed, snorted, pawed at his mouth, but he just couldn't rid himself of that dreadful taste; and increasingly it was obvious that he had me firmly tagged as the cause of all the trouble. As I left he flashed me a glance which said quite plainly, 'You rotten swine!'

There was something in that look which reminded me of Magnus from the Drovers, but the first sign that Timmy, unlike Magnus, wasn't going to be satisfied with vocal disapproval came within a few days. I was strolling meditatively down Trengate when a white missile issued from Gimber's Yard, nipped me on the ankle and disappeared as silently as he had come. I caught only a glimpse of the little form speeding on its short legs down the passage.

I laughed. Fancy his remembering! But it happened again and again and I realised that the little dog was indeed lying in wait for me. He never actually sank his teeth into me – it was a gesture more than anything – but it seemed to satisfy him to see me jump as he snatched briefly at my calf or trouser leg. I was a sitting bird because I was usually deep in thought as I walked down the street.

And when I thought about it, I couldn't blame Timmy. Looking at it from his point of view he had been sitting by his fireside digesting an unusual meal and minding his own business when a total stranger had pounced on him, hustled him from the comfort of his rug and poured mustard into him. It was outrageous and he just wasn't prepared to let the matter rest there.

For my part there was a certain satisfaction in being the object of a vendetta waged by an animal who would have been dead without my services. And unpleasantly dead because the victims of phosphorus poisoning had to endure long days and sometimes weeks of jaundice, misery and creeping debility before the inevitable end.

So I suffered the attacks with good grace. But when I remembered I crossed to the other side of the street to avoid the hazard of Gimber's Yard; and from there I could often see the little white dog peeping round the corner waiting for the moment when he would make me pay for that indignity.

Timmy, I knew, was one who would never forget.

# 35

I suppose there was a wry humour in the fact that my call-up papers arrived on my birthday, but I didn't see the joke at the time.

The event is preserved in my memory in a picture which is as clear to me today as when I walked into our 'dining room' that morning. Helen perched away up on her high stool at the end of the table, very still, eyes downcast. By the side of my plate my birthday present, a tin of Dobie's Blue Square tobacco, and next to it a long envelope. I didn't have to ask what it contained.

I had been expecting it for some time but it still gave me a jolt to find I had only a week before presenting myself at Lord's Cricket Ground, St John's Wood, London. And that week went by at frightening speed as I made my final plans, tidying up the loose ends in the practice, getting my Ministry of Agriculture forms sent off, arranging for our few possessions to be taken to Helen's old home where she would stay while I was away.

Having decided that I would finish work at teatime on Friday I had a call from old Arnold Summergill at about three o'clock that afternoon; and I knew that would be my very last job because it was always an expedition rather than a visit to his smallholding which clung to a bracken strewn slope in the depths of the hills. I didn't speak directly to Arnold but to Miss Thompson the postmistress in Hainby village.

'Mr Summergill wants you to come and see his dog,' she said over the phone.

'What's the trouble?' I asked.

I heard a muttered consultation at the far end.

'He says its leg's gone funny.'

'Funny? What d'you mean, funny?'

Again the quick babble of voices. 'He says it's kind of stickin' out.'

'All right,' I said. 'I'll be along very soon.'

It was no good asking for the dog to be brought in. Arnold had never owned a car. Nor had he ever spoken on a telephone – all our conversations had been carried on through the medium of Miss Thompson. Arnold would mount his rusty bicycle, pedal to Hainby and tell his troubles to the postmistress. And the symptoms; they were typically vague and I didn't suppose there would be anything either 'funny' or 'sticking out' about that leg when I saw it.

Anyway, I thought, as I drove out of Darrowby, I wouldn't mind having a last look at Benjamin. It was a fanciful name for a small farmer's dog and I never really found out how he had acquired it. But after all he was an unlikely breed for such a setting, a massive Old English Sheep Dog who would have looked more in place decorating the lawns of a stately home than following his master round Arnold's stony pastures. He was a classical example of the walking hearthrug and it took a second look to decide which end of him was which. But when

245

you did manage to locate his head you found two of the most benevolent eyes imaginable glinting through the thick fringe of hair.

Benjamin was in fact too friendly at times, especially in winter when he had been strolling in the farmyard mud and showed his delight at my arrival by planting his huge feet on my chest. He did the same thing to my car, too, usually just after I had washed it, smearing clay lavishly over windows and bodywork while exchanging pleasantries with Sam inside. When Benjamin made a mess of anything he did it right.

But I had to interrupt my musings when I reached the last stage of my journey. And as I hung on to the kicking, jerking wheel and listened to the creaking and groaning of springs and shock absorbers, the thought forced its way into my mind as it always did around here that it cost us money to come to Mr Summergill's farm. There could be no profit from the visit because this vicious track must knock at least five pounds off the value of the car on every trip. Since Arnold did not have a car himself he saw no reason why he should interfere with the primeval state of his road.

It was simply a six foot strip of earth and rock and it wound and twisted for an awful long way. The trouble was that to get to the farm you had to descend into a deep valley before climbing through a wood towards the house. I think going down was worse because the vehicle hovered agonisingly on the top of each ridge before plunging into the yawning ruts beyond; and each time, listening to the unyielding stone grating on sump and exhaust I tried to stop myself working out the damage in pounds shillings and pence.

And when at last, mouth gaping, eyes popping, tyres sending the sharp pebbles flying, I ground my way upwards in bottom gear over the last few yards leading to the house I was surprised to see Arnold waiting for me there alone. It was unusual to see him without Benjamin.

He must have read my questioning look because he jerked his thumb over his shoulder.

'He's in t'house,' he grunted, and his eyes were anxious.

246

I got out of the car and looked at him for a moment as he stood there in a typical attitude, wide shoulders back, head high. I have called him 'old' and indeed he was over seventy, but the features beneath the woollen tammy which he always wore pulled down over his ears were clean and regular and the tall figure lean and straight. He was a fine looking man and must have been handsome in his youth, yet he had never married. I often felt there was a story there but he seemed content to live here alone, a 'bit of a 'ermit' as they said in the village. Alone, that is, except for Benjamin.

As I followed him into the kitchen he casually shooed out a couple of hens who had been perching on a dusty dresser. Then I saw Benjamin and pulled up with a jerk.

The big dog was sitting quite motionless by the side of the table and this time the eyes behind the overhanging hair were big and liquid with fright. He appeared to be too terrified to move and when I saw his left fore leg I couldn't blame him. Arnold had been right after all; it was indeed sticking out with a vengeance, at an angle which made my heart give a quick double thud; a complete lateral dislocation of the elbow, the radius projecting away out from the humerus at an almost impossible obliquity.

I swallowed carefully. 'When did this happen, Mr Summergill?'

'Just an hour since.' He tugged worriedly at his strange headgear. 'I was changing the cows into another field and awd Benjamin likes to have a nip at their heels when he's behind 'em. Well he did it once ower often and one of them lashed out and got 'im on the leg.'

'I see.' My mind was racing. This thing was grotesque. I had never seen anything like it, in fact thirty years later I still haven't seen anything like it. How on earth was I going to reduce the thing away up here in the hills ? By the look of it I would need general anaesthesia and a skilled assistant.

'Poor old lad,' I said, resting my hand on the shaggy head as I tried to think. 'What are we going to do with you ?'

The tail whisked along the flags in reply and the mouth

opened in a nervous panting, giving a glimpse of flawlessly white teeth.

Arnold cleared his throat. 'Can you put 'im right?'

Well it was a good question. An airy answer might give the wrong impression yet I didn't want to worry him with my doubts. It would be a mammoth task to get the enormous dog down to Darrowby; he nearly filled the kitchen, never mind my little car. And with that leg sticking out and with Sam already in residence. And would I be able to get the joint back in place when I got there? And even if I did manage it I would still have to bring him all the way back up here. It would just about take care of the rest of the day.

Gently I passed my fingers over the dislocated joint and searched my memory for details of the anatomy of the elbow. For the leg to be in this position the processus anconeus must have been completely disengaged from the supracondyloid fossa where it normally lay; and to get it back the joint would have to be flexed until the anconeus was clear of the epicondyles.

'Now let's see,' I murmured to myself. 'If I had this dog anaesthetised and on the table I would have to get hold of him like this.' I grasped the leg just above the elbow and began to move the radius slowly upwards. Benjamin gave me a quick glance then turned his head away, a gesture typical of good-natured dogs, conveying the message that he was going to put up with whatever I thought it necessary to do.

I flexed the joint still further until I was sure the anconeus was clear, then carefully rotated the radius and ulna inwards.

'Yes . . . yes . . .' I muttered again. 'This must be about the right position . . .' But my soliloquy was interrupted by a sudden movement of the bones under my hand; a springing, flicking sensation.

I looked incredulously at the leg. It was perfectly straight.

Benjamin, too, seemed unable to take it in right away, because he peered cautiously round through his shaggy curtain before lowering his nose and sniffing around the elbow. Then he seemed to realise all was well and ambled over to his master.

And he was perfectly sound. Not a trace of a limp.

A slow smile spread over Arnold's face. 'You've mended him, then.'

'Looks like it, Mr Summergill.' I tried to keep my voice casual, but I felt like cheering or bursting into hysterical laughter. I had only been making an examination, feeling things out a little, and the joint had popped back into place. A glorious accident.

'Aye well, that's grand,' the farmer said. 'Isn't it, awd lad?' He bent and tickled Benjamin's ear.

I could have been disappointed by this laconic reception of my performance, but I realised it was a compliment to me that he wasn't surprised that I, James Herriot, his vet, should effortlessly produce a miracle when it was required.

A theatre-full of cheering students would have rounded off the incident or it would be nice to do this kind of thing to some millionaire's animal in a crowded drawing room, but it never happened that way. I looked around the kitchen, at the cluttered table, the pile of unwashed crockery in the sink, a couple of Arnold's ragged shirts drying before the fire, and I smiled to myself. This was the sort of setting in which I usually pulled off my spectacular cures. The only spectators here, apart from Arnold, were the two hens who had made their way back on to the dresser and they didn't seem particularly impressed.

'Well, I'll be getting back down the hill,' I said. And Arnold walked with me across the yard to the car.

'I hear you're off to join up,' he said as I put my hand on the door.

'Yes, I'm away tomorrow, Mr Summergill.'

'Tomorrow, eh?' he raised his eyebrows.

'Yes, to London. Ever been there?'

'Nay, nay, be damned!' The woollen cap quivered as he shook his head. 'That'd be no good to me.'

I laughed. 'Why do you say that?'

'Well now, I'll tell ye.' He scratched his chin ruminatively. 'Ah nobbut went once to Brawton and that was enough. Ah couldn't walk on t'street!'

'Couldn't walk?'

'Nay. There were that many people about. I 'ad to take big steps and little 'uns, then big steps and little 'uns again. Couldn't get goin'.'

I had often seen Arnold stalking over his fields with the long, even stride of the hillman with nothing in his way and I knew exactly what he meant. 'Big steps and little 'uns.' That put it perfectly.

I started the engine and waved and as I moved away the old man raised a hand.

'Tek care, lad,' he murmured.

I spotted Benjamin's nose just peeping round the kitchen door. Any other time he would have been out with his master to see me off the premises but it had been a strange day for him culminating with my descending on him and mauling his leg about. He wasn't taking any more chances.

I drove gingerly down through the wood and before starting up the track on the other side I stopped the car and got out with Sam leaping eagerly after me.

This was a little lost valley in the hills, a green cleft cut off from the wild country above. One of the bonuses in a country vet's life is that he sees these hidden places. Apart from old Arnold nobody ever came down here, not even the postman who left the infrequent mail in a box at the top of the track and nobody saw the blazing scarlets and golds of the autumn trees nor heard the busy clucking and murmuring of the beck among its clean-washed stones.

I walked along the water's edge watching the little fish darting and flitting in the cool depths. In the spring these banks were bright with primroses and in May a great sea of bluebells flowed among the trees but today, though, the sky was an untroubled blue and the clean air was touched with the sweetness of the dying year.

I climbed a little way up the hillside and sat down among the bracken now fast turning to bronze. Sam, as was his way, flopped by my side and I ran a hand over the silky hair of his ears. The far side of the valley rose steeply to where, above the gleaming ridge of limestone cliffs, I could just see the sunlit rim of the moor.

I looked back to where the farm chimney sent a thin tendril of smoke from behind the brow of the hill, and it seemed that the episode with Benjamin, my last job in veterinary practice before I left Darrowby, was a fitting epilogue. A little triumph, intensely satisfying but by no means world shaking; like all the other little triumphs and disasters which make up a veterinary surgeon's life but go unnoticed by the world.

Last night, after Helen had packed my bag I had pushed Black's Veterinary Dictionary in among the shirts and socks. It was a bulky volume but I had been gripped momentarily by a fear that I might forget the things I had learned, and conceived on an impulse the scheme of reading a page or two each day to keep my memory fresh. And here among the bracken the thought came back to me; that it was the greatest good fortune not only to be fascinated by animals but to know about them. Suddenly the knowing became a precious thing.

I went back and opened the car door. Sam jumped on to the seat and before I got in I looked away down in the other direction from the house to the valley's mouth where the hills parted to give a glimpse of the plain below. And the endless wash of pale tints, the gold of the stubble, the dark smudges of wood, the mottled greens of the pasture land were like a perfect water colour. I found myself staring greedily as if for the first time at the scene which had so often lifted my heart, the great wide clean-blown face of Yorkshire.

I would come back to it all, I thought as I drove away; back to my work . . . how was it that book had described it . . . my hard, honest and fine profession.

# 36

I had to catch the early train and Bob Cooper was at the door with his ancient taxi before eight o'clock next morning.

Sam followed me across the room expectantly as he always did but I closed the door gently against his puzzled face. Clattering down the long flight of stairs I caught a glimpse through the landing window of the garden with the sunshine beginning to pierce the autumn mist, turning the dewy grass into a glittering coverlet, glinting on the bright colours of the apples and the last roses.

In the passage I paused at the side door where I had started my day's work so many times since coming to Darrowby, but then I hurried past. This was one time I went out the front.

Bob pushed open the taxi door and I threw my bag in before looking up over the ivy-covered brick of the old house to our little room under the tiles. Helen was in the window. She was crying. When she saw me she waved gaily and smiled, but it was a twisted smile as the tears flowed. And as we drove round the corner and I swallowed the biggest ever lump in my throat a fierce resolve welled in me; men all over the country were leaving their wives and I had to leave Helen now, but nothing, nothing, nothing would ever get me away from her again.

The shops were still closed and nothing stirred in the market place. As we left I turned and looked back at the cobbled square with the old clock tower and the row of irregular roofs with the green fells quiet and peaceful behind, and it seemed that I was losing something for ever.

I wish I had known then that it was not the end of everything. I wish I had known it was only the beginning. But at that moment I knew only that soon I would be far from here; in London, pushing my way through the crowds. Taking big steps and little 'uns.

# Vet In A Spin

With love to
**Rosie, Jim and Gill**

# 1

This was a very different uniform. The wellingtons and breeches of my country vet days seemed far away as I climbed into the baggy flying suit and pulled on the sheepskin boots and the gloves – the silk ones first then the big clumsy pair on top. It was all new but I had a feeling of pride.

Leather helmet and goggles next, then I fastened on my parachute, passing the straps over my shoulders and between my legs and buckling them against my chest before shuffling out of the flight hut on to the long stretch of sunlit grass.

Flying Officer Woodham was waiting for me there. He was to be my instructor and he glanced at me apprehensively as though he didn't relish the prospect. With his dark boyish good looks he resembled all the pictures I had seen of Battle of Britain pilots and in fact, like all our instructors, he had been through this crisis in our history. They had been sent here as a kind of holiday after their tremendous experience but it was said that they regarded their operations against the enemy as a picnic compared with this. They had faced the might of the Luftwaffe without flinching but we terrified them.

As we walked over the grass I could see one of my friends coming in to land. The little biplane slewed and weaved crazily in the sky. It just missed a clump of trees, then about fifty feet from the ground it dropped like a stone, bounced high on its wheels, bounced twice again then zig-zagged to a halt. The helmeted head in the rear cockpit jerked and nodded as though it were making some pointed remarks to the head in front. Flying Officer Woodham's face was expressionless but I knew what he was thinking. It was his turn next.

The Tiger Moth looked very small and alone on the wide stretch of green. I climbed up and strapped myself into the cockpit while my instructor got in behind me. He went through the drill which I would soon know by heart like a piece of poetry. A fitter gave the propeller a few turns for priming. Then 'Contact!', the fitter swung the prop, the engine roared, the chocks were pulled away from the wheels and we were away, bumping over the grass, then suddenly and miraculously lifting and soaring high over the straggle of huts into the summer sky with the patchwork of the soft countryside of southern England unfolding beneath us.

I felt a sudden elation, not just because I liked the sensation but because I had waited so long for this moment. The months of drilling and marching and studying navigation had been leading up to the time when I would take to the air and now it had arrived.

FO Woodham's voice came over the intercom. 'Now you've got her. Take the stick and hold her steady. Watch the artificial horizon and keep it level. See that cloud ahead? Line yourself up with it and keep your nose on it.'

I gripped the joystick in my gauntleted hand. This was lovely. And easy, too. They had told me flying would be a simple matter and they had been right. It was child's play. Cruising along I glanced down at the grandstand of Ascot racecourse far below.

I was just beginning to smile happily when a voice crashed in my ear. 'Relax, for God's sake! What the hell are you playing at?'

I couldn't understand him. I felt perfectly relaxed and I thought I was doing fine, but in the mirror I could see my instructor's eyes glaring through his goggles.

'No, no, no! That's no bloody good! Relax, can't you hear me, relax!'

'Yes, sir,' I quavered and immediately began to stiffen up. I couldn't imagine what was troubling the man but as I began to stare with increasing desperation, now at the artificial horizon, then at the nose of the aircraft against the cloud ahead, the noises over the intercom became increasingly apoplectic.

I didn't seem to have a single problem, yet all I could hear were curses and groans and on one occasion the voice rose to a scream. 'Get your bloody finger out, will you!'

I stopped enjoying myself and a faint misery welled in me. And as always when that happened I began to think of Helen and the happier life I had left behind. In the open cockpit the wind thundered in my ears, lending vivid life to the picture forming in my mind.

The wind was thundering here, too, but it was against the window of our bedsitter. It was early November and a golden autumn had changed with brutal suddenness to arctic cold. For two weeks an icy rain had swept the grey towns and villages which huddled in the folds of the Yorkshire Dales, turning the fields into shallow lakes and the farmyards into squelching mud-holes.

Everybody had colds. Some said it was flu, but whatever it was it decimated the population. Half of Darrowby seemed to be in bed and the other half sneezing at each other.

I myself was on a knife edge, crouching over the fire, sucking an antiseptic lozenge and wincing every time I had to swallow. My throat felt raw and there was an ominous tickling at the back of my nose. I shivered as the rain hurled a drumming cascade of water against the glass. I was all alone in the practice. Siegfried had gone away for a few days and I just daren't catch cold.

It all depended on tonight. If only I could stay indoors and then have a good sleep I could throw this off, but as I glanced over at the phone on the bedside table it looked like a crouching beast ready to spring.

Helen was sitting on the other side of the fire, knitting. She didn't have a cold – she never did. And even in those early days of our marriage I couldn't help feeling it was a little unfair. Even now, thirty-five years later, things are just the same and, as I go around sniffling, I still feel tight-lipped at her obstinate refusal to join me.

I pulled my chair closer to the blaze. There was always a lot of night work in our kind of practice but maybe I would be lucky. It was eight o'clock with never a cheep, and perhaps fate had decreed that I would not be hauled out into that sodden darkness in my weakened state.

Helen came to the end of a row and held up her knitting. It was a sweater for me, about half done.

'How does it look, Jim?' she asked.

I smiled. There was something in her gesture that seemed to epitomize our life together. I opened my mouth to tell her it was simply smashing when the phone pealed with a suddenness which made me bite my tongue.

Tremblingly I lifted the receiver while horrid visions of calving heifers floated before me. An hour with my shirt off would just tip me nicely over the brink.

'This is Sowden of Long Pasture,' a voice croaked.

'Yes, Mr Sowden?' I gripped the phone tightly. I would know my fate in a moment.

'I 'ave a big calf 'ere. Looks very dowly and gruntin' bad. Will ye come?'

A long breath of relief escaped me. A calf with probable stomach trouble. It could have been a lot worse.

'Right, I'll see you in twenty minutes,' I said.

As I turned back to the cosy warmth of the little room the injustice of life smote me.

'I've got to go out, Helen.'

'Oh, no.'

'Yes, and I have this cold coming on,' I whimpered. 'And just listen to that rain.'

'Yes, you must wrap up well, Jim.'

I scowled at her. 'That place is ten miles away, and a cheerless dump if ever there was one. There's not a warm corner anywhere.' I fingered my aching throat. 'A trip out there's just what I need – I'm sure I've got a temperature.' I don't know if all veterinary surgeons blame their wives when they get an unwanted call, but heaven help me, I've done it all my life.

Instead of giving me a swift kick in the pants Helen smiled up at me. 'I'm really sorry, Jim, but maybe it won't take you long. And you can have a bowl of hot soup when you get back.'

I nodded sulkily. Yes, that was something to look forward to. Helen had made some brisket broth that day, rich and meaty, crowded with celery, leeks and carrots and with a flavour to bring a man back from the dead. I kissed her and trailed off into the night.

Long Pasture Farm was in the little hamlet of Dowsett and I had travelled this narrow road many times. It snaked its way high into the wild country and on summer days the bare lonely hills had a serene beauty; treeless and austere, but with a clean wind sweeping over the grassy miles.

But tonight as I peered unhappily through the streaming windscreen the unseen surrounding black bulk pressed close and I could imagine the dripping stone walls climbing high to the summits where the rain drove across the moorland, drenching the heather and bracken, churning the dark mirrors of the bog water into liquid mud.

When I saw Mr Sowden I realized that I was really quite fit. He had obviously been suffering from the prevalent malady for some time, but like most farmers he just had to keep going at his hard ceaseless work. He looked at me from swimming eyes, gave a couple of racking coughs that almost tore him apart and led me into the buildings. He held an oil lamp high as we entered a lofty barn and in the feeble light I discerned various rusting farm implements, a heap of potatoes and another of turnips and in a corner a makeshift pen where my patient stood.

It wasn't the two-week-old baby calf I had half expected, but a little animal of six months, almost stirk age, but not well grown. It had all the signs of a 'bad doer' – thin and pot-bellied with its light roan coat hanging in a thick overgrown fringe below its abdomen.

'Allus been a poor calf,' Mr Sowden wheezed between coughs. 'Never seemed to put on flesh. Rain stopped for a bit this after-noon, so ah let 'im out for a bit of fresh air and now look at 'im.'

I climbed into the pen and as I slipped the thermometer into the rectum I studied the little creature. He offered no resistance as I gently pushed him to one side, his head hung down and he gazed apathetically at the floor from deep sunk eyes. Worst of all was the noise he was making. It was more than a grunt – rather a long, painful groan repeated every few seconds.

'It certainly looks like his stomach,' I said. 'Which field was he in this afternoon?'

'I nobbut let 'im have a walk round t'orchard for a couple of hours.'

'I see.' I looked at the thermometer. The temperature was sub-normal. 'I suppose there's a bit of fruit lying around there.'

Mr Sowden went into another paroxysm, then leaned on the boards of the pen to recover his breath. 'Aye, there's apples and pears all over t'grass. Had a helluva crop this year.'

I put the stethoscope over the rumen and instead of the normal surge and bubble of the healthy stomach I heard only a deathly silence. I palpated the flank and felt the typical doughy fullness of impaction.

11

'Well, Mr Sowden, I think he's got a bellyful of fruit and it's brought his digestion to a complete halt. He's in a bad way.'

The farmer shrugged. 'Well, if 'e's just a bit bunged up, a good dose of linseed oil 'ud shift 'im.'

'I'm afraid it's not as simple as that,' I said. 'This is a serious condition.'

'Well, what are we goin' to do about it, then?' He wiped his nose and looked at me morosely.

I hesitated. It was bitterly cold in the old building and already I was feeling shivery and my throat ached. The thought of Helen and the bedsitter and the warm fire was unbearably attractive. But I had seen impactions like this before and tried treating them with purgatives and it didn't work. This animal's temperature was falling to the moribund level and he had a sunken eye – if I didn't do something drastic he would be dead by morning.

'There's only one thing will save him,' I said. 'And that's a rumenotomy.'

'A what?'

'An operation. Open up his first stomach and clear out all the stuff that shouldn't be there.'

'Are you sure? D'ye not think a good pint of oil would put 'im right. It 'ud be a lot easier.'

It would indeed. For a moment the fireside and Helen glowed like a jewel in a cave, then I glanced at the calf. Scraggy and long-haired, he looked utterly unimportant, infinitely vulnerable and dependent. It would be the easiest thing in the world to leave him groaning in the dark till morning.

'I'm quite sure, Mr Sowden. He's so weak that I think I'll do it under a local anaesthetic, so we'll need some help.'

The farmer nodded slowly. 'Awright, ah'll go down t'village and get George Hindley.' He coughed again, painfully. 'But by gaw, ah could do without this tonight. Ah'm sure I've got brown chitis.'

Brown chitis was a common malady among the farmers of those days and there was no doubt this poor man was suffering from it but my pang of sympathy faded as he left because he took the lamp with him and the darkness closed tightly on me.

There are all kinds of barns. Some of them are small, cosy and fragrant with hay, but this was a terrible place. I had been in here on sunny afternoons and even then the dank gloom of crumbling walls and rotting beams was like a clammy blanket and all warmth and softness seemed to disappear among the cobwebbed rafters high above. I used to feel that people with starry-eyed notions of farming ought to take a look inside that barn. It was evocative of the grim comfortless other side of the agricultural life.

I had it to myself now, and as I stood there listening to the wind rattling the door on its latch a variety of draughts whistled round me and a remorseless drip-drip from the broken pantiles on the roof sent icy droplets trickling over my head and neck. And as the minutes ticked away I began to hop from foot to foot in a vain effort to keep warm.

Dales farmers are never in a hurry and I hadn't expected a quick return, but after fifteen minutes in the impenetrable blackness bitter thoughts began to assail me. Where the hell was the man? Maybe he and George Hindley were brewing a pot of tea for themselves or perhaps settling down to a quick game of dominoes. My legs were trembling by the time the oil lamp reappeared in the entrance and Mr Sowden ushered his neighbour inside.

'Good evening, George,' I said. 'How are you?'

'Only moderate, Mr Herriot,' the newcomer sniffled. 'This bloody caud's just – ah – ah – whooosh – just getting' a haud o' me.' He blew lustily into a red handkerchief and gazed at me blearily.

I looked around me. 'Well let's get started. We'll need an operating table. Perhaps you could stack up a few straw bales?'

The two men trailed out and returned, carrying a couple of bales apiece. When they were built up they were about the right height but rather wobbly.

'We could do with a board on top.' I blew on my freezing fingers and stamped my feet. 'Any ideas?'

Mr Sowden rubbed his chin. 'Aye, we'll get a door.' He shuffled out into the yard with his lamp and I watched him struggling to lift one of the cow byre doors from its hinges. George went to give him a hand and as the two of them pulled and heaved I thought wearily that veterinary operations didn't trouble me all that much but getting ready for them was a killer.

Finally the men staggered back into the barn, laid the door on top of the bales and the theatre was ready.

'Let's get him up,' I gasped.

We lifted the unresisting little creature on to the improvised table and stretched him on his right side. Mr Sowden held his head while George took charge of the tail and the rear end.

Quickly I laid out my instruments, removed coat and jacket and rolled up my shirt sleeves. 'Damn! We've no hot water. Will you bring some, Mr Sowden?'

I held the head and again waited interminably while the farmer went to the house. This time it was worse without my warm clothing, and cold ate into me as I pictured the farm kitchen and the slow scooping of the water from the side boiler into a bucket, then the unhurried journey back to the buildings.

When Mr Sowden finally reappeared I added antiseptic to the bucket and scrubbed my arms feverishly. Then I clipped the hair on the left side and filled the syringe with local anaesthetic. But as I infiltrated the area I felt my hopes sinking.

'I can hardly see a damn thing.' I looked helplessly at the oil lamp balanced on a nearby turnip chopper. 'That light's in the wrong place.'

Wordlessly Mr Sowden left his place and began to tie a length of plough cord to a beam. He threw it over another beam and made it fast before suspending the lamp above the calf. It was a big improvement but it took a long time, and by the time he had finished I had abandoned all hope of ever throwing off my cold. I was frozen right through and a burning sensation had started in my chest. I would soon be in the same state as my helpers. Brown chitis was just round the corner.

Anyway, at least I could start now, and I incised skin, muscles, peritoneum and rumenal wall at record speed. I plunged an arm deep into the opened organ, through the fermenting mass of stomach contents, and in a flash all my troubles dissolved. Along the floor of the rumen apples and pears were spread in layers, some of them bitten but most of them whole and intact. Bovines take most of their food in big swallows and chew it over later at their leisure, but no animal could make cud out of this lot.

I looked up happily. 'It's just as I thought. He's full of fruit.'

'Hhrraaagh!' replied Mr Sowden. Coughs come in various forms but this one was tremendous and fundamental, starting at the soles of his hob-nailed boots and exploding right in my face.

I hadn't realized how vulnerable I was with the farmer leaning over the calf's neck, his head a few inches from mine. 'Hhrraaagh!' he repeated, and a second shower of virus-laden moisture struck me. Apparently Mr Sowden either didn't know or didn't care about droplet infection, but with my hands inside my patient there was nothing I could do about it.

Instinctively I turned my face a little in the other direction.

'Whoosh!' went George. It was a sneeze rather than a cough, but it sent a similar deadly spray against my other cheek. I realized there was no escape. I was hopelessly trapped between the two of them.

But as I say, my morale had received a boost. Eagerly I scooped out great handfuls of the offending fruit and within minutes the floor of the barn was littered with Bramley's seedlings and Conference pears.

'Enough here to start a shop,' I laughed.

'Hhrraaagh!' responded Mr Sowden.

'Whooosh!' added George, not to be outdone.

When I had sent the last apple and pear rolling into the darkness I scrubbed up again and started to stitch. This is the longest and most wearisome part of a rumenotomy. The excitement of diagnosis and discovery is over and it is a good time for idle chat, funny stories, anything to pass the time.

But there in the circle of yellow light with the wind whirling round my feet from the surrounding gloom and occasional icy trickles of rain running down my back I was singularly short of gossip, and my companions, sunk in their respective miseries, were in no mood for badinage.

I was halfway down the skin sutures when a tickle mounted at the back of my nose and I had to stop and stand upright.

'Ah – ah – ashooo!' I rubbed my forearm along my nose.

'He's startin',' murmured George with mournful satisfaction.

'Aye, 'e's off,' agreed Mr Sowden, brightening visibly.

I was not greatly worried. I had long since come to the conclusion that my cause was lost. The long session of freezing in my shirt sleeves would have done it without the incessant germ bombardment from either side. I was resigned to my fate and besides, when I inserted the last stitch and helped the calf down from that table I felt a deep thrill of satisfaction. That horrible groan had vanished and the little animal was looking around him as though he had been away for a while. He wasn't cheerful yet, but I knew his pain had gone and that he would live.

'Bed him up well, Mr Sowden.' I started to wash my instruments in the bucket. 'And put a couple of sacks round him to keep him warm. I'll call in a fortnight to take out the stitches.'

The fortnight seemed to last a long time. My cold, as I had confidently expected, developed into a raging holocaust which settled down into the inevitable brown chitis with an accompanying cough which rivalled Mr Sowden's.

Mr Sowden was never an ebullient man but I expected him to look a little happier when I removed the stitches. Because the calf was bright and lively I had to chase him around his pen to catch him.

Despite the fire in my chest I had that airy feeling of success.

'Well,' I said expansively. 'He's done very well. He'll make a good bullock some day.'

The farmer shrugged gloomily. 'Aye, reckon 'e will. But there was no need for all that carry on.'

'No need . . . ?'

'Naw. Ah've been talkin' to one or two folk about t'job and they all said it was daft to open 'im up like that. Ah should just 'ave given 'im a pint of oil like I said.'

'Mr Sowden, I assure you . . .'

'And now ah'll have a big bill to pay.' He dug his hands deep into his pockets.

'Believe me, it was worth it.'

'Nay, nay, never.' He started to walk away, then looked over his shoulder. 'It would've been better if you 'adn't come.'

I had done three circuits with FO Woodham and on this third one he had kept fairly quiet. Obviously I was doing all right now and I could start enjoying myself again. Flying was lovely.

The voice came over the intercom again. 'I'm going to let you land her yourself this time. I've told you how to do it. Right, you've got her.'

'I've got her,' I replied. He had indeed told me how to do it – again and again – and I was sure I would have no trouble.

As we lost height the tops of the trees appeared, then the

16

grass of the airfield came up to meet us. It was the moment of truth. Carefully I eased the stick back, then at what I thought was the right moment I slammed it back against my stomach. Maybe a bit soon because we bounced a couple of times and that made me forget to seesaw the rudder bar so that we careered from side to side over the turf before coming to a halt.

With the engine stilled I took a deep breath. That was my first landing and it hadn't been bad. In fact I had got better and better all the time and the conviction was growing in me that my instructor must have been impressed with my initial showing. We climbed out and after walking a few steps in silence FO Woodham halted and turned to me.

'What's your name?' he asked.

Ah yes, here was the proof. He knew I had done well. He was interested in me.

'Herriot, sir,' I replied smartly.

For a few moments he gave me a level stare. 'Well, Herriot,' he murmured, 'that was bloody awful.'

He turned and left me. I gazed down at my feet in their big sheepskin boots. Yes, the uniform was different, but things hadn't changed all that much.

# 2

'Takes all kinds, doesn't it, chum?'

The airman grinned at me across the flight hut table. We had been listening to a monologue from a third man who had just left us after telling us what he intended to do after gaining his wings. The impression he left was that he was almost going to win the war on his own.

There were certainly all kinds in the RAF and this 'line shooting' was a common phenomenon when different types were thrown together.

There were all kinds of animals, too. Many people think my

farm patients are all the same, but cows, pigs, sheep and horses can be moody, placid, vicious, docile, spiteful, loving.

There was one particular pig called Gertrude, but before I come to her I must start with Mr Barge.

Nowadays the young men from the pharmaceutical companies who call on veterinary surgeons are referred to as 'reps', but nobody would have dreamed of applying such a term to Mr Barge. He was definitely a 'representative' of Cargill and Sons, Manufacturers of Fine Chemicals since 1850, and he was so old that he might have been in on the beginning.

It was a frosty morning in late winter when I opened the front door at Skeldale House and saw Mr Barge standing on the front step. He raised his black homburg a few inches above the sparse strands of silver hair and his pink features relaxed into a smile of gentle benevolence. He had always treated me as a favourite son and I took it as a compliment because he was a man of immense prestige.

'Mr Herriot,' he murmured, and bowed slightly. The bow was rich in dignity and matched the dark morning coat, striped trousers and shiny leather briefcase.

'Please come in, Mr Barge,' I said, and ushered him into the house.

He always called at midday and stayed for lunch. My young boss, Siegfried Farnon, a man not easily overawed, invariably treated him with deference and in fact the visit was something of a state occasion.

The modern rep breezes in, chats briefly about blood levels of antibiotics and steroids, says a word or two about bulk discounts, drops a few data sheets on the desk and hurries away. In a way I feel rather sorry for these young men because, with a few exceptions, they are all selling the same things.

Mr Barge, on the other hand, like all his contemporaries, carried a thick catalogue of exotic remedies, each one peculiar to its own firm.

Siegfried pulled out the chair at the head of the dining table. 'Come and sit here, Mr Barge.'

'You are very kind.' The old gentleman inclined his head slightly and took his place.

As usual there was no reference to business during the meal

and it wasn't until the coffee appeared that Mr Barge dropped his brochure carelessly on the table as though this part of the visit was an unimportant afterthought.

Siegfried and I browsed through the pages, savouring the exciting whiff of witchcraft which has been blown from our profession by the wind of science. At intervals my boss placed an order.

'I think we'd better have a couple of dozen electuaries, Mr Barge.'

'Thank you so much.' The old gentleman flipped open a leather-bound notebook and made an entry with a silver pencil.

'And we're getting a bit low on fever drinks, aren't we, James ?' Siegfried glanced round at me. 'Yes, we'll need a gross of them if you please.'

'I am most grateful,' Mr Barge breathed, noting that down, too.

My employer murmured his requests as he riffled through the catalogue. A Winchester of spirits of nitre and another of formalin, castration clams, triple bromide, Stockholm tar – all the things we never use now – and Mr Barge responded gravely to each with 'I do thank you' or 'Thank you indeed,' and a flourish of his silver pencil.

Finally Siegfried lay back in his chair. 'Well now, Mr Barge, I think that's it – unless you have anything new.'

'As it happens, my dear Mr Farnon, we have.' The eyes in the pink face twinkled. 'I can offer you our latest product, "Soothitt", an admirable sedative.'

In an instant Siegfried and I were all attention. Every animal doctor is keenly interested in sedatives. Anything which makes our patients more amenable is a blessing. Mr Barge extolled the unique properties of Soothitt and we probed for further information.

'How about unmaternal sows ?' I asked. 'You know – the kind which savage their young. I don't suppose it's any good for that ?'

'My dear young sir,' Mr Barge gave me the kind of sorrowing smile a bishop might bestow on an erring curate, 'Soothitt is a specific for this condition. A single injection to a farrowing sow and you will have no problems.'

'That's great,' I said. 'And does it have any effect on car sickness in dogs ?'

The noble old features lit up with quiet triumph. 'Another classical indication, Mr Herriot. Soothitt comes in tablet form for that very purpose.'

'Splendid.' Siegfried drained his cup and stood up. 'Better send us a good supply then. And if you will excuse us, we must start the afternoon round, Mr Barge. Thank you so much for calling.'

We all shook hands, Mr Barge raised his homburg again on the front step and another gracious occasion was over.

Within a week the new supplies from Cargill and Sons arrived. Medicines were always sent in tea chests in those days and as I prised open the wooden lid I looked with interest at the beautifully packed phials and tablets of Soothitt. And it seemed uncanny that I had a call for the new product immediately.

That same day one of the town's bank managers, Mr Ronald Beresford, called to see me.

'Mr Herriot,' he said. 'As you know I have worked here for several years but I have been offered the managership of a bigger branch down south and I leave tomorrow for Portsmouth.' From his gaunt height he looked down at me with the unsmiling gaze which was characteristic of him.

'Portsmouth! Gosh, that's a long way.'

'Yes, it is – about three hundred miles. And I have a problem.'

'Really ?'

'I have, I fear. I recently purchased a six-month-old cocker spaniel and he is an excellent little animal but for the fact that he behaves peculiarly in the car.'

'In what way ?'

He hesitated. 'Well, he's outside now. If you've got a minute to spare I could demonstrate.'

'Of course,' I said. 'I'll come with you now.'

We went out to the car. His wife was in the passenger seat, as fat as her husband was thin, but with the same severe unbending manner. She nodded at me coldly but the attractive little animal on her lap gave me an enthusiastic welcome.

I stroked the long silky ears. 'He's a nice little fellow.'

Mr Beresford gave me a sidelong glance. 'Yes, his name is Coco and he really is quite charming. It's only when the engine is running that the trouble begins.'

I got in the back, he pressed the starter and we set off. And I saw immediately what he meant. The spaniel stiffened and raised his head till his nose pointed at the roof. He formed his lips into a cone and emitted a series of high-pitched howls.

'Hooo, hooo, hooo, hooo,' wailed Coco.

It really startled me because I had never heard anything quite like it. I don't know whether it was the perfectly even spacing of the hoots, their piercing, jarring quality, or the fact that they never stopped which drove the sound deep into my brain, but my head was singing after a two-minute circuit of the town. I was vastly relieved when we drew up again outside the surgery.

Mr Beresford switched off the engine and it was as though he had switched off the noise, too, because the little animal relaxed instantly and began to lick my hand.

'Yes,' I said. 'You have a problem without a doubt.'

He pulled nervously at his tie. 'And it gets louder the longer you drive. Let me take you a bit further round and . . .'

'No-no, no-no,' I put in hastily. 'That won't be necessary. I can see exactly how you are placed. But you say you haven't had Coco for long. He isn't much more than a pup. I'm sure he'll get used to the car in time.'

'Very possibly he will.' Mr Beresford's voice was taut with apprehension. 'But I'm thinking of tomorrow. I've got to drive all the way to Portsmouth with my wife and this dog and I've tried car sickness tablets without result.'

A full day with that appalling din was unthinkable but at that moment the image of Mr Barge rose before me. He had sprouted wings and floated in front of my eyes like an elderly guardian angel. What an incredible piece of luck!

'As it happens,' I said with a reassuring smile, 'there is something new for this sort of thing, and by coincidence we have just received a batch of it today. Come in and I'll fix you up.'

'Well, thank heavens for that.' Mr Beresford examined the box of tablets, 'I just give one, half an hour before the journey, and all will be well?'

'That's the idea,' I replied cheerfully. 'I've given you a few extra for future journeys.'

'I am most grateful, you've taken a great load off my mind.' He went out to the car and I watched as he started the engine. As if in response to a signal the little brown head on the back seat went up and the lips pursed.

'Hooo, hooo, hooo, hooo,' Coco yowled, and his master shot me a despairing look as he drove away.

I stood on the steps for some time, listening incredulously. Many people in Darrowby didn't like Mr Beresford very much, probably because of his cold manner, but I felt he wasn't a bad chap and he certainly had my sympathy. Long after the car had disappeared round the corner of Trengate I could still hear Coco.

'Hooo, hooo, hooo, hooo.'

About seven o'clock that evening I had a phone call from Will Hollin.

'Gertrude's started farrowin'!' he said urgently. 'And she's tryin' to worry her pigs!'

It was bad news. Sows occasionally attacked their piglets after birth and in fact would kill them if they were not removed from their reach. And of course it meant that suckling was impossible.

It was a tricky problem at any time but particularly so in this case because Gertrude was a pedigree sow – an expensive animal Will Hollin had bought to improve his strain of pigs.

'How many has she had?' I asked.

'Four – and she's gone for every one.' His voice was tense.

It was then I remembered Soothitt and again I blessed the coming of Mr Barge.

I smiled into the receiver. 'There's a new product I can use, Mr Hollin. Just arrived today. I'll be right out.'

I trotted through to the dispensary, opened the box of phials and had a quick read at the enclosed pamphlet. Ah yes, there it was. 'Ten cc intramuscularly and the sow will accept the piglets within twenty minutes.'

It wasn't a long drive to the Hollin farm but as I sped through the darkness I could discern the workings of fate in the day's events. The Soothitt had arrived this morning and right away I had two urgent calls for it. There was no doubt Mr Barge had been sent for a purpose – living proof, perhaps, that everything in our lives is preordained. It gave me a prickling at the back of my neck to think about it.

I could hardly wait to get the injection into the sow and climbed eagerly into the pen. Gertrude didn't appreciate having a needle rammed into her thigh and she swung round on me with an explosive bark. But I got the ten cc in before making my escape.

'We just wait twenty minutes, then ?' Will Hollin leaned on the rail and looked down anxiously at his pig. He was a hardworking smallholder in his fifties and I knew this meant a lot to him.

I was about to make a comforting reply when Gertrude popped out another pink, squirming piglet. The farmer leaned over and gently nudged the little creature towards the udder as the sow lay on her side, but as soon as the nose made contact with the teat the big pig was up in a flash, all growls and yellow teeth.

He snatched the piglet away quickly and deposited it with the others in a tall cardboard box. 'Well, you see how it is, Mr Herriot.'

'I certainly do. How many have you got in there now ?'

'There's six. And they're grand pigs, too.'

I peered into the box at the little animals. They all had the classical long-bodied shape. 'Yes, they are. And she looks as though she has a lot more in her yet.'

The farmer nodded and we waited.

It seemed to take a long time for the twenty minutes to pass but finally I lifted a couple of piglets and clambered into the pen. I was about to put them to the sow when one of them squealed. Gertrude rushed across with a ferocious roar, mouth gaping, and I leaped to safety with an agility which surprised me.

'She don't look very sleepy,' Mr Hollin said.

'No . . . no . . . she doesn't, does she ? Maybe we'd better wait a bit longer.'

We gave her another ten minutes and tried again with the same result. I injected a further ten cc of the Soothitt, then about an hour later a third one. By nine o'clock Gertrude had produced fifteen beautiful young pigs and had chased me and her family from the pen six times. She was, if anything, livelier and fiercer than when I started.

'Well, she's cleansed,' Mr Hollin said gloomily. 'So it looks like she's finished.' He gazed, sad-faced, into the box. 'And now I've got fifteen pigs to rear without their mother's milk. I could lose all this lot.'

'Nay, nay.' The voice came from the open doorway. 'You won't lose 'em.'

I looked round. It was Grandad Hollin, his puckish features set in their customary smile. He marched to the pen and poked Gertrude's ribs with his stick.

She responded with a snarl and a malignant glare and the old man's smile grew broader.

'Ah'll soon fettle the awd beggar,' he said.

'Fettle her ?' I shifted my feet uncomfortably. 'What do you mean ?'

'Why, she just wants quietin', tha knaws.'

I took a long breath. 'Yes, Mr Hollin, that's exactly what I've been trying to do.'

'Aye, but you're not doin' it the right way, young man.'

I looked at him narrowly. The know-all with his liberal advice in a difficult situation is a familiar figure most veterinary surgeons have to tolerate, but in Grandad Hollin's case I didn't feel the usual irritation. I liked him. He was a nice man, the head of a fine family. Will was the eldest of his four sons and he had several farmer grandsons in the district.

Anyway, I had failed miserably. I was in no position to be uppity.

'Well, I've given her the latest injection,' I mumbled.

He shook his head. 'She don't want injections, she wants beer.'

'Eh ?'

'Beer, young man. A drop o' good ale.' He turned to his son. 'Hasta got a clean bucket, Will, lad ?'

'Aye, there's a new-scalded one in t'milk house.'

'Right, ah'll slip down to the pub. Won't be long.' Grandad swung on his heel and strode briskly into the night. He must have been around eighty but from the back he looked like a twenty-five-year-old – upright, square-shouldered, jaunty.

Will Hollin and I didn't have much to say to each other. He was sunk in disappointment and I was awash with shame. It was a relief when Grandad returned bearing an enamel bucket brimming with brown liquid.

'By gaw,' he chuckled. 'You should've seen their faces down at t'Wagon and Horses. Reckon they've never heard of a two-gallon order afore.'

I gaped at him. 'You've got two gallons of beer ?'

'That's right, young man, and she'll need it all.' He turned again to his son. 'She hasn't had a drink for a bit, has she, Will ?'

'Naw, I was goin' to give her some water when she'd finished piggin' but I haven't done it yet.'

Grandad poised his bucket. 'She'll be nice and thirsty, then.' He leaned over the rail and sent a dark cascade frothing into the empty trough.

Gertrude ambled moodily across and sniffed at the strange fluid. After some hesitation she dipped her snout and tried a tentative swallow, and within seconds the building echoed with a busy slobbering.

'By heck, she likes it!' Will exclaimed.

'She should,' Grandad murmured wistfully. 'It's John Smith's best bitter.'

It took the sow a surprisingly short time to consume the two gallons and when she had finished she licked out every corner of the trough before turning away. She showed no inclination to return to her straw bed but began to saunter round the pen. Now and then she stopped at the trough to check that there was no more beer in it and from time to time she looked up at the three faces overhanging the timber walls.

On one of these occasions I caught her eye and saw with a sense of disbelief that the previously baleful little orb now registered only a gentle benevolence. In fact with a little effort I could have imagined she was smiling.

As the minutes passed her perambulations became increasingly erratic. There were times when she stumbled and almost fell and finally with an unmistakeable hiccup she flopped on the straw and rolled on to her side.

Grandad regarded her expressionlessly for a few moments, whistling tunelessly, then he reached out again and pushed his stick against the fleshy thigh, but the only response he received from the motionless animal was a soft grunt of pleasure.

Gertrude was stoned to the wide.

The old man gestured towards the cardboard box. 'Put the little 'uns in now.'

Will went into the pen with a wriggling armful, then another, and like all newborn creatures they didn't have to be told what to do. Fifteen ravenous little mouths fastened on to the teats and with mixed feelings I gazed at the sight which I had hoped to bring about with my modern veterinary skill, the long pink row filling their tiny stomachs with the life-giving fluid.

Well, I had fallen down on the job and an octogenarian farmer had wiped my eye with two gallons of strong ale. I didn't feel great.

Sheepishly I closed the box of Soothitt phials and was beating an unobtrusive retreat to my car when Will Hollin called after me.

'Come in and have a cup o' coffee afore you go, Mr Herriot.' His voice was friendly, with nothing to suggest that I had made no useful contribution all evening.

I made my way into the kitchen and as I went over to the table Will dug me in the ribs.

'Hey, look at this.' He held out the bucket in which a quantity of the good beer still sloshed around the bottom. 'There's summat better than coffee 'ere – enough for a couple of good drinks. I'll get two glasses.'

He was fumbling in the dresser when Grandad walked in. The old man hung his hat and stick on a hook on the wall and rubbed his hands.

'Tha can get another glass out, Will,' he said. 'Remember ah did the pourin' and ah left enough for three.'

Next morning I might have been inclined to dwell despondently on my chastening experience but I had a pre-breakfast call to a cow with a prolapsed uterus and there is nothing like an hour of feverish activity to rid the mind of brooding.

It was 8 a.m. when I drove back into Darrowby and I pulled in to the market place petrol station which was just opening. With a pleasantly blank mind I was watching Bob Cooper running the petrol in the tank when I heard the sound in the distance.

'Hooo, hooo, hooo, hooo.'

Tremblingly I scanned the square. There was no other vehicle in sight but the dread ululation approached inexorably until Mr Beresford's car rounded the far corner, heading my way.

I shrank behind a petrol pump but it was of no avail. I had been spotted and the car bumped over the strip of cobbles before screeching to a halt beside me.

'Hooo, hooo, hooo, hooo.' At close quarters the noise was insupportable.

I peeped round the pump and into the bulging eyes of the bank manager as he lowered his window. He switched off the engine and Coco stopped his howling and gave me a friendly wag through the glass.

His master, however, did not look at all friendly.

'Good morning, Mr Herriot,' he said, grim-faced.

'Good morning,' I replied hoarsely, then working up a smile I bent at the window. 'And good morning to you, Mrs Beresford.'

The lady withered me with a look and was about to speak when her husband went on.

'I administered one of the wonderful new tablets early this morning on your advice.' His chin quivered slightly.

'Oh, yes . . . ?'

'Yes, I did, and it had no effect, so I gave him another.' He paused. 'Since this produced a similar result I tried a third and a fourth.'

I swallowed. 'Really . . . ?'

'Indeed.' He gave me a cold stare. 'So I am driven to the conclusion that the tablets are useless.'

'Well . . . er . . . it certainly does look . . .'

He held up a hand. 'I cannot listen to explanations. I have already wasted enough time and there are three hundred miles' driving in front of me.'

'I'm truly sorry . . .' I began, but he was already closing the window. He started the engine and Coco froze immediately into his miniature wolf position, nose high, lips puckered into a small circle. I watched the car roll across the square and turn out of sight on the road to the south. For quite a while after it had gone I could still hear Coco.

'Hooo, hooo, hooo, hooo.'

Feeling suddenly weak, I leaned against the pump. My heart went out to Mr Beresford. As I have said, I felt sure he was a decent man.

In fact I quite liked him, but for all that I was profoundly grateful that I would probably never see him again.

*

Our audiences with Mr Barge usually took place every three months and it was mid-June before I saw him again at the head of our luncheon table. The silvery head gleamed under the summer sunshine as he sipped his coffee and murmured politenesses. At the end of the meal he dabbed his lips with a napkin and slid his brochure unhurriedly along the table cloth.

Siegfried reached for it and asked the inevitable question. 'Anything new, Mr Barge?'

'My dear sir.' The old gentleman's smile seemed to convey that the follies of the young, though incomprehensible to him, were still delightful. 'Cargill and Sons never send me to you without a host of new products, many of them specific, all of them efficient. I have many sovereign remedies to offer you.'

I must have uttered some sort of strangled sound because he turned and regarded me quizzically. 'Ah, Mr Herriot, did you say something, young sir?'

I swallowed a couple of times and opened my mouth as the waves of benevolence flowed over me, but against that dignity and presence I was helpless.

'No . . . no, not really, Mr Barge,' I replied. I knew I would never be able to tell him about the Soothitt.


# 3


Now that we were faced with the reality of life at flying school, the ties which bound me to my fellow airmen were strengthened. We had a common aim, a common worry.

The feeling of comradeship was very like my relationship with Siegfried, and his student brother, Tristan, back in Darrowby. But there, the pressures came not from learning to fly but from the daily challenge of veterinary practice. Our existence was ruled by sudden and unexpected alarms.

Tristan, however, didn't let it get him down. He and I were sitting in the big room at Skeldale House one night when the telephone burst into strident voice.

He reached from his chair and lifted the receiver.

'Allo, plis, oo is dis ?' he inquired.

He listened attentively for a few moments then shook his head.

'Naw, naw, verree sorry, but Meester Farnon no at home. Yis, yis, I tell heem when he come. Hokey dokey, bye bye.'

I looked across at him wonderingly from the other side of the fireplace as he replaced the instrument. These strange accents were only one facet of his constant determination to extract amusement from every situation. He didn't do it all the time, only when the mood was on him, but it was not unusual for farmers to say that 'some foreign feller' had answered the phone.

Tristan settled comfortably behind his *Daily Mirror* and was fumbling for a Woodbine when the ringing started again. He stretched out once more.

'Yaas, yaas, goot efening, howdy do. Vat you vant, huh ?'

I could just hear a deep rumble from the other end of the line and Tristan suddenly snapped upright in his chair. His *Daily Mirror* and cigarettes slithered to the floor.

'Yes, Mr Mouht,' he said smartly. 'No, Mr Mount. Yes indeed, Mr Mount, I shall pass on your message immediately. Thank you very much, goodbye.'

He fell back in the chair and blew out his cheeks. 'That was Mr Mount.'

'So I gathered. And he certainly wiped the smile off your face, Triss.'

'Yes . . . yes . . . just a little unexpected.' He recovered his Woodbines and lit one thoughtfully.

'Quite,' I said. 'What did he ring for, anyway ?'

'Oh, he has a cart horse to see tomorrow morning. Something wrong with its hind feet.'

I made a note on the pad and turned back to the young man. 'I don't know how you find the time in your hectic love life, but you're running around with that chap's daughter, aren't you ?'

Tristan took the cigarette from his mouth and studied the glowing end. 'Yes, as a matter of fact I have taken Deborah Mount out a few times. Why do you ask ?'

'Oh, no particular reason. Her old man seems a bit formidable, that's all.'

I could picture Mr Mount the last time I saw him. He was well named; a veritable massif of a man towering several inches over six feet. From shoulders like the great buttresses of the fell which overhung his farm rose a beetling cliff of head with craggy outcrops of jaw and cheek and brow. He had the biggest hands I have ever seen – approximately three times the size of my own.

'Oh, I don't know,' Tristan said. 'He's not a bad sort.'

'I agree, I've nothing against him.' Mr Mount was deeply religious and had the reputation of being hard but fair. 'It's just that I wouldn't like him to come up to me and ask if I was trifling with his daughter's affections.'

Tristan swallowed, and anxiety flitted briefly in his eyes. 'Oh, that's ridiculous. Deborah and I have a friendly relationship, that's all.'

'Well, I'm glad to hear it,' I said. 'I've been told her father is very protective about her and I'd hate to feel those big hands round my throat.'

Tristan gave me a cold stare. 'You're a sadistic bugger at times, Jim. Just because I occasionally enjoy a little female company ...'

'Oh, forget it, Triss, I'm only kidding. You've nothing to worry about. When I see old Mount tomorrow I promise I won't mention that Deborah is one of your harem.' I dodged a flying cushion and went through to the dispensary to stock up for the next day's round.

But I realized next morning that my joke was barbed when I saw Mr Mount coming out of the farmhouse. For a moment his bulk filled the doorway, then he advanced with measured tread over the cobbles till he loomed over me, blocking out the sunshine, throwing a large area around me into shade.

'That young man, Tristan,' he said without preamble. 'He was speakin' a bit funny like on the phone last night. What sort of a feller is he?'

I looked up at the great head poised above me, at the unwavering grey eyes probing into mine from beneath a bristling overhang of brow. 'Tristan?' I answered shakily. 'Oh, he's a splendid chap. A really fine type.'

'Mmm.' The huge man continued to look at me and one banana-like finger rubbed doubtfully along his chin. 'Does he drink?'

Mr Mount was renowned for his rigid antagonism to alcohol

and I thought it unwise to reply that Tristan was a popular and esteemed figure at most of the local hostelries.

'Oh, er—' I said. 'Hardly at all . . . in the strictest moderation . . .'

At that moment Deborah came out of the house and began to walk across the yard.

She was wearing a flowered cotton dress. About nineteen, shining golden hair falling below her shoulders, she radiated the healthy buxom beauty of the country girl. As she went by she flashed a smile at me and I had a heart-lifting glimpse of white teeth and warm brown eyes. It was in the early days before I had met Helen and I had as sharp an interest in a pretty lass as anybody. I found myself studying her legs appreciatively after she had passed.

It was then that I had an almost palpable awareness of her father's gaze upon me. I turned and saw a new expression there – a harsh disapproval which chilled me and left a deep conviction in my mind. Deborah was a little smasher all right, and she looked nice, too, but no . . . no . . . never. Tristan had more courage than I had.

Mr Mount turned away abruptly. 'This 'oss is in the stable,' he grunted.

In those late thirties the tractor had driven a lot of the draught horses from the land but most of the farmers kept a few around, perhaps because they had always worked horses and it was part of their way of life and maybe because of the sheer proud beauty of animals like the one which stood before me now.

It was a magnificent Shire gelding, standing all of eighteen hands. He was a picture of massively muscled power but when his master spoke, the great white-blazed face which turned to us was utterly docile.

The farmer slapped him on the rump. 'He's a good sort is Bobby and I think a bit about 'im. What ah noticed first was a strange smell about his hind feet and then ah had a look for meself. I've never seen owt like it.'

I bent and seized a handful of the long feathered hair behind the horse's pastern. Bobby did not resist as I lifted the huge spatulate foot and rested it on my knee. It seemed to occupy most of my lap but it was not the size which astonished me. Mr Mount had never seen owt like it and neither had I. The sole was a ragged, sodden mass with a stinking exudation oozing from the underrun horn, but what really bewildered me was the series of growths sprouting from every crevice.

They were like nightmare toadstools – long papillae with horny caps growing from the diseased surface. I had read about them in the books; they were called ergots, but I had never imagined them in such profusion. My thoughts raced as I moved behind the horse and lifted the other foot. It was just the same. Just as bad.

I had been qualified only a few months and was still trying to gain the confidence of the Darrowby farmers. This was just the sort of thing I didn't want.

'What is it ?' Mr Mount asked, and again I felt that unwinking gaze piercing me.

I straightened up and rubbed my hands. 'It's canker, but a very bad case.' I knew all about the theory of the thing, in fact I was bursting with theory, but putting it into practice with this animal was a bit different.

'How are you going to cure it ?' Mr Mount had an uncomfortable habit of going straight to the heart of things.

'Well, you see, all that loose horn and those growths will have to be cut away and then the surface dressed with caustic,' I replied, and it sounded easy when I said it.

'It won't get better on its own, then ?'

'No, if you leave it the sole will disintegrate and the pedal bone will come through. Also the discharge will work up under the wall of the hoof and cause separation.'

The farmer nodded. 'So he'd never walk again, and that would be the end of Bobby.'

'I'm afraid so.'

'Right, then.' Mr Mount threw up his head with a decisive gesture. 'When are you going to do it ?'

It was a nasty question, because I was preoccupied at that moment not so much with when I would do it but how I would do it.

'Well now, let's see,' I said huskily. 'Would it be . . .' The farmer broke in. 'We're busy hay-makin' all this week, and you'll be wantin' some men to help you. How about Monday next week?'

A wave of relief surged through me. Thank heavens he hadn't said tomorrow. I had a bit of time to think now.

'Very well, Mr Mount. That suits me fine. Don't feed him on the Sunday because he'll have to have an anaesthetic.'

Driving from the farm, a sense of doom oppressed me. Was I going to ruin that beautiful animal in my ignorance? Canker of the foot was unpleasant at any time and was not uncommon in the days of the draught horse, but this was something way out of the ordinary. No doubt many of my contemporaries have seen feet like Bobby's, but to the modern young veterinary surgeon it must be like a page from an ancient manual of farriery.

As is my wont when I have a worrying case I started mulling it over right away. As I drove, I rehearsed various procedures. Would that enormous horse go down with a chloroform muzzle? Or would I have to collect all Mr Mount's men and rope him and pull him down? But it would be like trying to pull down St Paul's Cathedral. And then how long would it take me to hack away all that horn – all those dreadful vegetations?

Within ten minutes my palms were sweating and I was tempted to throw the whole lot over to Siegfried. But I was restrained by the knowledge that I had to establish myself not only with the farmers but with my new boss. He wasn't going to think much of an assistant who couldn't handle a thing on his own.

I did what I usually did when I was worried: drove off the un-fenced road, got out of the car and followed a track across the moor. The track wound beneath the brow of the fell which over-looked the Mount farm and when I had left the road far behind I flopped on the grass and looked down on the sunlit valley floor a thousand feet below.

In most places you could hear something – the call of a bird, a car in the distance – but here there was a silence which was abso-lute, except when the wind sighed over the hilltop, rustling the bracken around me.

The farm lay in one of the soft places in a harsh countryside; lush flat fields where cattle grazed in comfort and the cut hay lay in long even swathes.

It was a placid scene, but it was up here in the airy heights that you found true serenity. Peace dwelt here in the high moorland, stealing across the empty miles, breathing from the silence and the tufted grass and the black, peaty earth.

The heady fragrance of the hay rose in the warm summer air and as always I felt my troubles dissolving. Even now, after all the years, I still count myself lucky that I can so often find tranquility of mind in the high places.

As I rose to go I was filled with a calm resolve. I would do the job somehow. Surely I could manage the thing without troubling Siegfried.

In any case Siegfried had other things on his mind when I met him over the lunch table.

'I looked in at Granville Bennett's surgery at Hartington this morning,' he said, helping himself to some new potatoes which had been picked that morning from the garden. 'And I must say I was very impressed with his waiting room. All those magazines. I know we don't have the numbers to cater for, but there's often a lot of farmers in there.' He poured gravy on to a corner of his plate. 'Tristan, I'll give you the job. Slip round to Garlow's and order a few suitable things to be delivered every week, will you?'

'Okay,' his student brother replied. 'I'll do it this afternoon.'

'Splendid.' Siegfried chewed happily. 'We must keep progressing in every way. Do have some more of these potatoes, James, they really are very good.'

Tristan went into action right away and within two days the table and shelves in our waiting room carried a tasteful selection of periodicals. The *Illustrated London News*, *Farmer's Weekly*, *The Farmer and Stockbreeder*, *Punch*. But as usual he had to embroider the situation.

'Look at this, Jim,' he whispered one afternoon, guiding me through the door. 'I've been having a little harmless sport.'

'What do you mean?' I looked around me uncomprehendingly.

Tristan said nothing, but pointed to one of the shelves. There, among the innocent journals was a German naturist magazine displaying a startling frontispiece of full frontal nudity. Even in these permissive days it would have caused a raised eyebrow but in rural Yorkshire in the thirties it was cataclysmic.

'Where the devil did you get this?' I gasped, leafing through it hurriedly. It was just the same inside. 'And what's the idea, anyway?'

Tristan repressed a giggle. 'A fellow at college gave it to me. And it's rather a lark to sneak in quietly and find some solid citizen having a peek when he thinks nobody's looking. I've had some very successful incursions. My best bags so far have been a town councillor, a Justice of the Peace and a lay preacher.'

I shook my head. 'I think you're sticking your neck out. What if Siegfried comes across it?'

'No fear of that,' he said. 'He rarely comes in here and he's always in too much of a hurry. Anyway, it's well out of the way.'

I shrugged. Tristan had been blessed with an agile intelligence which I envied, but so much of it was misapplied. However, at the moment I hadn't time for his tricks. My mind was feverishly preoccupied.

Mentally I had cast that horse by innumerable methods and operated on his feet a thousand times by night and day. In daylight, riding around in the car, it wasn't so bad, but the operations I carried out in bed were truly bizarre. All the time I had the feeling that something was wrong, that there was some fatal flaw in the picture of myself carving away those hideous growths in one session. Finally I buried my pride.

'Siegfried,' I said, one afternoon when the practice was slack. 'I have rather a weird horse case.'

My boss's eyes glinted and the mouth beneath the small sandy moustache crooked into a smile. The word 'horse' usually had this effect.

'Really, James? Tell me.'

I told him.

'Yes . . . yes . . .' he murmured. 'Maybe we'd better have a look together.'

The Mount farm was deserted when we arrived. Everybody was in the hayfields working frantically while the sunshine lasted.

'Where is he?' Siegfried asked.

'In here.' I led the way to the stable.

My boss lifted a hind foot and whistled softly. Then he moved round and examined the other one. For a full minute he gazed down at the obscene fungi thrusting from the tattered stinking horn. When he stood up he looked at me expressionlessly.

It was a few seconds before he spoke. 'And you were just going to pop round here on Monday, tip this big fellow on to the grass and do the job?'

'Yes,' I replied. 'That was the idea.'

A strange smile spread over my employer's face. It held something of wonder, sympathy, amusement and a tinge of admiration. Finally he laughed and shook his head.

'Ah, the innocence of youth,' he murmured.

'What do you mean?' After all, I was only six years younger than Siegfried.

He came over and patted my shoulder. 'I'm not mocking you, James. This is the worst case of canker I've ever seen and I've seen a few.'

'You mean I couldn't do it at one go?'

'That's exactly what I mean. There's six weeks' work here, James.'

'Six weeks...?'

'Yes, and there'll be three men involved. We'll have to get this horse into one of the loose boxes at Skeldale House and then the two of us plus a blacksmith will have a go at him. After that his feet will have to be dressed every day in the stocks.'

'I see.'

'Yes, yes.' Siegfried was warming to his subject. 'We'll use the strongest caustic – nitric acid – and he'll be shod with special shoes with a metal plate to exert pressure on the sole.' He stopped, probably because I was beginning to look bewildered, then he continued in a gentler tone. 'Believe me, James, all this is necessary. The alternative is to shoot a fine horse, because he can't go on much longer than this.'

I looked at Bobby, at the white face again turned towards us. The thought of a bullet entering that noble head was unbearable.

'All right, whatever you say, Siegfried,' I mumbled, and just then Mr Mount's vast bulk darkened the entrance to the stable.

'Ah, good afternoon to you, Mr Mount,' my boss said. 'I hope you're getting a good crop of hay.'

'Aye, thank ye, Mr Farnon. We're doing very nicely. We've been lucky with the weather.' The big man looked curiously from one of us to the other, and Siegfried went on quickly.

'Mr Herriot asked me to come and look at your horse. He's been thinking the matter over and has decided that it would be better to hospitalize him at our place for a few weeks. I must say I agree with him. It's a very bad case and the chances of a permanent cure would be increased.'

Bless you, Siegfried, I thought. I had expected to emerge from this meeting as the number one chump, but all was suddenly well. I congratulated myself, not for the first time, on having an employer who never let me down.

Mr Mount took off his hat and drew a forearm across his sweating brow. 'Aye well, if that's what you think, both of ye, we'd better do it. Ah want the best for Bobby. He's a favourite o' mine.'

'Yes, he's a grand sort, Mr Mount.' Siegfried went round the big animal, patting and stroking him, then as we walked back to the car he kept up an effortless conversation with the farmer. I had always found it difficult to speak to this formidable man, but in my colleague's presence he became quite chatty. In fact there were one or two occasions when he almost smiled.

Bobby came into the yard at Skeldale House the following day and when I saw the amount of sheer hard labour which the operation entailed I realized the utter impossibility of a single man doing it at one go.

Pat Jenner, the blacksmith, with his full tool kit was pressed into service and between us, taking it in turns, we removed all the vegetations and diseased tissue, leaving only healthy horn. Siegfried applied the acid to cauterize the area, then packed the sole with twists of tow which were held in place by the metal plate Pat had made to fit under the shoe. This pressure from the tow was essential to effect a cure.

After a week I was doing the daily dressings myself. This was when I began to appreciate the value of the stocks with their massive timbers sunk deep into the cobbles of the yard. It made everything so much easier when I was able to lead Bobby into the stocks, pull up a foot and make it fast in any position I wished.

Some days Pat Jenner came in to check on the shoes, and he and I were busy in the yard when I heard the familiar rattle of my little Austin in the back lane. The big double doors were open and I looked up as the car turned in and drew alongside us. Pat looked, too, and his eyes popped.

'Bloody 'ell!' he exclaimed, and I couldn't blame him, because the car had no driver. At least it looked that way since there was nobody in the seat as it swung in from the lane.

A driverless car in motion is quite a sight, and Pat gaped open-mouthed for a few seconds. Then just as I was about to explain, Tristan shot up from the floor with a piercing cry.

'Hi there!' he shrieked.

Pat dropped his hammer and backed away. 'God 'elp us!' he breathed.

I was unaffected by the performance because it was old stuff to me. Whenever I was in the yard and a call came in, Tristan would drive my car round from the front street and this happened so many times that inevitably he grew bored and tried to find a less orthodox method.

After a bit of practice he mastered the driverless technique. He crouched on the floor with a foot on the accelerator and one hand on the wheel and nearly frightened the life out of me the first time he did it. But I was used to it now, and blasé.

Within a few days I was able to observe another of Tristan's little jokes. As I turned the corner of the passage at Skeldale House I found him lurking by the waiting-room door which was slightly ajar.

'I think I've got a victim in there,' he whispered. 'Let's see what happens.' He gently pushed the door and tiptoed inside.

As I peeped through the crack I could see that he had indeed scored a success. A man was standing there with his back to him and he was poring over the nudist magazine with greatest absorption. As he slowly turned the pages his enthralment showed in the way he frequently moved the pictures towards the light from the french window, inclining his head this way and that to take in all the angles. He looked as though he would have been happy to spend all day there but when he heard Tristan's exquisitely timed cough he dropped the magazine as thought it was white hot, snatched hurriedly at the *Farmer's Weekly* and swung round.

That was when Tristan's victory went flat. It was Mr Mount.

The huge farmer loomed over him for a few seconds and the deep bass rumble came from between clenched teeth.

'It's you, is it?' He glanced quickly from the young man to the embarrassing magazine and back again and the eyes in the craggy face narrowed dangerously.

'Yes . . . yes . . . yes, Mr Mount,' Tristan replied unsteadily. 'And how are you, Mr Mount?'

'Ah'm awright.'

'Good . . . good . . . splendid.' Tristan backed away a few steps. 'And how is Deborah?'

The eyes beneath the sprouting bristles drew in further. 'She's awright.'

There was a silence which lingered interminably and I felt for my young friend. It was not a merry meeting.

At last he managed to work up a sickly smile. 'Ah well, yes, er . . . and what can we do for you, Mr Mount?'

'Ah've come to see me 'oss.'

'Yes indeed, of course, certainly. I believe Mr Herriot is just outside the room.'

I led the big man down the long garden into the yard. His encounter with Tristan had clearly failed to improve his opinion of the young man and he glowered as I opened the loose box.

But his expression softened when he saw Bobby eating hay contentedly. He went in and patted the arching neck. 'How's he goin' on then?'

'Oh, very well.' I lifted a hind foot and showed him the metal plate. 'I can take this off for you if you like.'

'Nay, nay, ah don't want to disturb the job. As long as all's well, that's all ah want to know.'

The dressings went on for a few more weeks till finally Siegfried was satisfied that the last remnants of the disease had been extirpated. Then he telephoned for Mr Mount to collect his horse the following morning.

It is always nice to be in on a little triumph, and I looked over my boss's shoulder as he lifted Bobby's feet and displayed the finished job to the owner. The necrotic jumble on the soles had been replaced by a clean, smooth surface with no sign of moisture anywhere.

Mr Mount was not enthusiastic by nature but he was obviously impressed. He nodded his head rapidly several times. 'Well now, that's champion. I'm right capped wi' that.'

Siegfried lowered the foot to the ground and straightened with a pleased smile. There was a general air of bonhomie in the yard, and then I heard my car in the back lane.

I felt a sudden tingle of apprehension. Oh no, Tristan, not this time, please. You don't know . . . My toes curled as I waited but I realized all was lost when the car turned in through the double doors. It had no driver.

With a dreadful feeling of imminent catastrophe I watched as it stopped within a few feet of Siegfried and Mr Mount who were staring at it in disbelief.

Nothing happened for a few seconds, then without warning Tristan catapulted like a jack-in-the-box into the open window.

'Yippeee!' he screeched, but his happy grin froze as he found himself gazing into the faces of his brother and Mr Mount. Siegfried's expression of exasperation was familiar to me, but the farmer's was infinitely more menacing. The eyes in the stony visage were mere slits, the jaw jutted, the great tangle of eyebrows bristled fiercely. There was no doubt he had finally made up his mind about Tristan.

I felt the young man had suffered enough, and I kept off the subject for a week or two afterwards, but we were sitting in the big room at Skeldale House when he mentioned casually that he wouldn't be taking Deborah out any more.

'Seems her father has forbidden it,' he said.

I shrugged in sympathy, but said nothing. After all, it had been an ill-starred romance from the beginning.


4


'Circuits and Bumps' they called it. Taking off, circling the field and landing, over and over and over. After an hour of it with FO Woodham in full voice I had had enough and it was a blessed relief when we climbed out at the end.

As my instructor walked away, one of his fellow officers

strolled by his side. 'How are you getting on with that chap, Woody?' he asked, smiling.

FO Woodham did not pause in his stride or turn his head. 'Oh, God!' he said with a hollow groan, and that was all.

I knew I wasn't meant to hear the words but they bit deep. My spirits did not rise till I entered the barrack hut and was greeted by the cheerful voices of my fellow airmen.

'Hello, Jim!' 'How's it going, Jim?' The words were like balm.

I looked around at the young men sprawled on their beds, reading or smoking and I realized that I needed them and their friendship.

Animals are the same. They need friends. Have you ever watched two animals in a field? They may be different species – a pony and a sheep – but they hang together. This comradeship between animals has always fascinated me, and I often think of Jack Sanders's two dogs as a perfect example of mutual devotion.

One of them was called Jingo and as I injected the local anaesthetic alongside the barbed wire tear in his skin the powerful bull terrier whimpered just once. Then he decided to resign himself to his fate and looked stolidly to the front as I depressed the plunger.

Meanwhile his inseparable friend, Skipper the corgi, gnawed gently at Jingo's hind leg. It was odd to see two dogs on the table at once, but I knew the relationship between them and made no comment as their master hoisted them both up.

After I had infiltrated the area around the wound I began to stitch and Jingo relaxed noticeably when he found that he could feel nothing.

'Maybe this'll teach you to avoid barbed wire fences in future, Jing,' I said.

Jack Sanders laughed. 'I doubt if it will, Mr Herriot. I thought the coast was clear when I took him down the lane this morning, but he spotted a dog on the other side of the fence and he was through like a bullet. Fortunately it was a greyhound and he couldn't catch it.'

'You're a regular terror, Jing.' I patted my patient, and the big Roman-nosed face turned to me with an ear-to-ear grin and at the other end the tail whipped delightedly.

'Yes, it's amazing, isn't it?' his master said. 'He's always looking for a fight, yet people and children can do anything with him. He's the best natured dog in the world.'

I finished stitching and dropped the suture needle into a kidney dish on the trolley. 'Well, you've got to remember that the bull terrier is the original English fighting dog and Jing is only obeying an age-old instinct.'

'Oh, I realize that. I'll just have to go on scanning the horizon every time I let him off the lead. No dog is safe from him.'

'Except this one, Jack.' I laughed and pointed to the little corgi who had tired of his companion's leg and was now chewing his ear.

'Yes, isn't it marvellous. I think he could bite Jing's ear off without reprisal.'

It was indeed rather wonderful. The corgi was eleven years old and beginning to show his age in stiffness of movement and impairment of sight, while the bull terrier was only three, at the height of his strength and power. A squat, barrel-chested bundle of bone and muscle, he was a formidable animal. But when the ear-chewing became too violent, all he did was turn and gently engulf Skipper's head in his huge jaws till the little animal desisted. Those jaws could be as merciless as a steel trap but they held the tiny head in a loving embrace.

Ten days later their master brought both dogs back to the surgery for the removal of the stitches. He looked worried as he lifted the animals on to the table.

'Jingo isn't at all well, Mr Herriot,' he said. 'He's been off his food for a couple of days and he looks miserable. Could that wound make him ill if it turned septic?'

'Yes it could, of course.' I looked down anxiously at the area of the flank where I had stitched, and my fingers explored the long scar. 'But there's not the slightest sign of infection here. No swelling, no pain. He's healed beautifully.'

I stepped back and looked at the bull terrier. He was strangely disconsolate, tail tucked down, eyes gazing ahead with total lack of interest. Not even the busy nibbling of his friend at one of his paws relieved his apathy.

Clearly Skipper didn't like being ignored in this fashion. He transferred his operations to the front end and started on the big dog's ear. As his efforts still went unnoticed he began to chew and tug harder, dragging the massive head down to one side, but as far as Jingo was concerned he might as well not have been there.

'Hey, that's enough, Skipper,' I said. 'Jing isn't in the mood for rough stuff today.' I lifted him gently to the floor where he paced indignantly around the table legs.

I examined the bull terrier thoroughly and the only significant finding was an elevated temperature.

'It's a hundred and five, Jack. He's very ill, there's no doubt about that.'

'But what's the matter with him?'

'With a high fever like that he must have some acute infection. But at the moment it's difficult to pinpoint.' I reached out and stroked the broad skull, running my fingers over the curving white face as my thoughts raced.

For an instant the tail twitched between his hocks and the friendly eyes rolled round to me and then to his master. It was that movement of the eyes which seized my whole attention. I quickly raised the upper lid. The conjunctiva appeared to be a normal pink, but in the smooth white sclera I could discern the faintest tinge of yellow.

'He's got jaundice,' I said. 'Have you noticed anything peculiar about his urine?'

Jack Sanders nodded. 'Yes, now you mention it. I saw him cock his leg in the garden and his water looked a bit dark.'

'Those are bile pigments.' I gently squeezed the abdomen and the dog winced slightly. 'Yes, he's definitely tender in there.'

'Jaundice?' His master stared at me across the table. 'Where would he get that?'

I rubbed my chin. 'Well, when I see a dog like this I think firstly of two things – phosphorus poisoning and leptospirosis. In view of the high temperature I go for the leptospirosis.'

'Would he catch it from another dog?'

'Possibly, but more likely from rats. Does he come into contact with any rats?'

'Yes, now and then. There's a lot of them in an old hen house at the foot of the lane and Jing sometimes gets in there after them.'

'Well, that's it.' I shrugged. 'I don't think we need to look any further for the cause.'

He nodded slowly. 'Anyway, it's something to know what's wrong with him. Now you can set about putting him right.'

I looked at him for a moment in silence. It wasn't like that at all. I didn't want to upset him, but on the other hand he was a highly intelligent and sensible man in his forties, a teacher at the local school. I felt I had to tell him the whole truth.

'Jack,' I said. 'This is a terrible condition to treat. If there's one thing I hate to see it's a jaundiced dog.'

'You mean it's serious ?'

'I'm afraid so. In fact the mortality rate is very high.'

I felt for him when I saw the sudden pain and concern in his face, but a warning now was better than a shock later, because I knew that Jingo could be dead within a few days. Even now, thirty years later, I quail when I see that yellowish discoloration in a dog's eyes. Penicillin and other antibiotics have some effect against the causal organism of leptospirosis but the disease is still very often fatal.

'I see . . . I see . . .' He was collecting his thoughts. 'But surely you can do something ?'

'Yes, yes, of course,' I said briskly. 'I'm going to give him a big shot of antileptospiral serum and some medicine to administer by the mouth. It isn't completely hopeless.'

I injected the serum in the knowledge that it didn't have much effect at this stage, but I had nothing else to offer. I gave Skipper a shot, too, with the happier feeling that it would protect him against the infection.

'One thing more, Jack,' I added. 'This disease also affects humans, so please take all hygienic precautions when handling Jingo. All right ?'

He nodded and lifted the bull terrier from the table. The big dog, as most of my patients do, tried to hurry away from the disturbing white-coat-and-antiseptic atmosphere of the surgery. As he trotted along the passage his master turned to me eagerly.

'Look at that! He doesn't seem too bad, does he ?'

I didn't say anything. I hoped with all my heart that he was right, but I was fighting off the conviction that this nice animal was doomed. At any rate I would soon know.

I knew, in fact, next day. Jack Sanders was on the phone before nine o'clock in the morning.

'Jing's not so good,' he said, but the tremor in his voice belied the lightness of his words.

'Oh.' I experienced the familiar drooping of the spirits. 'What is he doing?'

'Nothing, I'm afraid. Won't eat a thing . . . lying around . . . just lifeless. And every now and then he vomits.'

It was what I expected, but I still felt like kicking the desk by my side. 'Very well, I'll be right round.'

There were no tail wags from Jing today. He was crouched before the fire, gazing listlessly into the coals. The yellow in his eyes had deepened to a rich orange and his temperature still soared. I repeated the serum injection, but the big dog did not heed the entry of the needle. Before I left I ran my hand over the smooth white body and Skipper as ever kept burrowing in on his friend, but Jingo's thoughts were elsewhere, sunk in his inner misery.

I visited him daily and on the fourth day I found him stretched almost comatose on his side. The conjunctiva, sclera, and the mucous membranes of the mouth were a dirty chocolate colour.

'Is he suffering?' Jack Sanders asked.

I hesitated for a moment. 'I honestly don't think he's in pain. Sickness, nausea, yes, but I'd say that's all.'

'Well, I'd like to keep on trying,' he said. 'I don't want to put him down even though you think it's hopeless. You do . . . don't you?'

I made a non-committal gesture. I was watching Skipper who seemed bewildered. He had given up his worrying tactics and was sniffing round his friend in a puzzled manner. Only once did he pull very gently at the unresponsive ear.

I went through the motions with a feeling of helplessness and left with the unpleasant intuition that I would never see Jingo alive again.

And even though I was waiting for it, Jack Sanders' phone call next morning was a bad start to the day.

'Jing died during the night, Mr Herriot. I thought I'd better let you know. You said you were coming back this morning.' He was trying to be matter-of-fact.

'I'm sorry, Jack,' I said. 'I did rather expect...'

'Yes, I know. And thank you for what you did.'

It made it worse when people were nice at these times. The Sanders were a childless couple and devoted to their animals. I knew how he was feeling.

I stood there with the receiver in my hand. 'Anyway, Jack, you've still got Skipper.' It sounded a bit lame, but it did help to have the comfort of one remaining dog, even though he was old.

'That's right,' he replied. 'We're very thankful for Skipper.'

I went on with my work. Patients died sometimes and once it was over it was almost a relief, especially when I knew in Jingo's case that the end was inevitable.

But this thing wasn't over. Less than a week later Jack Sanders was on the phone again.

'It's Skipper,' he said. 'He seems to be going the same way as Jing.'

A cold hand took hold of my stomach and twisted it.

'But... but... he can't be! I gave him the protective injection!'

'Well, I don't know, but he's hanging around miserably and hardly eats a thing. He seems to be going down fast.'

I ran out and jumped into my car. And as I drove to the edge of the town where the Sanders lived my heart thudded and panicky thoughts jostled around in my mind. How could he have got the infection? I had little faith in the serum as a cure but as a prevention I felt it was safe. I had even given him a second shot to make sure. The idea of these people losing both their dogs was bad enough but I couldn't bear the thought that the second one might be my fault.

The little corgi trailed unhappily across the carpet when he saw me and I lifted him quickly on to the kitchen table. I almost snatched at his eyelids in my anxiety but there was no sign of jaundice in the sclera nor in the mucous membranes of the mouth. The temperature was dead normal and I felt a wave of relief.

'He hasn't got leptospirosis, anyway,' I said.

Mrs Sanders clasped her hands. 'Oh, thank God for that. We were sure it was the same thing. He looks so awful.'

I examined the little animal meticulously and when I finished I put my stethoscope in my pocket. 'Well, I can't find much wrong here. He's got a bit of a heart murmur but you've known that for some time. He's old, after all.'

'Do you think he could be fretting for Jing?' Jack Sanders asked.

'Yes, I do. They were such friends. He must feel lost.'

'But he'll get over that, won't he?'

'Oh, of course he will. I'll leave some mild sedative tablets for him and I'm sure they'll help.'

I met Jack a few days later in the market place.

'How is Skipper?' I asked.

He blew out his cheeks. 'About the same. Maybe a bit worse. The trouble is he eats practically nothing – he's getting very thin.'

I didn't see what else I could do but on the following day I looked in at the Sanders' as I was passing.

I was shocked at the little corgi's appearance. Despite his age he had been so cocky and full of bounce, and when Jing was alive he had been indisputably the boss dog. But now he was utterly deflated. He looked at me with lack-lustre eyes as I came in, then crept stiffly to his basket where he curled himself as though wishing to shut out the world.

I examined him again. The heart murmur seemed a little more pronounced but there was nothing else except that he looked old and decrepit and done.

'You know, I'm beginning to wonder if he really is fretting.' I said. 'It could be just his age catching up on him. After all, he'll be twelve in the spring, won't he?'

Mrs Sanders nodded. 'That's right. Then you think . . . this could be the end?'

'It's possible.' I knew what she was thinking. A couple of weeks ago two healthy dogs rolling around and playing in this house and now there could soon be none.

'But isn't there anything else you can do?'

'Well, I can give him a course of digitalis for his heart. And perhaps you would bring in a sample of his urine. I want to see how his kidneys are functioning.'

I tested the urine. There was a little albumen, but no more than you would expect in a dog of his age. I ruled out nephritis as a cause.

As the days passed I tried other things; vitamins, iron tonics, organo-phosphates, but the little animal declined steadily. It was about a month after Jing's death that I called to the house again.

Skipper was in his basket and when I called to him he slowly raised his head. His face was pinched and fleshless and the filmed eyes regarded me without recognition.

'Come on, lad,' I said encouragingly. 'Let's see you get out of there.'

Jack Sanders shook his head. 'It's no good, Mr Herriot. He never leaves his basket now and when we lift him out he's almost too weak to walk. Another thing . . . he makes a mess down here in the kitchen during the night. That's something he's never done.'

It was like the tolling of a sad bell. Everything he said pointed to a dog in the last stages of senility. I tried to pick my words.

'I'm sorry, Jack, but it all sounds as if the old chap has come to the end of the road. I don't think fretting could possibly cause all this.'

He didn't speak for a moment. He looked at his wife then down at the forlorn little creature. 'Well, of course, this has been in the back of our minds. But we've kept hoping he would start to eat. What . . . what do you suggest?'

I could not bring myself to say the fateful words. 'It seems to me that we can't stand by and let him suffer. He's just a little skeleton and I can't think he's getting any pleasure out of his life now.'

'I see,' he said. 'And I agree. He lies there all day – he has no interest in anything.' He paused and looked at his wife again. 'I tell you what, Mr Herriot. Let us think it over till tomorrow. But you do think there's no hope?'

'Yes, Jack, I do. Old dogs often go this way at the end. Skipper has just cracked up . . . he's finished, I'm afraid.'

He drew a long breath. 'Right, if you don't hear from me by eight o'clock tomorrow morning, please come and put him to sleep.'

I had small hope of the call coming and it didn't. In those early days of our marriage Helen worked as a secretary for one of the local millers. We often started our day together by descending the long flights of stairs from our bed-sitter and I would see her out of the front door before getting ready for my round.

This morning she gave me her usual kiss before going out into the street but then she looked at me searchingly. 'You've been quiet all through breakfast, Jim. What's the matter?'

'It's nothing, really. Just part of the job,' I said. But when she kept her steady gaze on me I told her quickly about the Sanders.

She touched my arm. 'It's such a shame, Jim, but you can't let your sad cases depress you. You'd never survive.'

'Aagh, I know that. But I'm a softy, that's my trouble. Sometimes I think I should never have been a vet.'

'You're wrong there,' she said. 'I couldn't imagine you as anything else. You'll do what you have to do, and you'll do it the right way.' She kissed me again, turned and ran down the steps.

It was mid-morning before I drew up outside the Sanders' home. I opened the car boot and took out the syringe and the bottle of concentrated anaesthetic which would give the old dog a peaceful and painless end.

The first thing I saw when I went into the kitchen was a fat white puppy waddling across the floor.

I looked down in astonishment. 'What's this . . . ?'

Mrs Sanders gave me a strained smile, 'Jack and I had a talk yesterday. We couldn't bear the idea of not having a dog at all, so we went round to Mrs Palmer who bred Jing and found she had a litter for sale. It seemed like fate. We've called him Jingo, too.'

'What a splendid idea!' I lifted the pup which squirmed in my hand, grunted in an obese manner and tried to lick my face. This, I felt, would make my unpleasant task easier. 'I think you've been very sensible.'

I lifted the bottle of anaesthetic unobtrusively from my pocket and went over to the basket in the corner. Skipper was still curled in the unheeding ball of yesterday and the comforting thought came to me that all I was going to do was push him a little further along the journey he had already begun.

I pierced the rubber diaphragm on the bottle with my needle and was about to withdraw the barbiturate when I saw that Skipper had raised his head. Chin resting on the edge of the basket, he seemed to be watching the pup. Wearily his eyes followed the tiny creature as it made its way to a dish of milk and began to lap busily. And there was something in his intent expression which had not been there for a long time.

I stood very still as the corgi made a couple of attempts then heaved himself to a standing position. He almost fell out of the basket and staggered on shaking legs across the floor. When he came alongside the pup he remained there, swaying, for some time, a gaunt caricature of his former self, but as I watched in disbelief, he reached forward and seized the little white ear in his mouth.

Stoicism is not a characteristic of pups and Jingo the Second yelped shrilly as the teeth squeezed. Skipper, undeterred, continued to gnaw with rapt concentration.

I dropped bottle and syringe back in my pocket. 'Bring him some food,' I said quietly.

Mrs Sanders hurried to the pantry and came back with a few pieces of meat on a saucer. Skipper continued his ear-nibbling for a few moments then sniffed the pup unhurriedly from end to end before turning to the saucer. He hardly had the strength to chew but he lifted a portion of meat and his jaws moved slowly.

'Good heavens!' Jack Sanders burst out. 'That's the first thing he's eaten for days!'

His wife seized my arm. 'What's happened, Mr Herriot? We only got the puppy because we couldn't have a house without a dog.'

'Well, it looks to me as though you've got two again.' I went over to the door and smiled back at the two people watching fascinated as the corgi swallowed then started determinedly on another piece of meat. 'Good morning, I'm going now.'

About eight months later, Jack Sanders came into the surgery and put Jingo Two on the table. He was growing into a fine animal with the wide chest and powerful legs of the breed. His good-natured face and whipping tail reminded me strongly of his predecessor.

'He's got a bit of eczema between his pads,' Jack said, then he bent and lifted Skipper up.

At that moment I had no eyes for my patient. All my attention was on the corgi, plump and bright-eyed, nibbling at the big dog's hind limbs with all his old bounce and vigour.

'Just look at that!' I murmured. 'It's like turning the clock back.'

Jack Sanders laughed. 'Yes, isn't it. They're tremendous friends – just like before.'

'Come here, Skipper.' I grabbed the little corgi and looked him over. When I had finished I held him for a moment as he tried to wiggle his way back to his friend. 'Do you know, I honestly think he'll go on for years yet.'

'Really?' Jack Sanders looked at me with a mischievous light in his eyes. 'But I seem to remember you saying quite a long time ago that his days were over – he was finished.'

I held up a hand, 'I know, I know. But sometimes it's lovely to be wrong.'


# 5


'That young Herriot's a bloody thick-'ead.'

It wasn't the sort of statement to raise one's morale and for a moment the good ale turned to vinegar in my mouth. I was having a quiet pint all alone in the 'snug' of the Crown and Anchor on my way home from an evening colic case, and the words came clearly through the hatch from the public bar.

I suppose it was the fact that I had come to the conclusion that my flying instructor, FO Woodham, considered me to be a person of low intelligence that brought the incident back to my mind.

I shifted my position slightly so that I could see into the brightly lit room. The speaker was Seth Pilling, a casual labourer and a well-known character in Darrowby. He was designated a labourer, but in truth he didn't labour unduly and his burly frame and red meaty face was a common sight around the Labour Exchange where he signed for his unemployment pay.

'Aye, 'e's got no idea. Knaws nowt about dogs.' The big man tipped about half a pint over his throat in one swallow.

'He's not a bad hand wi' cows,' another voice broke in.

'Aye, maybe, but I'm not talkin' about bloody awd cows,' Seth retorted witheringly. 'I'm talkin' about dogs. Ye need skill to doctor dogs.'

A third man spoke up. 'Well, 'e's a vitnery, isn't he?'

'Aye, a knaw he is, but there's all kind o' vitneries and this 'un's a dead loss. Ah could tell ye some tales about this feller.'

They say an eavesdropper never hears anything good about himself, and I knew the sensible thing would be to get out of there immediately rather than hear this man vilifying me in a crowded bar. But of course I didn't get out. I stayed, morbidly fascinated, listening with every nerve and fibre.

'What sort o' tales, Seth?' The company was as interested as I was.

'Well,' he replied. 'There's many a time folks 'ave brought dogs to me that he's made a mess of.'

'Tha knaws all about dogs, doesn't tha, Seth?'

It was perhaps wishful thinking that made me imagine a touch of sarcasm in the last remark, but if it were so it was lost on Mr Pilling. His big, stupid face creased into a self-satisfied smirk.

'Ah'll tell ye there's not a lot ah don't know about 'em. I've been among 'em all me life and I've studied t'job, too.' He slurped down more beer. 'I've got a houseful o' books and read 'em all. Ah ken everythin' about them diseases and the remedies.'

Another of the men in the bar spoke. 'Have you ever been beat wi' a dog job, Seth?'

There was a pause. 'Well, ah'm not goin' to say I never 'ave,' he said judicially. 'It's very rare I'm beat, but if I am I don't go to Herriot.' He shook his head. 'Nay, nay, ah slip through to Brawton and consult wi' Dennaby Broome. He's a big friend o' mine.'

In the quiet of the snug I sipped at my glass. Dennaby Broome was one of the many 'quacks' who flourished in those days. He had started in the building trade – as a plasterer to be exact – and had gravitated mysteriously and without formal training into the field of veterinary science where he now made a comfortable living.

I had nothing against him for that – we all have to live. In any case he rarely bothered me because Brawton was mainly outside our practice orbit, but my colleagues around there used some unkind words about him. I had a private conviction that a lot of his success was due to his resounding name. To me, the very words 'Dennaby Broome' were profoundly imposing.

'Aye, that's what ah do,' Seth continued. 'Dennaby and me's big friends and we oft consult about dogs. Matter of fact ah took me own dog to 'im once – he looks well, eh?'

I stood on tiptoe and peered into the bar. I could just see Seth's keeshound sitting at his feet. A handsome creature with a luxuriant glossy coat. The big man leaned over and patted the fox-like head. 'He's a vallible animal is that. Ah couldn't trust 'im to a feller like Herriot.'

'What's the matter wi' Herriot, any road?' somebody asked.

'Well, ah'll tell tha.' Seth tapped his head. 'He hasn't got ower much up 'ere.'

I didn't want to hear any more. I put down my glass and stole out into the night.

After that experience I took more notice of Seth Pilling. He was often to be seen strolling round the town because, despite his vast store of knowledge on many subjects, he was frequently out of work. He wasn't an expert only on dogs – he pontificated in the Crown and Anchor on politics, gardening, cage birds, agriculture, the state of the economy, cricket, fishing and many other matters. There were few topics which his wide intellect did not effortlessly embrace, so that it was surprising that employers seemed to dispense with his services after a very brief period.

He usually took his dog with him on his strolls, and the attractive animal began to appear to me as a symbol of my shortcomings. Instinctively I kept out of his way but one morning I came right up against him.

It was at the little shelter in the market place and a group of people were waiting for the Brawton bus. Among them was Seth Pilling and the keeshound, and as I passed within a few feet of them on my way to the post office I stopped involuntarily and stared. The dog was almost unrecognizable.

The dense, off-standing ash-grey coat I knew so well had become sparse and lustreless. The thick ruff, so characteristic of the breed, had shrunk to nothing.

'You're lookin' at me dog ?' Mr Pilling tightened the lead and pulled the little animal towards him protectively as though he feared I might put my contaminated hand on him.

'Yes . . . I'm sorry, but I couldn't help noticing. He has a skin condition . . . ?'

The big man looked down his nose at me. 'Aye, 'e has, a bit. I'm just takin' him through to Brawton to see Dennaby Broome.'

'I see.'

'Yes, ah thought ah'd better take 'im to somebody as knows summat about dogs.' He smirked as he looked around at the people in the shelter who were listening with interest. 'He's a vallible dog is that.'

'I'm sure he is,' I said.

He raised his voice further. 'Mind you, ah've been givin' him some of me own treatment.' He didn't have to tell me. There was a strong smell of tar, and the dog's hair was streaked with some oily substance. 'But it's maybe better to make sure. We're lucky to 'ave a man like Dennaby Broome to turn to.'

'Quite.'

He looked around his audience appreciatively. 'Especially with a vallible dog like this. You can't 'ave any Tom Dick or Harry muckin' around with 'im.'

'Well,' I said. 'I hope you get him put right.'

'Oh, ah will.' The big man was enjoying the interlude, and he laughed. 'Don't *you* worry about *that*.'

This little session did not enliven my day, but it gave me more reason to watch out for Mr Pilling. For the next two weeks I observed his movements with the deepest interest because his dog was losing its hair at an alarming rate. Not only that, but the animal's whole demeanour had changed and instead of tripping along in his old sprightly way he dragged one foot after another as though he were on the point of death.

Towards the end of the period I was horrified to see the big man with something like a shorn ewe on the end of the lead. It was all that was left of the beautiful keeshound, but as I started to walk towards him his master spotted me and hurried off in the opposite direction, dragging the unfortunate animal behind him.

I did, however, succeed in having a look at the dog a few days afterwards. He was in the waiting room at Skeldale House, and this time he was accompanied by his mistress instead of his master.

Mrs Pilling was sitting very upright, and when I asked her to come through to the consulting room she jumped to her feet, marched past me and stumped quickly along the passage in front of me.

She was quite small, but broad hipped and stocky, and she always walked rapidly, her head nodding forward aggressively at each step, her jaw thrust out. She never smiled.

I had heard it said that Seth Pilling was a big talker outside, but under his own roof he was scared to death of his little wife. And as the tight-mouthed fiery-eyed face turned to me I could believe it.

She bent, pushed powerful arms under the keeshound and hoisted him on to the table.

'Just look at me dog, Mr Herriot!' She rapped out.

I looked. 'Good heavens!' I gasped.

The little animal was almost completely bald. His skin was dry, scaly and wrinkled, and his head hung down as though he were under sedation.

'Aye, you're surprised, aren't you?' she barked. 'And no wonder. He's in a terrible state, isn't he?'

'I'm afraid so. I wouldn't have known him.'

'No, nobody would. Ah think the world 'o this dog and just look at 'im!' She paused and snorted a few times. 'And I know who's responsible, don't you?'

'Well...'

'Oh, you do. It's that husband o' mine.' She paused and glared at me, breathing rapidly. 'What d'you think of my husband, Mr Herriot?'

'I really don't know him very well. I...'

'Well, ah know 'im and he's a gawp. He's a great gawp. Knows everything and knows nowt. He's played around wi' me good dog till he's ruined 'im.'

I didn't say anything. I was studying the keeshound. It was the first time I had been able to observe him closely and I was certain I knew the cause of the trouble.

Mrs Pilling stuck her jaw out further and continued.

'First me husband said it was eczema. Is it?'

'No.'

'Then 'e said it was mange. Is it?'

'No.'

'D'you know what it is?'

'Yes.'

'Well, will you tell me please?'

'It's myxoedema.'

'Myx...?'

'Wait a minute,' I said. 'I'll just make absolutely sure.' I reached for my stethoscope and put it on the dog's chest. And the bradycardia was there as I expected, the slow, slow heartbeat of hypothyroidism. 'Yes, that's it. Not a shadow of a doubt about it.'

'What did you call it?'

'Myxoedema. It's a thyroid deficiency – there's a gland in his neck which isn't doing its job properly.'

'And that makes 'is hair fall out?'

'Oh yes. And it also causes this typical scaliness and wrinkling of the skin.'

'Aye, but he's half asleep all t'time. How about that?'

'Another classical symptom. Dogs with this condition become very lethargic – lose all their energy.'

She reached out and touched the dog's skin, bare and leathery where once the coat had grown in bushy glory. 'And can you cure it?'

'Yes.'

'Now Mr Herriot, don't take this the wrong way, but could you be mistaken? Are ye positive it's this myxi-whatever-it-is?'

'Of course I am. It's a straightforward case.'

'Straightforward to you, maybe.' She flushed and appeared to be grinding her teeth. 'But not straightforward to that clever husband o' mine. The great lubbert! When ah think what he's put me good dog through – ah could kill 'im.'

'Well, I suppose he thought he was acting for the best, Mrs Pilling.'

'Ah don't care what he thought, he's made this poor dog suffer, the big fool. Wait till ah get hold of 'im.'

I gave her a supply of tablets. 'These are thyroid extract, and I want you to give him one night and morning.' I also handed her a bottle of potassium iodide which I had found helpful in these cases.

She looked at me doubtfully. 'But surely he'll want summat rubbed on 'is skin.'

'No,' I replied. 'Applications to the skin do no good at all.'

'Then you mean.' She turned a dark purple colour and began snorting again. 'You mean all them bottles o' filthy stuff me husband put on 'im were a waste o' time ?'

'Afraid so.'

'Oh, ah'll murder 'im!' she burst out. 'Mucky, oily rubbish, it was. And that fancy feller in Brawton sent some 'orrible lotion – yeller it was, and stank the place out. Ruined me carpets and good chair covers an' all!'

Sulphur, whale oil and creosote, I thought. Splendid old-fashioned ingredients, but quite useless in this case and definitely antisocial.

Mrs Pilling heaved the keeshound to the floor and strode along the passage, head down, powerful shoulders hunched. I could hear her muttering to herself as she went.

'By gaw, just wait till ah get home. Ah'll sort 'im, by gaw ah will!'

I was naturally interested in the progress of my patient, and when I failed to see him around for the next fortnight I could only conclude that Seth Pilling was keeping out of my way. Indeed there was one occasion when I thought I saw him and the dog disappearing down an alley, but I couldn't be sure.

When I did see them both it was by accident. I was driving round the corner into the market place and I came upon a man and dog coming away from one of the stalls on the cobbles.

And as I peered through the window I caught my breath. Even in that short space of time the animal's skin was covered with a healthy down of new hair, and he was stepping out with something like his old vitality.

His master swung round as I slowed down. He gave me a single hunted look then tugged on the lead and scuttled away.

I could only imagine the turmoil in his mind, the conflict of emotions. No doubt he wanted to see his dog recover, but not this way. And as it turned out, the dice were loaded against the poor man because this was an unbelievably rapid recovery. I have seen some spectacular cures in myxoedema, but none so dramatic as that keeshound.

Mr Pilling's sufferings were communicated to me in various ways. For instance I heard he had changed his pub and now went to the Red Bear of an evening. In a little place like Darrowby, news fairly crackles around and I had a good idea that the farm men in the Crown and Anchor would have had a bit of quiet Yorkshire sport with the expert.

But his main martyrdom was at home. It was about six weeks after I had finished treating the dog that Mrs Pilling brought him to the surgery.

As before, she lifted him easily on to the table and looked at me, her face as always grim and unsmiling.

'Mr Herriot,' she said. 'Ah've just come to say thank ye, and ah thought you'd be interested to see me dog now.'

'I am indeed, Mrs Pilling. It's nice of you to come.' I gazed wonderingly at the thick coat, bushy, shining and new, and at the sparkling eyes and alert expression. 'I think you can say he's about back to normal.'

She nodded. 'That's what I thought and ah'm grateful to ye for what you've done.'

I walked with her to the front door and as she led her dog on to the street she turned her tough little face to me again. As the stern eyes met mine she looked very menacing.

'There's one thing,' she said. 'Ah'll never forgive that man o' mine for what he did to me dog. By gum, I've given 'im some stick, the great goof! He'll never hear the last of it from me.'

As she made off down the street, the little animal trotting briskly by her side, I brimmed with pleasant emotions. It is always warming to see a case recover so well, but in this instance there was an additional bonus.

For a long time little Mrs Pilling was going to give her husband pure hell.

# 6

'Today,' said FO Woodham, 'we're going to try a few new things. Spinning, sideslipping and how to come out of a stall.' His voice was gentle, and before he pulled on his helmet he turned his dark, fine-featured face towards me and smiled. Walking over the grass I thought what a likeable chap he was. I could have made a friend of him.

But he was always like that on the ground. He was altogether different in the air.

Yet I could never understand it. Flying was no trouble at all, and as we spun and dropped and soared about the summer sky his instructions appeared simple and easy to carry out. But the rot, as always, began to set in very soon.

'Didn't I tell you opposite rudder and stick to sideslip?' he bawled over the intercom.

'Yes, sir,' was all I replied, instead of the more appropriate, 'That's just what I'm doing, you stupid bugger!' which I might have used in civil life.

The goggled eyes bulged in the mirror. 'Well, why the bloody hell aren't you doing it?' His voice rose to a wild shriek.

'Sorry, sir.'

'Well, take her up. We'll try again. And for God's sake keep your wits about you!'

It was the same with the spins and stalls. I hadn't the slightest difficulty in pulling out of them but at times I thought my instructor was going out of his mind.

Berserk cries rang in my ears. 'Full opposite rudder and centralize the stick! Centralize it! Can't you hear me? Oh God, God!'

And of course the panic gradually crept in and I began to crack. One moment I could see a railway station in front of me whirling around in crazy circles, then there was nothing but the empty heavens and within seconds fields and trees would start to rush at me. Everything kept changing bewilderingly except the enraged eyes in the mirror and the exasperated yells.

'Centralize it, you bloody fool! Keep your eye on that cloud!

Watch your artificial horizon! Don't you know what the altimeter's for? I told you to keep at one thousand feet but it's like talking to a bloody wall!'

After a while a kind of numbness took over and the words rang meaninglessly in my head, one sentence seeming to contradict another. Desperately I tried to sort out the volleys of advice, but the whole thing began to slip from my grasp.

I had felt like this somewhere before. There was a familiar ring about this jumble in my brain. Then it came back to me. It was like being back at the Birtwhistles.

The trouble with the Birtwhistles was that they all spoke at once. Mr Birtwhistle invariably discussed his livestock, his wife concentrated on family matters and Len, their massive eighteen-year-old son, talked of nothing but football.

I was examining Nellie, the big white cow that always stood opposite the doorway in the grey stone byre. She had been lame for over a week and I didn't like the look of her.

'Lift her foot, will you, Len,' I said. It was wonderful to have a muscular giant to hoist the hind limb instead of going through the tedious business of hauling it up with a rope over a beam.

With the cloven hoof cradled in the great hands I could see that my fears were realized. The space between the cleats was clear but there was a significant swelling around the interphalangeal joint.

I looked up from my stooping position. 'Can you see that, Mr Birtwhistle? The infection is spreading upwards.'

'Aye . . . aye . . .' The farmer thrust a finger against the tumefied area and Nellie flinched. 'It's goin' up her leg on that side right enough. Ah thought it was nowt but a bit o' foul and I've been puttin' . . .'

'By gaw,' Len interjected. 'The lads 'ad a good win against Hellerby on Saturday. Johnnie Nudd got another couple o' goals and . . .'

' . . . puttin' that caustic lotion between 'er cleats.' Mr Birtwhistle didn't appear to have heard his son, but it was always like that. 'Done it regular night and mornin'. And ah'll tell ye the best way to do it. Get a hen feather an' . . .'

' . . . ah wouldn't be surprised if 'e scores a few more this

Saturday,' continued Len unheedingly. 'He's a right bobby dazzler when 'e . . .'

'. . . ye just dip it in t'lotion and push the feather in between t'cleats. It works like a . . .'

'. . . gets that ball on 'is right foot. He just whacks 'em in . . .'

I raised a hand. 'Wait a minute. You must realize this cow hasn't got foul. She has suppurative arthritis in this little joint just at the coronet here. I don't want to use a lot of big words but she has pus – matter – right inside the joint cavity, and it's a very nasty thing.'

Mr Birtwhistle nodded slowly. 'Sort of a abscess, you mean ? Well, maybe it ud be best to lance it. Once you let t'matter out it would . . .'

'. . . just like a rocket,' went on Len. 'Ah'll tell ye, Johnnie could get a trial for Darlington one o' these days and then . . .'

I always think it is polite to look at a person when they are talking to you, but it is difficult when they are both talking at once, especially when one of them is bent double and the other standing behind you.

'Thank you, Len,' I said. 'You can put her foot down now.' I straightened up and directed my gaze somewhere between them. 'The trouble with this condition is that you can't just stick a knife into it and relieve it. Very often the smooth surfaces of the joint are eaten away and it's terribly painful.'

Nellie would agree with me. It was the outside cleat which was affected and she was standing with her leg splayed sideways in an attempt to take the weight on the healthy inner digit.

The farmer asked the inevitable question. 'Well, what are we goin' to do ?'

I had an uncomfortable conviction that it wasn't going to make much difference what we did, but I had to make an effort.

'We'll give her a course of sulphanilamide powders and I also want you to put a poultice on that foot three times daily.'

'Poultice ?' The farmer brightened. 'Ah've been doin' that. Ah've been . . .'

'If Darlington signed Johnnie Nudd I reckon . . .'

'Hold on, Len,' I said. 'What poultice have you been using, Mr Birtwhistle ?'

'Cow shit,' the farmer replied confidently. 'Ye can't beat a good cow shit poultice to bring t'bad out. Ah've used it for them bad cases o' . . .'

'. . . ah'd have to go through to Darlington now and then instead of watchin' the Kestrels,' Len broke in. 'Ah'd have to see how Johnnie was gettin' on wi' them professionals because . . .'

I managed a twisted smile. I like football myself and I found it touching that Len ignored the great panorama of league football to concentrate on a village team who played in front of about twenty spectators. 'Yes, yes, Len, I quite understand how you feel.' Then I turned to his father. 'I was thinking of a rather different type of poultice, Mr Birtwhistle.'

The farmer's face lengthened and the corners of his mouth drooped. 'Well, ah've never found owt better than cow shit and ah've been among stock all me life.'

I clenched my teeth. This earthy medicament was highly regarded among the Dales farmers of the thirties and the damnable thing was that it often achieved its objective. There was no doubt that a sackful of bovine faeces applied to an inflamed area set up a tremendous heat and counter-irritation. In those days I had to go along with many of the ancient cures and keep my tongue between my teeth but I never prescribed cow shit and I wasn't going to start now.

'Maybe so,' I said firmly, 'but what I was thinking of was kaolin. You could call down at the surgery for some. You just heat the tin in a pan of hot water and apply the poultice to the foot. It keeps its heat for several hours.'

Mr Birtwhistle showed no great enthusiasm so I tried again.

'Or you could use bran. I see you've got a sack over there.'

He cheered up a little. 'Aye . . . that's right.'

'Okay, put on some hot bran three times a day and give her the powders and I'll see her again in a few days.' I knew the farmer would do as I said, because he was a conscientious stockman, but I had seen cases like this before and I wasn't happy. Nothing seems to pull a good cow down quicker than a painful foot. Big fat animals could be reduced to skeletons within weeks because of the agony of septic arthritis. I could only hope.

'Very good, Mr Herriot,' Mr Birtwhistle said. 'And now come into the house. T'missus has a cup o' tea ready for you.'

I seldom refuse such an invitation but as I entered the kitchen I knew this was where the going got really tough.

'Now then, Mr Herriot,' the farmer's wife said, beaming as she handed me a steaming mug. 'I was talkin' to your good lady in the market place yesterday, and she said . . .'

'And ye think them powders o' yours might do the trick?' Her husband looked at me seriously. 'I 'ope so, because Nellie's a right good milker. Ah reckon last lactation she gave . . .'

'Kestrels is drawn agin Dibham in t'Hulton cup.' Len chimed in. 'It'll be some game. Last time . . .'

Mrs Birtwhistle continued without drawing breath. '. . . you were nicely settled in at top of Skeldale House. It must be right pleasant up there with the lovely view and . . .'

'. . . five gallons when she fust calved and she kept it up for . . .'

'. . . they nearly kicked us off t'pitch, but by gaw ah'll tell ye, we'll . . .'

'. . . you can see right over Darrowby. But it wouldn't do for a fat body like me. I was sayin' to your missus that you 'ave to be young and slim to live up there. All them stairs and . . .'

I took a long draught from my cup. It gave me a chance to focus my eyes and attention on just one thing as the conversation crackled unceasingly around me. I invariably found it wearing trying to listen to all three Birtwhistles in full cry and of course it was impossible to look at them all simultaneously and adjust my expression to their different remarks.

The thing that amazed me was that none of them ever became angry at the others butting in. Nobody ever said, 'I'm speaking, do you mind?' or 'Don't interrupt!' or 'For Pete's sake, shut up!' They lived together in perfect harmony with all of them talking at once and none paying the slightest heed to what the other was saying.

When I saw the cow during the following week she was worse. Mr Birtwhistle had followed my instructions faithfully but Nellie could scarcely hobble as he brought her in from the field.

Len was there to lift the foot and I gloomily surveyed the increased swelling. It ran right round the coronet from the heel to the interdigital cleft in front, and the slightest touch from my finger caused the big cow to jerk her leg in pain.

I didn't say much, because I knew what was in store for Nellie and I knew too, that Mr Birtwhistle wasn't going to like it when I told him.

When I visited again at the end of the week I had only to look at the farmer's face to realize that everything had turned out as I feared. For once he was on his own and he led me silently to the byre.

Nellie was on three legs now, not daring even to bring the infected foot into momentary contact with the cobbled flooring. And worse, she was in an advanced state of emaciation, the sleek healthy animal of two weeks ago reduced to little more than bone and hide.

'I doubt she's 'ad it,' Mr Birtwhistle muttered.

Cow's hind feet are difficult to lift, but today I didn't need any help because Nellie had stopped caring. I examined the swollen digit. It was now vast – a great ugly club of tissue with a trickle of pus discharging down the wall.

'I see it's bust there.' The farmer poked a finger at the ragged opening. 'But it hasn't given 'er no relief.'

'Well, I wouldn't expect it to,' I said. 'Remember I told you the trouble is all inside the joint.'

'Well, these things 'appen,' he replied. 'Ah might as well telephone for Mallock. She's hardly givin' a drop o' milk, poor awd lass, she's nawt but a screw now.'

I always had to wait for the threat of the knacker man's humane killer before I said what I had to say now. Right from the start this had been a case for surgery, but it would have been a waste of time to suggest it at the beginning. Amputation of the bovine digit has always filled farmers with horror and even now I knew I would have trouble convincing Mr Birtwhistle.

'There's no need to slaughter her,' I said. 'There's another way of curing this.'

'Another way? We've tried 'ard enough, surely.'

I bent and lifted the foot again. 'Look at this.' I seized the inner cleat and moved it freely around. 'This side is perfectly healthy. There's nothing wrong with it. It would bear Nellie's full weight.'

'Aye, but . . . how about t'other 'orrible thing?'

'I could remove it.'

'You mean ... cut it off?'

'Yes.'

He shook his head vigorously 'Nay, nay, I'm not havin' that. She's suffered enough. Far better send for Jeff Mallock and get the job over.'

Here it was again. Farmers are anything but shrinking violets, but there was something about this business which appalled them.

'But Mr Birtwhistle,' I said. 'Don't you see – the pain is immediately relieved. The pressure is off and all the weight rests on the good side.'

'Ah said no, Mr Herriot, and ah mean no. You've done your best and I thank ye, but I'm not havin' her foot cut off and that's all about it.' He turned and began to walk away.

I looked after him helplessly. One thing I hate to do is talk a man into an operation on one of his beasts for the simple reason that if anything goes wrong I get the blame. But, as I was just about certain that an hour's work could restore this good cow to her former state, I couldn't let it go at this.

I trotted from the byre. The farmer was already halfway across the yard on his way to the phone.

I panted up to him as he reached the farmhouse door. 'Mr Birtwhistle, listen to me for a minute. I never said anything about cutting off her foot. Just one cleat.'

'Well that's half a foot, isn't it?' he looked down at his boots. 'And it's ower much for me.'

'But she wouldn't know a thing,' I pleaded. 'She'd be under a general anaesthetic. And I'm nearly sure it would be a success.'

'Mr Herriot, I just don't fancy it. I don't like t'idea. And even if it did work it would be like havin' a crippled cow walkin' about.'

'Not at all. She would grow a little stump of horn there and I'd like to bet you'd never notice a thing.'

He gave me a long sideways look and I could see he was weakening.

'Mr Birtwhistle,' I said, pressing home the attack. 'Within a month Nellie could be a fat cow again, giving five gallons of milk a day.'

This was silly talk, not to be recommended to any veterinary surgeon, but I was seized by a kind of madness. I couldn't bear the thought of that cow being cut up for dog food when I was convinced I could put it right. And there was another thing; I was already savouring the pleasure, childish perhaps, of instantly relieving an animal's pain, of bringing off a spectacular cure. There aren't many operations in the field of bovine surgery where you can do this but digit amputation is one of them.

Something of my fervour must have been communicated to the farmer because he looked at me steadily for a few moments then shrugged.

'When do you want to do it ?' he asked.

'Tomorrow.'

'Right. Will you need a lot o' fellers to help ?'

'No, just you and Len. I'll see you at ten o'clock.'

Next day the sun was warm on my back as I laid out my equipment on a small field near the house. It was a typical setting for many large animal operations I have carried out over the years; the sweet stretch of green, the grey stone buildings and the peaceful bulk of the fells rising calm and unheeding into the white scattering clouds.

It took a long time for them to lead Nellie out, though she didn't have far to go, and as the bony scarecrow hopped painfully towards me, dangling her useless limb, the brave words of yesterday seemed foolhardy.

'All right,' I said. 'Stop there. That's a good spot.' On the grass, nearby, lay my tray with the saw, chloroform, bandages, cotton wool and iodoform. I had my long casting rope too, which we used to pull cattle down, but I had a feeling Nellie wouldn't need it.

I was right. I buckled on the muzzle, poured some chloroform on to the sponge and the big white cow sank almost thankfully on to the cool green herbage.

'Kestrels had a smashin' match on Wednesday night,' Len chuckled happily. 'Johnnie Nudd didn't score but Len Bottomley . . .'

'I 'ope we're doin' t'right thing,' muttered Mr Birtwhistle. 'The way she staggered out 'ere I'd say it was a waste of time to . . .'

'. . . cracked in a couple o' beauties.' Len's face lit up at the memory. 'Kestrels is lucky to 'ave two fellers like . . .'

'Get hold of that bad foot, Len!' I barked, playing them at their own game. 'And keep it steady on that block of wood. And you, Mr Birtwhistle, hold her head down. I don't suppose she'll move, but if she does we'll have to give her more chloroform.'

Cows are good subjects for chloroform anaesthesia but I don't like to keep them laid out too long in case of regurgitation of food. I was in a hurry.

I quickly tied a bandage above the hoof, pulling it tight to serve as a tourniquet, then I reached back to the tray for the saw. The books are full of sophisticated methods of digit amputation with much talk of curved incisions, reflections of skin to expose the region of the articulations, and the like. But I have whipped off hundreds of cleats with a few brisk strokes of the saw below the coronary band with complete success.

I took a long breath. 'Hold tight, Len,' And set to work.

For a few moments there was silence except for the rhythmic grating of metal on bone, then the offending digit was lying on the grass, leaving a flat stump from which a few capillary vessels spurted. Using curved scissors I speedily disarticulated the remains of the bone from the second phalanx and held it up.

'Look at that!' I cried. 'Almost eaten away.' I pointed to the necrotic tissue in and around the joint. 'And d'you see all that rubbish? No wonder she was in pain.' I did a bit of quick curetting, dusted the surface with iodoform, applied a thick pad of cotton wool and prepared to bandage.

And as I tore the paper from the white rolls I felt a stab of remorse. In my absorption I had been rather rude. I had never replied to Len's remark about his beloved team. Maybe I could pass the next few minutes with a little gentle banter.

'Hey, Len,' I said. 'When you're talking about the Kestrels you never mention the time Willerton beat them five nil. How is that?'

In reply the young man hurled himself unhesitatingly at me, butting me savagely on the forehead. The assault of the great coarse-haired head against my skin was like being attacked by a curly-polled bull, and the impact sent me flying backwards on to the grass. At first the inside of my cranium was illuminated by a firework display but as consciousness slipped away my last sensation was of astonishment and disbelief.

I loved football myself but never had I thought that Len's devotion to the Kestrels would lead him to physical violence. He had always seemed a most gentle and harmless boy.

I suppose I was out for only a few seconds but I fancy I might have spent a good deal longer lying on the cool turf but for the fact that something kept hammering out the message that I was in the middle of a surgical procedure. I blinked and sat up.

Nellie was still sleeping peacefully against the green background of hills. Mr Birtwhistle, hands on her neck, was regarding me anxiously, and Len was lying unconscious face down across the cow's body.

'Has he hurt tha, Mr Herriot?'

'No . . . no . . . not really. What happened?'

'I owt to have told ye. He can't stand the sight o' blood. Great daft beggar.' The farmer directed an exasperated glare at his slumbering son. 'But ah've never seen 'im go down as fast as that. Pitched right into you, 'e did!'

I rolled the young man's inert form to one side and began again. I bandaged slowly and carefully because of the danger of post-operative haemorrhage. I finished with several layers of zinc oxide plaster then turned to the farmer.

'You can take her muzzle off now, Mr Birtwhistle. The job's done.'

I was starting to wash my instruments in the bucket when Len sat up almost as suddenly as he had slumped down. He was deathly pale but he looked at me with his usual friendly smile.

'What was that ye were sayin' about t'Kestrels, Mr Herriot?'

'Nothing, Len,' I replied hastily. 'Nothing at all.'

After three days I returned and removed the original dressing which was caked hard with blood and pus. I dusted the stump with powder again and bandaged on a clean soft pad of cotton wool.

'She'll feel a lot more comfortable now,' I said, and indeed Nellie was already looking vastly happier. She was taking some weight on the affected foot – rather gingerly, as though she couldn't believe that terrible thing had gone from her life.

As she walked away I crossed my fingers. The only thing that can ruin these operations is if the infection spreads to the other side. The inevitable result then is immediate slaughter and terrible disappointment.

But it never happened to Nellie. When I took off the second dressing she was almost sound and I didn't see her again until about five weeks after the operation.

I had finished injecting one of Mr Birtwhistle's pigs when I asked casually, 'And how's Nellie?'

'Come and 'ave a look at her,' the farmer replied. 'She's just in that field at side of t'road.'

We walked together over the grass to where the white cow was standing among her companions, head down, munching busily. And she must have done a lot of that since I saw her because she was fat again.

'Get on, lass.' The farmer gently nudged her rump with his thumb and she ambled forward a few paces before setting to work on another patch of grass. There wasn't the slightest trace of lameness.

'Well, that's grand,' I said. 'And is she milking well, too?'

'Aye, back to five gallons.' He pulled a much dented tobacco tin from his pocket, unscrewed the lid and produced an ancient watch. 'It's ten o'clock, young man. Len'll have gone into t'house for his tea, and 'lowance. Will ye come in and have a cup?'

I squared my shoulders and followed him inside, and the barrage began immediately.

'Summat right funny happened on Saturday,' Len said with a roar of laughter. 'Walter Gimmett was refereein' and 'e gave two penalties agin t'Kestrels. So what did the lads do, they...'

'Eee, wasn't it sad about old Mr Brent?' Mrs Birtwhistle put her head on one side and looked at me piteously. 'We buried 'im on Saturday and...'

'You know, Mr Herriot,' her husband put in. 'Ah thought you were pullin' ma leg when you said Nellie would be givin' five gallons again. I never...'

'... dumped the beggar in a 'oss trough. He won't give no more penalties agin t'Kestrels. You should 'ave seen...'

'. . . it would 'ave been his ninetieth birthday today, poor old man. He was well liked in t'village and there was a big congregation. Parson said . . .'

'. . . expected owt like that. Ah thought she might maybe put on a bit of flesh so we could get 'er off for beef. Ah'm right grateful to . . .'

At that moment, fingers clenched tensely around my cup, I happened to catch sight of my reflection in a cracked mirror above the kitchen sink. It was a frightening experience because I was staring glassily into space with my features contorted almost out of recognition. There was something of an idiot smile as I acknowledged the humour of Walter in the horse trough, a touch of sorrow at Mr Brent's demise, and, I swear, a suggestion of gratification at the successful outcome of Nellie's operation. And since I was also trying to look in three directions at once, I had to give myself full marks for effort.

But as I say, I found it a little unnerving and excused myself soon afterwards. The men were still busy with Mrs Birtwhistle's apple pie and scones and the conversation was raging unabated when I left. The closure of the door behind me brought a sudden peace. The feeling of tranquillity stayed with me as I got into my car and drove out of the yard and on to the narrow country road. It persisted as I stopped the car after less than a hundred yards and wound down the window to have a look at my patient.

Nellie was lying down now. She had eaten her fill and was resting comfortably on her chest as she chewed her cud. To a doctor of farm animals there is nothing more reassuring than that slow lateral grinding. It means contentment and health. She gazed at me across the stone wall and the placid eyes in the white face added to the restfulness of the scene, accentuating the silence after the babel of voices in the farmhouse.

Nellie couldn't talk, but those calmly moving jaws told me all I wanted to know.

# 7

To me there are few things more appealing than a dog begging. This one was tied to a lamp post outside a shop in Windsor. Its eyes were fixed steadfastly on the shop doorway, willing its owner to come out, and every now and then it sat up in mute entreaty.

Flying had been suspended for an afternoon. It gave us all a chance to relax and no doubt it eased the frayed nerves of our instructors, but as I looked at that dog all the pressures of the RAF fell away and I went back to Darrowby.

It was when Siegfried and I were making one of our market day sorties that we noticed the little dog among the stalls.

When things were quiet in the surgery we often used to walk together across the cobbles and have a word with the farmers gathered round the doorway of the Drovers' Arms. Sometimes we collected a few outstanding bills or drummed up a bit of work for the forthcoming week -- and if nothing like that happened we still enjoyed the fresh air.

The thing that made us notice the dog was that he was sitting up begging in front of the biscuit stall.

'Look at that little chap,' Siegfried said. 'I wonder where he's sprung from.'

As he spoke, the stallholder threw a biscuit which the dog devoured eagerly but when the man came round and stretched out a hand the little animal trotted away.

He stopped, however, at another stall which sold produce: eggs, cheese, butter, cakes and scones. Without hesitation he sat up again in the begging position, rock steady, paws dangling, head pointing expectantly.

I nudged Siegfried. 'There he goes again.'

My colleague nodded. 'Yes, he's an engaging little thing, isn't he ? What breed would you call him ?'

'A cross, I'd say. He's like a little brown sheepdog, but there's a touch of something else – maybe terrier.'

It wasn't long before he was munching a bun, and this time we walked over to him. And as we drew near I spoke gently.

'Here, boy,' I said, squatting down a yard away. 'Come on, let's have a look at you.'

He faced me and for a moment two friendly brown eyes gazed at me from a singularly attractive little face. The fringed tail waved in response to my words but as I inched nearer he turned and ambled unhurriedly among the market day crowd till he was lost to sight. I didn't want to make a thing out of the encounter because I could never quite divine Siegfried's attitude to the small animals. He was eminently wrapped up in his horse work and often seemed amused at the way I rushed around after dogs and cats.

At that time, in fact, Siegfried was strongly opposed to the whole idea of keeping animals as pets. He was quite vociferous on the subject – said it was utterly foolish – despite the fact that five assorted dogs travelled everywhere with him in his car. Now, thirty-five years later, he is just as strongly in favour of keeping pets, though he now carries only one dog in his car. So, as I say, it was difficult to assess his reactions in this field and I refrained from following the little animal.

I was standing there when a young policeman came up to me.

'I've been watching that little dog begging among the stalls all morning,' he said. 'But like you, I haven't been able to get near him.'

'Yes, it's strange. He's obviously friendly, yet he's afraid. I wonder who owns him.'

'I reckon he's a stray, Mr Herriot. I'm interested in dogs myself and I fancy I know just about all of them around here. But this 'un's a stranger to me.'

I nodded. 'I bet you're right. So anything could have happened to him. He could have been ill-treated by somebody and run away, or he could have been dumped from a car.'

'Yes,' he replied. 'There's some lovely people around. It beats me how anybody can leave a helpless animal to fend for itself like that. I've had a few goes at catching him myself but it's no good.'

The memory stayed with me for the rest of the day and even when I lay in bed that night I was unable to dispel the disturbing image of the little brown creature wandering in a strange world, sitting up asking for help in the only way he knew.

*

I was still a bachelor at that time and on the Friday night of the same week Siegfried and I were arraying ourselves in evening dress in preparation for the Hunt Ball at East Hirdsley, about ten miles away.

It was a tortuous business because those were the days of starched shirt fronts and stiff high collars and I kept hearing explosions of colourful language from Siegfried's room as he wrestled with his studs.

I was in an even worse plight because I had outgrown my suit and even when I had managed to secure the strangling collar I had to fight my way into the dinner jacket which nipped me cruelly under the arms. I had just managed to don the complete outfit and was trying out a few careful breaths when the phone rang.

It was the same young policeman I had been speaking to earlier in the week.

'We've got that dog round here, Mr Herriot. You know – the one that was begging in the market place.'

'Oh yes? Somebody's managed to catch him, then?'

There was a pause. 'No, not really. One of our men found him lying by the roadside about a mile out of town and brought him in. He's been in an accident.'

I told Siegfried. He looked at his watch. 'Always happens, doesn't it, James. Just when we're ready to go out. It's nine o'clock now and we should be on our way.' He thought for a moment. 'Anyway, slip round there and have a look and I'll wait for you. It would be better if we could go to this affair together.'

As I drove round to the police station I hoped fervently that there wouldn't be much to do. This Hunt Ball meant a lot to my boss because it would be a gathering of the horse-loving fraternity of the district and he would have a wonderful time just chatting and drinking with so many kindred spirits even though he hardly danced at all. Also, he maintained, it was good for business to meet the clients socially.

The kennels were at the bottom of a yard behind the station and the policeman led me down and opened one of the doors. The little dog was lying very still under the single electric bulb and when I bent and stroked the brown coat his tail stirred briefly among the straw of his bed.

'He can still manage a wag, anyway,' I said.

The policeman nodded. 'Aye, there's no doubt he's a good-natured little thing.'

I tried to examine him as much as possible without touching. I didn't want to hurt him and there was no saying what the extent of his injuries might be. But even at a glance certain things were obvious; he had multiple lacerations, one hind leg was crooked in the unmistakeable posture of a fracture and there was blood on his lips.

This could be from damaged teeth and I gently raised the head with a view to looking into his mouth. He was lying on his right side and as the head came round it was as though somebody had struck me in the face.

The right eye had been violently dislodged from its socket and it sprouted like some hideous growth from above the cheek bone, a great glistening orb with the eyelids tucked behind the white expanse of sclera.

I seemed to squat there for a long time, stunned by the obscenity, and as the seconds dragged by I looked into the little dog's face and he looked back at me – trustingly from one soft brown eye, glaring meaninglessly from the grotesque ball on the other side.

The policeman's voice broke my thoughts. 'He's a mess, isn't he?'

'Yes . . . yes . . . must have been struck by some vehicle – maybe dragged along by the look of all those wounds.'

'What d'you think, Mr Herriot?'

I knew what he meant. It was the sensible thing to ease this lost unwanted creature from the world. He was grieviously hurt and he didn't seem to belong to anybody. A quick overdose of anaesthetic – his troubles would be over and I'd be on my way to the dance.

But the policeman didn't say anything of the sort. Maybe, like me, he was looking into the soft depths of that one trusting eye.

I stood up quickly. 'Can I use your phone?'

At the other end of the line Siegfried's voice crackled with impatience. 'Hell, James, it's half-past nine! If we're going to this thing we've got to go now or we might as well not bother. A stray dog, badly injured. It doesn't sound such a great problem.'

'I know, Siegfried. I'm sorry to hold you up but I can't make up my mind. I wish you'd come round and tell me what you think.'

There was a silence then a long sigh. 'All right, James. See you in five minutes.'

He created a slight stir as he entered the station. Even in his casual working clothes Siegfried always managed to look distinguished, but as he swept into the station newly bathed and shaved, a camel coat thrown over the sparkling white shirt and black tie there was something ducal about him.

He drew respectful glances from the men sitting around, then my young policeman stepped forward.

'This way, sir,' he said, and we went back to the kennels.

Siegfried was silent as he crouched over the dog, looking him over as I had done without touching him. Then he carefully raised the head and the monstrous eye glared.

'My God!' he said softly, and at the sound of his voice the long fringed tail moved along the ground.

For a few seconds he stayed very still looking fixedly at the dog's face while in the silence, the whisking tail rustled the straw.

Then he straightened up. 'Let's get him round there,' he murmured.

In the surgery we anaesthetized the little animal and as he lay unconscious on the table we were able to examine him thoroughly. After a few minutes Siegfried stuffed his stethoscope into the pocket of his white coat and leaned both hands on the table.

'Luxated eyeball, fractured femur, umpteen deep lacerations, broken claws. There's enough here to keep us going till midnight, James.'

I didn't say anything.

My boss pulled the knot from his black tie and undid the front stud. He peeled off the stiff collar and hung it on the cross bar of the surgery lamp. . .

'By God, that's better,' he muttered, and began to lay out suture materials.

I looked at him across the table. 'How about the Hunt Ball?'

'Oh bugger the Hunt Ball,' Siegfried said. 'Let's get busy.'

We were busy, too, for a long time. I hung up my collar next to my colleague's and we began on the eye. I know we both felt the same – we wanted to get rid of that horror before we did anything else.

I lubricated the great ball and pulled the eyelids apart while Siegfried gently manoeuvred it back into the orbital cavity. I sighed as everything slid out of sight, leaving only the cornea visible.

Siegfried chuckled with satisfaction. 'Looks like an eye again, doesn't it.' He seized an ophthalmoscope and peered into the depths.

'And there's no major damage – could be as good as new again. But we'll just stitch the lids together to protect it for a few days.'

The broken ends of the fractured tibia were badly displaced and we had to struggle to bring them into apposition before applying the plaster of paris. But at last we finished and started on the long job of stitching the many cuts and lacerations.

We worked separately for this, and for a long time it was quiet in the operating room except for the snip of scissors as we clipped the brown hair away from the wounds. I knew and Siegfried knew that we were almost certainly working without payment, but the most disturbing thought was that after all our efforts we might still have to put him down. He was still in the care of the police and if nobody claimed him within ten days it meant euthanasia. And if his late owners were really interested in his fate, why hadn't they tried to contact the police before now . . .

By the time we had completed our work and washed the instruments it was after midnight. Siegfried dropped the last suture needle into its tray and looked at the sleeping animal.

'I think he's beginning to come round,' he said. 'Let's take him through to the fire and we can have a drink while he recovers.'

We stretchered the dog through to the sitting room on a blanket and laid him on the rug before the brightly burning coals. My colleague reached a long arm up to the glass-fronted cabinet above the mantelpiece and pulled down the whisky bottle and two glasses. Drinks in hand, collarless, still in shirt sleeves, with our starched white fronts and braided evening trousers to remind us of the lost dance we lay back in our chairs on either side of the fireplace and between us our patient stretched peacefully.

He was a happier sight now. One eye was closed by the protecting stitches and his hind leg projected stiffly in its white cast, but he was tidy, cleaned up, cared for. He looked as though he belonged to somebody – but then there was a great big doubt about that.

It was nearly one o'clock in the morning and we were getting well down the bottle when the shaggy brown head began to move.

Siegfried leaned forward and touched one of the ears and immediately the tail flapped against the rug and a pink tongue lazily licked his fingers.

'What an absolutely grand little dog,' he murmured, but his voice had a distant quality. I knew he was worried too.

I took the stitches out of the eyelids two days after and was delighted to find a normal eye underneath.

The young policeman was as pleased as I was. 'Look at that!' he exclaimed. 'You'd never know anything had happened there.'

'Yes, it's done wonderfully well. All the swelling and inflammation has gone.' I hesitated for a moment. 'Has anybody inquired about him?'

He shook his head. 'Nothing yet. But there's another eight days to go and we're taking good care of him here.'

I visited the police station several times and the little animal greeted me with undisguised joy, all his fear gone, standing upright against my legs on his plastered limb, his tail swishing.

But all the time my sense of foreboding increased, and on the tenth day I made my way almost with dread to the police kennels. I had heard nothing. My course of action seemed inevitable. Putting down old or hopelessly ill dogs was often an act of mercy but when it was a young healthy dog it was terrible. I hated it, but it was one of those things veterinary surgeons had to do.

The young policeman was standing in the doorway.

'Still no news?' I asked, and he shook his head.

I went past him into the kennel and the shaggy little creature stood up against my legs as before, laughing into my face, mouth open, eyes shining.

I turned away quickly. I'd have to do this right now or I'd never do it.

'Mr Herriot.' The policeman put his hand on my arm. 'I think I'll take him.'

'You?' I stared at him.

'Aye, that's right. We got a lot o' stray dogs in here and though I feel sorry for them you can't give them all a home, can you?'

'No, you can't,' I said. 'I have the same problem.'

He nodded slowly. 'But somehow this 'un's different, and it seems to me he's just come at the right time. I have two little girls and they've been at me for a bit to get 'em a dog. This little bloke looks just right for the job.'

Warm relief began to ebb through me. 'I couldn't agree more. He's the soul of good nature. I bet he'll be wonderful with children.'

'Good. That's settled then. I thought I'd ask your advice first.' He smiled happily.

I looked at him as though I had never seen him before. 'What's your name?'

'Phelps,' he replied. 'PC Phelps.'

He was a good-looking young fellow, clear-skinned, with cheerful blue eyes and a solid dependable look about him. I had to fight against an impulse to wring his hand and thump him on the back. But I managed to preserve the professional exterior.

'Well, that's fine.' I bent and stroked the little dog. 'Don't forget to bring him along to the surgery in ten days for removal of the stitches, and we'll have to get that plaster off in about a month.'

It was Siegfried who took out the stitches, and I didn't see our patient again until four weeks later.

PC Phelps had his little girls, aged four and six, with him as well as the dog.

'You said the plaster ought to come off about now,' he said, and I nodded.

He looked down at the children. 'Well, come on, you two, lift him on the table.'

Eagerly the little girls put their arms around their new pet and as they hoisted him the tail wagged furiously and the wide mouth panted in delight.

'Looks as though he's been a success,' I said.

He smiled. 'That's an understatement. He's perfect with these two. I can't tell you what pleasure he's given us. He's one of the family.'

I got out my little saw and began to hack at the plaster.

'It's worked both ways, I should say. A dog loves a secure home.'

'Well, he couldn't be more secure.' He ran his hand along the brown coat and laughed as he addressed the little dog. 'That's what you get for begging among the stalls on market day, my lad. You're in the hands of the law now.'

# 8

When I entered the RAF I had a secret fear. All my life I have suffered from vertigo and even now I have only to look down from the smallest height to be engulfed by that dreadful dizziness and panic. What would I feel, then, when I started to fly?

As it turned out, I felt nothing. I could gaze downwards from the open cockpit through thousands of feet of space without a qualm, so my fear was groundless.

I had my fears in veterinary practice, too, and in the early days the thing which raised the greatest terror in my breast was the Ministry of Agriculture.

An extraordinary statement, perhaps, but true. It was the clerical side that scared me – all those forms. As to the practical Ministry work itself, I felt in all modesty that I was quite good at it. My thoughts often turned back to all the tuberculin testing I used to do – clipping a clean little area from just the right place in the cow's neck, inserting the needle into the thickness of the skin and injecting one tenth of a cc of tuberculin.

It was on Mr Hill's farm, and I watched the satisfactory intradermal 'pea' rise up under my needle. That was the way it should be, and when it came up like that you knew you were really doing your job and testing the animal for tuberculosis.

'That 'un's number sixty-five,' the farmer said, then a slightly injured look spread over his face as I checked the number in the ear.

'You're wastin' your time, Mr Herriot. I 'ave the whole list, all in t'correct order. Wrote it out special for you so you could take it away with you.'

I had my doubts. All farmers were convinced that their herd records were flawless but I had been caught out before. I seemed to have the gift of making every possible clerical mistake and I didn't need any help from the farmers.

But still . . . it was tempting. I looked at the long list of figures dangling from the horny fingers. If I accepted it I would save a lot of time. There were still more than fifty animals to test here and I had to get through two more herds before lunch time.

I looked at my watch. Damn! I was well behind my programme and I felt the old stab of frustration.

'Right, Mr Hill, I'll take it and thank you very much.' I stuffed the sheet of paper into my pocket and began to move along the byre, clipping and injecting at top speed.

A week later the dread words leaped out at me from the open day book. 'Ring Min.' The cryptic phrase in Miss Harbottle's writing had the power to freeze my blood quicker than anything else. It meant simply that I had to telephone the Ministry of Agriculture office, and whenever our secretary wrote those words in the book it meant that I was in trouble again. I extended a trembling hand towards the receiver.

As always, Kitty Pattison answered my call and I could detect the note of pity in her voice. She was the attractive girl in charge of the office staff and she knew all about my misdemeanours. In fact when it was something very trivial she sometimes brought it to my attention herself, but when I had really dropped a large brick I was dealt with by the boss, Charles Harcourt, the Divisional Inspector.

'Ah, Mr Herriot,' Kitty said lightly. I knew she sympathized with me but she couldn't do a thing about it. 'Mr Harcourt wants a word with you.'

There it was. The terrible sentence that always set my heart thumping.

'Thank you,' I said huskily, and waited an eternity as the phone was switched through.

'Herriot!' The booming voice made me jump.

I swallowed. 'Good morning Mr Harcourt. How are you?'

'I'll tell you how I am, I'm bloody annoyed!' I could imagine vividly the handsome, high-coloured, choleric face flushing deeper, the greenish eyes glaring. 'In fact I'm hopping bloody mad!'

'Oh.'

'It's no use saying "oh". That's what you said the last time when you tested that cow of Frankland's that had been dead for two years! That was very clever – I don't know how you managed it. Now I've been going over your test at Hill's of High View and there are two cows here that you've tested – numbers 74 and 103. Now our records show that he sold both of them at Brawton Auction Mart six months ago, so you've performed another miracle.'

'I'm sorry . . .'

'Please don't be sorry, it's bloody marvellous how you do it. I have all the figures here – skin measurements, the lot. I see you found they were both thin-skinned animals even though they were about fifteen miles away at the time. Clever stuff!'

'Well I . . .'

'All right, Herriot, I'll dispense with the comedy. I'm going to tell you once more, for the last time, and I hope you're listening.' He paused and I could almost see the big shoulders hunching as he barked into the phone. '*Look in the bloody ears in future!*'

I broke into a rapid gabble. 'I will indeed, Mr Harcourt, I assure you from now on . . .'

'All right, all right, but there's something else.'

'Something else?'

'Yes, I'm not finished yet.' The voice took on a great weariness. 'Can I ask you to cast your mind back to that cow you took under the TB order from Wilson of Low Parks?'

I dug my nails into my palm. We were heading for deep water. 'Yes – I remember it.'

'Well now, Herriot, lad, do you remember a little chat we had about the forms?' Charles was trying to be patient, because he was a decent man, but it was costing him dearly. 'Didn't anything I told you sink in?'

'Well, yes, of course.'

'Then why, why didn't you send me a receipt for slaughter?'

'Receipt for . . . didn't I . . . ?'

'No, you didn't,' he said. 'And honestly I can't understand it.

I went over it with you step by step last time when you forgot to forward a copy of the valuation agreement.'

'Oh dear, I really am sorry.'

A deep sigh came from the other end. 'And there's nothing to it.' He paused. 'Tell you what we'll do. Let's go over the procedure once more, shall we?'

'Yes, by all means.'

'Very well,' he said. 'First of all, when you find an infected animal you serve B 205 DT, Form A, which is the notice requiring detention and isolation of the animal. Next,' and I could hear the slap of finger on palm as he enumerated his points, 'next, there is B 207 DT, Form C, Notice of intended slaughter. Then B 208 DT, Form D, Post-mortem Certificate. Then B 196 DT, Veterinary Inspector's report. Then B 209 DT, Valuation agreement, and in cases where the owner objects, there is B 213 DT, Appointment of valuer. Then we have B 212 DT, Notice to owner of time and place of slaughter, followed by B 227 DT, Receipt for animal for slaughter, and finally B 230 DT, Notice requiring cleansing and disinfection. Dammit, a child could understand that. It's perfectly simple, isn't it?'

'Yes, yes, certainly, absolutely.' It wasn't simple to me, but I didn't mention the fact. He had calmed down nicely and I didn't want to inflame him again.

'Well thank you, Mr Harcourt,' I said. 'I'll see it doesn't happen again.' I put down the receiver with the feeling that things could have turned out a lot worse, but for all that my nerves didn't stop jangling for some time. The trouble was that the Ministry work was desperately important to general practitioners. In fact, in those precarious days it was the main rent payer.

This business of the Tuberculosis Order. When a veterinary surgeon came upon a cow with open TB it was his duty to see that the animal was slaughtered immediately because its milk could be a danger to the public. That sounds easy, but unfortunately the law insisted that the demise of each unhappy creature be commemorated by a confetti-like shower of the doom-laden forms.

It wasn't just that there were so many of these forms, but they had to be sent to an amazing variety of people. Sometimes I used to think that there were very few people in England who didn't get one. Apart from Charles Harcourt, other recipients included the farmer concerned, the police, the Head Office of the Ministry, the knacker man, the local authority. I nearly always managed to forget one of them. I used to have nightmares about standing in the middle of the market place, throwing the forms around me at the passers-by and laughing hysterically.

Looking back, I can hardly believe that for all this wear and tear on the nervous system the payment was one guinea plus ten and sixpence for the post-mortem.

It was a mere two days after my interview with the Divisional Inspector that I had to take another cow under the TB Order. When I came to fill in the forms I sat at the surgery desk in a dither of apprehension, going over them again and again, laying them out side by side and enclosing them one by one in their various envelopes. This time there must be no mistake.

I took them over to the post myself and uttered a silent prayer as I dropped them into the box. Charles would have them the following morning, and I would soon know if I had done it again. When two days passed without incident I felt I was safe, but midway through the third morning I dropped in at the surgery and read the message in letters of fire. 'RING MIN!'

Kitty Pattison sounded strained. She didn't even try to appear casual. 'Oh yes, Mr Herriot,' she said hurriedly. 'Mr Harcourt asked me to call you. I'm putting you through now.'

My heart almost stopped as I waited for the familiar bellow, but when the quiet voice came on the line it frightened me even more.

'Good morning, Herriot.' Charles was curt and impersonal. 'I'd like to discuss that last cow you took under the Order.'

'Oh yes ?' I croaked.

'But not over the telephone. I want to see you here in the office.'

'In the . . . the office ?'

'Yes, right away if you can.'

I put down the phone and went out to the car with my knees knocking. Charles Harcourt was really upset this time. There was a kind of restrained fury in his words, and this business of going to the office – that was reserved for serious transgressions.

Twenty minutes later my footsteps echoed in the corridor of

the Ministry building. Marching stiffly like a condemned man I passed the windows where I could see the typists at work, then I read 'Divisional Inspector' on the door at the end.

I took one long shuddering breath, then knocked.

'Come in.' The voice was still quiet and controlled.

Charles looked up unsmilingly from his desk as I entered. He motioned me to a chair and directed a cold stare at me.

'Herriot,' he said unemotionally. 'You're really on the carpet this time.'

Charles had been a major in the Punjabi Rifles and he was very much the Indian Army officer at this moment. A fine looking man, clear-skinned and ruddy, with massive cheek bones above a powerful jaw. Looking at the dangerously glinting eyes it struck me that only a fool would trifle with somebody like him – and I had a nasty feeling that I had been trifling.

Dry-mouthed, I waited.

'You know, Herriot,' he went on. 'After our last telephone conversation about TB forms I thought you might give me a little peace.'

'Peace . . . ?'

'Yes, yes, it was silly of me, I know, but when I took all that time to go over the procedure with you I actually thought you were listening.'

'Oh I was, I was!'

'You were? Oh good.' He gave me a mirthless smile. 'Then I suppose it was even more foolish of me to expect you to act upon my instructions. In my innocence I thought you cared about what I was telling you.'

'Mr Harcourt, believe me, I do care, I . . .'

'*Then why*,' he bawled without warning, bringing his great hand flailing down on the desk with a crash that made pens and inkwells dance, '*why the bloody hell do you keep making a balls of it?*'

I resisted a strong impulse to run away. 'Making a . . . I don't quite understand.'

'You don't?' He kept up his pounding on the desk. 'Well I'll tell you. One of my veterinary officers was on that farm, and he found that you hadn't served a Notice of cleansing and disinfection!'

'Is that so?'

'Yes, it bloody well is so! You didn't give one to the farmer but you sent one to me. Maybe you want me to go and disinfect the place, is that it? Would you like me to slip along there and get busy with a hosepipe – I'll go now if it'll make you feel any happier!'

'Oh no, no, no . . . no.'

He was apparently not satisfied with the thunderous noise he was making because he began to use both hands, bringing them down simultaneously with sickening force on the wood while he glared wildly.

'Herriot!' he shouted. 'There's just one thing I want to know from you – do you want this bloody work or don't you? Just say the word and I'll give it to another practice and then maybe we'd both be able to live a quiet life!'

'Please, Mr Harcourt, I give you my word, I . . . we . . . we do want the work very much.' And I meant it with all my heart.

The big man slumped back in his chair and regarded me for a few moments in silence. Then he glanced at his wrist watch.

'Ten past twelve,' he murmured. 'Just time to have a beer at the Red Lion before lunch.'

In the pub lounge he took a long pull at his glass, placed it carefully on the table in front of him, then turned to me with a touch of weariness.

'You know, Herriot, I do wish you'd stop doing this sort of thing. It takes it out of me.'

I believed him. His face had lost a little of its colour and his hand trembled slightly as he raised his glass again.

'I'm truly sorry, Mr Harcourt, I don't know how it happened. I did try to get it right this time and I'll do my best to avoid troubling you in future.'

He nodded a few times, then clapped me on the shoulder. 'Good, good – let's just have one more.'

He moved over to the bar, brought back the drinks then fished out a brown paper parcel from his pocket.

'Little wedding present, Herriot. Understand you're getting married soon – this is from my missus and me with our best wishes.'

I didn't know what to say. I fumbled the wrapping away and uncovered a small square barometer.

Shame engulfed me as I muttered a few words of thanks. This man was the head of the Ministry in the area while I was the newest and lowest of his minions. Not only that, but I was pretty sure I caused him more trouble than all the others put together – I was like a hair shirt to him. There was no earthly reason why he should give me a barometer.

This last experience deepened my dread of form filling to the extent that I hoped it would be a long time before I encountered another tuberculous animal, but fate decreed that I had some concentrated days of clinical inspections and it was with a feeling of inevitability that I surveyed Mr Moverley's Ayrshire cow.

It was the soft cough which made me stop and look at her more closely, and as I studied her my spirits sank. This was another one. The skin stretched tightly over the bony frame, the slightly accelerated respirations and that deep careful cough. Mercifully you don't see cows like that now, but in those days they were all too common.

I moved along her side and examined the wall in front of her. The tell-tale blobs of sputum were clearly visible on the rough stones and I quickly lifted a sample and smeared it on a glass slide.

Back at the surgery I stained the smear by Ziehl-Nielson's method and pushed the slide under the microscope. The red clumps of tubercle bacilli lay among the scattered cells, tiny, iridescent and deadly. I hadn't really needed the grim proof but it was there.

Mr Moverley was not amused when I told him next morning the animal would have to be slaughtered.

'It's nobbut got a bit of a chill,' he grunted. The farmers were never pleased when one of their milk producers was removed by a petty bureaucrat like me. 'But ah suppose it's no use arguin'.'

'I assure you, Mr Moverley, there's no doubt about it. I examined that sample last night and . . .'

'Oh, never mind about that.' The farmer waved an impatient hand. 'If t'bloody government says me cow's got to go she's got to go. But ah get compensation, don't I ?'

'Yes, you do.'

'How much ?'

I thought rapidly. The rules stated that the animal be valued as if it were up for sale in the open market in its present condition. The minimum was five pounds and there was no doubt that this emaciated cow came into that category.

'The statutory value is five pounds,' I said.

'Shit!' replied Mr Moverley.

'We can appoint a valuer if you don't agree.'

'Oh 'ell, let's get t'job over with.' He was clearly disgusted and I thought it imprudent to tell him that he would only get a proportion of the five pounds, depending on the post-mortem.

'Very well,' I said. 'I'll tell Jeff Mallock to collect her as soon as possible.'

The fact that I was unpopular with Mr Moverley didn't worry me as much as the prospect of dealing with the dreaded forms. The very thought of sending another batch winging hopefully on its way to Charles Harcourt brought me out in a sweat.

Then I had a flash of inspiration. Such things don't often happen to me, but this struck me as brilliant. I wouldn't send off the forms till I'd had them vetted by Kitty Pattison.

I couldn't wait to get the plan under way. Almost gleefully I laid the papers out in a long row, signed them and laid them by their envelopes, ready for their varied journeys. Then I phoned the Ministry office.

Kitty was patient and kind. I am sure she realized that I did my work conscientiously but that I was a clerical numbskull and she sympathized.

When I had finished going through the list she congratulated me. 'Well done, Mr Herriot, you've got them right this time! All you need now is the knacker man's signature and your post-mortem report and you're home and dry.'

'Bless you, Kitty,' I said. 'You've made my day.'

And she had. The airy sensation of relief was tremendous. The knowledge that there would be no come-back from Charles this time was like the sun bursting through dark clouds. I felt like singing as I went round to Mallock's yard and arranged with him to pick up the cow.

'Have her ready for me to inspect tomorrow, Jeff,' I said, and went on my way with a light heart.

I couldn't understand it when Mr Moverley waved me down

from his farm gate next day. As I drew up I could see he was extremely agitated.

'Hey!' he cried. 'Ah've just got back from the market and my missus tells me Mallock's been!'

I smiled. 'That's right, Mr Moverley. Remember I told you I was going to send him round for your cow.'

'Aye, ah know all about that!' He paused and glared at me. 'But he's took the wrong one!'

'Wrong . . . wrong what?'

'Wrong cow, that's what! He's off wi' the best cow in me herd. Pedigree Ayrshire – ah bought 'er in Dumfries last week and they only delivered 'er this mornin'.'

Horror drove through me in a freezing wave. I had told the knacker man to collect the Ayrshire which would be isolated in the loose box in the yard. The new animal would be in a box, too, after her arrival. I could see Jeff and his man leading her up the ramp into his wagon with a dreadful clarity.

'This is your responsibility, tha knaws!' The farmer waved a threatening finger. 'If he kills me good cow you'll 'ave to answer for it!'

He didn't have to tell me. I'd have to answer for it to a lot of people, including Charles Harcourt.

'Get on the phone to the knacker yard right away!' I gasped.

The farmer waved his arms about. 'Ah've tried that and there's no reply. Ah tell ye he'll shoot 'er afore we can stop 'im. Do you know how much ah paid for that cow?'

'Never mind about that! Which way did he go?'

'T'missus said he went towards Grampton – about ten minutes ago.'

I started my engine. 'He'll maybe be picking up other beasts – I'll go after him.'

Teeth clenched, eyes popping, I roared along the Grampton road. The enormity of this latest catastrophe was almost more than I could assimilate. The wrong form was bad enough, but the wrong cow was unthinkable. But it had happened. Charles would crucify me this time. He was a good bloke but he would have no option, because the higher-ups in the Ministry would get wind of an immortal boner like this and they would howl for blood.

Feverishly but vainly I scanned each farm entrance in Grampton village as I shot through, and when I saw the open countryside ahead of me again the tension was almost unbearable. I was telling myself that the whole thing was hopeless when in the far distance above a row of trees I spotted the familiar top of Mallock's wagon.

It was a high, wooden-sided vehicle and I couldn't mistake it. Repressing a shout of triumph I put my foot on the boards and set off in that direction with the fanatical zeal of the hunter. But it was a long way off and I hadn't travelled a mile before I realized I had lost it.

Over the years many things have stayed in my memory, but the Great Cow Chase is engraven deeper than most. The sheer terror I felt is vivid to this day. I kept sighting the wagon among the maze of lanes and side roads, but by the time I had cut across country my quarry had disappeared behind a hillside or dipped into one of the many hollows in the wide vista. I was constantly deceived by the fact that I expected him to be turning towards Darrowby after passing through a village, but he never did. Clearly he had other business on the way.

The whole thing seemed to last a very long time and there was no fun in it for me. I was gripped throughout by a cold dread, and the violent swings – the alternating scents of hope and despair – were wearing to the point of exhaustion. I was utterly drained when at last I saw the tall lorry rocking along a straight road in front of me.

I had him now! Forcing my little car to the limit, I drew abreast of him, sounding my horn repeatedly till he stopped. Breathlessly I pulled up in front of him and ran round to offer my explanations. But as I looked up into the driver's cab my eager smile vanished. It wasn't Jeff Mallock at all. I had been following the wrong man.

It was the 'ket feller'. He had exactly the same type of wagon as Mallock and he went round a wide area of Yorkshire picking up the nameless odds and ends of the dead animals which even the knacker men didn't want. It was a strange job and he was a strange-looking man. The oddly piercing eyes glittered uncannily from under a tattered army peaked cap.

'Wot's up, guvnor?' He removed a cigarette from his mouth and spat companionably into the roadway.

My throat was tight. 'I – I'm sorry. I thought you were Jeff Mallock.'

The eyes did not change expression, but the corner of his mouth twitched briefly. 'If tha wants Jeff he'll be back at his yard now, ah reckon.' He spat again and replaced his cigarette.

I nodded dully. Jeff would be there now all right – long ago. I had been chasing the wrong wagon for about an hour and that cow would be dead and hanging up on hooks at this moment. The knacker man was a fast and skilful worker and wasted no time when he got back with his beasts.

'Well, ah'm off 'ome now,' the ket feller said. 'So long, boss.' He winked at me, started his engine and the big vehicle rumbled away.

I trailed back to my car. There was no hurry now. And strangely, now that all was lost my mood relaxed. In fact, as I drove away, a great calm settled on me and I began to assess my future with cool objectivity. I would be drummed out of the Ministry's service for sure, and idly I wondered if they had any special ceremony for the occasion – perhaps a ritual stripping of the Panel Certificates or something of the sort.

I tried to put away the thought that more than the Ministry would be interested in my latest exploit. How about the Royal College ? Did they strike you off for something like this ? Well, it was possible, and in my serene state of mind I toyed with the possibilities of alternative avenues of employment. I had often thought it must be fun to run a secondhand book shop and now that I began to consider it seriously I felt sure there was an opening for one in Darrowby. I experienced a comfortable glow at the vision of myself sitting under the rows of dusty volumes, pulling one down from the shelf when I felt like it or maybe just looking out into the street through the window from my safe little world where there were no forms or telephones or messages saying, 'Ring Min.'

In Darrowby I drove round without haste to the knacker yard. I left my car outside the grim little building with the black smoke drifting from its chimney. I pulled back the sliding door and saw Jeff seated at his ease on a pile of cow hides, holding a slice of apple pie in blood-stained fingers. And, ah yes, there, just behind him hung the two great sides of beef and on the floor, the lungs, bowels and other viscera – the sad remnants of Mr Moverley's pedigree Ayrshire.

'Hello, Jeff,' I said.

'Now then, Mr Herriot.' He gave me the beatific smile which mirrored his personality so well. 'Ah'm just havin' a little snack. I allus like a bite about this time.' He sank his teeth into the pie and chewed appreciatively.

'So I see.' I sorrowfully scanned the hanging carcass. Just dog meat and not even much of that. Ayrshires were never very fat. I was wondering how to break the news to him when he spoke again.

'Ah'm sorry you've caught me out this time, Mr Herriot,' he said, reaching for a greasy mug of tea.

'What do you mean?'

'Well, I allus reckon to have t'beast dressed and ready for you but you've come a bit early.'

I stared at him. 'But . . . everything's here, surely.' I waved a hand around me.

'Nay, nay, that's not 'er.'

'You mean . . . that isn't the cow from Moverley's.'

'That's right.' He took a long draught from the mug and wiped his mouth with the back of his hand. 'I 'ad to do this 'un first. Moverley's cow's still in t'wagon out at the back.'

'Alive?'

He looked mildly surprised. 'Aye, of course. She's never had a finger on 'er. Nice cow for a screw, too.'

I could have fainted with relief. 'She's no screw, Jeff. That's the wrong cow you've got there?'

'Wrong cow?' Nothing ever startled him but he obviously desired more information. I told him the whole story.

When I had finished, his shoulders began to shake gently and the beautiful clear eyes twinkled in the pink face.

'Well, that's a licker,' he murmured, and continued to laugh gently. There was nothing immoderate in his mirth and indeed nothing I had said disturbed him in the least. The fact that he had wasted his journey or that the farmer might be annoyed was of no moment to him.

Again, looking at Jeff Mallock, it struck me, as many times before, that there was nothing like a lifetime of dabbling among diseased carcasses and lethal bacteria for breeding tranquillity of mind.

'You'll slip back and change the cow ?' I said.

'Aye, in a minute or two. There's nowt spoilin'. Ah never likes to hurry me grub.' He belched contentedly. 'And how about you, Mr Herriot ? You could do with summat to keep your strength up.' He produced another mug and broke off a generous wedge of pie which he offered to me.

'No ... no ... er ... no, thank you, Jeff. It's kind of you, but no ... no ... not just now.'

He shrugged his shoulders and smiled as he stretched an arm for his pipe which was balanced on a sheep's skull. Flicking away some shreds of stray tissue from the stem he applied a match and settled down blissfully on the hides.

'I'll see ye later, then,' he said. 'Come round tonight and everything'll be ready for you.' He closed his eyes and again his shoulders quivered. 'Ah'd better get the right 'un this time.'

It must be more than twenty years since I took a cow under the TB Order, because the clinical cases so rarely exist now. 'Ring Min' no longer has the power to chill my blood, and the dread forms which scarred my soul lie unused and yellowing in the bottom of a drawer.

All these things have gone from my life. Charles Harcourt has gone too, but I think of him every day when I look at the little barometer which still hangs on my wall.

# 9

'Oh Mr Herriot!' Mrs Ridge said delightedly. 'Somebody stole our car last night.' She looked at me with a radiant smile.

I was lying on my bed in the barrack hut at Winkfield listening to somebody on the radio adjuring people to immobilize their cars in wartime when this lady's strange remark bubbled back from my veterinary days.

I stopped in the doorway of her house. 'Mrs Ridge, I'm terribly sorry. How . . . ?'

'Yes, yes, oh I can't wait to tell you!' Her voice trembled with excitement and joy. 'There must have been some prowlers around here last night, and I'm such a silly about leaving the car unlocked.'

'I see . . . how unfortunate.'

'But do come in,' she giggled. 'Forgive me for keeping you standing on the step, but I'm all of a dither!'

I went past her into the lounge. 'Well, it's very understandable. It must have been quite a shock.'

'Shock? Oh, but you don't see what I mean. It's wonderful!'

'Eh?'

'Yes, of course!' She clasped her hands and looked up at the ceiling. 'Do you know what happened?'

'Well, yes,' I said. 'You've just told me.'

'No, I haven't told you half.'

'You haven't?'

'No, but do sit down. I know you'll want to hear all about it.'


To explain this I have to go back ten days to the afternoon when Mrs Ridge ran tearfully up the steps of Skeldale House.

'My little dog's had an accident,' she gasped.

I looked past her. 'Where is he?'

'In the car. I didn't know whether I should move him.'

I crossed the pavement and opened the door. Her Cairn terrier, Joshua, lay very still on a blanket on the back seat.

'What happened?' I asked.

She put a hand over her eyes. 'Oh, it was terrible. You know he often plays in the farmer's field opposite our house – well, about half an hour ago he started to chase a rabbit and ran under the wheels of a tractor.'

I looked from her face to the motionless animal and back again. 'Did the wheels go over him?'

She nodded as the tears streamed down her cheeks.

I took her by the arm. 'Mrs Ridge, this is important. Are you absolutely sure that wheel passed right over his body?'

'Yes, I am – quite certain. I saw it happen. I couldn't believe he'd be alive when I ran to pick him up.' She took a long breath. 'I don't suppose he can live after that, can he?'

I didn't want to depress her but it seemed impossible that a small dog like this could survive being crushed under that great weight. Massive internal damage would be inevitable apart altogether from broken bones. It was sad to see the little sandy form lying still and unheeding when I had watched him so often running and leaping in the fields.

'Let's have a look at him,' I said.

I climbed into the car and sat down on the seat beside him. With the utmost care I felt my way over the limbs, expecting every moment to feel the crepitus which would indicate a fracture. I put my hand underneath him very slowly, supporting his weight every inch of the way. The only time Joshua showed any reaction was when I moved the pelvic girdle.

The best sign of all was the pinkness of the mucous membranes of eye and mouth and I turned to Mrs Ridge rather more hopefully.

'Miraculously he doesn't seem to have an internal haemorrhage and there are no limb bones broken. I'm pretty sure he has a fractured pelvis, but that's not so bad.'

She drew her fingers over the smears on her cheeks and looked at me, wide-eyed. 'You really think he has a chance?'

'Well, I don't want to raise your hopes unduly, but at this moment I can't find any sign of severe injury.'

'But it doesn't seem possible.'

I shrugged. 'I agree, it doesn't, but if he has got away with it I can only think it was because he was on soft ground which yielded as the wheel squeezed him down. Anyway, let's get him X-rayed to make sure.'

At that time, in common with most large animal practices, we didn't have an X-ray machine, but the local hospital helped us out in times of need. I took Joshua round there and the picture confirmed my diagnosis of pelvic fracture.

'There's not much I can do,' I said to his mistress. 'This type of injury usually heals itself. He'll probably have difficulty in standing on his hind legs for a while and for several weeks he'll be weak in the rear end, but with rest and time he ought to recover.'

'Oh, marvellous!' She watched me place the little animal back on the car seat. 'I suppose it's just a matter of waiting, then?'

'That's what I hope.'

My fears that Joshua might have some internal damage were finally allayed when I saw him two days later. His membranes were a rich deep pink and all natural functions were operating.

Mrs Ridge, however, was still worried. 'He's such a sorrowful little thing,' she said. 'Just look at him – he's lifeless.'

'Well you know he must be bruised and sore after that squashing he had. And he was very shocked, too. You must be patient.'

As I spoke, the little dog stood up, wobbled a few feet across the carpet and flopped down again. He showed no interest in me or his surroundings.

Before I left I gave his mistress some salicylate tablets to give him. 'These will ease his discomfort,' I said. 'Let me know if he doesn't improve.'

She did let me know – within forty-eight hours. 'I wish you'd come and see Joshua again,' she said on the phone. 'I'm not at all happy about him."

The little animal was as before. I looked down at him as he lay dejectedly on the rug, head on his paws, looking into the fireplace.

'Come on, Joshua, old lad,' I said. 'You must be feeling better now.' I bent and rubbed my fingers along the wiry coat, but neither word or gesture made an impression. I might as well not have been there.

Mrs Ridge turned to me worriedly. 'That's what he's like all the time. And you know how he is normally.'

'Yes, he's always been a ball of fire.' Again I recalled him jumping round my legs, gazing up at me eagerly. 'It's very strange.'

'And another thing,' she went on. 'He never utters a sound. And you know, that worries me more than anything because he's always been such a good little watch dog. We used to hear him barking when the early post came, he barked at the milk boy, the dustman, everybody. He was never a yappy dog, but he let us know when anybody was around.'

'Yes . . .' That was another thing I remembered. The tumult of sound from within whenever I rang the door bell.

'And now there's just this dreadful silence. People come and go but he never even looks up.' She shook her head slowly. 'Oh, if only he'd bark! Just once! I think it would mean he was getting better.'

'It probably would,' I said.

'Is there something else wrong with him, do you think?' she asked.

I thought for a moment or two. 'No, I'm convinced there isn't. Not physically, anyway. He's had a tremendous fright and he has withdrawn within himself. He'll come out of it in time.'

As I left I had the feeling I was trying to convince myself as much as Mrs Ridge. And as, over the next few days, she kept phoning me with bad reports about the little dog my confidence began to ebb.

It was a week after the accident that she begged me to come to the house again. Joshua was unchanged. Apathetic, tail tucked down, sad-eyed – and still soundless.

His mistress was obviously under strain.

'Mr Herriot,' she said. 'What are we going to do? I can't sleep for thinking about him.'

I produced stethoscope and thermometer and examined the little animal again. Then I palpated him thoroughly from head to tail. When I had finished I squatted on the rug and looked up at Mrs Ridge.

'I can't find anything new. You'll just have to be patient.'

'But that's what you said before, and I feel I can't go on much longer like this.'

'Still no barking?'

She shook her head. 'No, and that's what I'm waiting for. He eats a little, walks around a little, but we never hear a sound from him. I know I'd stop worrying if I heard him bark, just once, but otherwise I have a horrible feeling he's going to die . . .'

*

I had hoped that my next visit would be more cheerful but though I was greatly relieved at Mrs Ridge's high spirits I was surprised, too.

I sat down in one of the comfortable chairs in the lounge.

'Well, I hope you'll soon recover your car,' I said.

She waved a hand negligently. 'Oh, it'll turn up somewhere, I'm sure.'

'But still – you must be very upset.'

'Upset? Not a bit! I'm so happy!'

'Happy? About losing the car . . . ?'

'No, not about that. About Joshua.'

'Joshua?'

'Yes.' She sat down in the chair opposite and leaned forward. 'Do you know what he did when those people were driving the car away?'

'No, tell me.'

'He *barked*, Mr Herriot! Joshua *barked*!'

# 10

The food was so good at the Winkfield flying school that it was said that those airmen whose homes were within visiting distance wouldn't take a day's leave because they might miss some culinary speciality. Difficult to believe, maybe, but I often think that few people in wartime Britain fared as well as the handful of young men in the scatter of wooden huts on that flat green stretch outside Windsor.

It wasn't as though we had a French chef, either. The cooking was done by two grizzled old men – civilians who wore cloth caps and smoked pipes and went about their business with unsmiling taciturnity.

It was rumoured that they were two ex-army cooks from the First World War, but whatever their origins they were artists. In their hands, simple stews and pies assumed a new significance and it was possible to rhapsodize even over the perfect flouriness of their potatoes.

So it was surprising when at lunchtime my neighbour on the left threw down his spoon, pushed away his plate and groaned. We ate on trestle tables, sitting in rows on long forms, and I was right up against the young man.

'What's wrong?' I asked. 'This apple dumpling is terrific.'

'Ah, it's not the grub.' He buried his face in his hands for a few seconds then looked at me with tortured eyes. 'I've been doing circuits and bumps this morning with Routledge and he's torn the knackers off me – all the time, it never stopped.'

Suddenly my own meal lost some of its flavour. I knew just what he meant. FO Woodham did the same to me.

He gave me another despairing glance, then stared straight ahead.

'I know one thing, Jim. I'll never make a bloody pilot.'

His words sent a chill through me. He was voicing the conviction which had been gradually growing in me. I never seemed to make any progress – whatever I did was wrong, and I was losing heart. Like all the others I was hoping to be graded pilot, but after every session with FO Woodham the idea of ever flying an aeroplane all on my own seemed more and more ludicrous. And I had another date with him at 2 p.m.

He was as quiet and charming as ever when I met him – till we got up into the sky and the shouting started again.

'Relax! For heavens sake, relax!' or 'Watch your height! Where the hell d'you think you're going?' or 'Didn't I tell you to centralize the stick? Are you bloody deaf or something?' And finally, after the first circuit when we juddered to a halt on the grass. 'That was an absolutely bloody ropy landing! Take off again!'

On the second circuit he fell strangely silent. And though I should have felt relieved I found something ominous in the unaccustomed peace. It could mean only one thing – he had finally given me up as a bad job. When we landed he told me to switch off the engine and climbed out of the rear cockpit. I was about to unbuckle my straps and follow him when he signalled me to remain in my seat.

'Stay where you are,' he said. 'You can take her up now.'

I stared down at him through my goggles. 'What . . . ?'

'I said take her up.'

'You mean, on my own . . . ? Go solo . . . ?'

'Yes, of course. Come and see me in the flight hut after you've landed and taxied in.' He turned and walked away over the green. He didn't look back.

After a few minutes a fitter came over to where I sat trembling in my seat. He spat on the turf then looked at me with deep distaste.

'Look, mate,' he said. 'That's a — good aircraft you've got there.'

I nodded agreement.

'Well I don't want it — well smashed up, okay ?'

'Okay.'

He gave me a final disgusted glance, then went round to the propeller.

Panic-stricken though I was, I did not forget the cockpit drill which had been dinned in to me so often. I never thought I'd have to use it in earnest but now I automatically tested the controls – rudder, ailerons and elevator. Fuel on, switch off, throttle closed, then switch on, throttle slightly open.

'Contact !' I cried.

The fitter swung the propeller and the engine roared. I pushed the throttle full open and the Tiger Moth began to bump its way over the grass. As we gathered speed I eased the stick forward to lift the tail, then as I pulled it back again the bumping stopped and we climbed smoothly into the air with the long dining hut at the end of the airfield flashing away beneath.

I was gripped by exhilaration and triumph. The impossible had happened. I was up here on my own, flying, really flying at last. I had been so certain of failure that the feeling of relief was over-powering. In fact it intoxicated me, so that for a long time I just sailed along, grinning foolishly to myself.

When I finally came to my senses I looked down happily over the side. It must be time to turn now, but as I stared downwards cold reality began to roll over me in a gathering flood. I couldn't recognize a thing in the great hazy tapestry beneath me. And everything seemed smaller than usual. Dry-mouthed, I looked at the altimeter. I was well over two thousand feet.

And suddenly it came to me that FO Woodham's shouts had not been meaningless; he had been talking sense, giving me good advice, and as soon as I got up in the air by myself I had ignored it all. I hadn't lined myself up on a cloud, I hadn't watched my artificial horizon. I hadn't kept an eye on the altimeter. And I was lost.

It was a terrible feeling, this sense of utter isolation as I desperately scanned the great chequered landscape for a familiar object. What did you do in a case like this? Soar around southern England till I found some farmer's field big enough to land in, then make my own abject way back to Winkfield? But that way I was going to look the complete fool, and also I'd stand an excellent chance of smashing up that fitter's beloved aeroplane and maybe myself.

It seemed to me that one way or another I was going to make a name for myself. Funny things had happened to some of the other lads – many had been air-sick and vomited in the cockpit, one had gone through a hedge, another on his first solo had circled the airfield again and again – seven times he had gone round – trying to find the courage to land while his instructor sweated blood and cursed on the ground. But nobody had really got lost like me. Nobody had flown off into the blue and returned on foot without his aeroplane.

My visions of my immediate fate were reaching horrific proportions and my heart was hammering uncontrollably when far away on my left I spotted the dear familiar bulk of the big stand on Ascot racecourse. Almost weeping with joy, I turned towards it and within minutes I was banking above its roof as I had done so often.

And there, far below and approaching with uncomfortable speed was the belt of trees which fringed the airfield, and beyond the windsock blowing over the wide green. But I was still far too high – I could never drop down there in time to hit that landing strip, I would have to go round again.

The ignominy of it went deep. They would all be watching on the ground and some would have a good laugh at the sight of Herriot over-shooting the field by several hundred feet and cruising off again into the clouds. But what was I thinking about?

There was a way of losing height rapidly and, bless you FO Woodham, I knew how to do it.

Opposite rudder and stick. He had told me a hundred times how to side slip and I did it now as hard as I could, sending the little machine slewing like an airborne crab down, down towards those trees.

And by golly it worked! The green copse rushed up at me and before I knew I was almost skimming the branches. I straightened up and headed for the long stretch of grass. At fifty feet I rounded out, then checked the stick gradually back till just above the ground, when I slammed it into my abdomen. The undercarriage made contact with the earth with hardly a tremor and I worked the rudder bar to keep straight until I came to a halt. Then I taxied in, climbed from the cockpit and walked over to the flight hut.

FO Woodham was sitting at a table, cup in hand, and he looked up as I entered. He had got out of his flying suit and was wearing a battle dress jacket with the wings we all dreamed about and the ribbon of the DFC.

'Ah, Herriot, I'm just having some coffee. Will you join me ?'
'Thank you, sir.'

I sat down and he pushed a cup towards me.
'I saw your landing,' he said. 'Delightful, quite delightful.'
'Thank you, sir.'

'And that sideslip.' One corner of his mouth twitched upwards. 'Very good indeed, really masterly.'

He reached for the coffee pot and went on. 'You've done awfully well, Herriot. Solo after nine hours' instruction, eh ? Splendid. But then I never had the slightest doubt about you at any time.'

He poised the pot over my cup. 'How do you like your coffee – black or white ?'

# 11

I was only the third man in our Flight of fifty to go solo and it was a matter of particular pride to me because so many of my comrades were eighteen- and nineteen-year-olds. They didn't say so but I often had the impression that they felt that an elderly gentleman like me in my twenties with a wife and baby had no right to be there, training for aircrew. In the nicest possible way they thought I was past it.

Of course, in many ways they had a point. The pull I had from home was probably stronger than theirs. When our sergeant handed out the letters on the daily parade I used to secrete mine away till I had a few minutes of solitude to read about how fast little Jimmy was growing, how much he weighed, the unmistakable signs of outstanding intelligence, even genius, which Helen could already discern in him.

I was missing his babyhood and it saddened me. It is still something I deeply regret because it comes only once and is gone so quickly. But I still have the bundles of letters which his proud mother wrote to keep me in touch with every fascinating stage, and when I read them now it is almost as though I had been there to see it all.

At the time, those letters pulled me back almost painfully to the comforts of home but on the other hand there were occasions when life in Darrowby hadn't been all that comfortable . . .

I think it was the early morning calls in the winter which were the worst. It was a fairly common experience to be walking sleepy-eyed into a cow byre at 6 a.m. for a calving, but at Mr Blackburn's farm there was a difference. In fact, several differences.

Firstly, there was usually an anxious-faced farmer to greet me with news of how the calf was coming, when labour had started, but today I was like an unwelcome stranger. Secondly, I had grown accustomed to the sight of a few cows tied up in a cobbled byre with wooden partitions and an oil lamp, and now I was gazing down a long avenue of concrete under blazing electric light with a seemingly endless succession of bovine backsides protruding from tubular metal standings. Thirdly, instead of the early morning peace there was a clattering of buckets, the rhythmic pulsing of a milking machine and the blaring of a radio loud-speaker. There was also a frantic scurrying of white-coated, white-capped men, but none of them paid the slightest attention to me.

This was one of the new big dairy farms. In place of a solitary figure on a milk stool, head buried in the cow's side, pulling forth the milk with a gentle 'hiss-hiss' there was this impersonal hustle and bustle.

I stood just inside the doorway while out in the yard a particularly cold snow drifted from the blackness above. I had left a comfortable bed and a warm wife to come here and it seemed somebody ought at least to say 'hello'. Then I noticed the owner hurrying past with a bucket. He was moving as fast as any of his men.

'Hey, Mr Blackburn!' I cried. 'You rang me – you've got a cow calving?'

He stopped and looked at me uncomprehendingly for a moment. 'Oh aye . . . aye . . . she's down there on t'right.' He pointed to a light roan animal halfway along the byre. She was easy to pick out – the only one lying down.

'How long has she been on?' I asked, but when I turned round Mr Blackburn had gone. I trotted after him, cornered him in the milk house and repeated my question.

'Oh, she should've calved last night. Must be summat amiss.' He began to pour his bucket of milk over the cooler into the churn.

'Have you had a feel inside her?'

'Nay, haven't had time.' He turned harassed eyes towards me. 'We're a bit behind with milkin' this mornin'. We can't be late for t'milk man.'

I knew what he meant. The drivers who collected the churns for the big dairy companies were a fierce body of men. Probably kind husbands and fathers at normal times but subject to violent outbursts of rage if they were kept waiting even for an instant. I couldn't blame them, because they had a lot of territory to cover and many farms to visit, but I had seen them when provoked and their anger was frightening to behold.

'All right,' I said. 'Can I have some hot water, soap and a towel, please?'

Mr Blackburn jerked his head at the corner of the milk house. 'You'll 'ave to help yourself. There's everythin' there. Ah must get on.' He went off again at a brisk walk. Clearly he was more in fear of the milk man than he was of me.

I filled a bucket, found a piece of soap and threw a towel over my shoulder. When I reached my patient I looked in vain for some sign of a name. So many of the cows of those days had their names printed above their stalls but there were no Marigolds, Alices or Snowdrops here, just numbers.

Before taking off my jacket I looked casually in the ear where the tattoo marks stood out plainly against the creamy white surface. She was number eighty-seven.

I was in more trouble when I stripped off my shirt. In a modern byre like this there were no nails jutting from the walls to serve as hangers. I had to roll my clothes into a ball and carry them through to the milk house. There I found a sack which I tied round my middle with a length of binder twine.

Still ignored by everybody, I returned, soaped my arm and inserted it into the cow. I had to go a long way in to reach the calf, which was strange considering the birth should have taken place last night. It was the top of the little creature's head I touched first; the nose was tucked downwards instead of thrusting its way along the vagina towards the outside world, and the legs were similarly coiled under the body.

And I noticed something else. The entry of my arm did not provoke any answering strain from the cow, nor did she try to rise to her feet. There was something else troubling Number Eighty-Seven.

Lying flat on the concrete, still buried to the shoulder in the cow, I raised my head and looked along the shaggy back with its speckle of light red and white hairs, and when I reached the neck I knew I need seek no further. The lateral kink was very obvious. Number Eighty-Seven, slumped on her chest, was gazing wearily and without interest at the wall in front of her but there was that funny little bend in her neck that told me everything.

I got up, washed and dried my arm and looked for Mr Blackburn. I found him bending by the side of a fat brown animal, pulling the cups from her teats. I tapped him on the shoulder.

'She's got milk fever.' I said.

'Oh, aye,' he replied, then he hoisted the bucket, brushed past me and made off down the byre.

I kept pace with him. 'That's why she can't strain. Her uterus has lost its tone. She'll never calve till she gets some calcium.'

'Right.' He still didn't look at me. 'Ye'll give 'er some, then ?'

'Yes,' I said to his retreating back.

The snow still swirled in the outer darkness and I toyed with the idea of getting dressed. But I'd only have to strip again so I decided to make a dash for it. With the car boot open, it seemed to take a long time to fish out the bottles and flutter valve with the flakes settling thickly on my naked flesh.

Back in the byre I looked around for a spare man to help me but there was no lessening of the feverish activity. I would have to roll this cow on to her side and inject into her milk vein without assistance. It all depended on how comatose she was.

And she must have been pretty far gone because when I braced my feet against the tubular steel and pushed both hands against her shoulder she flopped over without resistance. To keep her there I lay on top of her as I pushed in the needle and ran the calcium into the vein.

One snag was that my sprawling position took me right underneath the neighbouring cow on the right, a skittish sort of animal who didn't welcome the rubber-booted legs tangling with her hind feet. She expressed her disapproval by treading painfully on my ankles and giving me a few smart kicks on the thigh, but I dared not move because the calcium was flowing in beautifully.

When the bottle was empty I kneed my patient back on to her chest and ran another bottle of calcium magnesium and phosphorus under her skin. By the time I had finished and rubbed away the subcutaneous fluid Number Eighty-Seven was looking decidedly happier.

I didn't hurry over cleaning and putting away my injection outfit and re-soaping my arms because I knew that every minute would bring back strength to my patient.

The lightning response to intravenous calcium has always afforded me a simple pleasure and when I pushed my arm in again the difference was remarkable. The previously flaccid uterus gripped at my hand and as the cow went into a long expulsive effort she turned her head, looked back at me and opened her mouth in a muffled bellow. It was not a sound of pain but rather as though she was saying, 'I'm back in business now.'

'All right, my lass,' I replied. 'I'll stay with you till it's all over.'

At other times I might have been a little chary of being over-heard conversing with a cow, but with the clamour of buckets and the nonstop blasting of the radio there was no chance of that happening.

I knew that I had to guide the calf back into the correct position and that it would take time, but I had a strange sense of one-ness with this animal because neither of us seemed to be of the slightest importance in the present setting. As I lay there face down on the concrete which grew harder all the time and with the milkers stumbling over my prostrate form I felt very much alone. There was just myself and Number Eighty-Seven for it.

Another thing I missed was the sense of occasion. There was a compensation in many an arduous calving in the feeling of a little drama being enacted; the worried farmer, attentive stockmen, the danger of losing the calf or even the mother – it was a gripping play and there was no doubt the vet was the leading man. He may even be the villain but he was number one. And here I was now, a scrabbling nonentity with hardly a mention in the cast. It was the shape of things to come.

And yet . . . and yet . . . the job was still there. I lifted the calf's lower jaw and as the cow gave a heave I eased it over the brim of the pelvis. Then I groped for the tiny legs and straightened them as another expulsive effort pushed the little creature towards me. He was definitely on his way now.

I didn't rush things – just lay there and let the cow get on with it. My worst moment was when one of the men came to put the milking machine on the temperamental animal on my right. As he tried to step up beside her she swung round, cocked her tail and sent a jet of faeces cascading across my back.

The man pushed her back into place, slipped on the teat cups then lifted the hose which was lying ready for swilling down the byre. A moment later I felt the icy flow of water playing from my shoulders to my hips, then the application of a spare udder cloth as the helpful fellow cleaned me off.

'Thanks very much,' I gasped. And I was really grateful. It was the only attention I had received all morning.

Within half an hour the feet appeared at the vulva followed by a wet nose whose nostrils twitched reassuringly. But they were big feet – this would be a bull calf and his final entry into the world could be a tight squeeze.

I got into a sitting position and gripped a slippery cloven hoof in each hand. Leaning back, feet against the dung channel, I addressed Number Eighty-Seven again.

'Come on, old lass. A couple of good shoves and we're there.'

She responded with a mighty inflation of the abdomen and the calf surged towards me as I pulled, giving me a glimpse of a broad forehead and a pair of slightly puzzled eyes. For a moment I thought the ears were going to slip through but then the cow relaxed and the head disappeared back inside.

'Once more, girl!' I pleaded, and this time it seemed that she had decided to stop playing around and get the job over with. She gave a prolonged strain which sent head and shoulders through, and as I hauled away I had only that momentary panic I always feel that the hips might jam in the pelvis. But this one didn't stick and came sliding beautifully on to my lap.

Puffing slightly, I got to my feet and parted the hind legs. Sure enough the little scrotum was there; he was a fine bull calf. I pulled some hay from the rack and dried him off and within minutes he was sitting up, sniffing and snorting, looking around him with interest.

He wasn't the only interested party. His mother, craning round in her neck chain, gazed fascinatedly at the new arrival before releasing a deafening bello . I seized the front feet again and pulled the calf up to the front of the stall where the cow, after a brief examination, began to lick him from head to tail. Then as I watched, entranced, she suddenly rose to her feet so that she could reach some of the little creature's more inaccessible corners.

I smiled to myself. So that was that. She had got over the milk fever and had a nice live calf, too. All was well with Number Eighty-Seven.

Mr Blackburn came up and stood by my side and I realized that the noise in the byre had subsided. The milking was finished.

The farmer took off his white hat and wiped away the sweat

from his brow. 'By gaw, that was a rush. We were short-handed this mornin' and I was sure we were goin' to miss that milk feller. He's a terror – won't wait a minute, and I've had to chase after 'im in a tractor with the churns afore now.'

As he finished speaking a hen leaped with a squawk from the rack. Mr Blackburn reached forward and lifted a warm new-laid egg out of the hay.

He inspected it for a moment then turned to me. 'Have you 'ad your breakfast?'

'No, of course not.'

'Well, tell your missus to put this in the fryin' pan,' he said, handing me the egg.

'Oh, thank you very much, Mr Blackburn, I'll enjoy that.'

He nodded and continued to stand there, gazing at the cow and calf. Dairy farming is one of the hardest ways of making a living and this pre-dawn turmoil was an everyday occurrence in his life. But I knew he was pleased with my efforts because he faced me suddenly and his weathered features broke into a delighted grin. Without warning he gave me a friendly thump on the chest.

'Good old Jim!' he said, and walked away.

I dressed, got into the car and placed my egg with the utmost care on the dash, then I eased myself gingerly on to the seat, because that hosing had sent a pint or two of dirty water down into my underpants and sitting down was intensely uncomfortable.

As I drove away the darkness was thinning into the grey beginning of a new day and around me the white bulk of the fells began to lift from the half light – massive, smooth and inexpressibly cold.

I looked at the egg rocking gently on the dash, and smiled to myself. I could still see Mr Blackburn's sudden grin, still feel his punch on the chest, and my main sensation was of reassurance.

Systems may be changing, but cows and calves and Yorkshire farmers were just the same.

# 12

On my wage of seven and threepence a day, out of which was deducted maintenance for wife and child, I was unable to indulge in high living even if I had wanted to, but one evening in Windsor I decided to allow myself the luxury of one glass of beer, and as I pushed open the pub doorway the first thing I saw was a man sitting at the corner of the bar with a small dog under his chair.

Little things like that could lift me effortlessly back to my old life, and I could almost hear George Wilks, the auctioneer, in the Drovers' Arms at Darrowby.

'I reckon that's the best pub terrier I've ever seen.' He bent down from the bar counter and patted Theo's shaggy head as it protruded from beneath his master's stool.

It struck me that 'pub terrier' wasn't a bad description. Theo was small and mainly white, though there were odd streaks of black on his flanks, and his muzzle had a bushy outgrowth of hair which made him undeniably attractive but still more mysterious.

I warmed to a Scottish colleague recently who, when pressed by a lady client to diagnose her dog's breed and lineage replied finally, 'Madam, I think it would be best just to call him a wee broon dug.'

By the same token Theo could be safely be described as a wee white dug, but in Yorkshire the expression 'pub terrier' would be more easily understood.

His master, Paul Cotterell, looked down from his high perch.

'What's he saying about you, old chap?' he murmured languidly, and at the sound of his voice the little animal leaped, eager and wagging, from his retreat.

Theo spent a considerable part of his life between the four metal legs of that stool, as did his master on the seat. And it often seemed to me to be a waste of time for both of them. I often took my own dog, Sam, into pubs and he could squat beneath my seat, but whereas it was an occasional thing with me – maybe once or twice a week – with Paul Cotterell it was an unvarying ritual. Every night from eight o'clock onwards he could be found sitting there at the end of the bar of the Drovers' Arms, pint glass in front of him, little curly pipe drooping over his chin.

For a young man like him – he was a bachelor in his late thirties – and a person of education and intelligence, it seemed a sterile existence.

He turned to me as I approached the counter. 'Hello, Jim, let me get you a drink.'

'That's very kind of you, Paul,' I replied. 'I'll have a pint.'

'Splendid.' He turned to the barmaid with easy courtesy. 'Could I trouble you, Moyra?'

We sipped our beer and we chatted. This time it was about the music festival at Brawton and then we got on to music in general. As with any other topic I had discussed with him he seemed to know a lot about it.

'So you're not all that keen on Bach?' he inquired lazily.

'No, not really. Some of it, yes, but on the whole I like something a bit more emotional. Elgar, Beethoven, Mozart. Even Tchaikovsky – I suppose you highbrows look down your noses at him?'

He shrugged, puffed his little pipe and regarded me with a half-smile, one eyebrow raised. He often looked like that and it made me feel he ought to wear a monocle. But he didn't enthuse about Bach, though it seemed he was his favourite composer. He never enthused about anything, and he listened with that funny look on his face while I rhapsodized about the Elgar violin concerto.

Paul Cotterell was from the south of England, but the locals had long since forgiven him for that because he was likeable, amusing, and always ready to buy anybody a drink from his corner in the Drovers'. To me, he had a charm·which was very English; casual, effortless. He never got excited, he was always polite and utterly self-contained.

'While you're here, Jim,' he said. 'I wonder if you'd have a look at Theo's foot?'

'Of course.' It is one of a vet's occupational hazards that wherever he goes socially it is taken for granted that there is nothing he would rather do than dole out advice or listen to symptoms. 'Let's have him up.'

'Here, boy, come on.' Paul patted his knee and the little dog jumped up and sat there, eyes sparkling with pleasure. And I thought as I always did that Theo should be in pictures. He was the perfect film dog with that extraordinarily fuzzy laugh-face. People paid good money to see dogs just like him in cinemas all over the world.

'All right, Theo,' I said, scooping him from his master's knee. 'Where's the trouble?'

Paul indicated the right forefoot with the stem of his pipe. 'It's that one. He's been going a bit lame off and on for the last few days.'

'I see.' I rolled the little animal on his back and then laughed. 'Oh, he's only got a broken claw. There's a little bit hanging off here. He must have caught it on a stone. Hang on a minute.' I delved in my pocket for the scissors which always dwelt there. A quick snip and the job was done.

'Is that all?' asked Paul.

'Yes, that's it.'

One eyebrow went up mockingly as he looked at Theo. 'So that's what you were making all the fuss about, eh? Silly old trout.' He snapped his fingers. 'Back you go.'

The little dog obediently leaped to the carpet and disappeared into his sanctuary beneath the stool. And at that moment I had a flash of intuition about Paul – about his charm which I had often admired and envied. He didn't really care. He was fond of his dog, of course. He took him everywhere with him, exercised him regularly by the river, but there was none of the anxiety, the almost desperate concern which I had so often seen in the eyes of my clients when I dealt with even the most trivial of their ailments. They cared too much – as I have always done with my own animals.

And of course he was right. It was an easier and more comfortable way to live. Caring made you vulnerable, while Paul cruised along, impregnable. That attractive casualness, the nonchalant good manners, the imperturbability – they all had their roots in the fact that nothing touched him very deeply.

And despite my snap diagnosis of his character I still envied him. I have always been blown around too easily by my emotions; it must be lovely to be like Paul. And the more I thought about it the more I realized how everything fitted in. He had never cared enough to get married. Even Bach, with his mathematical music, was part of the pattern.

'I think that major operation deserves another pint, Jim.' He smiled his lop-sided smile. 'Unless you demand a higher fee ?'

I laughed. I would always like him. We are all different and we have to act as we are made, but as I started my second glass I thought again of his carefree life. He had a good job in the government offices in Brawton, no domestic responsibilities, and every night he sat on that same stool drinking beer with his dog underneath. He hadn't a worry in the world.

Anyway, he was part of the Darrowby scene, part of something I liked, and since I have always hated change it was in a sense reassuring to know that no matter what night you went into the Drovers' you would find Paul Cotterell in the corner and Theo's shaggy muzzle peeping from below.

I felt like that one night when I dropped in near closing time.

'D'you think he's got worms ?' The question was typically off-hand.

'I don't know, Paul. Why do you ask ?'

He drew on his pipe. 'Oh, I just thought he looked a bit thin lately. Come up, Theo !'

The little dog, perched on his master's knee, looked as chirpy as ever and when I reached over and lifted him he licked my hand. But his ribs did feel rather prominent.

'Mmm, yes,' I said. 'Maybe he has lost a bit of weight. Have you noticed him passing any worms ?'

'I haven't, actually.'

'Not even little bits – whitish segments sticking round his rear ?'

'No, Jim.' He shook his head and smiled. 'But I haven't looked all that closely, old boy.'

'Okay,' I said. 'Let's worm him, just in case. I'll bring in some tablets tomorrow night. You'll be here . . . ?'

The eyebrow went up. 'I think that's highly probable.'

Theo duly got his worm tablets and after that there was a space of several weeks when I was too busy to visit the Drovers'. When I finally did get in it was a Saturday night and the Athletic Club dance was in full spate. A rhythmic beat drifted from the ballroom, the little bar was packed, and the domino players were under pressure, squashed into a corner by the crush of dinner jackets and backless dresses.

In the noise and heat I struggled towards the bar, thinking that the place was unrecognizable. But there was one feature unchanged – Paul Cotterell on his stool at the far end of the counter.

I squeezed in next to him and saw he was wearing his usual tweed jacket. 'Not dancing, Paul ?'

He half closed his eyes, shook his head slowly and smiled at me over his bent little pipe. 'Not for me, old boy,' he murmured. 'Too much like work.'

I glanced down and saw that something else hadn't changed. Theo was there, too, keeping his nose well clear of the milling feet. I ordered two beers and we tried to converse, but it was difficult to shout above the babel. Arms kept poking between us towards the counter, red faces pushed into ours and shouted greetings. Most of the time we just looked around us.

Then Paul leaned close and spoke into my ear. 'I gave Theo those pills but he's still getting thinner.'

'Really ?' I shouted back. 'That's unusual.'

'Yes . . . perhaps you'd have a look at him ?'

I nodded, he snapped his fingers and the little dog was on his knee in an instant. I reached and lifted him on to mine and I noticed immediately that he was lighter in my hands.

'You're right,' I said. 'He's still losing weight.'

Balancing the dog in my lap, I pulled down an eyelid and saw that the conjunctiva was pale.

I shouted again. 'He's anaemic.' I felt my way back over his face and behind the angle of the jaw I found that the post-pharyngeal lymph glands were greatly enlarged. This was strange. Could he have some form of mouth or throat infection ? I looked helplessly around me, wishing fervently that Paul wouldn't invariably consult me about his dog in a pub. I wanted to examine the animal, but I couldn't very well deposit him among the glasses on the bar.

I was trying to get a better grip with a view to looking down his throat when my hand slipped behind his foreleg and my heart gave a sudden thump as I encountered the axillary gland. It, too, was grossly enlarged. I whipped my fingers back into his groin and there was the inguinal gland, prominent as an egg. The pre-scapular was the same, and as I groped feverishly I realized that every superficial lymph gland was several times its normal size.

Hodgkin's disease. For a few moments I was oblivious of the shouting and laughter, the muffled blare of music. Then I looked at Paul who was regarding me calmly as he puffed his pipe. How could I tell him in these surroundings? He would ask me what Hodgkin's disease was and I would have to explain that it was a cancer of the lymphatic system and that his dog was surely going to die.

As my thoughts raced I stroked the shaggy head and Theo's comic whiskered face turned towards me. People jostled past, hands reached out and bore gins and whiskies and beers past my face, a fat man threw his arm round my neck.

I leaned across. 'Paul,' I said.

'Yes, Jim?'

'Will you . . . will you bring Theo round to the surgery to-morrow morning. It's ten o'clock on a Sunday.'

Momentarily the eyebrow twitched upwards, then he nodded. 'Right, old boy.'

I didn't bother to finish my drink. I began to push my way towards the door and as the crush closed around me I glanced back. The little dog's tail was just disappearing under the stool.

Next day I had one of those early waking mornings when I started tossing around at six o'clock and finished by staring at the ceiling.

Even after I had got my feet on the ground and brought Helen a cup of tea, the waiting was interminable until the moment arrived which I had been dreading – when I faced Paul across the surgery table with Theo standing between us.

I told him straight away. I couldn't think of any easy way to lead up to it.

His expression did not change, but he took his pipe out of his mouth and looked steadily at me, then at the dog and back again at me.

'Oh,' he said at last. 'I see.'

I didn't say anything and he slowly ran his hand along the little animal's back. 'Are you quite sure, Jim?'

'Absolutely. I'm terribly sorry.'

'Is there no treatment?'

'There are various palliatives, Paul, but I've never seen any of them do any good. The end result is always the same.'

'Yes . . .' He nodded slowly. 'But he doesn't look so bad. What will happen if we don't do anything?'

I paused. 'Well, as the internal glands enlarge, various things will happen. Ascites – dropsy – will develop in the abdomen. In fact you see he's a little bit pot-bellied now.'

'Yes . . . I do see, now you mention it. Anything else?'

'As the thoracic glands get bigger he'll begin to pant.'

'I've noticed that already. He's breathless after a short walk.'

'And all the time he'll get thinner and thinner and more debilitated.'

Paul looked down at his feet for a few moments then faced me. 'So what it amounts to is that he's going to be pretty miserable for the rest of his life.' He swallowed. 'And how long is that going to be?'

'A few weeks. It varies. Maybe up to three months.'

'Well, Jim.' He smoothed back his hair. 'I can't let that happen. It's my responsibility. You must put him to sleep now, before he really starts to suffer. Don't you agree?'

'Yes, Paul, it's the kindest thing to do.'

'Will you do it immediately – as soon as I am out of that door?'

'I will,' I replied. 'And I promise you he won't know a thing.'

His face held a curious fixity of expression. He put his pipe in his mouth, but it had gone out so he stuffed it into his pocket. Then he leaned forward and patted his dog once on the head. The bushy face with the funny shock of hair round the muzzle turned to him and for a few seconds they looked at each other.

Then, 'Goodbye, old chap,' he muttered and strode quickly from the room.

I kept my promise.

'Good lad, good old Theo,' I murmured, and stroked the face and ears again and again as the little creature slipped peacefully away. Like all vets I hated doing this, painless though it was, but to me there has always been a comfort in the knowledge that the last thing these helpless animals knew was the sound of a friendly voice and the touch of a gentle hand.

Sentimental, maybe. Not like Paul. He had been practical and utterly rational in the way he had acted. He had been able to do the right thing because he was not at the mercy of his emotions.

Later, over a Sunday lunch which I didn't enjoy as much as usual I told Helen about Theo.

I had to say something because she had produced a delicious pot roast on the gas ring which was our only means of cooking and I wasn't doing justice to her skill.

Sitting at our bench I looked down at her. It was my turn for the high stool.

'You know, Helen,' I said, 'that was an object lesson for me. The way Paul acted, I mean. If I'd been in his position I'd have shilly-shallied – tried to put off something which was inevitable.'

She thought for a moment. 'Well, a lot of people would.'

'Yes, but he didn't.' I put down my knife and fork and stared at the wall. 'He behaved in a mature way. I suppose Paul has one of those personalities you read about. Well-adjusted, completely adequate.'

'Come on, Jim, eat your lunch. I know it was a sad thing but it had to be done and you mustn't start criticizing yourself. Paul is Paul and you are you.'

I started again on the meat but I couldn't repress the rising sense of my own inadequacy. Then as I glanced to one side I saw that my wife was smiling up at me.

I felt suddenly reassured. It seemed that she at least didn't seem to mind that I was me.


That was on the Sunday, and on Tuesday morning I was handing out some wart lotion to Mr Sangster who kept a few dairy cows down by the station.

'Dab that on the udder night and morning after milking,' I said. 'I think you'll find that the warts will start to drop off after a week or two.'

'Thank ye.' He handed over half a crown and I was dropping it into the desk drawer when he spoke again.

'Bad job about Paul Cotterell, wasn't it?'

'What do you mean?'

'Ah thought you'd have heard,' he said. 'He's dead.'

'Dead!' I stared at him stupidly. 'How . . . what . . . ?'

'Found 'im this mornin'. He did away with 'isself.'

I leaned with both hands on the desk. 'Do you mean . . . suicide?'

'Aye, that's what they say. Took a lot o' pills. It's all ower t'town.'

I found myself hunching over the day book, sightlessly scanning the list of calls while the farmer's voice seemed to come from far away.

'It's a bad job, right enough. He were a nice feller. Reckon everybody liked 'im.'

Later that day I was passing Paul's lodgings when I saw his landlady, Mrs Clayton, in the doorway. I pulled up and got out of the car.

'Mrs Clayton,' I said. 'I still can't believe this.'

'Nor can I, Mr Herriot, it's terrible.' Her face was pale, her eyes red. 'He was with me six years, you know – he was like a son.'

'But why on earth . . . ?'

'Oh, it was losin' his dog that did it. He just couldn't stand it.'

A great wave of misery rose and engulfed me and she put her hand on my arm.

'Don't look like that, Mr Herriot. It wasn't your fault. Paul told me all about it and nobody could have saved Theo. People die of that, never mind dogs.'

I nodded dumbly and she went on.

'But I'll tell your something in confidence, Mr Herriot. Paul wasn't able to stand things like you or me. It was the way he was made – you see he suffered from depression.'

'Depression! Paul . . . ?'

'Oh yes, he's been under the doctor for a long time and takin' pills regular. He allus put a brave face on, but he's had nervous trouble off and on for years.'

'Nervous trouble . . . I'd never have dreamed . . .'

'No, nobody would, but that's how it was. He had an unhappy childhood from what I made out. Maybe that's why he was so fond of his dog. He got too attached to him, really.'

'Yes . . . yes . . .'

She took out a screwed up handkerchief and blew her nose. 'Well, as I said, the poor lad had a rough time most of his life, but he was brave.'

There didn't seem anything else to say. I drove away out of the town and the calm green hills offered a quiet contrast to the turmoil which can fill a man's mind. So much for Herriot as a judge of character. I couldn't have been more wrong, but Paul had fought his secret battle with a courage which had deceived everybody.

I reflected on the object lesson which I thought he had given me, but in fact it was a lesson of another kind and one which I have never forgotten; that there are countless people like Paul who are not what they seem.

# 13

The shock of Paul Cotterell's death stayed with me for a long time, and in fact I know I have never quite got over it because even now when the company in the bar of the Drovers' has changed and I am one of the few old faces left from thirty-five years ago I can still see the jaunty figure on the corner stool and the bushy face peeping from beneath.

It was the kind of experience I didn't want repeated in my lifetime yet, uncannily, I ran into the same sort of thing almost immediately afterwards.

It couldn't have been more than a week after Paul's funeral that Andrew Vine brought his fox terrier to the surgery.

I put the little dog on the table and examined each of his eyes carefully in turn.

'I'm afraid he's getting worse,' I said.

Without warning the man slumped across the table and buried his face in his hands.

I put my hand on his shoulder. 'What is it, Andrew? What on earth's the matter?'

At first he did not answer but stayed there, huddled grotesquely by the side of his dog as great sobs shook his body.

When he spoke at last it was into his hands and his voice was hoarse and desperate. 'I can't stand it! If Digger goes blind I'll kill myself!'

I looked down at the bowed head in horrified disbelief. It couldn't be happening again. Not so soon after Paul. And yet there were similarities. Andrew was another bachelor in his thirties and the terrier was his constant companion. He lived in lodgings and appeared to have no worries though he was a shy, diffident man with a fragile look about his tall stooping frame and pallid face.

He had first consulted me about Digger several months ago.

'I call him that because he's dug large holes in the garden ever since his puppy days,' he said with a half-smile, looking at me almost apprehensively from large dark eyes.

I laughed. 'I hope you haven't brought him to me to cure that, because I've never read anything in the books about it.'

'No, no, it's about something else – his eyes. And he's had that trouble since he was a pup, too.'

'Really? Tell me.'

'Well, when I first got him he had sort of mattery eyes, but the breeder said he'd probably just got some irritant in them and it would soon clear up. And in fact it did. But he's never been quite right. He always seems to have a little discomfort in his eyes.'

'How do you mean?'

'He rubs the side of his face along the carpet and he blinks in bright light.'

'I see.' I pulled the little animal's face round towards me and looked intently at the eyelids. My mind had been busy as he spoke and I was fairly sure I should find either entropion (inversion of the eyelids) or distichiasis (an extra row of lashes rubbing against the eyeball), but there was no sign of either. The surface of the cornea, too, looked normal, except perhaps that the deeper structure of lens and iris were not as easy to define as usual.

I moved over to a cupboard for the ophthalmoscope. 'How old is he now?'

'About a year.'

'So he's had this for about ten months?'

'Yes, about that. But it varies a lot. Most of the time he seems normal, then there are days when he goes and lies in his basket with his eyes half closed and you can tell there's something wrong. Not pain, really. More like discomfort, as I said.'

I nodded and hoped I was looking wise but none of this added up to anything familiar. I switched on the little light on the ophthalmoscope and peered into the depths of that most magical and delicate of all organs, down through the lens to the brilliant tapestry of the retina with its optic papilla and branching blood vessels. I couldn't find a thing wrong.

'Does he still dig holes?' I asked. When baffled I often snatch at straws and I wondered if the dog was suffering from a soil irritation.

Andrew shook his head. 'No, very seldom now, and anyway, his bad days are never associated with his digging.'

'Is that so?' I rubbed my chin. The man was obviously ahead of me with his thinking and I had an uncomfortable feeling of bewilderment. People were always bringing their dogs in with 'bad eyes' and there was invariably something to be seen, some cause to be found. 'And would you say that this was one of his bad days?'

'Well I thought so this morning, but he seems a bit better now. Still, he's a bit blinky, don't you think?'

'Yes . . . maybe so.' Digger did appear to be reluctant to open his eyes fully to the sunshine streaming through the surgery window. And occasionally he kept them closed for a second or two as though he wasn't very happy. But damn it, nothing gave me the slightest clue.

I didn't tell the owner that I hadn't the faintest idea what was wrong with his dog. Such remarks do not inspire confidence. Instead, I took refuge in businesslike activity.

'I'm going to give you some lotion,' I said briskly. 'Put a few drops into his eyes three times daily. And let me know how he goes on. It's possible he has some long-standing infection in there.'

I handed over a bottle of two per cent boric acid solution and patted Digger's head. 'I hope that will clear things up for you, lad,' I said, and the stumpy tail wagged in reply. He was a sharp looking little animal, attractive and good-natured and a fine specimen of the smooth-haired breed with his long head and neck, pointed nose and beautifully straight limbs.

He jumped from the table and leaped excitedly around his master's legs.

I laughed. 'He's eager to go, like most of my patients.' I bent and slapped him playfully on the rump. 'My word, doesn't he look fit!'

'He is fit.' Andrew smiled proudly. 'In fact I often think that apart from those eyes he's a perfect little physical machine. You should see him out in the fields – he can run like a whippet.'

'I'll bet he can. Keep in touch, will you?' I waved them out of the door and turned to my other work, mercifully unaware that I had just embarked on one of the most frustrating and traumatic cases of my career.

After that first time I took special notice of Digger and his owner. Andrew, a sensitive likeable man, was a representative for a firm of agricultural chemists and, like myself, spent most of his time driving around the Darrowby district. His dog was always with him and I had been perfunctorily amused by the fact that the little animal was invariably peering intently through the windscreen, his paws either on the dash or balanced on his master's hand as he operated the gear lever.

But now that I was personally interested I could discern the obvious delight which the little animal derived from taking in every detail of his surroundings. He missed nothing in his daily journeys. The road ahead, the houses and people, trees and fields which flashed by the windows – these made up his world.

I met him one day when I was exercising Sam up on the high moors which crown the windy summits of the fells. But this was May, the air was soft and a week's hot sunshine had dried the green paths which wandered among the heather. I saw Digger flashing like a white streak over the velvet turf and when he spotted Sam he darted up to him, set himself teasingly for a moment, then shot back to Andrew who was standing in a natural circular glade among the harsh brown growth.

Here gorse bushes blazed in full yellow glory and the little dog hurtled round and round the arena, exulting in his health and speed.

'That's what I'd call sheer joy of living,' I said.

Andrew smiled shyly. 'Yes, isn't he beautiful,' he murmured.

'How are the eyes ?' I asked.

He shrugged. 'Sometimes good, sometimes not so good. Much the same as before. But I must say he seems easier whenever I put the drops in.'

'But he still has days when he looks unhappy ?'

'Yes . . . I have to say yes. Some days they bother him a lot.'

Again the frustration welled in me. 'Let's walk back to the car,' I said. 'I might as well have a look at him.'

I lifted Digger on to the bonnet and examined him again. There wasn't a single abnormality in the eyelids – I had wondered if I had missed something last time – but as the bright sunshine slanted across the eyeballs I could just discern the faintest cloudiness in the cornea. There was a slight keratitis there which hadn't been visible before. But why . . . why ?

'He'd better have some stronger lotion.' I rummaged in the car boot. 'I've got some here. We'll try silver nitrate this time.'

Andrew brought him in about a week later. The corneal discoloration had gone – probably the silver nitrate had moved it – but the underlying trouble was unchanged. There was still something sadly wrong. Something I couldn't diagnose.

That was when I started to get really worried. As the weeks passed I bombarded those eyes with everything in the book; oxide of mercury, chinosol, zinc sulphide, ichthyol and a host of other things which are now buried in history.

I had none of the modern sophisticated antibiotic and steroid applications but it would have made no difference if I had. I know that now.

The real nightmare started when I saw the first of the pigment cells beginning to invade the cornea. Sinister brown specks gathering at the limbus and pushing out dark tendrils into the smooth membrane which was Digger's window on the world. I had seen cells like them before. When they came they usually stayed. And they were opaque.

Over the next month I fought them with my pathetic remedies, but they crept inwards, slowly but inexorably, blurring and narrowing Digger's field of vision. Andrew noticed them too, and when he brought the little dog into the surgery he clasped and unclasped his hands anxiously.

'You know, he's seeing less all the time, Mr Herriot. I can tell. He still looks out of the car windows but he used to bark at all sorts of things he didn't like – other dogs for instance – and now he just doesn't spot them. He's – he's losing his sight.'

I felt like screaming or kicking the table, but since that wouldn't have helped I just looked at him.

'It's that brown stuff isn't it?' he said. 'What is it?'

'It's called pigmentary keratitis, Andrew. It sometimes happens when the cornea – the front of the eyeball – has been inflamed over a long period, and it is very difficult to treat. I'll do the best I can.'

My best wasn't enough. That slow, creeping tide was pitiless, and as the pigment cells were laid down thicker and thicker the resulting layer was almost black, lowering a dingy curtain between Digger and all the things he had gazed at so eagerly.

And all the time I suffered a long gnawing worry, a helpless wretchedness as I contemplated the inevitable.

It was when I examined the eyes five months after I had first seen them that Andrew broke down. There was hardly anything to be seen of the original corneal structure now; just a brown-black opacity which left only minute chinks for moments of sight. Blindness was not far away.

I patted the man's shoulder again. 'Come on, Andrew. Come over here and sit down.' I pulled over the single wooden chair in the consulting room.

He staggered across the floor and almost collapsed on the seat. He sat there, head in hands, for some time then raised a tear-stained face to me. His expression was distraught.

'I can't bear the thought of it,' he gasped. 'A friendly little thing like Digger – he loves everybody. What has he ever done to deserve this?'

'Nothing, Andrew. It's just one of the sad things which happen. I'm terribly sorry.'

He rolled his head from side to side. 'Oh God, but it's worse for him. You've seen him in the car – he's so interested in everything. Life wouldn't be worth living for him if he lost his sight. And I don't want to live any more either!'

123

'You mustn't talk like that, Andrew,' I said. 'That's going too far.' I hesitated. 'Please don't be offended, but you ought to see your doctor.'

'Oh, I'm always at the doctor,' he replied dully. 'I'm full of pills right now. He tells me I have a depression.'

The word was like a mournful knell. Coming so soon after Paul it sent a wave of panic through me.

'How long have you been like this?'

'Oh, weeks. I seem to be getting worse.'

'Have you ever had it before?'

'No, never.' He wrung his hands and looked at the floor. 'The doctor says that if I keep on taking the pills I'll get over it, but I'm reaching the end of my tether now.'

'But the doctor is right, Andrew. You've got to stick it and you'll be as good as new.'

'I don't believe it,' he muttered. 'Every day lasts a year. I never enjoy anything. And every morning when I wake up I dread having to face the world again.'

I didn't know what to say or how to help. 'Can I get you a glass of water?'

'No . . . no thanks.'

He turned his deathly pale face up to me again and the dark eyes held a terrible blankness. 'What's the use of going on? I know I'm going to be miserable for the rest of my life.'

I am no psychiatrist but I knew better than to tell somebody in Andrew's condition to snap out of it. And I had a flash of intuition.

'All right,' I said. 'Be miserable for the rest of your life, but while you're about it you've got to look after this dog.'

'Look after him? What can I do? He's going blind. There's nothing anybody can do for him now.'

'You're wrong, Andrew. This is where you start doing things for him. He's going to be lost without your help.'

'How do you mean?'

'Well, you know all those walks you take him – you've got to get him used to the same tracks and paths so that he can trot along on familiar ground without fear. Keep him clear of holes and ditches.'

He screwed up his face. 'Yes, but he won't enjoy the walks any more.'

'He will,' I said. 'You'll be surprised.'

'Oh, but . . .'

'And that nice big lawn at the back of your house where he runs. You'll have to be on the lookout all the time in case there are things left lying around on the grass that he might bump into. And the eye drops – you say they make him more comfortable. Who's going to put them in if you don't ?'

'But Mr Herriot . . . you've seen how he always looks out of the car when he's with me . . .'

'He'll still look out.'

'Even if he can't see ?'

'Yes.' I put my hand on his arm. 'You must understand, Andrew, when an animal loses his sight he doesn't realize what's happened to him. It's a terrible thing, I know, but he doesn't suffer the mental agony of a human being.'

He stood up and took a long shuddering breath. 'But I'm having the agony. I've been dreading this happening for so long. I haven't been able to sleep for thinking about it. It seems so cruel and unjust for this to strike a helpless animal – a little creature who's never done anybody any harm.' He began to wring his hands again and pace about the room.

'You're just torturing yourself!' I said sharply. 'That's part of your trouble. You're using Digger to punish yourself instead of doing something useful.'

'Oh, but what can I do that will really help ? All those things you talked about – they can't give him a happy life.'

'Oh, but they can. Digger can be happy for years and years if you really work at it. It's up to you.'

Like a man in a dream he bent and gathered his dog into his arms and shuffled along the passage to the front door. As he went down the steps into the street I called out to him.

'Keep in touch with your doctor, Andrew. Take your pills regularly – and remember,' I raised my voice to a shout, 're-member you've got a job to do with that dog!'

*

After Paul, I was on a knife edge of apprehension but this time there was no tragic news to shatter me. Instead I saw Andrew Vine frequently, sometimes in the town with Digger on a lead, occasionally in his car with the little white head framed always in the windscreen, and most often in the fields by the river where he seemed to be carrying out my advice by following the good open tracks again and again.

It was by the river that I stopped him one day. 'How are things going, Andrew?'

He looked at me unsmilingly. 'Oh, he's finding his way around not too badly. I keep my eye on him. I always avoid that field over there – there's a lot of boggy places in it.'

'Good, that's the idea. And how are you yourself?'

'Do you really want to know?'

'Yes, of course.'

He tried to smile. 'Well, this is one of my good days. I'm just tense and dreadfully unhappy. On my bad days I'm terror-stricken, despairing, utterly desolate.'

'I'm sorry, Andrew.'

He shrugged. 'Don't think I'm wallowing in self-pity. You asked me. Anyway, I have a system. Every morning I look at myself in the mirror and I say, 'Okay, Vine, here's another bloody awful day coming up, but you're going to do your job and you're going to look after your dog.'

'That's good, Andrew. And it will all pass. The whole thing will go away and you'll be all right one day.'

'That's what the doctor says.' He gave me a sidelong glance. 'But in the meantime . . .' He looked down at his dog. 'Come on, Digger.'

He turned and strode away abruptly with the little dog trotting after him, and there was something in the set of the man's shoulders and the forward thrust of his head which gave me hope. He was a picture of fierce determination.

My hopes were fulfilled. Both Andrew and Digger won through. I knew that within months, but the final picture in my mind is of a meeting I had with the two of them about two years later. It was on the flat table-land above Darrowby where I had first seen Digger hurtling joyously among the gorse bushes.

He wasn't doing so badly now, running freely over the smooth green turf, sniffing among the herbage, cocking a leg now and then with deep contentment against the drystone wall which ran along the hillside.

Andrew laughed when he saw me. He had put on weight and looked a different person. 'Digger knows every inch of this walk,' he said. 'I think it's just about his favourite spot – you can see how he's enjoying himself.'

I nodded. 'He certainly looks a happy little dog.'

'Yes, he's happy all right. He had a good life and honestly I often forget that he can't see.' He paused. 'You were right, that day in your surgery. You said this would happen.'

'Well, that's great, Andrew,' I said. 'And you're happy, too, aren't you?'

'I am, Mr Herriot. Thank God, I am.' A shadow crossed his face. 'When I think how it was then, I can't believe my luck. It was like being in a dark valley, and bit by bit I've climbed out into the sunshine.'

'I can see that. You're as good as new, now.'

He smiled. 'I'm better than that – better than I was before. That terrible experience did me good. Remember you said I was torturing myself? I realized I had spent all my days doing that. I used to take every little mishap of life and beat myself over the head with it.'

'You don't have to tell me, Andrew,' I said ruefully. 'I've always been pretty good at that myself.'

'Well, yes, I suppose a lot of us are. But I became an expert and see where it got me. It helped so much to have Digger to look after.' His face lit up and he pointed over the grass. 'Just look at that!'

The little dog had been inspecting an ancient fence, a few rotting planks which were probably part of an old sheep-fold, and as we watched he leaped effortlessly between the spars to the other side.

'Marvellous!' I said delightedly. 'You'd think there was nothing wrong with him.'

Andrew turned to me. 'Mr Herriot, when I see a thing like that it makes me wonder. Can a blind dog do such a thing. Do you think . . . do you think there's a chance he can see just a little?'

I hesitated. 'Maybe he can see a bit through that pigment, but it can't be much – a flicker of light and shade, perhaps. I really don't know. But in any case, he's become so clever in his familiar surroundings that it doesn't make much difference.'

'Yes . . . yes.' He smiled philosophically. 'Anyway, we must get on our way. Come on, Digger!'

He snapped his fingers and set off along a track which pushed a vivid green finger through the heather, pointing clean and unbroken to the sunny skyline. His dog bounded ahead of him, not just at a trot but at a gallop.

I have made no secret of the fact that I never really knew the cause of Digger's blindness, but in the light of modern developments in eye surgery I believe it was a condition called keratitis sicca. This was simply not recognized in those early days and anyway, if I had known, I could have done little about it. The name means 'dryness of the cornea' and it occurs when the dog is not producing enough tears. At the present time it is treated by instilling artificial tears or by an intricate operation whereby the salivary ducts are transferred to the eyes. But even now, despite these things, I have seen that dread pigmentation taking over in the end.

When I look back on the whole episode my feeling is of thankfulness. All sorts of things help people to pull out of a depression. Mostly it is their family – the knowledge that wife and children are dependent on them – sometimes it is a cause to work for, but in Andrew Vine's case it was a dog.

I often think of the dark valley which closed around him at that time and I am convinced he came out of it on the end of Digger's lead.

# 14

Now that I had done my first solo I was beginning to appreciate the qualities of my instructor. There was no doubt FO Woodham was a very good teacher.

There was a war on and no time for niceties. He had to get green young men into the air on their own without delay and he had done it with me.

I used to fancy myself as a teacher, too, with the boys who came to see practice in Darrowby. I could see myself now, smiling indulgently at one of my pupils.

'You don't see this sort of thing in country practice, David,' I said. He was one of the young people who occasionally came with me on my rounds. Fifteen years old, and like all the others he thought he wanted to be a veterinary surgeon. But at the moment he looked a little bewildered.

I really couldn't blame him. It was his first visit and he had expected to spend a day with me in the rough and tumble of large animal practice in the Yorkshire Dales and now there was this lady with the poodle and Emmeline. The lady's progress along the passage to the consulting room had been punctuated by a series of squeaking noises produced by her squeezing a small rubber doll. At each squeak Lucy advanced a few reluctant steps until a final pressure lured her on to the table. There she stood trembling and looking soulfully around her.

'She won't go anywhere without Emmeline,' the lady explained.

'Emmeline?'

'The doll.' She held up the rubber toy. 'Since this trouble started Lucy has become devoted to her.'

'I see. And what trouble is that?'

'Well, it's been going on for about two weeks now. She's so listless and strange, and she hardly eats anything.'

I reached behind me to the trolley for the thermometer. 'Right, we'll have a look at her. There's something wrong when a dog won't eat.'

The temperature was normal. I went over her chest thoroughly

129

with my stethoscope without finding any unusual sounds. The heart thudded steadily in my ears. Careful palpation of the abdomen revealed nothing out of the way.

The lady stroked Lucy's curly poll and the little animal looked up at her with sorrowful liquid eyes. 'I'm getting really worried about her. She doesn't want to go walks. In fact we can't even entice her from the house without Emmeline.'

'Eh ?'

'I say she won't take a step outside unless we squeak Emmeline at her, and then they both go out together. Even then she just trails along like an old dog, and she's only three after all. You know how lively she is normally.'

I nodded. I did know. This little poodle was a bundle of energy. I had seen her racing around the fields down by the river, jumping to enormous heights as she chased a ball. She must be suffering from something pretty severe, but so far I was baffled.

And I wished the lady woudn't keep on about Emmeline and the squeaking. I shot a side glance at David. I had been holding forth to him, telling him how ours was a scientific profession and that he would have to be really hot at physics, chemistry and biology to gain entrance to a veterinary school, and it didn't fit in with all this.

Maybe I could guide the conversation along more clinical lines. 'Any more symptoms ?' I asked. 'Any cough, constipation, diarrhoea ? Does she ever cry out in pain ?'

The lady shook her head. 'No, nothing like that. She just moons around looking at us with such a pitiful expression and searching for Emmeline.'

Oh dear, there it was again. I cleared my throat. 'She never vomits at all ? Especially after a meal ?'

'Never. When she does eat a little she goes straight away to find Emmeline and takes her to her basket.'

'Really ? Well I can't see that that has anything to do with it. Are you sure she isn't lame at times ?'

The lady didn't seem to be listening. 'And when she gets Emmeline into her basket she sort of circles around, scratching the blanket as though she was making a bed for the little thing.'

I gritted my teeth. Would she never stop ? Then a light flashed in the darkness.

'Wait a minute,' I said. 'Did you say making a bed?'

'Yes, she scratches around for ages then puts Emmeline down.'

'Ah yes.' The next question would settle it. 'When was she last in season?'

The lady tapped a finger against her cheek. 'Let me see. It was in the middle of May – that would be about nine weeks ago.'

There wasn't a mystery any more.

'Roll her over, please,' I said.

With Lucy stretched on her back, her eyes regarding the surgery ceiling with deep emotion, I ran my fingers over the mammary glands. They were turgid and swollen. I gently squeezed one of the teats and a bead of milk appeared.

'She's got false pregnancy,' I said.

'What on earth is that?' The lady looked at me, round-eyed.

'Oh, it's quite common in bitches. They get the idea they are going to have pups and around the end of the gestation period they start this business. Making a bed for the pups is typical, but some of them actually swell in the abdomen. They do all sorts of peculiar things.'

'My goodness, how extraordinary!' The lady began to laugh. 'Lucy, you silly little thing, worrying us over nothing.' She looked at me across the table. 'How long is she going to be like this?'

I turned on the hot tap and began to wash my hands. 'Not for long. I'll give you some tablets for her. If she's not much better in a week come back for more. But you needn't worry – even if it takes a little bit longer she'll be her old self in the end.'

I went through to the dispensary, put the tablets in a box and handed them over. The lady thanked me then turned to her pet who was sitting on the tiled floor looking dreamily into space.

'Come along, Lucy,' she said, but the poodle took no notice. 'Lucy! Do you hear me? We're going now!' She began to walk briskly along the passage but the little animal merely put her head on one side and appeared to be hearkening to inward music. After a minute her mistress reappeared and regarded her with some exasperation. 'Oh really, you are naughty. I suppose there's only one way.' She opened her handbag and produced the rubber toy.

'Squeak-squeak,' went Emmeline and the poodle raised her eyes with misty adoration. 'Squeak-squeak, squeak-squeak.' The sound retreated along the passage and Lucy followed entranced until she disappeared round the corner.

I turned to David with an apologetic grin. 'Right,' I said, 'we'll get out on the road. I know you want to see farm practice and I assure you it's vastly different from what you've seen here.'

Sitting in the car, I continued. 'Mind you, don't get me wrong. I'm not decrying small animal work. In fact I'd have to admit that it is the most highly skilled branch of the profession and I personally think that small animal surgery is tremendously demanding. Just don't judge it all by Emmeline. Anyway, we have one doggy visit before we go out into the country.'

'What's that?' the lad asked.

'Well, I've had a call from a Mr Rington to say that his dalmatian bitch has completely altered her behaviour. In fact she's acting so strangely that he doesn't want to bring her to the surgery.'

'What do you think that might be?'

I thought for a moment. 'It seems a bit silly, but the first thing that comes to my mind is rabies. This is the most dreadful dog disease of all, but thank heaven we've managed to, keep it out of this country so far by strict quarantine regulations. But at college it was hammered into us so forcibly that it is always at the back of my mind even though I don't really expect to see it. But this case of the dalmatian could be anything. I only hope she hasn't turned savage because that's the sort of thing that leads to a dog being put down and I hate that.'

Mr Rington's opening remark didn't cheer me.

'Tessa's become really fierce lately, Mr Herriot. Started moping about and growling a few days ago and frankly I daren't trust her with strangers now. She nailed the postman by the ankle this morning. Most embarrassing.'

My spirits sank lower. 'Actually bit somebody! It's unbelievable – she's such a softie. I've always been able to do anything with her.'

'I know, I know,' he muttered. 'She's marvellous with children, too. I can't understand it. But come and have a look at her.'

The dalmatian was sitting in a corner of the lounge and she glanced up sulkily as we entered. She was a favourite patient and I approached her confidently.

'Hello, Tessa,' I said, and held out my hand. I usually had a tail-lashing, tongue-lolling welcome from this animal but today she froze into complete immobility and her lips withdrew silently from her teeth. It wasn't an ordinary snarl – it was as though the upper lip was operated by strings and there was something unnerving about it.

'What's the matter, old girl?' I inquired, and again the gleaming incisors were soundlessly exposed. And as I stared uncomprehendingly I could see that the eyes were glaring at me with blazing primitive hatred. Tessa was unrecognizable.

'Mr Herriot—' Her owner looked at me apprehensively. 'I don't think I'd go any nearer if I were you.'

I withdrew a pace. 'Yes, I'm inclined to agree with you. I don't think she'd cooperate if I tried to examine her. But never mind, tell me all about her.'

'Well, there's really nothing more to tell,' Mr Rington said helpless. 'She's just different – like this.'

'Appetite good?'

'Yes, fine. Eats everything in front of her.'

'No unusual symptoms at all?'

'None, apart from the altered temperament. The family can handle her, but quite frankly I think she'd bite any stranger who came too near.'

I ran my fingers through my hair. 'Any change in family circumstances? New baby? Different domestic help? Unusual people coming to the house?'

'No, nothing like that. There's been no change.'

'I ask because animals sometimes act like this out of jealousy or disapproval.'

'Sorry.' Mr Rington shrugged his shoulders. 'Everything is just as it's always been. Only this morning my wife was wondering if Tessa was still cross with us because we kept her indoors for three weeks while she was in season. But that was a long time ago – about two months now.'

I whipped round and faced him. 'Two months?'

'Yes, about that.'

'Surely not again!' I gestured to the owner. 'Would you please lift her up so that she's standing on her hind legs?'

'Like this?' He put his arms round the dalmatian's chest and hoisted till she was in the upright position with her abdomen facing me.

And it was as if I knew beforehand. Because I felt not the slightest surprise when I saw the twin row of engorged teats. It was unnecessary, but I leaned forward, grasped a little nipple and sent a white jet spurting.

'She's bulging with milk,' I said.

'Milk?'

'Yes, she's got false pregnancy. This is one of the more unusual side effects, but I'll give you some tablets and she'll soon be the docile Tessa again.'

As we got back into the car I had a good idea what the schoolboy was thinking. He would be wondering where the chemistry, physics and biology came in.

'Sorry about that, David,' I said. 'I've been telling you all about the constant variety of a vet's life and the first two cases you see are the same condition. But we are going out to the farms now and, as I said, you'll find it very different. I mean, those two cases were really psychological things. You don't get that in country practice. It's a bit rough but it's real and down to earth.'

As we drove into the farmyard I saw the farmer carrying a bag of meal over the cobbles.

I got out of the car with David. 'You've got a pig ill, Mr Fisher?'

'Aye, a big sow. She's in 'ere.' He led the way into a pen and pointed to a huge white pig lying on her side.

'She's been off it for a few days,' he said. 'Hardly eats owt – just picks at her food. And she just lays there all t'time. Ah don't think she's got strength to get to her feet.'

My thermometer had been in the pig's rectum as he spoke and I fished it out and read the temperature. It was 102.2 – dead normal. I auscultated the chest and palpated the abdomen with growing puzzlement. Nothing wrong. I looked over at the trough nearby. It was filled to the brim with fresh meal and water – untouched. And pigs do love their food.

I nudged her thigh with my fist. 'Come on, lass, get up.' And I followed it with a brisk slap across the rump. A healthy pig would have leaped to her feet but the sow never moved.

I tried not to scratch my head. There was something very funny here. 'Has she ever been ill before, Mr Fisher?'

'Nay, never ailed a thing and she's allus been a real lively pig, too. Ah can't reckon it up.'

Nor could I. 'What beats me,' I said, 'is that she doesn't look like a sick animal. She's not trembling or anxious, she's lying there as if she hadn't a care in the world.'

'Aye, you're right, Mr Herriot. She's as 'appy as Larry, but she'll neither move nor eat. It's a rum 'un, isn't it?'

It was very rum indeed. I squatted on my heels, watching the big sow. She reached forward and pushed gently with her snout at the straw bedding round her head. Sick pigs never did that. It was a gesture of well-being. And those little grunts which issued from deep in her chest. They were grunts of deep contentment and there was something familiar about the sound of them . . . something lurking at the back of my mind which wouldn't come forward. It was the same with the way the sow eased herself further on to her side, pushing the great stretch of abdomen outward as though in offering.

I had heard and seen it so many times before – the happy sounds, the careful movements. Then I remembered. Of course! She was like a sow with a litter, only there was no litter.

A wave of disbelief flowed over me. Oh no, no, please not a third time! It was dark in the pen and I couldn't get a clear view of the mammary glands.

I turned to the farmer. 'Open the door a little will you, please.'

As the sunshine flooded in everything was obvious. It was mere routine to reach out to the long tumefied udder and squirt the milk against the wall.

I straightened up wearily and was about to make my now commonplace announcement when David did it for me.

'False pregnancy?' he said.

I nodded dumbly.

'What was that?' enquired Mr Fisher.

'Well, your sow has got it into her head that she is pregnant,' I said. 'Not only that, but she thinks she has given birth to a litter and she's suckling the imaginary piglets now. You can see it, can't you?'

135

The farmer gave a long soft whistle. 'Aye . . . aye . . . you're right. That's what she's doin' . . . enjoyin' it, too.' He took off his cap, rubbed the top of his head and put the cap on again. 'Well, there's allus summat new, isn't there ?'

It wasn't new to David, of course. Old stuff, in fact, and I didn't want to bore him further with a lengthy dissertation.

'Nothing to worry about, Mr Fisher,' I said hastily. 'Call down to the surgery and I'll give you something to put in her food. She'll soon be back to normal.'

As I left the pen the sow gave a deep sigh of utter fulfilment and moved her position with the utmost care to avoid crushing her phantom family. I looked back at her and I could almost see the long pink row of piglets sucking busily. I shook my head to dispel the vision and went out to the car.

I was opening the door when the farmer's wife trotted towards me. 'I've just had a phone call from your surgery, Mr Herriot. They want you to go to Mr Rogers of East Farm. There's a cow calving.'

An emergency like this in the middle of a round was usually an irritant, but today the news came as a relief. I had promised this schoolboy some genuine country practice and I was beginning to feel embarrassed.

'Well, David,' I said with a light laugh as we drove away. 'You must be thinking all my patients are neurotic. But you're going to see a bit of the real thing now – there's nothing airy-fairy about a calving cow. This is where the hard work of our job comes in. It's often pretty tough fighting against a big straining cow, but you must remember the vet only sees the difficult cases where the calf is laid wrong.'

The situation of East Farm seemed to add weight to my words. We were bumping up the fellside along a narrow track which was never meant for motor cars and I winced as the exhaust grated against the jutting rocks.

The farm was perched almost on the edge of the hilltop and behind it the sparse fields, stolen from the moorland, rolled away to the skyline. The crumbling stonework and broken roof tiles testified to the age of the squat grey house.

I pointed to some figures, faintly visible on the massive stone lintel above the front door. 'What does that date mean to you, David ?'

'Sixteen sixty-six, the Great Fire of London,' he replied promptly.

'Well done. Strange to think they were building this place in the same year as old London burned down.'

Mr Rogers appeared, carrying a steaming bucket and a towel. 'She's out in t'field, Mr Herriot, but she's a quiet cow and easy to catch.'

'All right.' I followed him through the gate. It was another little annoyance when the farmer didn't have the cow inside for me but again I felt that if David wanted to be a vet he ought to know that a lot of our work was carried out in the open, often in the cold and rain.

Even now on this July morning a cool breeze whipped round my chest and back as I pulled off my shirt. It was never very warm in the high country of the Dales but I felt at home here. With the cow standing patiently as the farmer held her halter, the bucket perched among the tufts of wiry grass, and only a few stunted wind-bent trees breaking the harsh sweep of green, it seemed that at last this boy was seeing me in my proper place.

I soaped my arms to the shoulders. 'Hold the tail, will you, David. This is where I find out what kind of job it's going to be.'

As I slipped my hand into the cow it struck me that it would be no bad thing if it was a hard calving. If the lad saw me losing a bit of sweat it would give him a truer picture of the life in front of him.

'Sometimes these jobs take an hour or more,' I said. 'But you have the reward of delivering a new living creature. Seeing a calf wriggling on the ground at the end of it is the biggest thrill in practice.'

I reached forward, my mind alive with the possibilities. Posterior ? Head back ? Breech ? But as I groped through the open cervix into the uterus I felt a growing astonishment. There was nothing there.

I withdrew my arm and leaned for a moment on the hairy rump. The day's events were taking on a dreamlike quality. Then I looked up at the farmer.

'There's no calf in this cow, Mr Rogers.'

'Eh?'

'She's empty. She's calved already.'

The farmer gazed around him, scanning the acres of bare grass. 'Well where the hangment is the thing? This cow was messin' about last night and I thought she'd calve, but there was nowt to find this morning'.'

His attention was caught by a cry from the right.

'Hey, Willie! Just a minute, Willie!' It was Bob Sellars from the next farm. He was leaning over the drystone wall about twenty yards away.

'What's matter, Bob?'

'Ah thowt ah'd better tell ye. Ah saw that cow hidin' her calf this morning'.'

'Hidin' . . . ? What are ye on about?'

'Ah'm not jokin' nor jestin', Willie. She hid it on yon gutter ower there and every time t'calf tried to get out she pushed it back in again.'

'But . . . nay, nay, I can't 'ave that. I've never heard of such a thing. Have you, Mr Herriot?'

I shook my head, but the whole thing seemed to fit in with the air of fantasy which had begun to pervade the day's work.

Bob Sellars began to climb over the wall. 'Awright, if ye won't believe me I'll show ye.'

He led the way to the far end of the field where a dry ditch ran along the base of the wall. 'There 'e is!' he said triumphantly.

And there indeed he was. A tiny red and white calf half concealed by the long herbage. He was curled comfortably in his grassy bed, his nose resting on his forelegs.

When the little creature saw his mother he staggered to his feet and clambered shakily up the side of the ditch, but no sooner had he gained the level of the field than the big cow, released now from her halter, lowered her head and gently nudged him back in again.

Bob waved his arm. 'There y'are, she's hidin' it, isn't she?'

Mr Rogers said nothing and I merely shrugged my shoulders, but twice more the calf managed to scramble from the ditch and twice more his mother returned him firmly with her head.

'Well it teks a bit o' believin,' the farmer murmured, half to himself. 'She's had five calves afore this and we've taken 'em straight away from 'er as we allus do. Maybe she wants to keep this 'un for 'erself? I dunno . . . I dunno . . .' His voice trailed away.

Later, as we rattled down the stony track, David turned to me. 'Do you think that cow really hid her calf . . . so that she could keep it for herself?'

I stared helplessly through the glass of the windscreen. 'Well, anybody would tell you it's impossible, but you saw what happened. I'm like Mr Rogers, I just don't know.' I paused as the car dipped into a deep rut and sent us bobbing about. 'But you see some funny things at our job.'

The schoolboy nodded thoughtfully. 'Yes, it seems to me that yours is a funny life altogether.'

# 15

'Would you care to come and dice with death?'
Flight Lieutenant Cramond looked down at me, his puckish features creased into a mischievous smile. I was sitting at a table in my flying suit waiting to be called for a grading test and I stood up hurriedly.

'You mean . . . go up with you, sir?'

'Yes, that's right.'

'Well, I'm just waiting for . . .'

'Oh I know all about that.' He waved a careless hand. 'But there's no hurry. You've time for a bit of fun first.'

'Just as you say, sir,' I said, and followed him out of the hut. Nobody was quite sure of Flt Lt Cramond's status at the flying school. He wasn't one of the regular instructors – he was a much older man – but he was obviously regarded with respect by his fellow officers and seemed to adopt a freelance role.

He occasionally descended on an unsuspecting trainee pilot with his familiar request, 'Would you care to dice with death?'

and this was invariably followed by a joy ride round the sky, a dazzling display of aerobatics which looked wonderful from the ground but could be shattering in the air.

I had seen pupils tottering green-faced from the Tiger Moth after these sessions, and there seemed to be no particular reason why he did it at all. But there was no doubt he was a brilliant flyer. It was rumoured that he had been a stunt pilot with Alan Cobham's famous air circus, but there were so many rumours in the RAF – like the one about the bromide in the tea – that I never really knew if it was true.

However, I got into the aircraft with a feeling of pleasant anticipation. Whatever happened I wouldn't feel ill, being blessed with a stomach which never got queasy with motion. Over-indulgence can have disastrous effects on my digestive apparatus but otherwise I am immune. I have been on little cattle boats in force nine gales when even the crew were groaning in their bunks, but land-lubber Herriot was still enjoying his four meals a day. It was the same in the air.

I soon had reason to be grateful for this blessing because Flt Lt Cramond threw the little aircraft around the sky in an alarming manner, climbing high, then fluttering earthwards like a falling autumn leaf, doing repeated loops and spins. Most of it I enjoyed because he was a likeable man and the eyes in the mirror were humorous and friendly.

He kept up a running commentary as he went through his repertoire.

'This is Cramond's famous hangover cure,' he announced before going into a violent manoeuvre which involved a lot of flying upside down. To a novice like myself it was a strange sensation to be hanging in my straps, looking up at farmhouses and down at the cloud-strewn sky.

That was the only time I didn't feel too happy, because those canvas straps were attached to the sides of the cockpit by frayed wires which twanged and groaned disturbingly as I hung there. It was a long way to the ground and I kept a hand on the parachute release just in case.

I was wondering how long we were going to stay in this position when he rolled over and went into a long dive. Down and down we roared, heading nose first for the peaceful farm land,

and just as I had concluded that we must certainly plunge straight into the earth he levelled off and we skimmed through a long cornfield with the wheels of the undercarriage trailing among the golden ears.

'This is nice, isn't it ?' Flt Lt Cramond murmured.

And it was nice, too. There was no crop spraying in those days and the scent of the wild flowers growing among the corn drifted into the open cockpit. The heady fragrance took me back in a moment to that picnic with Helen.

There were many things leading up to the picnic. It all started when I caught Helen in the pantry, stealing the porridge oats. She was standing with the packet in her hand, scooping the contents into her mouth with a spoon, and she started guiltily when she saw me.

'You're at it again!' I exclaimed. I snatched the packet from her fingers. 'It's nearly empty! How many do you go through a week ?'

She looked at me with a striken face and shook her head. 'I don't know.'

'But Helen – raw porridge oats! You're not supposed to eat them that way. Not a packet at a time, anyway. You'll give yourself indigestion.'

'I'm all right so far.' Her spoon twitched and I could see she wanted more.

'But why don't you cook them and eat ordinary porridge – do you good that way.'

She pouted. 'Don't want ordinary porridge.'

I gave her an exasperated stare and left her to it. I'd had no experience with pregnant women but I had heard of these cravings and no doubt they were to be respected. With Helen it had started with oranges – oranges morning noon and night – and I was rather pleased because I thought they would be good for her with all those vitamins. But it wasn't long before she went off the oranges and on to the porridge and I started to worry.

However it was needless. Within a week or two the porridge had lost all its attractions and Helen was on the custard. And it was cooked custard, good wholesome stuff made with plenty of milk, and though Helen drank it by the gallon instead of the pint I felt sure it must be beneficial.

The custard phase lasted for some time. Whatever I was doing around our bed-sitter Helen would be crouched over her bowl of custard, imbibing it effortlessly, spoonful by spoonful, watching me with inward-looking eyes. When I was working in the garden I had only to glance up to the little window under the tiles to see that rapt face looking out at me and the spoon rising and falling from the custard bowl.

Such nourishing material, I thought, could do nothing but good both for my wife and for our first born, but before I knew where I was the trouble with the smells began.

It was totally unexpected. We both accepted the fact that our dining arrangements were somewhat primitive. Bare boards, a wooden bench against the wall and a gas ring was all we had. But it was all we wanted, so that it was something of a shock to me when Helen complained.

It was one lunchtime and she looked around her, sniffing suspiciously. 'There's a funny smell in here,' she said.

'A funny smell? What do you mean?' I was utterly at a loss because just about the only thing that annoyed me about my new wife was that she spent far too much time scrubbing and cleaning our premises. There just couldn't be any smells.

But it began to happen every day. Each lunchtime when we climbed the long flights of stairs to our kitchen Helen's nose began to wrinkle almost as soon as the door closed behind her. Matters came to a head at the end of a week.

'Jim,' she said mournfully. 'I can't eat here any more. Not with this smell about.'

It was a problem. Lunch was our main meal of the day and she had almost stopped eating breakfast. Also, the reassuring consumption of custard had dwindled. If this went on she would suffer from malnutrition. Then I had one of my infrequent ideas.

'Let's go out to lunch,' I said.

'Where?'

'The Lilac Café. They say it's very good.'

She nodded uncertainly. 'All right, we'll try it. I just can't eat up here, anyway.'

For a couple of weeks I was sure the problem was solved. The food at the Lilac was excellent and didn't put any strain on our limited financial resources. You could get soup, meat, potatoes and two veg, apple pie and cream, coffee and biscuits all for one and sixpence. Helen enjoyed it all and I was triumphant.

It was only on market days that the Lilac was full, with the farmers and their wives packing the place, and it was on a market day that the blow fell. I was sipping my coffee and making conversation with two stout ladies at the next table when my wife nudged me.

'Jim,' she whispered, and I felt a premonition as I saw the familiar hunted look on her face. 'There's a funny smell in here.'

I stared at her. 'What kind of smell – the same as the one at home?'

'No.' She shook her head miserably. 'But it's funny.'

'But Helen, this is pure imagination.' I raised my head and gave a few ostentatious sniffs. 'There's nothing here at all.'

But she was already on her way out and I realized with a sense of loss that that was the end of the Lilac.

For the next few days we tried the Dickon Street Café. It was much smaller and the food was definitely uninspiring but Helen seemed content, so I was thankful. After all, I told myself as I chewed at a toughish piece of rump steak, she was the one who was having the baby and it was only right that I should humour her. And I was just thinking that matters could be a lot worse when she leaned across the table.

'Can't you smell it?' she asked, wide-eyed.

I felt a surge of despair. 'Smell what?'

'That funny smell. Surely you must be able to . . .' She gazed at me appealingly.

'No, I can't,' I said. 'But never mind, we'll try somewhere else tomorrow.'

Darrowby didn't run to many cafés and there was only one left. It was known simply as Mrs Ackerley's and consisted of one tiny room in that lady's house down a side street. The cuisine there was frankly sub-standard and Mrs Ackerley herself didn't seem to have much faith in its because she invariably added 'Praps not' to every suggestion.

'Would you like some liver – or praps not? Or some toad-in-the-hole – or praps not?' Then for dessert it would be the same. 'How about prunes and rice – or praps not?'

Everything was badly cooked and yet it fascinated me that she had her faithful clientele; an old man who worked at the shoe shop, a middle-aged spinster school teacher and a pale dyspeptic-looking young man whom I recognized as a clerk from the bank. They came every day and I realized I was exploring a hitherto unknown stratum of Darrowby society.

Helen seemed to find some humour in the situation. 'Let's get round to Praps Not's,' she would say each day and I hoped this was a good sign. But I could not stifle the lurking conviction within me that Mrs Ackerley wouldn't last.

I was pushing some particularly tired-looking cabbage round my plate when I heard a sharp intake of breath. My wife was sitting bolt upright, snuffing the air like a hound on the scent.

'Jim,' she muttered urgently, 'There's a . . .'

I held up a hand. 'Okay, okay, you don't have to tell me. Let's go.'

Our position was critical. We had run out of cafés and yet we couldn't live without eating. It was Helen who found the answer.

'It's lovely weather,' she said, slipping her arm through mine. 'Let's have a picnic tomorrow.'

One thing about living in Darrowby is that you don't have to drive very far to leave the town behind. Next day we sat down on a grassy bank and as we opened our packet of sandwiches the September sun flooded down, warming the grey stones of the wall behind us, slanting dazzlingly against the tumbling water of the river far below.

Beyond the wall lay the wide golden sweep of a cornfield and a little breeze stirred the ripe ears into a long slow whisper, bringing with it the sweet scent of a thousand growing things.

Helen sliced a tomato, shook some salt on to it and drew a long contented breath.

'Nice smell here,' she said.

# 16

The doctor put down the folder containing my case history and gave me a friendly smile across the desk.

'I'm sorry, Herriot, but you've got to have an operation.'

His words, though gentle, were like a slap in the face. After flying school we had been posted to Heaton Park, Manchester, and I heard within two days that I had been graded pilot. Everything seemed at last to be going smoothly.

'An operation . . . are you sure?'

'Absolutely, I'm afraid,' he said, and he looked like a man who knew his business. He was a Wing Commander, almost certainly a specialist in civilian life, and I had been sent to him after a medical inspection by one of the regular doctors.

'This old surgical scar they mention in your documents,' he went on. 'You've already had surgery there, haven't you?'

'Yes, a few years ago.'

'Well, I'm afraid the thing is opening up again and needs attention.'

I seemed to have run out of words and could think of only one. 'When?'

'Immediately. Within a few days, anyway.'

I stared at him. 'But my flight's going overseas at the end of the week.'

'Ah well, that's a pity.' He spread his hands and smiled again. 'But they'll be going without you. You will be in hospital.'

I had a sudden feeling of loss, of something coming to an end, and it lingered after I had left the Wing Commander's office. I realized painfully that the fifty men with whom I had sweated my way through all those new experiences had become my friends. The first breaking-in at St John's Wood in London, the hard training at Scarborough ITW, the 'toughening course' in Shropshire and the final flying instruction at Winkfield; it had bound us together and I had come to think of myself not as an individual but as part of a group. My mind could hardly accept the fact that I was going to be on my own.

The others were sorry, too, my own particular chums looking

almost bereaved, but they were all too busy to pay me much attention. They were being pushed around all over the place, getting briefed and kitted out for their posting, and it was a hectic time for the whole flight – except me. I sat on my bed in the Nissen hut while the excitement billowed around me.

I thought my departure would go unnoticed but when I got my summons and prepared to leave I found, tucked in the webbing of my pack, an envelope filled with the precious coupons with which we drew our ration of cigarettes in those days. It seemed that nearly everybody had chipped in and the final gesture squeezed at my throat as I made my lonely way from the camp.

The hospital was at Creden Hill, near Hereford, and I suppose it is one of the consolations of service life that you can't feel lonely for very long. The beds in the long ward were filled with people like myself who had been torn from their comrades and were eager to be friendly.

In the few days before my operation we came to know each other pretty well. The young man in the bed on my left spent his time writing excruciating poetry to his girlfriend and insisted on reading it out to me, stanza by stanza. The lad on the right seemed a pensive type. Everybody addressed him as 'Sammy' but he replied only in grunts.

When he found out I was a vet he leaned from the sheets and beckoned to me.

'I got fed up wi' them blokes callin' me Sammy,' he muttered in a ripe Birmingham accent. 'Because me name's not Sammy, it's Desmond.'

'Really ? Why do they do it, then ?'

He leaned out further. 'That's what I want to talk to you about. You bein' a vet – you'll know about these things. It's because of what's wrong with me – why I'm in 'ere.'

'Well, why are you here ? What's your trouble ?'

He looked around him then spoke in a confidential whisper. 'I gotta big ball.'

'A what ?'

'A big ball. One of me balls is a right whopper.'

'Ah, I see, but I still don't understand . . .'

'Well, it's like this,' he said. 'All the fellers in the ward keep sayin' the doctor's goin' to cut it off – then I'd be like Sammy Hall.'

I nodded in comprehension. Memories from my college days filtered back. It had been a popular ditty at the parties. 'My name is Sammy Hall and I've only got one ball . . .'

'Oh, nonsense, they're pulling your leg,' I said. 'An enlarged testicle can be all sorts of things. Can you remember what the doctor called it ?'

He screwed up his face. 'It was a funny name. Like vorry or varry something.'

'Do you mean varicocele ?'

'That's it !' He threw up an arm. 'That's the word !'

'Well, you can stop worrying,' I said. 'It's quite a simple little operation. Trifling, in fact.'

'You mean they won't cut me ball off ?'

'Definitely not. Just remove a few surplus blood vessels, that's all. No trouble.'

He fell back on the pillow and gazed ecstatically at the ceiling. 'Thanks, mate,' he breathed. 'You've done me a world o' good. I'm gettin' done tomorrow and I've been dreadin' it.'

He was like a different person all that day, laughing and joking with everybody, and next morning when the nurse came to give him his pre-med injection he turned to me with a last appeal in his eyes.

'You wouldn't kid me, mate, would you ? They're not goin' to . . . ?'

I held up a hand. 'I assure you, Sammy – er – Desmond, you've nothing to worry about. I give you my word.'

Again the beatific smile crept over his face and it stayed there until the 'blood wagon', the operating room trolley, pushed by a male orderly, came to collect him.

The blood wagon was very busy each morning and it was customary to raise a cheer as each man was wheeled out. Most of the victims responded with a sleepy wave before the swing doors closed behind them, but when I saw Desmond grinning cheerfully and giving the thumbs-up sign I felt I had really done something.

Next morning it was my turn. I had my injection at around eight o'clock and by the time the trolley appeared I was pleasantly woozy. They removed my pyjamas and arrayed me in a sort of nightgown with laces at the neck and pulled thick woollen socks over my feet. As the orderly wheeled me away the inmates of the ward broke into a ragged chorus of encouragement and I managed the ritual flourish of an arm as I left.

It was a cheerless journey along white-tiled corridors until the trolley pushed its way into the anaesthetics room. As I entered, the doors at the far end parted as a doctor came towards me bearing a loaded syringe. I had a chilling glimpse of the operating theatre beyond, with the lights beating on the long table and the masked surgeons waiting.

The doctor pushed up my sleeve and swabbed my forearm with surgical spirit. I decided I had seen enough and closed my eyes, but an exclamation from above made me open them.

'Good God, it's Jim Herriot!'

I looked up at the man with the syringe. It was Teddy McQueen. He had been in my class at school and I hadn't seen him since the day I left.

My throat was dry after the injection but I felt I had to say something.

'Hello, Teddy,' I croaked.

His eyes were wide. 'What the hell are you doing here?'

'What the hell do you think?' I rasped crossly. 'I'm going in there for an operation.'

'Oh, I know that – I'm the anaesthetist here – but I remember you telling me at school that you were going to be a vet.'

'That's right. I am a vet.'

'You are?' His face was a picture of amazement. 'But what the devil is a vet doing in the RAF?'

It was a good question. 'Nothing very much, Teddy,' I replied.

He began to laugh. Obviously he found the whole situation intriguing.

'Well, Jim, I can't get over this!' He leaned over me and giggled uncontrollably. 'Imagine our meeting here after all these years. I think it's an absolute hoot!' His whole body began to shake and he had to dab away the tears from his eyes.

Lying there on the blood wagon in my nightie and woolly socks I didn't find it all that funny, and my numbed brain was searching for a withering riposte when a voice barked from the theatre.

'What's keeping you, McQueen? We can't wait all morning!'

Teddy stopped laughing. 'Sorry, Jim, old chum,' he said. 'But your presence is requested within.' He pushed the needle into my vein and my last memory as I drifted away was of his lingering amused smile.

I spent three weeks at Creden Hill and towards the end of that time those of us who were almost fully recovered were allowed out to visit the nearby town of Hereford. This was embarrassing because we were all clad in the regulation suit of hospital blue with white shirt and red tie and it was obvious from the respectful glances we received that people thought we had been wounded in action.

When a veteran of the First World War came up to me and asked, 'Where did you get your packet, mate?' I stopped going altogether.

I left the RAF hospital with a feeling of gratitude – particularly towards the hard-working, cheerful nurses. They gave us many a tongue lashing for chattering after lights out, for smoking under the blankets, for messing up our beds, but all the time I marvelled at their dedication.

I used to lie there and wonder what it was in a girl's character that made her go in for the arduous life of nursing. A concern for people's welfare? A natural caring instinct? Whatever it was, I was sure a person was born with it.

This trait is part of the personalities of some animals and it was exemplified in Eric Abbot's sheepdog, Judy.

I first met Judy when I was treating Eric's bullock for wooden tongue. The bullock was only a young one and the farmer admitted ruefully that he had neglected it because it was almost a walking skeleton.

'Damn!' Eric grunted. 'He's been runnin' out with that bunch in the far fields and I must have missed 'im. I never knew he'd got to this state.'

When actinobacillosis affects the tongue it should be treated right at the start, when the first symptoms of salivation and swelling beneath the jaw appear. Otherwise the tongue becomes harder and harder till finally it sticks out of the front of the mouth, as unyielding as the wood which gives the disease its ancient name.

This skinny little creature had reached that state, so that he not only looked pathetic but also slightly comic as though he were making a derisive gesture at me. But with a tongue like that he just couldn't eat and was literally starving to death. He lay quietly as though he didn't care.

'There's one thing, Eric,' I said. 'Giving him an intravenous injection won't be any problem. He hasn't the strength to resist.'

The great new treatment at that time was sodium iodide into the vein – modern and spectacular. Before that the farmers used to paint the tongue with tincture of iodine, a tedious procedure which sometimes worked and sometimes didn't. The sodium iodide was a magical improvement and showed results within a few days.

I inserted the needle into the jugular and tipped up the bottle of clear fluid. Two drachms of the iodide I used to use, in eight ounces of distilled water and it didn't take long to flow in. In fact the bottle was nearly empty before I noticed Judy.

I had been aware of a big dog sitting near me all the time, but as I neared the end of the injection a black nose moved ever closer till it was almost touching the needle. Then the nose moved along the rubber tube up to the bottle and back again, sniffing with the utmost concentration. When I removed the needle the nose began a careful inspection of the injection site. Then a tongue appeared and began to lick the bullock's neck methodically.

I squatted back on my heels and watched. This was something more than mere curiosity; everything in the dog's attitude suggested intense interest and concern.

'You know, Eric,' I said. 'I have the impression that this dog isn't just watching me. She's supervising the whole job.'

The farmer laughed. 'You're right there. She's a funny old bitch is Judy – sort of a nurse. If there's anything amiss she's on duty. You can't keep her away.'

Judy looked up quickly at the sound of her name. She was a handsome animal; not the usual colour, but a variegated brindle with waving lines of brown and grey mingling with the normal black and white of the farm collie. Maybe there was a cross somewhere but the result was very attractive and the effect was heightened by her bright-eyed, laughing-mouthed friendliness.

I reached out and tickled the backs of her ears and she wagged mightily – not just her tail but her entire rear end. 'I suppose she's just good-natured.'

'Oh aye, she is,' the farmer said. 'But it's not only that. It sounds daft but I think Judy feels a sense of responsibility to all the stock on t'farm.'

I nodded. 'I believe you. Anyway, let's get this beast on to his chest.'

We got down in the straw and with our hands under the backbone, rolled the bullock till he was resting on his sternum. We balanced him there with straw bales on either side then covered him with a horse rug.

In that position he didn't look as moribund as before, but the emaciated head with the useless jutting tongue lolled feebly on his shoulders and the saliva drooled uncontrolled on to the straw. I wondered if I'd ever see him alive again.

Judy however didn't appear to share my pessimism. After a thorough sniffing examination of rug and bales she moved to the front, applied an encouraging tongue to the shaggy forehead then stationed herself comfortably facing the bullock, very like a night nurse keeping an eye on her patient.

'Will she stay there?' I closed the half-door and took a last look inside.

'Aye, nothing'll shift her till he's dead or better,' Eric replied. 'She's in her element now.'

'Well, you never know, she may give him an interest in life, just sitting there. He certainly needs some help. You must keep him alive with milk or gruel till the injection starts to work. If he'll drink it it'll do him most good but otherwise you'll have to bottle it into him. But be careful – you can choke a beast that way.'

A case like this had more than the usual share of the old fascination because I was using a therapeutic agent which really worked – something that didn't happen too often at that time. So I was

151

eager to get back to see if I had been able to pull that bullock from the brink of death. But I knew I had to give the drug a chance and kept away for five days.

When I walked across the yard to the box I knew there would be no further doubts. He would either be dead or on the road to recovery.

The sound of my steps on the cobbles hadn't gone unnoticed. Judy's head, ears cocked, appeared above the half-door. A little well of triumph brimmed in me. If the nurse was still on duty then the patient must be alive. And I felt even more certain when the big dog disappeared for a second, then came soaring effortlessly over the door and capered up to me, working her hind end into convolutions of delight. She seemed to be doing her best to tell me all was well.

Inside the box the bullock was still lying down but he turned to look at me and I noticed a strand of hay hanging from his mouth. The tongue itself had disappeared behind the lips.

'Well, we're winnin', aren't we ?' Eric Abbot came in from the yard.

'Without a doubt,' I said. 'The tongue's much softer and I see he's been trying to eat hay.'

'Aye, can't quite manage it yet, but he's suppin' the milk and gruel like a good 'un. He's been up a time or two but he's very wobbly on his pins.'

I produced another bottle of sodium iodide and repeated the injection with Judy's nose again almost touching the needle as she sniffed avidly. Her eyes were focused on the injection site with fierce concentration and so intent was she on extracting the full savour that she occasionally blew out her nostrils with a sharp blast before recommencing her inspection.

When I had finished she took up her position at the head and as I prepared to leave I noticed a voluptuous swaying of her hips which were embedded in the straw. I was a little puzzled until I realized she was wagging in the sitting position.

'Well, Judy's happy at the way things are going,' I said.

The farmer nodded. 'Yes, she is. She likes to be in charge. Do you know, she gives every newborn calf a good lick over as soon as it comes into t'world and it's the same whenever one of our cats 'as kittens.'

'Bit of a midwife, too, eh?'

'You could say that. And another funny thing about 'er – she lives with the livestock in the buildings. She's got a nice warm kennel but she never bothers with it – sleeps with the beasts in the straw every night.'

I revisited the bullock a week later and this time he galloped round the box like a racehorse when I approached him. When I finally trapped him in a corner and caught his nose I was breathless but happy. I slipped my fingers into his mouth; the tongue was pliable and almost normal.

'One more shot, Eric', I said. 'Wooden tongue is the very devil for recurring if you don't get it cleared up thoroughly.' I began to unwind the rubber tube. 'By the way, I don't see Judy around.'

'Oh, I reckon she feels he's cured now, and anyway, she has summat else on her plate this mornin'. Can you see her over there?'

I looked through the doorway. Judy was stalking importantly across the yard. She had something in her mouth – a yellow fluffy object.

I craned out further. 'What is she carrying?'

'It's a chicken.'

'A chicken?'

'Aye, there's a brood of them runnin' around just now. They're only a month old and t'awd bitch seems to think they'd be better off in the stable. She's made a bed for them in there and she keeps tryin' to curl herself round them. But the little things won't 'ave it.'

I watched Judy disappear into the stable. Very soon she came out, trotted after a group of tiny chicks which were pecking happily among the cobbles and gently scooped one up. Busily she made her way back to the stable but as she entered the previous chick reappeared in the doorway and pottered over to rejoin his friends.

She was having a frustrating time but I knew she would keep at it because that was the way she was.

Judy, the nurse dog, was still on duty.

# 17

My experience in the RAF hospital made me think. As a veterinary surgeon I had become used to being on the other end of the knife and I preferred it that way.

As I remembered, I was quite happy that morning a couple of years ago as I poised my knife over a swollen ear. Tristan, one elbow leaning wearily on the table, was holding an anaesthetic mask over the nose of the sleeping dog when Siegfried came into the room.

He glanced briefly at the patient. 'Ah yes, that haematoma you were telling me about, James.' Then he looked across the table at his brother. 'Good God, you're a lovely sight this morning! When did you get in last night?'

Tristan raised a pallid countenance. He eyes were bloodshot slits between puffy lids. 'Oh, I don't quite know. Fairly late, I should think.'

'Fairly late! I got back from a farrowing at four o'clock and you hadn't arrived then. Where the hell were you, anyway?'

'I was at the Licensed Victuallers' Ball. Very good do, actually.'

'I bet it was!' Siegfried snorted. 'You don't miss a thing, do you? Darts Team Dinner, Bellringers' Outing, Pigeon Club Dance and now it's the Licensed Victuallers' Ball. If there's a good booze-up going on anywhere you'll find it.'

When under fire Tristan always retained his dignity and he drew it around him now like a threadbare cloak.

'As a matter of fact,' he said, 'many of the Licensed Victuallers are my friends.'

His brother flushed. 'I believe you. I should think you're the best bloody customer they've ever had!'

Tristan made no reply but began to make a careful check of the flow of oxygen into the ether bottle.

'And another thing,' Siegfried continued. 'I keep seeing you slinking around with about a dozen different women. And you're supposed to be studying for an exam.'

'That's an exaggeration.' The young man gave him a pained

look. 'I admit I enjoy a little female company now and then – just like yourself.'

Tristan believed in attack as the best form of defence, and it was a telling blow because there was a constant stream of attractive girls laying siege to Siegfried at Skeldale House.

But the elder brother was only temporarily halted. 'Never mind me!' he shouted. 'I've passed all my exams. I'm talking about you! Didn't I see you with that new barmaid from the Drovers' the other night ? You dodged rapidly into a shop doorway but I'm bloody sure it was you.'

Tristan cleared his throat. 'It quite possibly was. I have recently become friendly with Lydia – she's a very nice girl.'

'I'm not saying she isn't. What I am saying is that I want to see you indoors at night with your books instead of boozing and chasing women. Is that clear ?'

'Quite.' The young man inclined his head gracefully and turned down the knob on the anaesthetic machine.

His brother regarded him balefully for a few moments, breathing deeply. These remonstrations always took it out of him. Then he turned away quickly and left.

Tristan's façade crumbled as soon as the door closed.

'Watch the anaesthetic for a minute, Jim,' he croaked. He went over to the basin in the corner, filled a measuring jar with cold water and drank it at a long gulp. Then he soaked some cotton wool under the tap and applied it to his brow.

'I wish he hadn't come in just then. I'm in no mood for the raised voices and angry words.' He reached up to a large bottle of aspirins, swallowed a few and washed them down with another gargantuan draught. 'All right then, Jim,' he murmured as he returned to the table and took over the mask again. 'Let's go.'

I bent once more over the sleeping dog. He was a Scottie called Hamish and his mistress, Miss Westerman, had brought him in two days ago.

She was a retired school teacher and I always used to think she must have had little trouble in keeping her class in order. The chilly pale eyes looking straight into mine reminded me that she was as tall as I was and the square jaw between the muscular shoulders completed a redoubtable presence.

'Mr Herriot,' she barked. 'I want you to have a look at Hamish. I do hope it's nothing serious but his ear has become very swollen and painful. They don't get – er – cancer there, do they?' For a moment the steady gaze wavered.

'Oh, that's most unlikely.' I lifted the little animal's chin and looked at the left ear which was drooping over the side of his face. His whole head, in fact, was askew as though dragged down by pain.

Carefully I lifted the ear and touched the tense swelling with a forefinger. Hamish looked round at me and whimpered.

'Yes, I know, old chap. It's tender, isn't it?' As I turned to Miss Westerman I almost bumped into the close-cropped iron-grey head which was hovering close over the little dog.

'He's got an aural haematoma,' I said.

'What on earth is that?'

'It's when the little blood vessels between the skin and cartilage of the ear rupture and the blood flows out and causes this acute distension.'

She patted the jet black shaggy coat. 'But what causes it?'

'Canker, usually. Has he been shaking his head lately?'

'Yes, now you mention it he has. Just as though he had got something in his ear and was trying to get rid of it.'

'Well that's what bursts the blood vessels. I can see he has a touch of canker though it isn't common in this breed.'

She nodded. 'I see. And how can you cure it?'

'Only by an operation, I'm afraid.'

'Oh dear!' She put her hand to her mouth. 'I'm not keen on that.'

'That's nothing to worry about,' I said. 'It's just a case of letting the blood out and stitching the layers of the ear together. If we don't do this soon he'll suffer a lot of pain and finish up with a cauliflower ear, and we don't want that because he's a bonny little chap.'

I meant it, too. Hamish was a proud-strutting, trim little dog. The Scottish terrier is an attractive creature and I often lament that there are so few around in these modern days.

After some hesitation Miss Westerman agreed and we fixed a date two days from then. When she brought him in for the operation she deposited Hamish in my arms, stroked his head again and again, then looked from Tristan to me and back again.

'You'll take care of him, won't you,' she said, and the jaw jutted and the pale blue eyes stabbed. For a moment I felt like a little boy caught in mischief, and I think my colleague felt the same because he blew out his breath as the lady departed.

'By gum, Jim, that's a tough baby,' he muttered. 'I wouldn't like to get on the wrong side of her.'

I nodded. 'Yes, and she thinks all the world of this dog, so let's make a good job of him.'

After Siegfried's departure I lifted the ear which was now a turgid cone and made an incision along the inner skin. As the pent up blood gushed forth I caught it in an enamel dish, then I squeezed several big clots through the wound.

'No wonder the poor little chap was in pain,' I said softly. 'He'll feel a lot better when he wakes up.'

I filled the cavity between skin and cartilage with sulphanilamide then began to stitch the layers together, using a row of buttons. You had to do something like this or the thing filled up again within a few days. When I first began to operate on aural haematomata I used to pack the interior with gauze, then bandage the ear to the head. The owners often made little granny-hats to try to keep the bandage in place, but a frisky dog usually had it off very soon.

The buttons were a far better idea and kept the layers in close contact, lessening the chance of distortion.

By lunchtime Hamish had come round from the anaesthetic and though still slightly dopey he already seemed to be relieved that his bulging ear had been deflated. Miss Westerman had gone away for the day and was due to pick him up in the evening. The little dog, curled in his basket, waited philosophically.

At teatime, Siegfried glanced across the table at his brother. 'I'm going off to Brawton for a few hours, Tristan,' he said. 'I want you to stay in the house and give Miss Westerman her dog when she arrives. I don't know just when she'll come.' He scooped out a spoonful of jam. 'You can keep an eye on the patient and do a bit of studying, too. It's about time you had a night at home.'

Tristan nodded. 'Right, I'll do that.' But I could see he wasn't enthusiastic.

When Siegfried had driven away Tristan rubbed his chin and gazed reflectively through the french window into the darkening garden. 'This is distinctly awkward, Jim.'

'Why?'

'Well, Lydia has tonight off and I promised to see her.' He whistled a few bars under his breath. 'It seems a pity to waste the opportunity just when things are building up nicely. I've got a strong feeling that girl fancies me. In fact she's nearly eating out of my hand.'

I looked at him wonderingly. 'My God, I thought you'd want a bit of peace and quiet and an early bed after last night!'

'Not me,' he said. 'I'm raring to go again.'

And indeed he looked fresh and fit, eyes sparkling, roses back in his cheeks.

'Look, Jim,' he went on. 'I don't suppose you could stick around with this dog?'

I shrugged. 'Sorry, Triss. I'm going back to see that cow of Ted Binns' – right at the top of the Dale. I'll be away for nearly two hours.'

For a few moments he was silent, then he raised a finger. 'I· think I have the solution. It's quite simple, in fact it's perfect. I'll bring Lydia in here.'

'What! Into the house?'

'Yes, into this very room. I can put Hamish in his basket by the fire and Lydia and I can occupy the sofa. Marvellous! What could be nicer on a cold winter's night. Cheap, too.'

'But Triss! How about Siegfried's lecture this morning? What if he comes home early and catches the two of you here?'

Tristan lit a Woodbine and blew out an expansive cloud. 'Not a chance. You worry about such tiny things, Jim. He's always late when he goes to Brawton. There's no problem at all.'

'Well, please yourself,' I said. 'But I think you're asking for trouble. Anyway, shouldn't you be doing a bit of bacteriology? The exams are getting close.'

He smiled seraphically through the smoke. 'Oh, I'll have a quick read through it all in good time.'

I couldn't argue with him there. I always had to go over a thing about six times before it finally sank in, but with his brain the quick read would no doubt suffice. I went out on my call.

I got back about eight o'clock and as I opened the front door my mind was far from Tristan. Ted Binns's cow wasn't responding to my treatment and I was beginning to wonder if I was on the right track. When in doubt I liked to look the subject up and the books were on the shelves in the sitting room. I hurried along the passage and threw open the door.

For a moment I stood there bewildered, trying to reorientate my thoughts. The sofa was drawn close to the bright fire, the atmosphere was heavy with cigarette smoke and the scent of perfume, but there was nobody to be seen.

The most striking feature was the long curtain over the french window. It was wafting slowly downwards as though some object had just hurtled through it at great speed. I trotted over the carpet and peered out into the dark garden. From somewhere in the gloom I heard a scuffling noise, a thud and a muffled cry, then there was a pitter-patter followed by a shrill yelping. I stood for some time listening, then as my eyes grew accustomed to the darkness I walked down the long path under the high brick wall to the yard at the foot. The yard door was open as were the big double doors into the back lane, but there was no sign of life.

Slowly I retraced my steps to the warm oblong of light at the foot of the tall old house. I was about to close the french window when I heard a stealthy movement and an urgent whisper.

'Is that you, Jim?'

'Triss! Where the hell have you sprung from?'

The young man tiptoed past me into the room and looked around him anxiously. 'It was you, then, not Siegfried?'

'Yes, I've just come in.'

He flopped on the sofa and sunk his head in his hands. 'Oh damn! I was just lying here a few minutes ago with Lydia in my arms. At peace with the world. Everything was wonderful. Then I heard the front door open.'

'But you knew I was coming back.'

'Yes, and I'd have given you a shout, but for some reason I thought, "God help us, it's Siegfried!" It sounded like his step in the passage.'

'Then what happened?'

He churned his hair around with his fingers. 'Oh, I panicked. I was whispering lovely things into Lydia's ear, then the next second I grabbed her, threw her off the couch and out of the french window.'

'I heard a thud . . .'

'Yes, that was Lydia falling into the rockery.'

'And then some sort of high-pitched cries . . .'

He signed and closed his eyes. 'That was Lydia in the rose bushes. She doesn't know the geography of the place, poor lass.'

'Gosh, Triss,' I said. 'I'm really sorry. I shouldn't have burst in on you like that. I was thinking of something else.'

He rose wearily and put a hand on my shoulder. 'Not your fault, Jim, not your fault. You did warn me.' He reached for his cigarettes. 'I don't know how I'm going to face that girl again. I just chucked her out into the lane and told her to beat it home with all speed. She must think I'm stone barmy.' He gave a hollow groan.

I tried to be cheerful. 'Oh, you'll get round her again. You'll have a laugh about it later.'

But he wasn't listening. His eyes, wide with horror, were staring past me. Slowly he raised a trembling finger and pointed towards the fireplace. His mouth worked for a few seconds before he spoke.

'Christ, Jim, it's gone!' he gasped.

For a moment I thought the shock had deranged him. 'Gone . . . ? What's gone?'

'The bloody dog! He was there when I dashed outside. Right there!'

I looked down at the empty basket and a cold hand clutched at me. 'Oh no! He must have got out through the open window. We're in trouble.'

We rushed into the garden and searched in vain. We came back for torches and searched once more, prowling around the yard and back lane, shouting the little dog's name with diminishing hope.

After ten minutes we trailed back to the brightly lit room and stared at each other.

Tristan was the first to voice our thoughts. 'What do we tell Miss Westerman when she calls?'

I shook my head. My mind fled from the thought of informing that lady that we had lost her dog.

Just at that moment the front door bell pealed in the passage and Tristan almost leaped in the air.

'Oh God!' he quavered. 'That'll be her now. Go and see her, Jim. Tell her it was my fault – anything you like – but I daren't face her.'

I squared my shoulders, marched over the long stretch of tiles and opened the door. It wasn't Miss Westerman, it was a well-built platinum blonde and she glared at me angrily.

'Where's Tristan?' she rasped in a voice which told me we had more than one tough female to deal with tonight.

'Well, he's – er—.'

'Oh, I know he's in there!' As she brushed past me I noticed she had a smear of soil on her cheek and her hair was sadly disarranged. I followed her into the room where she stalked up to my friend.

'Look at my bloody stockings!' she burst out. 'They're ruined!'

Tristan peered nervously at the shapely legs. 'I'm sorry, Lydia. I'll get you another pair. Honestly, love, I will.'

'You'd better, you bugger!' she replied. 'And don't "love" me – I've never been so insulted in my life. What did you think you were playing at?'

'It was all a misunderstanding. Let me explain . . .' Tristan advanced on her with a brave attempt at a winning smile, but she backed away.

'Keep your distance,' she said frigidly. 'I've had enough of you for one night.'

She swept out and Tristan leaned his head against the mantelpiece. 'The end of a lovely friendship, Jim.' Then he shook himself. 'But we've got to find that dog. Come on.'

I set off in one direction and he went in the other. It was a moonless night of impenetrable darkness and we were looking for a jet black dog. I think we both knew it was hopeless but we had to try.

In a little town like Darrowby you are soon out on the country roads where there are no lights and as I stumbled around peering vainly over invisible fields the utter pointlessness of the activity became more and more obvious.

Occasionally I came within Tristan's orbit and heard his despairing cries echoing over the empty landscape. 'Haamiish! Haamiish! Haamiish . . . !'

After half an hour we met at Skeldale House. Tristan faced me and as I shook my head he seemed to shrink within himself. His chest heaved as he fought for breath. Obviously he had been running while I had been walking and I suppose that was natural enough. We were both in an awkward situation but the final devastating blow would inevitably fall on him.

'Well, we'd better get out on the road again,' he gasped, and as he spoke the front door bell rang again.

The colour drained rapidly from his face and he clutched my arm. 'That must be Miss Westerman this time. God almighty, she's coming in!'

Rapid footsteps sounded in the passage and the sitting room door opened. But it wasn't Miss Westerman, it was Lydia again. She strode over to the sofa, reached underneath and extracted her handbag. She didn't say anything but merely shrivelled Tristan with a sidelong glance before leaving.

'What a night!' he moaned, putting a hand to his forehead. 'I can't stand much more of this.'

Over the next hour we made innumerable sorties but we couldn't find Hamish and nobody else seemed to have seen him. I came in to find Tristan collapsed in an armchair. His mouth hung open and he showed every sign of advanced exhaustion. I shook my head and he shook his then I heard the telephone.

I lifted the receiver, listened for a minute and turned to the young man. 'I've got to go out, Triss. Mr Drew's old pony has colic again.'

He reached out a hand from the depth of his chair. 'You're not going to leave me, Jim ?'

'Sorry, I must. But I won't be long. It's only a mile away.'

'But what if Miss Westerman comes ?'

I shrugged. 'You'll just have to apologize. Hamish is bound to turn up – maybe in the morning.'

'You make it sound easy . . .' He ran a hand inside his collar. 'And another thing – how about Siegfried ? What if he arrives and asks about the dog ? What do I tell him ?'

'Oh, I shouldn't worry about that.' I replied airily. 'Just say you were too busy on the sofa with the Drovers' barmaid to bother about such things. He'll understand.'

But my attempt at jocularity fell flat. The young man fixed me with a cold eye and ignited a quivering Woodbine. 'I believe I've told you this before, Jim, but there's a nasty cruel streak in you.'

Mr Drew's pony had almost recovered when I got there but I gave it a mild sedative injection before turning for home. On the way back a thought struck me and I took a road round the edge of the town to the row of modern bungalows where Miss Westerman lived. I parked the car and walked up the path of number ten.

And there was Hamish in the porch, coiled up comfortably on the mat, looking up at me with mild surprise as I hovered over him.

'Come on, lad,' I said. 'You've got more sense than we had. Why didn't we think of this before?'

I deposited him on the passenger seat and as I drove away he hoisted his paws on to the dash and gazed out interestedly at the road unfolding in the headlights. Truly a phlegmatic little hound.

Outside Skeldale House I tucked him under my arm and was about to turn the handle of the front door when I paused. Tristan had notched up a long succession of successful pranks against me – fake telephone calls, the ghost in my bedroom and many others – and in fact, good friends as we were, he never neglected a chance to take the mickey out of me. In this situation, with the positions reversed, he would be merciless. I put my finger on the bell and leaned on it for several long seconds.

For some time there was neither sound nor movement from within and I pictured the cowering figure mustering his courage before marching to his doom. Then the light came on in the passage and as I peered expectantly through the glass a nose appeared round the far corner followed very gingerly by a wary eye. By degrees the full face inched into view and when Tristan recognized my grinning countenance he unleashed a cry of rage and bounded along the passage with upraised fist.

I really think that in his distraught state he would have attacked me, but the sight of Hamish banished all else. He grabbed the hairy creature and began to fondle him.

'Good little dog, nice little dog,' he crooned as he trotted through to the sitting room. 'What a beautiful thing you are.' He laid him lovingly in the basket, and Hamish, after a 'heigh-ho, here we are again' glance around him, put his head along his side and promptly went to sleep.

Tristan fell limply into the armchair and gazed at me with glazed eyes.

'Well, we're saved, Jim,' he whispered. 'But I'll never be the same after tonight. I've run bloody miles and I've nearly lost my voice with shouting. I tell you I'm about knackered.'

I, too, was vastly relieved, and the nearness of catastrophe was brought home to us when Miss Westerman arrived within ten minutes.

'Oh, my darling!' she cried as Hamish leaped at her, mouth open, short tail wagging furiously. 'I've been so worried about you all day.'

She looked tentatively at the ear with its rows of buttons. 'Oh, it does look a lot better without that horrid swelling – and what a nice neat job you have made. Thank you, Mr Herriot, and thank you, too, young man.'

Tristan, who had staggered to his feet, bowed slightly as I showed the lady out.

'Bring him back in six weeks to have the stitches out,' I called to her as she left, then I rushed back into the room.

'Siegfried's just pulled up outside! You'd better look as if you've been working.'

He rushed to the bookshelves, pulled down Gaiger and Davis's *Bacteriology* and a notebook and dived into a chair. When his brother came in he was utterly engrossed.

Siegfried moved over to the fire and warmed his hands. He looked pink and mellow.

'I've just been speaking to Miss Westerman,' he said. 'She's really pleased. Well done, both of you.'

'Thank you,' I said, but Tristan was too busy to reply, scanning the pages anxiously and scribbling repeatedly in the notebook.

Siegfried walked behind the young man's chair and looked down at the open volume.

'Ah, yes, Clostridium septique,' he murmured, smiling indulgently. 'That's a good one to study. Keeps coming up in exams.'

He rested a hand briefly on his brother's shoulder. 'I'm glad to see you at work. You've been raking about too much lately and it's getting you down. A night at your books will have been good for you.'

He yawned, stretched, and made for the door. 'I'm off to bed. I'm rather sleepy.' He paused with his hand on the door. 'You know, Tristan, I quite envy you – there's nothing like a nice restful evening at home.'

# 18

When I was discharged from hospital I expected to be posted straight overseas and I wondered if I would be able to catch up with my old flight and my friends.

However, I learned with surprise that I had to go to a convalescent home for a fortnight before any further action could be taken. This was in Puddlestone, near Leominster – a lovely mansion house in acres of beautiful gardens. It was presided over by a delightful old matron with whom we fortunate airmen played sedate games of croquet or walked in the cool woods; it was easy to imagine there was no such thing as a war. Two weeks of this treatment left me feeling revitalized. It wouldn't be long, I felt, before I was back on the job.

From Puddlestone it was back to Manchester and Heaton Park again and this time it was strange to think that in all the great sprawl of huts and the crowding thousands of men in blue there wasn't a soul who knew me.

Except, of course, the Wing Commander who had sent me to hospital in the first place. I had an interview with him on my arrival and he came straight to the point.

'Herriot,' he said. 'I'm afraid you can't fly any more.'

'But . . . I've had the operation . . . I'm a lot better.'

'I know that, but you can no longer be classed as one hundred per cent fit. You have been officially downgraded and I'm sure you realize that pilots have to be grade one.'

'Yes . . . of course.'

He glanced at the file in his hand. 'I see you are a veterinary surgeon. Mmm – this poses a problem. Normally when an air-crew is grounded he remusters on the ground staff, but yours is a reserved occupation. You really can't serve in any capacity but aircrew. Yes . . . yes . . . we'll have to see.'

It was all very impersonal and businesslike. Those few words coming from a man like him left no room for argument and they obliterated at a stroke every picture I had ever had of my future in the RAF.

I was fairly certain that if my flying days were over I would be discharged from the service and as I left the Wing Commander's office and walked slowly back to my hut at the other end of the park I pondered on my contribution to the war effort.

I hadn't fired a shot in anger. I had peeled mountains of potatoes, washed countless dishes, shovelled coke, mucked out pigs, marched for miles, drilled interminably, finally and magically learned to fly and now it was all for nothing. I passed the big dining hall and the RAF march blared out at me from the loud-speakers.

The familiar sound reminded me of so many experiences, so many friends, and suddenly I felt intensely lonely. I wanted some-body to talk to. It was a new sensation for me, and there, in those unlikely surroundings, I began to realize how much I used to enjoy chatting to the farmers during my veterinary calls.

It is one of the nicest things about country practice, but you have to keep your mind on the job at the same time or you could be in trouble. And at Mr Duggleby's I nearly landed in the big-gest trouble of all. He was a smallholder who kept a few sows and reared the litters to pork weight in some ramshackle sheds behind the railway line outside Darrowby.

He was also a cricket fanatic, steeped in the lore and history of the game, and he would talk about it for hours on end. He never tired of it.

I was a willing listener because cricket has always fascinated me, even though I grew up in Scotland where it is little played. As I moved among the young pigs only part of my attention was focused on the little animals – most of me was out on the great green oval at Headingley with the Yorkshire heroes.

'By gaw, you should've seen Len Hutton on Saturday,' he breathed reverently. 'A hundred and eighty and never gave a chance. It was lovely to watch 'im.' He gave a fair imitation of the great man's cover drive.

'Yes, I can imagine it.' I nodded and smiled. 'You said these pigs were lame, Mr Duggleby ?'

'Aye, noticed a few of 'em hoppin' about with a leg up this mornin'. And you know, Maurice Leyland was nearly as good. Not as classy as Len, tha knows, but by heck 'e can clump 'em.'

'Yes, he's a lion-hearted little player is Maurice,' I said. I reached down, grabbed a pig by the tail and thrust my thermometer into its rectum. 'Remember him and Eddie Paynter in the test match against Australia ?'

He gave a dreamy smile. 'Remember it ? By gaw, that's summat I'll never forget. What a day that was.'

I withdrew the thermometer. 'This little chap's got a temperature of a hundred and five. Must be some infection somewhere – maybe a touch of joint ill.' I felt my way along the small pink limbs. 'And yet it's funny, the joints aren't swollen.'

'Ah reckon Bill Bowes'll skittle Somerset out when they start their innings today. This wicket's just to 'is liking.'

'Yes, he's a great bowler, isn't he ?' I said. 'I love watching a good fast bowler. I suppose you'll have seen them all – Larwood, Voce, G. O. Allen and the rest ?'

'Aye, that I have. I could go on all day about those men.'

I caught another of the lame pigs and examined it. 'This is rather strange, Mr Duggleby. About half the pigs in this pen seem to be lame but there's nothing to see.'

'Aye well, happen it's like you said – joint ill. You can give 'em a jab for that, can't you ? And while you're doin' it I'll tell you of the time I saw Wilfred Rhodes take eight wickets in an afternoon.'

I filled a syringe. 'Right, we'd better give them all a shot. Have you got a marking pencil there ?'

The farmer nodded and lifted one of the little animals which promptly unleashed a protesting scream. 'There was never anybody like awd Wilfred,' he shouted above the noise. 'It was about half past two and the wicket had had a shower of rain on it when t'skipper threw 'im the ball.'

I smile and raised my syringe. It passed the time so pleasantly

167

listening to these reminiscences. Well content, I was about to plunge the needle into the pink thigh when one of the pigs began to nibble at the heel of my wellington. I looked down at a ring of the little creatures all looking up at me, alarmed by the shrill screeches of their friend.

My mind was still with Wilfred Rhodes when I noticed what looked like a small white knob on one of the uptilted snouts. And there was another on that one – and that one . . . I had been unable to see their faces until now because they had been trying to run away from me, but a warning bell clanged suddenly in my head.

I reached down and seized a pig, and as I squeezed the swelling on the snout a cold wind blew through me, scattering the gentle vision of cricket and sunshine and green grass. It wasn't a knob, it was a vesicle, a delicate blister which ruptured easily on pressure.

I could feel my arms shaking as I turned the piglet up and began to examine the tiny cloven feet. There were more vesicles there, flatter and more diffuse, but telling the same dread story.

Dry-mouthed, I lifted two other pigs. They were just the same. As I turned to the farmer I felt bowed down by a crushing weight of pity, almost of guilt. He was still smiling eagerly, anxious to get on with his tale, and I was about to give him the worst news a veterinary surgeon can give a stockman.

'Mr Duggleby,' I said. 'I'm afraid I'll have to telephone the Ministry of Agriculture.'

'The Ministry . . . ? What for ?'

'To tell them I have a case of suspected Foot and Mouth Disease.'

'Foot and Mouth ? Never !'

'Yes, I'm terribly sorry.'

'Are you sure ?'

'It's not up to me to be definite about it, Mr Duggleby. One of the Ministry officers will have to do that – I must phone them right away.'

It was an unlikely place to find a telephone but Mr Duggleby ran a little coal delivery round on the side. I was quickly through to the Ministry and I spoke to Neville Craggs, one of the full-time officers.

He groaned. 'Sounds awfully like it, Jim. Anyway, stay put till I see you.'

In the farm kitchen Mr Duggleby looked at me inquiringly. 'What now?'

'You'll just have to put up with me for a bit,' I said. 'I can't leave till I get the verdict.'

He was silent for a moment. 'What happens if it's what you think?'

'I'm afraid your pigs will have to be slaughtered.'

'Every one of 'em?'

'That is the law – I'm sorry. But you'll get compensation.'

He scratched his head. 'But they can get better. Why do you have to kill 'em all?'

'You're quite right.' I shrugged. 'Many animals do recover, but Foot and Mouth is fiercely infectious. While you were treating them it would have spread to neighbouring farms, then all over the country.'

'Aye, but look at the expense. Slaughtering must cost thousands o' pounds.'

'I agree, but it would cost a lot more the other way. Apart from the animals that die, just think of the loss of milk, loss of flesh in cows, pigs and sheep. It would come to millions every year. It's lucky Britain is an island.'

'Reckon you'll be right.' He felt for his pipe. 'And you're pretty sure I've got it?'

'Yes.'

'Aye well,' he murmured. 'These things 'appen.'

The old Yorkshire words. I had heard them so often under circumstances which would make most city folk, including myself, beat their heads against a wall. Mr Duggleby's smallholding would soon be a silent place of death, but he just chewed his pipe and said, 'These things 'appen.'

It didn't take the Ministry long to make up their minds. The source of the infection was almost certainly some imported meat which Mr Duggleby hadn't boiled properly with his swill. The disease was confirmed and a fifteen-mile radius standstill order was imposed. I disinfected myself and my car and went home. I undressed, my clothes were taken away for fumigation and I climbed into a hot antiseptic bath.

Lying there in the steam, I pondered on what might have been. If I had failed to spot the disease I would have gone merrily on my way, spreading destruction and havoc. I always washed my boots before leaving a farm, but how about those little pigs nibbling round the hem of my long coat, how about my syringe, even my thermometer? My next call was to have been to Terence Bailey's pedigree herd of dairy shorthorns – two hundred peerless cows, a strain built up over generations. Foreigners came from all over the world to buy them and I could have been the cause of their annihilation.

And then there was Mr Duggleby himself. I could picture him rattling around the farms in his coal wagon. He would have done his bit of spreading, too. And like as not he would have taken a few store pigs to the auction mart this week, sending the deadly contagion all over Yorkshire and beyond. It was easy to see how a major outbreak could have started – a disaster of national importance costing millions.

If I hadn't been sweating already I would have started now at the very thought of it. I would have joined the unhappy band of practitioners who had missed Foot and Mouth.

I knew of some of these people and my heart bled for them. It could happen so easily. Busy men trying to examine kicking, struggling animals in dark buildings with perhaps part of their mind on the list of calls ahead. And the other hazards – the total unexpectedness, the atypical case, various distractions. My distraction had been cricket and it had nearly caused my downfall. But I had escaped and, huddling lower in the hot water, I said a silent prayer of thanks.

Later, with a complete change of clothes and instruments, I continued on my rounds and as I stood in Terence Bailey's long byre I realized my luck again. The long rows of beautiful animals, meticulously groomed, firm high udders pushing between their hocks, delicate heads, fine legs deep in straw; they were a picture of bovine perfection and quite irreplaceable.

Once Foot and Mouth is confirmed in a district there is a tense period of waiting. Farmers, veterinary surgeons and most of all, Ministry officials are on the rack, wondering if there has been any dissemination before diagnosis, bracing themselves against the telephone message which could herald the raging spread which they dreaded and which would tear their lives apart.

To the city dwellers a big Foot and Mouth outbreak is something remote which they read about in the newspapers. To the country folk it means the transformation of the quiet farms and fields into charnel houses and funeral pyres. It means heartbreak and ruin.

We waited in Darrowby. And as the days passed and no frightening news of lame or salivating animals came over the wires it seemed that the Duggleby episode was what we hoped – an isolated case caused by a few shreds of imported meat.

I almost bathed in disinfectant on every farm, sloshing a strong solution of Lysol over my boots and protective clothing so that my car reeked of the stuff and I caused wrinkled noses when I entered a shop, the post office, the bank.

After nearly two weeks I had begun to feel reasonably safe, but when I had a call from the famous Bailey farm I felt a twinge of apprehension.

It was Terence Bailey himself. 'Will you come and see one of my cows, Mr Herriot. She's got blisters on one of her teats.'

'Blisters!' My heart went bump. 'Is she slavering, is she lame?'

'Nay, nay, she just has these nasty blisters. Seem to have fluid in them.'

I was breathless as I put down the receiver. One nasty blister would be enough. It sometimes started like that in cows. I almost ran out to my car and on the journey my mind beat about like a trapped bird.

Bailey's was the farm I had visited straight from Duggleby's. Could I possibly have carried it there? But the change of clothes, the bath, the fresh thermometer and instruments. What more could I do? How about my car wheels? Well, I had disinfected them, too – I couldn't possibly be blamed, but ... but ...

It was Mr Bailey's wife who met me.

'I noticed this cow when I was milking this morning, Mr Herriot.' The herd was still hand-milked and in the hardworking family tradition Mrs Bailey did her stint night and morning with her husband and the farm men.

'As soon as I got hold of the teats I could see the cow was uneasy,' she continued. 'Then I saw there was a lot of little blisters and one big one. I managed to milk her and most of the little blisters burst, but the big one's still there.'

I bent and peered anxiously at the udder. It was as she said – lots of small ruptured vesicles and one large one, intact and fluctuating. It was all horribly evocative and without speaking I moved along, grasped the cow's nose and pulled her head round. I prised the mouth open and stared desperately at lips, cheek and dental pad. I think I would have fainted if I had found anything in there but it was all clean and normal.

I lifted each forefoot in turn and scrubbed out the clefts with soap and water – nothing. I tied a rope round the hind leg, threw it over a beam and with the help of one of the men pulled the foot up. More scrubbing and searching without success then the same with the other hind foot. When I finished I was perspiring but no further forward.

I took the temperature and found it slightly elevated, then I walked up and down the byre.

'Is there any trouble among these other cows?' I asked.

Mrs Bailey shook her head. 'No, there's just this one.' She was a good-looking woman in her thirties with the red, roughened complexion of the outdoor worker. 'What do you think it is?'

I didn't dare tell her. I had a cow with vesicles on the teats right in the middle of a district under Foot and Mouth restrictions. I just couldn't take a chance. I had to bring the Ministry in.

Even then I was unable to speak the dread words. All I could say was, 'Can I use your phone, please?'

She looked surprised, but smiled quickly. 'Yes, of course. Come into the house.'

As I walked down the byre I looked again at the beautiful cows and then beyond, at the fold yard where I could see the young heifers and the tiny calves in their pens. All of them carrying the Bailey blood which had been produced and perfected by generations of careful breeding and selection. But a humane killer is no respecter of such things and if my fears were realized a quick series of bang-bangs would wipe out all this in an hour or two.

We went into the farm kitchen and Mrs Bailey pointed to the door at the far end.

'The phone's through there in the front room,' she said.

I kicked off my wellingtons and was padding across the floor in my stockinged feet when I almost fell over Giles, the lusty one-year-old baby of the family, as he waddled across my path. I bent to ease him out of the way and he looked up at me with an enormous cheesy grin.

His mother laughed. 'Just look at him. Full of the devil, and he's had such a painful arm since his smallpox vaccination.'

'Poor lad,' I said absently, patting his head as I opened the door, my mind already busy with the uncomfortable conversation ahead. I had taken a few strides over the carpet beyond, when I halted abruptly.

I turned and looked back into the kitchen. 'Did you say smallpox vaccination ?'

'Yes, all our other children have been done when they were his age but they've never reacted like this. I've had to change his dressing every day.'

'You changed his dressing . . . and you milked that cow . . . ?'

'Yes, that's right.'

A great light beamed suddenly, spilling sunshine into my dark troubled world. I returned to the kitchen and closed the door behind me.

Mrs Bailey looked at me for a moment in silence, then she spoke hesitantly. 'Aren't you going to use the phone ?'

'No . . . no . . .' I replied. 'I've changed my mind.'

'I see.' She raised her eyebrows and seemed at a loss for words. Then she smiled and lifted the kettle. 'Well, maybe you'll have a cup of tea, then ?'

'Thank you, that would be lovely.' I sank happily on to one of the hard wooden chairs.

Mrs Bailey put the kettle on and turned to me. 'By the way, you've never told me what's wrong with that cow.'

'Oh yes, of course, I'm sorry,' I said airily as though I'd just forgotten to mention it. 'She's got cow pox. In fact you gave it to her.'

'I gave it . . . ? What do you mean ?'

'Well, the vaccine they use for babies is made from the cow pox virus. You carried it on your hands from the baby to the cow.' I smiled, enjoying my big moment.

Her mouth fell open slightly, then she began to giggle. 'Oh dear, I don't know what my husband's going to say. I've never heard of anything like that.' She wiggled her fingers in front of her eyes. 'And I'm always so careful, too. But I've been a bit harassed with the poor little chap's arm.'

'Oh well, it isn't serious,' I said. 'I've got some ointment in the car which will cure it quite quickly.'

I sipped my tea and watched Giles's activities. In a short time he had spread chaos throughout the kitchen and at the moment was busily engaged in removing all the contents of a cupboard in the corner. Bent double, small bottom out-thrust, he hurled pans, lids, brushes behind him with intense dedication till the cupboard was empty. Then, as he looked around for further employment, he spotted me and tacked towards me on straddled legs.

My stocking-clad toes seemed to fascinate him and as I wiggled them at him he grasped at them with fat little hands. When he had finally trapped my big toe he looked up at me with his huge grin in which four tiny teeth glittered.

I smiled back at him with sincere affection as the relief flowed through me. It wasn't just that I was grateful to him – I really liked him. I still like Giles today. He is one of my clients, a burly farmer with a family of his own, a deep love and knowledge of pedigree cows and the same big grin, except that there are a few more teeth in it.

But he'll never know how near his smallpox vaccination came to giving me heart failure.

# 19

I looked around me at the heap of boots, the piled mounds of shirts, the rows of empty shelves and pigeon holes. I was employed in the stores at Heaton Park, living proof that the RAF was finding me something of a problem.

The big war machine was rumbling along pretty smoothly by this time, turning out pilots, navigators, air-gunners in a steady stream and slotting them into different jobs if they failed to make the grade. It ticked over like a well-oiled engine as long as nothing disturbed the rhythm.

I was like a speck of sand in the works, and I could tell from various interviews that I had caused the administrators a certain amount of puzzlement. I don't suppose Mr Churchill was losing any sleep over me but since I wasn't allowed to fly and was ineligible for the ground staff I was obviously a bit of a nuisance. Nobody seemed to have come across a grounded vet before.

Of course it was inevitable that I would be sent back to my practice, but I could see that it was going to take some time for the RAF to regurgitate me into civil life. Apparently I had to go through the motions even though some of them were meaningless.

One of the interviews was with three officers. They were very nice and they sat behind a table, beaming, friendly, reassuring. Their task, apparently, was to find out what ground staff job might suit me. I think they were probably psychologists and they asked me all kinds of questions, nodding and smiling kindly all the time.

'Well now, Herriot,' the middle officer said. 'We are going to put you through a series of aptitude tests. It will last two days, starting tomorrow, and by the end of it I think we'll know all about you.' He laughed. 'It's nothing to worry about. You might rather enjoy it.'

I did enjoy it, in fact. I filled up great long sheets with my answers, I drew diagrams, fitted odd-shaped pieces of wood into holes. It was fun.

I had to wait another two days before I was called before the tribunal again. The three were if anything more charming than before and I seemed to sense an air of subdued excitement about them this time. They were all smiling broadly as the middle one spoke.

'Herriot, we have really found out something about you,' he said.

'You have?'

'Yes, indeed. We have found that you have an outstanding mechanical aptitude.'

I stared at him. This was a facer, because if ever there was a mechanical idiot that man is J. Herriot. I have a loathing for engines, wheels, pistons, cylinders, cogs. I can't mend anything and if a garage mechanic tries to explain something to me I just can't take it in.

I told the officers this and the three smiles became rather fixed.

'But surely,' said the one on the left, 'you drive a car in the course of your professional work?'

'Yes, sir, I do. I've driven one for years, but I still don't know how it works and if I break down I have to scream for help.'

'I see, I see.' The smiles were very thin now and the three heads came together for a whispered consultation.

Finally the middle one leaned across the table.

'Tell you what, Herriot. How would you like to be a meteorologist?'

'Fine,' I replied.

I sympathized with them, because they were obviously kind men, but I've never had any faith in aptitude tests since then.


Of course there was never the slightest chance of my becoming a meteorologist and I suppose that's how I landed in the stores. It was one of the bizarre periods of my life, mercifully brief but vivid. They had told me to report to Corporal Weekes at the stores hut and I made my way through the maze of roads of a Heaton Park populated by strangers.

Corporal Weekes was fat and he gave me a quick look over with crafty eyes.

'Herriot, eh? Well you can make yourself useful around 'ere. Not much to do, really. This ain't a main stores – we deal mainly wiv laundry and boot repairs.'

As he spoke a fair-haired young man came in.

'AC2 Morgan, Corporal,' he said. 'Come for my boots. They've been re-soled.'

Weekes jerked his head and I had my first sight of the boot mountain. 'They're in there. They'll be labelled.'

The young man looked surprised but he came round behind the counter and began to delve among the hundreds of identical black objects. It took him nearly an hour to find his own pair during which the corporal puffed at cigarettes with a total lack of interest. When the boots were finally unearthed he wordlessly ticked off the name on a long list.

'This is the sort of thing you'll be doin', he said to me. 'Nothin' to it.'

He wasn't exaggerating. There was nothing to life in those stores. It took me only a day or two to realize the sweet existence Weekes had carved out for himself. Store-bashing is an honourable trade but not the way he did it. The innumerable compartments, niches and alcoves around the big hut were all marked with letters or numbers and there is no doubt the incoming boots and shirts should have been tucked away in order for easy recovery. But that would have involved work and the corporal was clearly averse to that.

When the boots came in they were tipped out in the middle of the floor and the string-tied packages of laundry were stacked, shirts-uppermost where they formed a blue tumulus reaching almost to the roof.

After three days I could stand it no longer.

'Look,' I said. 'It would pass the time if I had something to do. Do you mind if I start putting all this stuff on the shelves ? It would be a lot easier to hand out.'

Weekes continued to study his magazine – he was a big reader – and at first I thought he hadn't heard me. Then he tongued his cigarette to the corner of his mouth and glanced at me through the smoke.

'Now just get this through your 'ead, mate,' he drawled. 'If I want any — thing doin' I'll — well tell you. I'm the boss in 'ere and I give the — orders, awright ?' He resumed his perusal of the magazine.

I subsided in my chair. Clearly I had offended my overseer and I would have to leave things as they were.

But overseer is a misnomer for Weekes because on the following day, after a final brain-washing that the procedure must remain unchanged, he disappeared and except for a few minutes each morning he left me on my own. I had nothing to do but sit there behind the wooden counter, ticking off the comings and going of the boots and shirts and I had the feeling that I was only one of many displaced persons who had fallen under his thrall.

I found it acutely embarrassing to watch the lads scrabbling for their belongings and the strongest impression left with me was of the infinite tolerance of the British race. Since I was in charge they thought I was responsible for the whole system but despite the fact that I was of lowly rank nobody attacked me physically. Most of them muttered and grumbled as they searched and one large chap came over to the counter and said, 'You should be filing away these boots in their proper order instead of sitting there on your arse, you lazy sod!' But he didn't punch me on the nose and I marvelled at it.

But still, the knowledge that great numbers of decent young men shared his opinion was uncomfortable and I found I was developing a permanently ingratiating smile.

The only time I came very near to being lynched was when a mob suddenly appeared one afternoon. An unexpected leave pass had been granted and there were hundreds of men milling around on the tarmac and grass outside the stores. They wanted their laundry – and quick, because they had trains to catch.

For a moment panic seized me. I couldn't let them all inside to fight for their shirts. Then inspiration came. I grabbed an armful of the flat packets from the table and shouted the name on the label.

'Walters!' And from somewhere among the surging heads an eager voice replied, 'Here!'

I located the source, held the packet between thumb and finger and with a back-hand flick sent it skimming over the crowd.

'Reilly!'

'Here!'

'McDonald!'

'Here!'

'Gibson!'

'Here!'

I was getting quite skilful at it, propelling the blue oblongs unerringly towards their owners, but it was a slow method of distribution. Also, there were occasional disasters when the strings broke in mid-air, sending a shower of collars on the upturned faces. Sometimes the shirts themselves burst free from their wrapping and plunged to earth.

It wasn't long before the voices had turned from eager to angry. As my projectiles planed and glided, volleys of abuse came back at me.

'You've made me miss my train, you useless bugger!'

'Bloody skiver, you want locking up!'

Much of it was in stronger language which I would rather not record here, but I have a particularly vivid memory of one young man scraping up his laundry from the dusty ground and approaching me with rapid strides. He pushed his face to within inches of mine. Despite the rage which disfigured it I could see it was a gentle, good-natured face. He looked a well-bred lad, the type who didn't even swear, but as he stared into my eyes his lips trembled and his cheeks twitched.

'This is a . . .' he stammered. 'This is a . . . a *bastard* system!'

He spat the words out and strode away.

I agreed entirely with him, of course, but continued to hurl the packets doggedly while somewhere in the back of my mind a little voice kept inquiring how James Herriot, Member of the Royal College of Veterinary Surgeons and trainee pilot, had ever got into this.

After half an hour there was no appreciable dimunution in the size of the multitude and I began to be aware of an increasing restlessness among the medley of waiting faces.

Suddenly there was a concerted movement and the packed mass of men surged at me in a great wave. I shrank back, clutching an armful of shirts, quite certain that this was when they rushed me and beat me up, but my fears were groundless. All they wanted was a speedier delivery and about a dozen of them swept past me behind the counter and began to follow my example.

Whereas there had been only a single missile winging over the heads the sky was now dark with the flying objects. Mid-air collisions were frequent. Collars sprayed, handkerchiefs fluttered, underpants parachuted gracefully, but after an unbearably long period of chaos the last airman had picked up his scattered laundry, given me a disgusted glance and departed.

I was left alone in the hut with the sad knowledge that my prestige was very low and the equally sad conviction that the RAF still did not know what do do with me.

# 20

Occasionally my period in limbo was relieved when I was allowed out of camp into the city of Manchester. And I suppose it was the fact that I was a new-fangled parent that made me look at the various prams in the streets. Mostly the prams were pushed by women, but now and then I saw a man doing the job.

I suppose it isn't unusual to see a man pushing a pram in a town, but on a lonely moorland road the sight merits a second glance. Especially when the pram contains a large dog.

That was what I saw in the hills above Darrowby one morning and I slowed down as I drove past. I had noticed the strange combination before – on several occasions over the last few weeks – and it was clear that man and dog had recently moved into the district.

As the car drew abreast of him the man turned, smiled and raised his hand. It was a smile of rare sweetness in a very brown face. A forty-year-old face, I thought, above a brown neck which bore neither collar nor tie, and a faded striped shirt lying open over a bare chest despite the coldness of the day.

I couldn't help wondering who or what he was. The outfit of scuffed suede golf jacket, corduroy trousers and sturdy boots didn't give much clue. Some people might have put him down as an ordinary tramp, but there was a businesslike energetic look about him which didn't fit the term.

I wound the window down and the thin wind of a Yorkshire March bit at my cheeks.

'Nippy this morning,' I said.

The man seemed surprised. 'Aye,' he replied after a moment. 'Aye, reckon it is.'

I looked at the pram, ancient and rusty, and at the big animal sitting upright inside it. He was a lurcher, a cross-bred greyhound, and he gazed back at me with unruffled dignity.

'Nice dog,' I said.

'Aye, that's Jake.' The man smiled again, showing good regular teeth. 'He's a grand 'un.'

I waved and drove on. In the mirror I could see the compact figure stepping out briskly, head up, shoulders squared, and, rising like a statue from the middle of the pram, the huge brindled form of Jake.

I didn't have to wait long to meet the unlikely pair again. I was examining a carthorse's teeth in a farmyard when on the hillside beyond the stable I saw a figure kneeling by a dry stone wall. And by his side, a pram and a big dog sitting patiently on the grass.

'Hey, just a minute.' I pointed at the hill. 'Who is that?'

The farmer laughed. 'That's Roddy Travers. D'you ken 'im?'

'No, no I don't. I had a word with him on the road the other day, that's all.'

'Aye, on the road.' He nodded knowingly. 'That's where you'd see Roddy, right enough.'

'But what is he? Where does he come from?'

'He comes from somewhere in Yorkshire, but ah don't rightly know where and ah don't think anybody else does. But I'll tell you this – he can turn 'is hand to anything.'

'Yes,' I said, watching the man expertly laying the flat slabs of stone as he repaired a gap in the wall. 'There's not many can do what he's doing now.'

'That's true. Wallin' is a skilled job and it's dying out, but Roddy's a dab hand at it. But he can do owt – hedgin', ditchin', lookin' after stock, it's all the same to him.'

I lifted the tooth rasp and began to rub a few sharp corners off the horse's molars. 'And how long will he stay here?'

'Oh, when he's finished that wall he'll be off. Ah could do with 'im stoppin' around for a bit but he never stays in one place for long.'

'But hasn't he got a home anywhere?'

'Nay, nay.' The farmer laughed again. 'Roddy's got nowt. All 'e has in the world is in that there pram.'

Over the next weeks as the harsh spring began to soften and the sunshine brought a bright speckle of primroses on to the grassy banks I saw Roddy quite often, sometimes on the road, occasionally wielding a spade busily on the ditches around the fields. Jake was always there, either loping by his side or watching him at work. But we didn't actually meet again till I was inoculating Mr Pawson's sheep for pulpy kidney.

There were three hundred to do and they drove them in batches into a small pen where Roddy caught and held them for me. And I could see he was an expert at this, too. The wild hill sheep whipped past him like bullets but he seized their fleece effortlessly, sometimes in mid-air, and held the foreleg up to expose that bare clean area of skin behind the elbow that nature seemed to provide for the veterinary surgeon's needle.

Outside, on the windy slopes the big lurcher sat upright in typical pose, looking with mild interest at the farm dogs prowling intently around the pens, but not interfering in any way.

'You've got him well trained,' I said.

Roddy smiled. 'Yes, ye'll never find Jake dashin' about, annoyin' people. He knows 'e has to sit there till I'm finished and there he'll sit.'

'And quite happy to do so, by the look of him.' I glanced again at the dog, a picture of contentment. 'He must live a wonderful life, travelling everywhere with you.'

'You're right there,' Mr Pawson broke in as he ushered another bunch of sheep into the pen. 'He hasn't a care in t'world, just like his master.'

Roddy didn't say anything, but as the sheep ran in he straightened up and took a long steady breath. He had been working hard and a little trickle of sweat ran down the side of his forehead but as he gazed over the wide sweep of moor and fell I could read utter serenity in his face. After a few moments he spoke.

'I reckon that's true. We haven't much to worry us, Jake and me.'

Mr Pawson grinned mischievously. 'By gaw, Roddy, you never spoke a truer word. No wife, no kids, no life insurance, no overdraft at t'bank – you must have a right peaceful existence.'

'Ah suppose so,' Roddy said. 'But then ah've no money either.'

The farmer gave him a quizzical look. 'Aye, how about that, then? Wouldn't you feel a bit more secure, like, if you had a bit o' brass put by?'

'Nay, nay. Ye can't take it with you and any road, as long as a man can pay 'is way, he's got enough.'

There was nothing original about the words, but they have

stayed with me all my life because they came from his lips and were spoken with such profound assurance.

When I had finished the inoculations and the ewes were turned out to trot back happily over the open fields I turned to Roddy. 'Well, thanks very much. It makes my job a lot quicker when I have a good catcher like you.' I pulled out a packet of Gold Flake. 'Will you have a cigarette?'

'No, thank ye, Mr Herriot. I don't smoke.'

'You don't?'

'No – don't drink either.' He gave me his gentle smile and again I had the impression of physical and mental purity. No drinking, no smoking, a life of constant movement in the open air without material possessions or ambitions – it all showed in the unclouded eyes, the fresh skin and the hard muscular frame. He wasn't very big but he looked indestructible.

'C'mon, Jake, it's dinnertime,' he said and the big lurcher bounded around him in delight. I went over and spoke to the dog and he responded with tremendous body-swaying wags, his handsome face looking up at me, full of friendliness.

I stroked the long pointed head and tickled the ears. 'He's a beauty, Roddy – a grand 'un, as you said.'

I walked to the house to wash my hands and before I went inside I glanced back at the two of them. They were sitting in the shelter of a wall and Roddy was laying out a thermos flask and a parcel of food while Jake watched eagerly. The hard bright sunshine beat on them as the wind whistled over the top of the wall. They looked supremely comfortable and at peace.

'He's independent, you see,' the farmer's wife said as I stood at the kitchen sink. 'He's welcome to come in for a bit o' dinner but he'd rather stay outside with his dog.'

I nodded. 'Where does he sleep when he's going round the farms like this?'

'Oh, anywhere,' she replied. 'In hay barns or granaries or sometimes out in the open, but when he's with us he sleeps upstairs in one of our rooms. Ah know for a fact any of the farmers would be willin' to have him in the house because he allus keeps himself spotless clean.'

'I see.' I pulled the towel from behind the door. 'He's quite a character, isn't he?'

She smiled ruminatively. 'Aye, he certainly is. Just him and his dog!' She lifted a fragrant dishful of hot roast ham from the oven and set it on the table. 'But I'll tell you this. The feller's all right. Everybody likes Roddy Travers – he's a very nice man.'

Roddy stayed around the Darrowby district throughout the summer and I grew used to the sight of him on the farms or pushing his pram along the roads. When it was raining he wore a tattered over-long gaberdine coat, but at other times it was always the golf jacket and corduroys. I don't know where he had accumulated his wardrobe. It was a safe bet he had never been on a golf course in his life and it was just another of the little mysteries about him.

I saw him early one morning on a hill path in early October. It had been a night of iron frost and the tussocky pastures beyond the walls were held in a pitiless white grip with every blade of grass stiffly ensheathed in rime.

I was muffled to the eyes and had been beating my gloved fingers against my knees to thaw them out, but when I pulled up and wound down the window the first thing I saw was the bare chest under the collarless unbuttoned shirt.

'Mornin', Mr Herriot,' he said. 'Ah'm glad I've seen ye.' He paused and gave me his tranquil smile. 'There's a job along t'road for a couple of weeks, then I'm movin' on.'

'I see.' I knew enough about him now not to ask where he was going. Instead I looked down at Jake who was sniffling the herbage. 'I see he's walking this morning.'

Roddy laughed. 'Yes, sometimes 'e likes to walk, sometimes 'e likes to ride. He pleases 'imself.'

'Right, Roddy,' I said. 'No doubt we'll meet again. All the best to you.'

He waved and set off jauntily over the icebound road and I felt that a little vein of richness had gone from my life.

But I was wrong. That same evening about eight o'clock the front door bell rang. I answered it and found Roddy on the front doorsteps. Behind him, just visible in the frosty darkness, stood the ubiquitous pram.

'I want you to look at me dog, Mr Herriot,' he said.

'Why, what's the trouble?'

'Ah don't rightly know. He's havin' sort of . . . faintin' fits.'

'Fainting fits? That doesn't sound like Jake. Where is he, anyway?'

He pointed behind him 'In t'pram, under t'cover.'

'All right.' I threw the door wide. 'Bring him in.'

Roddy adroitly manhandled the rusty old vehicle up the steps and pushed it, squeaking and rattling, along the passage to the consulting room. There, under the bright lights he snapped back the fasteners and threw off the cover to reveal Jake stretched beneath.

His head was pillowed on the familiar gaberdine coat and around him lay his master's worldly goods; a string-tied bundle of spare shirt and socks, a packet of tea, a thermos, knife and spoon and an ex-army haversack.

The big dog looked up at me with terrified eyes and as I patted him I could feel his whole frame quivering.

'Let him lie there a minute, Roddy,' I said. 'And tell me exactly what you've seen.'

He rubbed his palms together and his fingers trembled. 'Well, it only started this afternoon. He was right as rain, larkin' about on the grass, then he went into a sort o' fit.'

'How do you mean?'

'Just kind of seized up and toppled over on 'is side. He lay there for a bit, gaspin' and slaverin'. Ah'll tell ye, I thought he was a goner.' His eyes widened and a corner of his mouth twitched at the memory.

'How long did that last?'

'Nobbut a few seconds. Then he got up and you'd say there was nowt wrong with 'im.'

'But he did it again?'

'Aye, time and time again. Drove me near daft. But in between 'e was normal. Normal, Mr Herriot!'

It sounded ominously like the onset of epilepsy. 'How old is he?' I asked.

'Five gone last February.'

Ah well, it was a bit old for that. I reached for a stethoscope and auscultated the heart. I listened intently but heard only the racing beat of a frightened animal. There was no abnormality. My thermometer showed no rise in temperature.

'Let's have him on the table, Roddy. You take the back end.'

The big animal was limp in our arms as we hoisted him on to the smooth surface, but after lying there for a moment he looked timidly around him then sat up with a slow and careful movement. As we watched he reached out and licked his master's face while his tail flickered between his legs.

'Look at that!' the man exclaimed. 'He's all right again. You'd think he didn't ail a thing.'

And indeed Jake was recovering his confidence rapidly. He peered tentatively at the floor a few times then suddenly jumped down, trotted to his master and put his paws against his chest.

I looked at the dog standing there, tail wagging furiously. 'Well, that's a relief, anyway. I didn't like the look of him just then, but whatever's been troubling him seems to have righted itself. I'll . . .'

My happy flow was cut off. I stared at the lurcher. His forelegs were on the floor again and his mouth was gaping as he fought for breath. Frantically he gasped and retched then he blundered across the floor, collided with the pram wheels and fell on his side.

'What the hell . . .! Quick, get him up again!' I grabbed the animal round the middle and we lifted him back on to the table.

I watched in disbelief as the huge form lay there. There was no fight for breath now – he wasn't breathing at all, he was unconscious. I pushed my fingers inside his thigh and felt the pulse. It was still going, rapid and feeble, but yet he didn't breathe.

He could die any moment and I stood there helpless, all my scientific training useless. Finally my frustration burst from me and I struck the dog on the ribs with the flat of my hand.

'Jake!' I yelled. 'Jake, what's the matter with you ?'

As though in reply, the lurcher immediately started to take great wheezing breaths, his eyelids twitched back to consciousness and he began to look about him. But he was still mortally afraid and he lay prone as I gently stroked his head.

There was a long silence while the animal's terror slowly subsided, then he sat up on the table and regarded us placidly.

'There you are,' Roddy said softly. 'Same thing again. Ah can't reckon it up and ah thought ah knew summat about dogs.'

186

I didn't say anything. I couldn't reckon it up either, and I was supposed to be a veterinary surgeon.

I spoke at last. 'Roddy, that wasn't a fit. He was choking. Something was interfering with his air flow.' I took my hand torch from my breast pocket. 'I'm going to have a look at his throat.'

I pushed Jake's jaws apart, depressed his tongue with a forefinger and shone the light into the depths. He was the kind of good-natured dog who offered no resistance as I prodded around, but despite my floodlit view of the pharynx I could find nothing wrong. I had been hoping desperately to come across a bit of bone stuck there somewhere but I ranged feverishly over pink tongue, healthy tonsils and gleaming molars without success. Everything looked perfect.

I was tilting his head a little further when I felt him stiffen and heard Roddy's cry.

'He's goin' again!'

And he was, too. I stared in horror as the brindled body slid away from me and lay prostrate once more on the table. And again the mouth strained wide and froth bubbled round the lips. As before, the breathing had stopped and the rib cage was motionless. As the seconds ticked away I beat on the chest with my hand but it didn't work this time. I pulled the lower eyelid down from the staring orb – the conjunctiva was blue, Jake hadn't long to live. The tragedy of the thing bore down on me. This wasn't just a dog, he was this man's family and I was watching him die.

It was at that moment that I heard the faint sound. It was a strangled cough which barely stirred the dog's lips.

'Damn it!' I shouted. 'He *is* choking. There must be something down there.'

Again I seized the head and pushed my torch into the mouth and I shall always be thankful that at that very instant the dog coughed again, opening the cartilages of the larynx and giving me a glimpse of the cause of all the trouble. There, beyond the drooping epiglottis I saw for a fleeting moment a smooth round object no bigger than a pea.

'I think it's a pebble,' I gasped. 'Right inside his larynx.'

'You mean, in 'is Adam's apple ?'

'That's right, and it's acting like a ball valve, blocking his windpipe every now and then.' I shook the dog's head. 'You see, look, I've dislodged it for the moment. He's coming round again.'

Once more Jake was reviving and breathing steadily.

Roddy ran his hand over the head, along the back and down the great muscles of the hind limbs. 'But . . . but . . . it'll happen again, won't it ?'

I nodded. 'I'm afraid so.'

'And one of these times it isn't goin' to shift and that'll be the end of 'im ?' He had gone very pale.

'That's about it, Roddy, I'll have to get that pebble out.'

'But how . . . ?'

'Cut into the larynx. And right now – it's the only way.'

'All right.' He swallowed. 'Let's get on. I don't think ah could stand it if he went down again.'

I knew what he meant. My knees had begun to shake, and I had a strong conviction that if Jake collapsed once more then so would I.

I seized a pair of scissors and clipped away the hair from the ventral surface of the larynx. I dared not use a general anaesthetic and infiltrated the area with local before swabbing with antiseptic. Mercifully there was a freshly boiled set of instruments lying in the sterilizer and I lifted out the tray and set it on the trolley by the side of the table.

'Hold his head steady,' I said hoarsely, and gripped a scalpel.

I cut down through skin, fascia and the thin layers of the sterno-hyoid and omo-hyoid muscles till the ventral surface of the larynx was revealed. This was something I had never done to a live dog before, but desperation abolished any hesitancy and it took me only another few seconds to incise the thin membrane and peer into the interior.

And there it was. A pebble right enough – grey and glistening and tiny, but big enough to kill.

I had to fish it out quickly and cleanly without pushing it into the trachea. I leaned back and rummaged in the tray till I found some broad-bladed forceps, then I poised them over the wound. Great surgeons' hands, I felt sure, didn't shake like this, nor did such men pant as I was doing. But I clenched my teeth, introduced the forceps and my hand magically steadied as I clamped them over the pebble.

I stopped panting, too. In fact I didn't breathe at all as I bore the shining little object slowly and tenderly through the opening and dropped it with a gentle rat-tat on the table.

'Is that it?' asked Roddy, almost in a whisper.

'That's it.' I reached for needle and suture silk. 'All is well now.'

The stitching took only a few minutes and by the end of it Jake was bright-eyed and alert, paws shifting impatiently, ready for anything. He seemed to know his troubles were over.

Roddy brought him back in ten days to have the stitches removed. It was, in fact, the very morning he was leaving the Darrowby district, and after I had picked the few loops of silk from the nicely healed wound I walked with him to the front door while Jake capered round our feet.

On the pavement outside Skeldale House the ancient pram stood in all its high, rusted dignity. Roddy pulled back the cover.

'Up, boy,' he murmured, and the big dog leaped effortlessly into his accustomed place.

Roddy took hold of the handle with both hands and as the autumn sunshine broke suddenly through the clouds it lit up a picture which had grown familiar and part of the daily scene. The golf jacket, the open shirt and brown chest, the handsome animal sitting up, looking around him with natural grace.

'Well, so long, Roddy,' I said. 'I suppose you'll be round these parts again.'

He turned and I saw that smile again. 'Aye, reckon ah'll be back.'

He gave a push and they were off, the strange vehicle creaking, Jake swaying gently as they went down the street. The memory came back to me of what I had seen under the cover that night in the surgery. The haversack, which would contain his razor, towel, soap and a few other things. The packet of tea and the thermos. And something else – a tiny dog collar. Could it have belonged to Jake as a pup or to another loved animal? It added a little more mystery to the man . . . and explained other things, too. That farmer had been right – all Roddy possessed was in that pram.

And it seemed it was all he desired, too, because as he turned the corner and disappeared from my view I could hear him whistling.


# 21


They had sent me to Eastchurch on the Isle of Sheppey and I knew it was the last stop.

As I looked along the disorderly line of men I realized I wouldn't be taking part in many more parades. And it came to me with a pang that at the Scarborough Initial Training Wing this would not have been classed as a parade at all. I could remember the ranks of blue outside the Grand Hotel, straight as the Grenadier Guards and every man standing stiffly, looking neither to left nor right. Our boots gleaming, buttons shining like gold and not a movement anywhere as the flight sergeant led the officer round on morning inspection.

I had moaned as loudly as anybody at the rigid discipline, the 'bull', the scrubbing and polishing, marching and drilling, but now that it had all gone it seemed good and meaningful and I missed it.

Here the files of airmen lounged, chatted among themselves and occasionally took a surreptitious drag at a cigarette as a sergeant out in front called the names from a list and gave us our leisurely instructions for the day.

This particular morning he was taking a long time over it, consulting sheaves of papers and making laboured notes with a pencil. A big Irishman on my right was becoming increasingly restive and finally he shouted testily:

'For — sake, sergeant, get us off this — square. Me — feet's killin' me!'

The sergeant didn't even look up. 'Shut your mouth, Brady,'

he replied. 'You'll get off the square when I say so and not before.'

It was like that at Eastchurch, the great filter tank of the RAF, where what I had heard described as the 'odds and sods' were finally sorted out. It was a big sprawling camp filled with a widely varied mixture of airmen who had one thing in common; they were all waiting – some of them for remuster, but most for discharge from the service.

There was a resigned air about the whole place, an acceptance of the fact that we were all just putting in time. There was a token discipline but it was of the most benign kind. And as I said, every man there was just waiting . . . waiting . . .

Little Ned Finch in his remote corner of the high Yorkshire Dales always seemed to me to be waiting, too. I could remember his boss yelling at him.

'For God's sake, shape up to t'job! You're not farmin' at all!' Mr Daggett grabbed hold of a leaping calf and glared in exasperation.

Ned gazed back at him impassively. His face registered no particular emotion, but in the pale blue eyes I read the expression that was always there – as though he was waiting for something to happen, but without much hope. He made a tentative attempt to catch a calf but was brushed aside, then he put his arms round the neck of another one, a chunky little animal of three months, and was borne along a few yards before being deposited on his back in the straw.

'Oh, dang it, do this one, Mr Herriot!' Mr Daggett barked, turning the hairy neck towards me. 'It looks as though I'll have to catch 'em all myself.'

I injected the animal. I was inoculating a batch of twenty with preventive pneumonia vaccine and Ned was suffering. With his diminutive stature and skinny, small-boned limbs he had always seemed to me to be in the wrong job; but he had been a farm worker all his life and he was over sixty now, grizzled, balding and slightly bent, but still battling on.

Mr Daggett reached out and as one of the shaggy creatures sped past he scooped the head into one of his great hands and seized the ear with the other. The little animal seemed to realize it was useless to struggle and stood unresisting as I inserted the needle. At the other end Ned put his knee against the calf's rear and listlessly pushed it against the wall. He wasn't doing much good and his boss gave him a withering glance.

We finished the bunch with hardly any help from the little man, and as we left the pen and came out into the yard Mr Daggett wiped his brow. It was a raw November day but he was sweating profusely and for a moment he leaned his gaunt six-foot frame against the wall as the wind from the bare moorland blew over him.

'By gaw, he's a useless little beggar is that,' he grunted. 'Ah don't know how ah put up with 'im.' He muttered to himself for a few moments, then gave tongue again. 'Hey, Ned!'

The little man who had been trailing aimlessly over the cobbles turned his pinched face and looked at him with his submissive but strangely expectant eyes.

'Get them bags o' corn up into the granary!' his boss ordered.

Wordlessly Ned went over to a cart and with an effort shouldered a sack of corn. As he painfully mounted the stone steps to the granary his frail little legs trembled and bent under the weight.

Mr Daggett shook his head and turned to me. His long cadaverous face was set in its usual cast of melancholy.

'You know what's wrong wi' Ned? he murmured confidentially.

'What do you mean?'

'Well, you know why 'e can't catch them calves?'

My own view was that Ned wasn't big enough or strong enough and anyway he was naturally ineffectual, but I shook my head.

'No,' I said. 'Why is it?'

'Well, I'll tell ye.' Mr Daggett glanced furtively across the yard then spoke from behind his hand. 'He's ower fond of t'bright lights.'

'Eh?'

'Ah'm tellin' ye, he's crazed over t'bright lights.'

'Bright ... what ... where ... ?'

Mr Daggett leaned closer. 'He gets over to Briston every night.'

'Briston . . . ?' I looked across from the isolated farm to the village three miles away on the other side of the Dale. It was the only settlement in that bleak vista – a straggle of ancient houses dark and silent against the green fellside. I could recall that at night the oil lamps made yellow flickers of light in the windows but they weren't very bright. 'I don't understand.'

'Well . . . 'e gets into t'pub.'

'Ah, the pub.'

Mr Daggett nodded slowly and portentously but I was still puzzled. The Hulton Arms was a square kitchen where you could get a glass of beer and where a few old men played dominoes of an evening. It wasn't my idea of a den of vice.

'Does he get drunk there?' I asked.

'Nay, nay.' The farmer shook his head. 'It's not that. It's the hours 'e keeps.'

'Comes back late, eh?'

'Aye, that 'e does!' The eyes widened in their cavernous sockets. 'Sometimes 'e doesn't get back till 'alf past nine or ten o'clock!'

'Gosh, is that so?'

'Sure as ah'm standin' here. And there's another thing. He can't get out of 'is bed next day. Ah've done half a day's work before 'e starts.' He paused and glanced again across the yard. 'You can believe me or believe me not, but sometimes 'e isn't on the job till seven o'clock in t'morning!'

'Good heavens!'

He shrugged wearily. 'Aye well, you see how it is. Come into t'house, you'll want to wash your hands.'

In the huge flagged kitchen I bent low over the brown earthenware sink. Scar Farm was four hundred years old and the various tenants hadn't altered it much since the days of Henry the Eighth. Gnarled beams, rough whitewashed walls and hard wooden chairs. But comfort had never been important to Mr Daggett or his wife who was ladling hot water from the primitive boiler by the side of the fire and pouring it into her scrubbing bucket.

She clopped around over the flags in her clogs, hair pulled back tightly from her weathered face into a bun, a coarse sacking apron tied round her waist. She had no children but her life was one of constant activity; indoors or outside, she worked all the time.

At one end of the room wooden steps led up through a hole in the ceiling to a loft where Ned slept. That had been the little man's room for nearly fifty years, ever since he had come to work for Mr Daggett's father as a boy from school. And in all that time he had never travelled further than Darrowby, never done anything outside his daily routine. Wifeless, friendless, he plodded through his life, endlessly milking, feeding and mucking out, and waiting, I suspected with diminishing hope for something to happen.

With my hand on the car door I looked back at Scar Farm, at the sagging roof tiles, the great stone lintel over the door. It typified the harshness of the lives of the people within. Little Ned was no bargain as a stockman, and his boss's exasperation was understandable. Mr Daggett was not a cruel or an unjust man. He and his wife had been hardened and squeezed dry by the pitiless austerity of their existence in this lonely corner of the high Pennines.

There was no softness up here, no frills. The stone walls, sparse grass and stunted trees; the narrow road with its smears of cow muck. Everything was down to fundamentals, and it was a miracle to me that most of the Dalesmen were not like the Daggetts but cheerful and humorous.

But as I drove away, the sombre beauty of the place overwhelmed me. The lowering hillsides burst magically into life as a shaft of sunshine stabbed through the clouds, flooding the bare flanks with warm gold. Suddenly I was aware of the delicate shadings of green, the rich glowing bronze of the dead bracken spilling from the high tops, the whole peaceful majesty of my work-a-day world.

I hadn't far to drive to my next call – just about a mile – and it was in a vastly different atmosphere. Miss Tremayne, a rich lady from the south, had bought a tumbledown manor house and spent many thousands of pounds in converting it into a luxury home. As my feet crunched on the gravel I looked up at the large windows with their leaded panes, at the smooth, freshly-pointed stones.

Elsie opened the door to me. She was Miss Tremayne's cook-housekeeper, and one of my favourite people. Aged about fifty, no more than five feet high and as round as a ball with short bandy legs sticking out from beneath a tight black dress.

'Good morning, Elsie,' I said, and she burst into a peal of

laughter. This, more than her remarkable physical appearance, was what delighted me. She laughed uproariously at every statement and occurrence; in fact she laughed at the things she said herself.

'Come in, Mr Herriot, ha-ha-ha,' she said. 'It's been a bit nippy today, he-he, but I think it'll get out this afternoon, ho-ho-ho.'

All the mirth may have seemed somewhat unnecessary, and indeed, it made her rather difficult to understand, but the general effect was cheering. She led me into the drawing room and her mistress rose with some difficulty from her chair.

Miss Tremayne was elderly and half crippled with arthritis but bore her affliction without fuss.

'Ah, Mr Herriot,' she said. 'How good of you to come.' She put her head on one side and beamed at me as though I was the most delightful thing she had seen for a long time.

She, too, had a bubbling, happy personality, and since she owned three dogs, two cats and an elderly donkey I had come to know her very well in her six months' residence in the Dale.

My visit was to dress the donkey's overgrown hoofs, and a pair of clippers and a blacksmith's knife dangled from my right hand.

'Oh, put those grisly instruments down over there,' she said. 'Elsie's bringing some tea – I'm sure you've time for a cup.'

I sank willingly into one of the brightly covered armchairs and was looking round the comfortable room when Elsie reappeared, gliding over the carpet as though on wheels. She put the tray on the table by my side.

'There's yer tea,' she said, and went into a paroxysm so hearty that she had to lean on the back of my chair. She had no visible neck and the laughter caused the fat little body to shake all over.

When she had recovered she rolled back into the kitchen and I heard her clattering about with pans. Despite her idiosyncrasies she was a wonderful cook and very efficient in all she did.

I spent a pleasant ten minutes with Miss Tremayne and the tea, then I went outside and attended to the donkey. When I had finished I made my way round the back of the house and as I was passing the kitchen I saw Elsie at the open window.

'Many thanks for the tea, Elsie,' I said.

The little woman gripped the sides of the sink to steady herself. 'Ha-ha-ha, that's all right. That's, he-he, quite all right, ha-ha-ho-ho-ho.'

Wonderingly I got into the car and as I drove away, the disturbing thought came to me that one day I might say something really witty to Elsie and cause her to do herself an injury.

I was called back to Mr Daggett's quite soon afterwards to see a cow which wouldn't get up. The farmer thought she was paralysed.

I drove there in a thin drizzle and the light was fading at about four o'clock in the afternoon when I arrived at Scar Farm.

When I examined the cow I was convinced she had just got herself into an awkward position in the stall with her legs jammed under the broken timbers of the partition.

'I think she's sulking, Mr Daggett,' I said. 'She's had a few goes at rising and now she's decided not to try any more. Some cows are like that.'

'Maybe you're right,' the farmer replied. 'She's allus been a stupid bitch.'

'And she's a big one, too. She'll take a bit of moving.' I lifted a rope from the byre wall and tied it round the hocks. 'I'll push the feet from the other side while you and Ned pull the legs round.'

'Pull ?' Mr Daggett gave the little man a sour look. 'He couldn't pull the skin off a rice puddin'.'

Ned said nothing, just gazed dully to his front, arms hanging limp. He looked as though he didn't care, wasn't even there with us. His mind was certainly elsewhere if his thoughts were mirrored in his eyes – vacant, unheeding, but as always, expectant.

I went behind the partition and thrust steadily at the feet while the men pulled. At least Mr Daggett pulled, mouth open, gasping with effort, while Ned leaned languidly on the rope.

Inch by inch the big animal came round till she was lying almost in the middle of the stall, but as I was about to call a halt the rope broke and Mr Daggett flew backwards on to the hard cobbles. Ned of course did not fall down because he hadn't been trying, and his employer, stretched flat, glared up at him with frustrated rage.

'Ye little bugger, ye let me do that all by meself! Ah don't know why ah bother with you, you're bloody useless.'

At that moment the cow, as I had expected, rose to her feet, and the farmer gesticulated at the little man. 'Well, go on, dang ye, get some straw and rub her legs! They'll be numb.'

Meekly Ned twisted some straw into a wisp and began to do a bit of massage. Mr Daggett got up stiffly, felt gingerly along his back, then walked up beside the cow to make sure the chain hadn't tightened round her neck. He was on his way back when the big animal swung round suddenly and brought her cloven hoof down solidly on the farmer's toe.

If he had been wearing heavy boots it wouldn't have been so bad, but his feet were encased in ancient cracked wellingtons which offered no protection.

'Ow! Ow! Ow!' yelled Mr Daggett, beating on the hairy back with his fists. 'Gerroff, ye awd bitch!' He heaved, pushed and writhed but the ten hundredweight of beef ground down inexorably.

The farmer was only released when the cow slid off his foot, and I know from experience that that sliding is the worst part.

Mr Daggett hopped around on one leg, nursing the bruised extremity in his hands. 'Bloody 'ell,' he moaned. 'Oh, bloody 'ell.'

Just then I happened to glance towards Ned and was amazed to see the apathetic little face crinkle suddenly into a wide grin of unholy glee. I couldn't recall him even smiling before, and my astonishment must have shown in my face because his boss whipped round suddenly and stared at him. As if by magic the sad mask slipped back into place and he went on with his rubbing.

Mr Daggett hobbled out to the car with me and as I was about to leave he nudged me.

'Look at 'im,' he whispered.

Ned, milk pail in hand, was bustling along the byre with unwonted energy.

His employer gave a bitter smile. 'It's t'only time 'e ever hurries. Can't wait to get out to t'pub.'

'Oh well, you say he doesn't get drunk. There can't be any harm in it.'

The deep sunk eyes held me. 'Don't you believe it. He'll come to a bad end gaddin' about the way 'e does.'

'But surely the odd glass of beer . . .'

'Ah but there's more than that to it.' He glanced around him. 'There's women!'

I laughed incredulously. 'Oh come now, Mr Daggett, what women ?'

'Over at t'pub,' he muttered. 'Them Bradley lasses.'

'The landlord's daughters ? Oh really, I can't believe . . .'

'All right, ye can say what ye like. He's got 'is eye on 'em. Ah knaw – ah've only been in that pub once but ah've seen for meself.'

I didn't know what to say, but in any case I had no opportunity because he turned and strode into the house.

Alone in the cold darkness I looked at the gaunt silhouette of the old farmhouse above me. In the dying light of the November day the rain streamed down the rough stones and the wind caught at the thin tendril of smoke from the chimney, hurling it in ragged streamers across the slate blue pallor of the western sky. The fell hung over everything, a black featureless bulk, oppressive and menacing.

Through the kitchen window I could see the oil lamp casting its dim light over the bare table, the cheerless hearth with its tiny flicker of fire. In the shadows at the far end the steps rose into Ned's loft and I could imagine the little figure clambering up to get changed and escape to Briston.

Across the valley the single street of the village was a broken grey thread in the gloom but in the cottage windows the lamps winked faintly. These were Ned Finch's bright lights and I could understand how he felt. After Scar Farm, Briston would be like Monte Carlo.

The image stayed in my mind so vividly that after two more calls that evening I decided to go a few miles out of my way as I returned homeward. I cut across the Dale and it was about half past eight when I drove into Briston. It was difficult to find the Hulton Arms because there was no lighted entrance, no attempt to advertise its presence, but I persevered because I had to find out what was behind Mr Daggett's tale of debauchery.

I located it at last. Just like the door of an ordinary house with a faded wooden sign hanging above it. Inside, the usual domino game was in progress, a few farmers sat chatting quietly. The Misses Bradley, plain but pleasant-faced women in their forties, sat on either side of the fire, and sure enough there was Ned with a half pint glass in front of him.

I sat down by his side. 'Hello, Ned.'

'Now then, Mr Herriot,' he murmured absently, glancing at me with his strange expectant eyes.

One of the Bradley ladies put down her knitting and came over. 'Pint of bitter, please,' I said. 'What will you have, Ned?'

'Nay, thank ye, Mr Herriot. This'll do for me. It's me second and ah'm not a big drinker, tha knows.'

Miss Bradley laughed. 'Yes, he nobbut has 'is two glasses a night, but he enjoys them, don't you, Ned?'

'That's right, ah do.' He looked up at her and she smiled kindly down at him before going for my beer.

He took a sip at his glass. 'Ah really come for t'company, Mr Herriot.'

'Yes, of course,' I said. I knew what he meant. He probably sat on his own most of the time, but around him was warmth and comfort and friendliness. A great log sent flames crackling up to the wide chimney, there was electric light and shining mirrors with whisky slogans painted on their surface. It wasn't anything like Scar Farm.

The little man said very little. He spun out his drink for another hour, looking around him as the dominoes clicked and I lowered another contemplative pint. The Misses Bradley knitted and brewed tea in a big black kettle over the fire and when they had to get up to serve their customers they occasionally patted Ned playfully on the cheek as they passed.

By the time he tipped down the last drop and rose to go it was a quarter to ten and he still had to cycle across to the other side of the Dale. Another late night for Ned.

It was a Tuesday lunchtime in early spring. Helen always cooked steak and kidney pie on Tuesdays and I used to think about it all morning on my rounds. My thoughts that morning had been particularly evocative because lambing had started and I had spent most of the time in my shirt sleeves in the biting wind as my hunger grew and grew.

Helen cut into her blissful creation and began to scoop the fragrant contents on to my plate.

'I met Miss Tremayne in the market place this morning, Jim.'

'Oh yes ?' I was almost drooling as my wife stopped shovelling out the pie, sliced open some jacket potatoes and dropped pats of farm butter on to the steaming surfaces.

'Yes, she wants you to go out there this afternoon and put some canker drops in Wilberforce's ears if you have time.'

'Oh I have time for that,' I said. Wilberforce was Miss Tremayne's ancient tabby cat and it was just the kind of job I wanted after my arm-aching morning.

I was raising a luscious forkful when Helen spoke again. 'Oh, and she had an interesting item of news.'

'Really ?' But I had begun to chew and my thoughts were distant.

'Its' about the little woman who works for her – Elsie. You know her ?'

I nodded and took another mouthful. 'Of course, of course.'

'Well, it's quite unexpected, I suppose, but Elsie's getting married.'

I choked on my pie. 'What!'

'It's true. And maybe you know the bridegroom.'

'Tell me.'

'He works on one of the neighbouring farms. His name is Ned Finch.'

This time my breath was cut off completely and Helen had to beat me on the back as I spluttered and retched. It wasn't until an occluding morsel of potato skin had shot down my nose that I was able to utter a weak croak. 'Ned Finch ?'

'That's what she said.'

I finished my lunch in a dream, but by the end of it I had accepted the extraordinary fact. Helen and Miss Tremayne were two sensible people – there couldn't be any mistake. And yet . . . even as I drew up outside the old Manor House a feeling of unreality persisted.

Elsie opened the door as usual. I looked at her for a moment.

'What's this I hear, Elsie?'

She started a giggle which rapidly spread over her spherical frame.

I put my hand on her shoulder. 'Is it true?'

The giggle developed into a mighty gale of laughter, and if she hadn't been holding the handle I am sure she would have fallen over.

'Aye, it's right enough,' she gasped. 'Ah've found a man at last and ah'm goin' to get wed!' She leaned helplessly on the door.

'Well, I'm pleased to hear it, Elsie. I hope you'll be very happy.'

She hadn't the strength to speak but merely nodded as she lay against the door. Then she led me to the drawing room.

'In ye go,' she chuckled. 'Ah'll bring ye some tea.'

Miss Tremayne rose to greet me with parted lips and shining eyes. 'Oh, Mr Herriot, have you heard?'

'Yes, but how ...?'

'It all started when I asked Mr Daggett for some fresh eggs. He sent Ned on his bicycle with the eggs and it was like fate.'

'Well, how wonderful.'

'Yes, and I actually saw it happen. Ned walked in that door with his basket, Elsie was clearing the table here, and, Mr Herriot—' She clasped her hands under her chin, smiled ecstatically and her eyes rolled upwards. 'Oh, Mr Herriot, it was love at first sight!'

'Yes ... yes, indeed. Marvellous!'

'And ever since that day Ned has been calling round and now he comes every evening and sits with Elsie in the kitchen. Isn't it romantic!'

'It certainly is. And when did they decide to get married?'

'Oh, he popped the question within a month, and I'm so happy for Elsie because Ned is such a dear little man, don't you think so?'

'Yes, he is.' I said. 'He's a very nice chap.'

Elsie simpered and tittered her way in with the tea then put her hand over her face and fled in confusion, and as Miss Tremayne began to pour I sank into one of the armchairs and lifted Wilberforce on to my lap.

The big cat purred as I instilled a few drops of lotion into his ear. He had a chronic canker condition – not very bad but now and then it became painful and needed treatment. It was because Miss Tremayne didn't like putting the lotion in that I was pressed into service.

As I turned the ear over and gently massaged the oily liquid into the depths, Wilberforce groaned softly with pleasure and rubbed his cheek against my hand. He loved this anointing of the tender area beyond his reach and when I had finished he curled up on my knee.

I leaned back and sipped my tea. At that moment, with my back and shoulders weary and my hands red and chapped with countless washings on the open hillsides this seemed to be veterinary practice at its best.

Miss Tremayne continued. 'We shall have a little reception after the wedding and then the happy couple will take up residence here.'

'You mean, in this house ?'

'Yes, of course. There's heaps of room in this big old place, and I have furnished two rooms for them on the east side. I'm sure they'll be very comfortable. Oh, I'm so excited about it all!'

She refilled my cup. 'Before you go you must let Elsie show you where they are going to live.'

On my way out the little woman took me through to the far end of the house.

'This, hee-hee-hee,' she said, 'is where we'll sit of a night, and this, ha-ha-ho-ho, oh dear me, is our bedroom.' She staggered around for a bit, wiped her eyes and turned to me for my opinion.

'It's really lovely, Elsie,' I said.

There were bright carpets, chairs with flowered covers and a fine mahogany-ended bed. It was nothing like the loft.

And as I looked at Elsie I realized the things Ned would see in his bride. Laughter, warmth, vivacity, and – I had no doubt at all – beauty and glamour.


I seemed to get round to most farms that lambing time and in due course I landed at Mr Daggett's. I delivered a fine pair of twins for him but it didn't seem to cheer him at all. Lifting the towel from the grass he handed it to me.

'Well, what did ah tell ye about Ned, eh? Got mixed up wi' a woman just like ah said.' He sniffed disapprovingly. 'All that rakin' and chasin' about – ah knew he'd get into mischief at t'finish.'

I walked back over the sunlit fields to the farm and as I passed the byre door Ned came out pushing a wheelbarrow.

'Good morning, Ned,' I said.

He glanced up at me in his vague way. 'How do, Mr Herriot.'

There was something different about him and it took me a few moments to discern what it was; his eyes had lost the expectant look which had been there for so long, and, after all, that was perfectly natural.

Because it had happened at last for Ned.


# 22


Despite the crowds of men milling around Eastchurch I felt cut off and apart. It made me think of old Mr Potts from my veterinary days. He must have felt like that.

'How are you, Mr Herriot?'

Ordinary words, but the eagerness, almost desperation in the old man's voice made them urgent and meaningful.

I saw him nearly every day. In my unpredictable life it was difficult to do anything regularly but I did like a stroll by the river before lunch and so did my beagle, Sam. That was when we met Mr Potts and Nip, his elderly sheepdog – they seemed to have the same habits as us. His house backed on to the riverside fields and he spent a lot of time just walking around with his dog.

Many retired farmers kept a bit of land and a few stock to occupy their minds and ease the transition from their arduous existence to day-long leisure, but Mr Potts had bought a little bungalow with a scrap of garden and it was obvious that time dragged.

Probably his health had dictated this. As he faced me he leaned on his stick and his bluish cheeks rose and fell with his breathing. He was a heart case if ever I saw one.

'I'm fine, Mr Potts,' I replied. 'And how are things with you ?'

'Nobbut middlin', lad. Ah soon get short o' wind.' He coughed a couple of times then asked the inevitable question.

'And what have you been doin' this mornin' ?' That was when his eyes grew intent and wide. He really wanted to know.

I thought for a moment. 'Well now, let's see.' I always tried to give him a detailed answer because I knew it meant a lot to him and brought back the life he missed so much. 'I've done a couple of cleansings, seen a lame bullock, treated two cows with mastitis and another with milk fever.'

He nodded eagerly at every word.

'By gaw!' he exclaimed. 'It's a beggar, that milk fever. When I were a lad, good cows used to die like flies with it. Allus good milkers after their third or fourth calf. Couldn't get to their feet and we used to dose 'em with all sorts, but they died, every one of 'em.'

'Yes,' I said. 'It must have been heartbreaking in those days.'

'But then—' He smiled delightedly, digging a forefinger into my chest. 'Then we started blowin' up their udders wi' a bicycle pump, and d'you know – they jumped up and walked away. Like magic it were.' His eyes sparkled at the memory.

'I know, Mr Potts, I've blown up a few myself, only I didn't use a bicycle pump – I had a special little inflation apparatus.'

That black box with its shining cylinders and filter is now in my personal museum, and it is the best place for it. It had got me out of some difficult situations but in the background there had always been the gnawing dread of transmitting tuberculosis. I had heard of it happening and was glad that calcium borogluconate had arrived.

As we spoke, Sam and Nip played on the grass beside us. I watched as the beagle frisked round the old animal while Nip pawed at him stiff-jointedly, his tail waving with pleasure. You could see that he enjoyed these meetings as much as his master and for a brief time the years fell away from him as he rolled on his back with Sam astride him, nibbling gently at his chest.

I walked with the old farmer as far as the little wooden bridge,

204

then I had to turn for home. I watched the two of them pottering slowly over the narrow strip of timber to the other side of the river. Sam and I had our work pressing, but they had nothing else to do.

I used to see Mr Potts at other times, too. Wandering aimlessly among the stalls on market days or standing on the fringe of the group of farmers who always gathered in front of the Drovers' Arms to meet cattle dealers, cow feed merchants, or just to talk business among themselves.

Or I saw him at the auction mart, leaning on his stick, listening to the rapid-fire chanting of the auctioneer, watching listlessly as the beasts were bought and sold. And all the time I knew there was an emptiness in him, because there were none of his cattle in the stalls, none of his sheep in the long rows of pens. He was out of it all, old and done.

I saw him the day before he died. It was in the usual place and I was standing at the river's edge watching a heron rising from a rush-lined island and flapping lazily away over the fields.

The old man stopped as he came abreast of me and the two dogs began their friendly wrestling.

'Well now, Mr Herriot.' He paused and bowed his head over the stick which he had dug into the grass of his farm for half a century. 'What have you been doin' today ?'

Perhaps his cheeks were a deeper shade of blue and the breath whistled through his pursed lips as he exhaled, but I can't recall that he looked any worse than usual.

'I'll tell you, Mr Potts,' I said. 'I'm feeling a bit weary. I ran into a real snorter of a foaling this morning – took me over two hours and I ache all over.'

'Foaling, eh ? Foal would be laid wrong, I reckon ?'

'Yes, crossways on, and I had a struggle to turn it.'

'By gaw, yes, it's hard work is that.' He smiled reminiscently. 'Doesta remember that Clydesdale mare you foaled at ma place ? Must 'ave been one of your first jobs when you came to Darrowby.'

'Of course I do,' I replied. And I remembered too, how kind the old man had been. Seeing I was young and green and unsure of myself he had taken pains, in his quiet way, to put me at my ease and give me confidence. 'Yes,' I went on, 'it was late on a Sunday night and we had a right tussle with it. There was just the two of us but we managed, didn't we?'

He squared his shoulders and for a moment his eyes looked past me at something I couldn't see. 'Aye, that's right. We made a job of 'er, you and me. Ah could push and pull a bit then.'

'You certainly could. There's no doubt about that.'

He sucked the air in with difficulty and blew it out again with that peculiar pursing of the lips. Then he turned to me with a strange dignity.

'They were good days, Mr Herriot, weren't they?'

'They were, Mr Potts, they were indeed.'

'Aye, aye.' He nodded slowly. 'Ah've had a lot o' them days. Hard but good.' He looked down at his dog. 'And awd Nip shared 'em with me, didn't ye, lad?'

His words took me back to the very first time I had seen Mr Potts. He was perched on a stool, milking one of his few cows, his cloth-capped head thrusting into the hairy flank, and as he pulled at the teats old Nip dropped a stone on the toe of his boot. The farmer reached down, lifted the stone between two fingers and flicked it out through the open door into the yard. Nip scurried delightedly after it and was back within seconds, dropping the stone on the boot and panting hopefully.

He wasn't disappointed. His master repeated the throw automatically as if it was something he did all the time, and as I watched it happening again and again I realized that this was a daily ritual between the two. I had a piercing impression of infinite patience and devotion.

'Right, then, Mr Herriot, we'll be off,' Mr Potts said, jerking me back to the present. 'Come on, Nip.' He waved his stick and I watched him till a low-hanging willow branch hid man and dog from my sight.

That was the last time I saw him. Next day the man at the petrol pumps mumbled casually. 'See old Mr Potts got his time in, eh?'

And that was it. There was no excitement, and only a handful of his old friends turned up at the funeral.

For me it was a stab of sorrow. Another familiar face gone, and I should miss him as my busy life went on. I knew our daily conversations had cheered him but I felt with a sad finality that there was nothing else I could do for Mr Potts.

It was about a fortnight later and as I opened the gate to let Sam into the riverside fields I glanced at my watch. Twelve-thirty – plenty of time for our pre-lunch walk and the long stretch of green was empty. Then I noticed a single dog away on the left. It was Nip, and as I watched he got up, took a few indeterminate steps over the grass then turned and sat down again at the gate of his back garden.

Instead of taking my usual route I cut along behind the houses till I reached the old dog. He had been looking around him aimlessly but when we came up to him he seemed to come to life, sniffing Sam over and wagging his tail at me.

On the other side of the gate Mrs Potts was doing a bit of weeding, bending painfully as she plied her trowel.

'How are you, Mrs Potts ?' I said.

With an effort she straightened up. 'Oh, not too bad, thank you, Mr Herriot.' She came over and leaned on the gate. 'I see you're lookin' at the awd dog. My word he's missin' his master.'

I didn't say anything and she went on. 'He's eating all right and I can give him plenty of good food, but what I can't do is take 'im for walks.' She rubbed her back. 'I'm plagued with rheumaticks, Mr Herriot, and it takes me all my time to get around the house and garden.'

'I can understand that,' I said. 'And I don't suppose he'll walk by himself.'

'Nay, he won't. There's the path he went along every day.' She pointed to the winding strip of beaten earth among the grass. 'But he won't go more'n a few yards.'

'Ah well, dogs like a bit of company just the same as we do.' I bent and ran my hand over the old animal's head and ears. 'How would you like to come with us, Nip ?'

I set off along the path and he followed unhesitatingly, trotting alongside Sam with swinging tail.

'Eee, look !' the old lady cried. 'Isn't that grand to see !'

I followed his usual route down to the river where the water ran dark and silent under the branches of the gnarled willows. Then we went over the bridge and in front of us the river widened into pebbly shallows and murmured and chattered among the stones.

It was peaceful down there with only the endless water sound and the piping of birds in my ears and the long curtain of leaves parting here and there to give glimpses of the green flanks of the fells.

I watched the two dogs frisking ahead of me and the decision came to me quite naturally; I would do this regularly. From that day I altered my route and went along behind the houses first. Nip was happy again, Sam loved the whole idea, and for me there was a strange comfort in the knowledge that there was still something I could do for Mr Potts.

# 23

I had plenty of time on my hands at Eastchurch, plenty of time to think, and like most servicemen I thought of home. Only my home wasn't there any more.

When I left Darrowby Helen had gone back to live with her father and the little rooms under the tiles of Skeldale House would be empty and dusty now. But they lived on in my mind, clear in every detail.

I could see the ivy-fringed window looking over the tumble of roofs to the green hills, our few pieces of furniture, the bed and side table and the old wardrobe which only stayed shut with the aid of one of my socks jammed in the door. Strangely, it was that dangling woollen toe which gave me the sharpest stab as I remembered.

And even though it was all gone I could hear the bedside radio playing, my wife's voice from the other side of the fire and on that winter evening Tristan shouting up the stairs from the passage far below.

'Jim! Jim!'

I went out and stuck my head over the banisters. 'What is it, Triss?'

'Sorry to bother you, Jim, but could you come down for a minute?' The upturned face had an anxious look.

I went down the long flights of steps two at a time and when I arrived slightly breathless on the ground floor Tristan beckoned me through to the consulting room at the back of the house. A teenage girl was standing by the table, her hand resting on a stained roll of blanket.

'It's a cat,' Tristan said. He pulled back a fold of the blanket and I looked down at a large, deeply striped tabby. At least he would have been large if he had had any flesh on his bones, but ribs and pelvis stood out painfully through the fur and as I passed my hand over the motionless body I could feel only a thin covering of skin.

Tristan cleared his throat. 'There's something else, Jim.'

I looked at him curiously. For once he didn't seem to have a joke in him. I watched as he gently lifted one of the cat's hind legs and rolled the abdomen into view. There was a gash on the ventral surface through which a coiled cluster of intestines spilled grotesquely on to the cloth. I was still shocked and staring when the girl spoke.

'I saw this cat sittin' in the dark, down Brown's yard. I thought 'e looked skinny, like, and a bit quiet and I bent down to give 'im a pat. Then I saw 'e was badly hurt and I went home for a blanket and brought 'im round to you.'

'That was kind of you,' I said. 'Have you any idea who he belongs to?'

The girl shook her head. 'No, he looks like a stray to me.'

'He does indeed.' I dragged my eyes away from the terrible wound. 'You're Marjorie Simpson, aren't you?'

'Yes.'

'I know your Dad well. He's our postman.'

'That's right.' She gave a half-smile, then her lips trembled. 'Well, I reckon I'd better leave 'im with you. You'll be goin' to put him out of his misery. There's nothing anybody can do about ... about that?'

I shrugged and shook my head. The girl's eyes filled with tears, she stretched out a hand and touched the emaciated animal then turned and walked quickly to the door.

'Thanks again, Marjorie,' I called after the retreating back. 'And don't worry – we'll look after him.'

In the silence that followed, Tristan and I looked down at the shattered animal. Under the surgery lamp it was all too easy to see. He had almost been disembowelled and the pile of intestines was covered in dirt and mud.

'What d'you think did this?' Tristan said at length. 'Has he been run over?'

'Maybe,' I replied. 'Could be anything. An attack by a big dog or somebody could have kicked him or struck him.' All things were possible with cats because some people seemed to regard them as fair game for any cruelty.

Tristan nodded. 'Anyway, whatever happened, he must have been on the verge of starvation. He's a skeleton. I bet he's wandered miles from home.'

'Ah well,' I signed. 'There's only one thing to do. Those guts are perforated in several places. It's hopeless.'

Tristan didn't say anything but he whistled under his breath and drew the tip of his forefinger again and again across the furry cheek. And, unbelievably, from somewhere in the scraggy chest a gentle purring arose.

The young man looked at me, round eyes. 'My God, do you hear that?'

'Yes . . . amazing in that condition. He's a good-natured cat.'

Tristan, head bowed, continued his stroking. I knew how he felt because, although he preserved a cheerfully hard-boiled attitude to our patients he couldn't kid me about one thing; he had a soft spot for cats. Even now, when we are both around the sixty mark, he often talks to me over a beer about the cat he has had for many years. It is a typical relationship – they tease each other unmercifully – but it is based on real affection.

'It's no good, Triss,' I said gently. 'It's got to be done.' I reached for the syringe but something in me rebelled against plunging a needle into that mutilated body. Instead I pulled a fold of the blanket over the cat's head.

'Pour a little ether on to the cloth,' I said. 'He'll just sleep away.'

Wordlessly Tristan unscrewed the cap of the ether bottle and poised it above the head. Then from under the shapeless heap of blanket we heard it again; the deep purring which increased in volume till it boomed in our ears like a distant motor cycle.

Tristan was like a man turned to stone, hand gripping the

bottle rigidly, eyes staring down at the mound of cloth from which the purring rose in waves of warm friendly sound.

At last he looked up at me and gulped. 'I don't fancy this much, Jim. Can't we do something?'

'You mean, put that lot back?'

'Yes.'

'But the bowels are damaged – they're like a sieve in parts.'

'We could stitch them, couldn't we?'

I lifted the blanket and looked again. 'Honestly, Triss, I wouldn't know where to start. And the whole thing is filthy.'

He didn't say anything, but continued to look at me steadily.

And I didn't need much persuading. I had no more desire to pour ether on to that comradely purring than he had.

'Come on, then,' I said. 'We'll have a go.'

With the oxygen bubbling and the cat's head in the anaesthetic mask we washed the whole prolapse with warm saline. We did it again and again but it was impossible to remove every fragment of caked dirt. Then we started the painfully slow business of stitching the many holes in the tiny intestines, and here I was glad of Tristan's nimble fingers which seemed better able to manipulate the small round-bodied needles than mine.

Two hours and yards of catgut later, we dusted the patched up peritoneal surface with sulphonamide and pushed the entire mass back into the abdomen. When I had sutured muscle layers and skin everything looked tidy but I had a nasty feeling of sweeping undesirable things under the carpet. The extensive damage, all that contamination – peritonitis was inevitable.

'He's alive, anyway, Triss,' I said as we began to wash the instruments. 'We'll put him on to sulphapyridine and keep our fingers crossed.' There were still no antibiotics at that time but the new drug was a big advance.

The door opened and Helen came in. 'You've been a long time, Jim.' She walked over to the table and looked down at the sleeping cat. 'What a poor skinny little thing. He's all bones.'

'You should have seen him when he came in.' Tristan switched off the sterilizer and screwed shut the valve on the anaesthetic machine. 'He looks a lot better now.'

She stroked the little animal for a moment. 'Is he badly injured?'

'I'm afraid so, Helen,' I said. 'We've done our best for him but I honestly don't think he has much chance.'

'What a shame. And he's pretty, too. Four white feet and all those unusual colours.' With her finger she traced the faint bands of auburn and copper-gold among the grey and black.

Tristan laughed. 'Yes, I think that chap has a ginger tom somewhere in his ancestry.'

Helen smiled, too, but absently, and I noticed a broody look about her. She hurried out to the stock room and returned with an empty box.

'Yes . . . yes . . .' she said thoughtfully. 'I can make a bed in this box for him and he'll sleep in our room, Jim.'

'He will?'

'Yes, he must be warm, mustn't he?'

'Of course.'

Later, in the darkness of our bedsitter, I looked from my pillow at a cosy scene; Sam in his basket on one side of the flickering fire and the cat cushioned and blanketed in his box on the other.

As I floated off into sleep it was good to know that my patient was so comfortable, but I wondered if he would be alive in the morning . . .

I knew he was alive at 7.30 a.m. because my wife was already up and talking to him. I trailed across the room in my pyjamas and the cat and I looked at each other. I rubbed him under the chin and he opened his mouth in a rusty miaow. But he didn't try to move.

'Helen,' I said. 'This little thing is tied together inside with catgut. He'll have to live on fluids for a week and even then he probably won't make it. If he stays up here you'll be spooning milk into him umpteen times a day.'

'Okay, okay.' She had that broody look again.

It wasn't only milk she spooned into him over the next few days. Beef essence, strained broth and a succession of sophisticated baby foods found their way down his throat at regular intervals. One lunch time I found Helen kneeling by the box.

'We shall call him Oscar,' she said.

'You mean we're keeping him?'

'Yes.'

I am fond of cats but we already had a dog in our cramped

quarters and I could see difficulties. Still I decided to let it go.

'Why Oscar?'

'I don't know.' Helen tipped a few drops of chop gravy on to the little red tongue and watched intently as he swallowed.

One of the things I like about women is their mystery, the unfathomable part of them, and I didn't press the matter further. But I was pleased at the way things were going. I had been giving the sulphapyridine every six hours and taking the temperature night and morning, expecting all the time to encounter the roaring fever, the vomiting and the tense abdomen of peritonitis. But it never happened.

It was as though Oscar's animal instinct told him he had to move as little as possible because he lay absolutely still day after day and looked up at us – and purred.

His purr became part of our lives and when he eventually left his bed, sauntered through to our kitchen and began to sample Sam's dinner of meat and biscuit it was a moment of triumph. And I didn't spoil it by wondering if he was ready for solid food; I felt he knew.

From then on it was a sheer joy to watch the furry scarecrow fill out and grow strong, and as he ate and ate and the flesh spread over his bones the true beauty of his coat showed in the glossy medley of auburn, black and gold. We had a handsome cat on our hands.

Once Oscar had recovered, Tristan was a regular visitor.

He probably felt, and rightly, that he, more than I, had saved Oscar's life in the first place and he used to play with him for long periods. His favourite ploy was to push his leg round the corner of the table and withdraw it repeatedly just as the cat pawed at it.

Oscar was justifiably irritated by this teasing but showed his character by lying in wait for Tristan one night and biting him smartly in the ankle before he could start his tricks.

From my own point of view Oscar added many things to our ménage. Sam was delighted with him and the two soon became firm friends, Helen adored him and each evening I thought afresh that a nice cat washing his face by the hearth gave extra comfort to a room.

Oscar had been established as one of the family for several

weeks when I came in from a late call to find Helen waiting for me with a stricken face.

'What's happened ?' I asked.

'It's Oscar – he's gone!'

'Gone ? what do you mean ?'

'Oh, Jim, I think he's run away.'

I stared at her. 'He wouldn't do that. He often goes down to the garden at night. Are you sure he isn't there ?'

'Absolutely. I've searched right into the yard. I've even had a walk round the town. And remember.' Her chin quivered. 'He ... he ran away from somewhere before.'

I looked at my watch. 'Ten o'clock. Yes, that is strange. He shouldn't be out at this time.'

As I spoke the front door bell jangled. I galloped down the stairs and as I rounded the corner in the passage I could see Mrs Heslington, the vicar's wife, through the glass. I threw open the door. She was holding Oscar in her arms.

'I believe this is your cat, Mr Herriot,' she said.

'It is indeed, Mrs Heslington. Where did you find him ?'

She smiled. 'Well, it was rather odd. We were having a meeting of the Mothers' Union at the church house and we noticed the cat sitting there in the room.'

'Just sitting ... ?'

'Yes, as though he were listening to what we were saying and enjoying it all. It was unusual. When the meeting ended I thought I'd better bring him along to you.'

'I'm most grateful, Mrs Heslington.' I snatched Oscar and tucked him under my arm. 'My wife is distraught – she thought he was lost.'

It was a little mystery. Why should he suddenly take off like that ? But since he showed no change in his manner over the ensuing week we put it out of our minds.

Then one evening a man brought in a dog for a distemper inoculation and left the front door open. When I went up to our flat I found that Oscar had disappeared again. This time Helen and I scoured the market place and side alleys in vain and when we returned at half past nine we were both despondent. It was nearly eleven and we were thinking of bed when the door bell rang.

It was Oscar again, this time resting on the ample stomach of Jack Newbould. Jack was leaning against a doorpost and the fresh country air drifting in from the dark street was richly intermingled with beer fumes.

Jack was a gardener at one of the big houses. He hiccuped gently and gave me a huge benevolent smile. 'Brought your cat, Mr Herriot.'

'Gosh, thanks, Jack!' I said, scooping up Oscar gratefully. 'Where the devil did you find him ?'

'Well, s'matter o' fact, 'e sort of found me.'

'What do you mean ?'

Jack closed his eyes for a few moments before articulating carefully. 'Thish is a big night, tha knows, Mr Herriot. Darts championship. Lots of t'lads round at t'Dog and Gun – lotsh and lotsh of 'em. Big gatherin'.'

'And our cat was there ?'

'Aye, he were there, all right. Sittin' among t'lads. Shpent t'whole evenin' with us.'

'Just sat there, eh ?'

'That 'e did.' Jack giggled reminiscently. 'By gaw 'e enjoyed isself. Ah gave 'im a drop o' best bitter out of me own glass and once or twice ah thought 'e was goin' to have a go at chuckin' a dart. He's some cat.' He laughed again.

As I bore Oscar upstairs I was deep in thought. What was going on here ? These sudden desertions were upsetting Helen and I felt they could get on my nerves in time.

I didn't have long to wait till the next one. Three nights later he was missing again. This time Helen and I didn't bother to search – we just waited.

He was back earlier than usual. I heard the door bell at nine o'clock. It was the elderly Miss Simpson peering through the glass. And she wasn't holding Oscar – he was prowling on the mat waiting to come in.

Miss Simpson watched with interest as the cat stalked inside and made for the stairs. 'Ah, good, I'm so glad he's come home safely. I knew he was your cat and I've been intrigued by his behaviour all evening.'

'Where . . . may I ask ?'

'Oh, at the Women's Institute. He came in shortly after we started and stayed till the end.'

'Really? What exactly was your programme, Miss Simpson?'

'Well, there was a bit of committee stuff, then a short talk with lantern slides by Mr Walters from the water company and we finished with a cake-making competition.'

'Yes . . . yes . . . and what did Oscar do?'

She laughed. 'Mixed with the company, apparently enjoyed the slides and showed great interest in the cakes.'

'I see. And you didn't bring him home?'

'No, he made his own way here. As you know, I have to pass your house and I merely rang your bell to make sure you knew he had arrived.'

'I'm obliged to you, Miss Simpson. We were a little worried.'

I mounted the stairs in record time. Helen was sitting with the cat on her knee and she looked up as I burst in.

'I know about Oscar now,' I said.

'Know what?'

'Why he goes on these nightly outings. He's not running away – he's visiting.'

'Visiting?'

'Yes,' I said. 'Don't you see? He likes getting around, he loves people, especially in groups, and he's interested in what they do. He's a natural mixer.'

Helen looked down at the attractive mound of fur curled on her lap. 'Of course . . . that's it . . . he's a socialite!'

'Exactly, a high stepper!'

'A cat-about-town!'

It all afforded us some innocent laughter and Oscar sat up and looked at us with evident pleasure, adding his own throbbing purr to the merriment. But for Helen and me there was a lot of relief behind it; ever since our cat had started his excursions there had been the gnawing fear that we would lose him, and now we felt secure.

From that night our delight in him increased. There was endless joy in watching this facet of his character unfolding. He did the social round meticulously, taking in most of the activities of the town. He became a familiar figure at whist drives, jumble sales, school concerts and scout bazaars. Most of the time he was made welcome, but was twice ejected from meetings of the Rural

District Council who did not seem to relish the idea of a cat sitting in on their deliberations.

At first I was apprehensive about his making his way through the streets but I watched him once or twice and saw that he looked both ways before tripping daintily across. Clearly he had excellent traffic sense and this made me feel that his original injury had not been caused by a car.

Taking it all in all, Helen and I felt that it was a kind stroke of fortune which had brought Oscar to us. He was a warm and cherished part of our home life. He added to our happiness.

When the blow fell it was totally unexpected.

I was finishing the evening surgery. I looked round the door and saw only a man and two little boys.

'Next please,' I said.

The man stood up. He had no animal with him. He was middle-aged, with the rough weathered face of a farm worker. He twirled a cloth cap nervously in his hands.

'Mr Herriot?' he said.

'Yes, what can I do for you?'

He swallowed and looked me straight in the eyes. 'Ah think you've got ma cat.'

'What?'

'Ah lost ma cat a bit since.' He cleared his throat. 'We used to live at Missdon but ah got a job as ploughman to Mr Horne of Wederly. It was after we moved to Wederly that t'cat went missin.' Ah reckon he was tryin' to find 'is way back to his old home.'

'Wederly? That's on the other side of Brawton – over thirty miles away.'

'Aye, ah knaw, but cats is funny things.'

'But what makes you think I've got him?'

He twisted the cap around a bit more. 'There's a cousin o' mine lives in Darrowby and ah heard tell from 'im about this cat that goes around to meetin's. I 'ad to come. We've been huntin' everywhere.'

'Tell me,' I said. 'This cat you lost. What did he look like?'

'Grey and black and sort o' gingery. Right bonny 'e was. And 'e was allus goin' out to gatherin's.'

A cold hand clutched at my heart. 'You'd better come upstairs. Bring the boys with you.'

Helen was putting some coal on the fire of the bedsitter.

'Helen,' I said. 'This is Mr – er – I'm sorry, I don't know your name.'

'Gibbons, Sep Gibbons. They called me Septimus because ah was the seventh in family and it looks like ah'm goin' t'same way 'cause we've got six already. These are our two youngest.' The two boys, obvious twins of about eight, looked up at us solemnly.

I wished my heart would stop hammering. 'Mr Gibbons thinks Oscar is his. He lost his cat some time ago.'

My wife put down her little shovel. 'Oh . . . oh . . . I see.' She stood very still for a moment then smiled faintly. 'Do sit down. Oscar's in the kitchen, I'll bring him through.'

She went out and reappeared with the cat in her arms. She hadn't got through the door before the little boys gave tongue.

'Tiger!' they cried. 'Oh, Tiger, Tiger!'

The man's face seemed lit from within. He walked quickly across the floor and ran his big work-roughened hand along the fur.

'Hullo, awd lad,' he said, and turned to me with a radiant smile. 'It's 'im, Mr Herriot, It's 'im awright, and don't 'e look well!'

'You call him Tiger, eh ?' I said.

'Aye,' he replied happily. 'It's them gingery stripes. The kids called 'im that. They were broken-hearted when we lost 'im.'

As the two little boys rolled on the floor our Oscar rolled with them, pawing playfully, purring with delight.

Sep Gibbons sat down again. 'That's the way 'e allus went on wi' the family. They used to play with 'im for hours. By gaw we did miss 'im. He were a right favourite.'

I looked at the broken nails on the edge of the cap, at the decent, honest, uncomplicated Yorkshire face so like the many I had grown to like and respect. Farm men like him got thirty shillings a week in those days and it was reflected in the threadbare jacket, the cracked, shiny boots and the obvious hand-me-downs of the boys.

But all three were scrubbed and tidy, the man's face like a red beacon, the children's knees gleaming and their hair carefully

218

slicked across their foreheads. They looked like nice people to me. I didn't know what to say.

Helen said it for me. 'Well, Mr Gibbons.' Her tone had an unnatural brightness. 'You'd better take him.'

The man hesitated. 'Now then, are ye sure, Missis Herriot?'

'Yes . . . yes, I'm sure. He was your cat first.'

'Aye, but some folks 'ud say finders keepers or summat like that. Ah didn't come 'ere to demand 'im back or owt of t'sort.'

'I know you didn't, Mr Gibbons, but you've had him all those years and you've searched for him so hard. We couldn't possibly keep him from you.'

He nodded quickly. 'Well, that's right good of ye.' He paused for a moment, his face serious, then he stooped and picked Oscar up. 'We'll have to be off if we're goin' to catch the eight o'clock bus.'

Helen reached forward, cupped the cat's head in her hands and looked at him steadily for a few seconds. Then she patted the boys' heads. 'You'll take good care of him, won't you?'

'Aye, missis, thank ye, we will that.' The two small faces looked up at her and smiled.

'I'll see you down the stairs, Mr Gibbons,' I said.

On the descent I tickled the furry cheek resting on the man's shoulder and heard for the last time the rich purring. On the front door step we shook hands and they set off down the street. As they rounded the corner of Trengate they stopped and waved, and I waved back at the man, the two children and the cat's head looking back at me over the shoulder.

It was my habit at that time in my life to mount the stairs two or three at a time but on this occasion I trailed upwards like an old man, slightly breathless, throat tight, eyes prickling.

I cursed myself for a sentimental fool but as I reached our door I found a flash of consolation. Helen had taken it remarkably well. She had nursed that cat and grown deeply attached to him, and I'd have thought an unforeseen calamity like this would have upset her terribly. But no, she had behaved calmly and rationally. You never knew with women, but I was thankful.

It was up to me to do as well. I adjusted my features into the semblance of a cheerful smile and marched into the room.

Helen had pulled a chair close to the table and was slumped face down against the wood. One arm cradled her head while the other was stretched in front of her as her body shook with an utterly abandoned weeping.

I had never seen her like this and I was appalled. I tried to say something comforting but nothing stemmed the flow of racking sobs.

Feeling helpless and inadequate I could only sit close to her and stroke the back of her head. Maybe I could have said something if I hadn't felt just about as bad myself.

You get over these things in time. After all, we told ourselves, it wasn't as though Oscar had died or got lost again – he had gone to a good family who would look after him. In fact he had really gone home.

And, of course, we still had our much-loved Sam, although he didn't help in the early stages by sniffing disconsolately where Oscar's bed used to lie, then collapsing on the rug with a long lugubrious sigh.

There was one other thing, too. I had a little notion forming in my mind, an idea which I would spring on Helen when the time was right. It was about a month after that shattering night and we were coming out of the cinema at Brawton at the end of our half-day. I looked at my watch.

'Only eight o'clock,' I said. 'How about going to see Oscar?'

Helen looked at me in surprise. 'You mean – drive on to Wederly?'

'Yes, it's only about five miles.'

A smile crept slowly across her face. 'That would be lovely. But do you think they would mind?'

'The Gibbons? No, I'm sure they wouldn't. Let's go.'

Wederly was a big village and the ploughman's cottage was at the far end a few yards beyond the Methodist chapel. I pushed open the garden gate and we walked down the path.

A busy-looking little woman answered my knock. She was drying her hands on a striped towel.

'Mrs Gibbons?' I said.

'Aye, that's me.'

'I'm James Herriot – and this is my wife.'

Her eyes widened uncomprehendingly. Clearly the name meant nothing to her.

'We had your cat for a while,' I added.

Suddenly she grinned and waved her towel at us. 'Oh aye, ah remember now. Sep told me about you. Come in, come in!'

The big kitchen-living room was a tableau of life with six children and thirty shillings a week. Battered furniture, rows of much-mended washing on a pulley, black cooking range and a general air of chaos.

Sep got up from his place by the fire, put down his newspaper, took off a pair of steel-rimmed spectacles and shook hands.

He waved Helen to a sagging armchair. 'Well, it's right nice to see you. Ah've often spoke of ye to t'missis.'

His wife hung up her towel. 'Yes, and I'm glad to meet ye both. I'll get some tea in a minnit.'

She laughed and dragged a bucket of muddy water into a corner. 'I've been washin' football jerseys. Them lads just handed them to me tonight – as if I haven't enough to do.'

As she ran the water into the kettle I peeped surreptitiously around me and I noticed Helen doing the same. But we searched in vain. There was no sign of a cat. Surely he couldn't have run away again? With a growing feeling of dismay I realized that my little scheme could backfire devastatingly.

It wasn't until the tea had been made and poured that I dared to raise the subject.

'How—' I asked diffidently. 'How is – er – Tiger?'

'Oh he's grand,' the little woman replied briskly. She glanced up at the clock on the mantelpiece. 'He should be back any time now, then you'll be able to see 'im.'

As she spoke, Sep raised a finger. 'Ah think ah can hear 'im now.'

He walked over and opened the door and our Oscar strode in with all his old grace and majesty. He took one look at Helen and leaped on to her lap. With a cry of delight she put down her cup and stroked the beautiful fur as the cat arched himself against her hand and the familiar purr echoed round the room.

'He knows me,' she murmured. 'He knows me.'

Sep nodded and smiled. 'He does that. You were good to 'im. He'll never forget ye, and we won't either, will we mother?'

'No, we won't, Mrs Herriot,' his wife said as she applied butter to a slice of gingerbread. 'That was a kind thing ye did for us and I 'ope you'll come and see us all whenever you're near.'

'Well, thank you,' I said. 'We'd love to – we're often in Brawton.'

I went over and tickled Oscar's chin, then I turned again to Mrs Gibbons. 'By the way, it's after nine o'clock. Where has he been till now ?'

She poised her butter knife and looked into space.

'Let's see, now,' she said. 'It's Thursday, isn't it ? Ah yes, it's 'is night for the Yoga class.'

# 24

I knew it was the end of the chapter when I slammed the carriage door behind me and squeezed into a seat between a fat WAAF and a sleeping corporal.

I suppose I was an entirely typical discharged serviceman. They had taken away my blue uniform and fitted me with a 'demob suit', a ghastly garment of stiff brown serge with purple stripes which made me look like an old-time gangster, but they had allowed me to retain my RAF shirt and tie and the shiny boots which were like old friends.

My few belongings, including Black's *Veterinary Dictionary*, lay in the rack above in a small cardboard suitcase of a type very popular among the lower ranks of the services. They were all I possessed and I could have done with a coat because it was cold in the train and a long journey stretched between Eastchurch and Darrowby.

It took an age to chug and jolt as far as London then there was a lengthy wait before I boarded the train for the north. It was about midnight when we set off, and for seven hours I sat there in the freezing darkness, feet numb, teeth chattering.

The last lap was by bus and it was the same rattling little

vehicle which had carried me to my first job those years ago. The driver was the same, too, and the time between seemed to melt away as the fells began to rise again from the blue distance in the early light and I saw the familiar farmhouses, the walls creeping up the grassy slopes, the fringe of trees by the river's edge.

It was mid-morning when we rumbled into the market place and I read 'Darrowby Co-operative Society' above the shop on the far side. The sun was high, warming the tiles of the fretted line of roofs with their swelling green background of hills. I got out and the bus went on its way, leaving me standing by my case.

And it was just the same as before. The sweet air, the silence and the cobbled square deserted except for the old men sitting around the clock tower. One of them looked up at me.

'Now then, Mr Herriot,' he said quietly as though he had seen me only yesterday.

Before me Trengate curved away till it disappeared round the grocer's shop on the corner. Most of the quiet street with the church at its foot was beyond my view and it was a long time since I had been down there, but with my eyes closed I could see Skeldale House with the ivy climbing over the old brick walls to the little rooms under the eaves.

That was where I would have to make another start; where I would find out how much I had forgotten, whether I was fit to be an animal doctor again. But I wouldn't go along there yet, not just yet . . .

A lot had happened since that first day when I arrived in Darrowby in search of a job but it came to me suddenly that my circumstances hadn't changed much. All I had possessed then was an old case and the suit I stood in and it was about the same now. Except for one great and wonderful thing. I had Helen and Jimmy.

That made all the difference. I had no money, not even a house to call my own, but any roof which covered my wife and son was personal and special. Sam would be with them, too, waiting for me. They were outside the town and it was a fair walk from here, but I looked down at the blunt toes of my boots sticking from the purple striped trousers. The RAF hadn't only taught me to fly, they had taught me to march, and a few miles didn't bother me.

I took a fresh grip on my cardboard case, turned towards the exit from the square and set off, left-right, left-right, left-right, on the road for home.

# Vets Might Fly

to my dogs,
**Hector** and **Dan**
faithful companions of the daily round

# one

'Move!' bawled the drill corporal. 'Come on, speed it up!' He sprinted effortlessly to the rear of the gasping, panting column of men and urged us on from there.

I was somewhere in the middle, jog-trotting laboriously with the rest and wondering how much longer I could keep going. And as my ribs heaved agonizingly and my leg muscles protested, I tried to work out just how many miles we had run.

I had suspected nothing when we lined up outside our billets. We weren't clad in PT kit but in woollen pullovers and regulation slacks and it seemed unlikely that anything violent was imminent. The corporal, too, a cheerful little cockney, appeared to regard us as his brothers. He had a kind face.

'Awright, lads,' he had cried, smiling over the fifty new airmen. 'We're just going to trot round to the park, so follow me. Le-eft turn! At the double, qui-ick march! 'eft-ight, 'eft-ight, 'eft-ight!'

That had been a long, long time ago and we were still reeling through the London streets with never a sign of a park anywhere. The thought hammered in my brain that I had been under the impression that I was fit. A country vet, especially in the Yorkshire Dales, never had the chance to get out of condition; he was always on the move, wrestling with the big animals, walking for miles between the fell-side barns; he was hard and tough. That's what I thought.

But now other reflections began to creep in. My few months of married life with Helen had been so much lotus eating. She was too good a cook and I was too faithful a disciple of her art. Just lounging by our bed-sitter's fireside was the sweetest of all occupations. I had tried to ignore the disappearance of my abdominal muscles, the sagging of my pectorals, but it was all coming home to me now.

'It's not far now, lads,' the corporal chirped from the rear, but he struck no responsive chords in the toiling group. He

7

had said it several times before and we had stopped believing him.

But this time it seemed he really meant it, because as we turned into yet another street I could see iron railings and trees at the far end. The relief was inexpressible. I would just about have the strength to make it through the gates – to the rest and smoke which I badly needed because my legs were beginning to seize up.

We passed under an arch of branches which still bore a few autumn leaves and stopped as one man, but the corporal was waving us on.

'Come on, lads, round the track!' he shouted and pointed to a broad earthen path which circled the park.

We stared at him. He couldn't be serious! A storm of protest broke out.

'Aw no, corp . . . !' 'Have a heart, corp . . . !'

The smile vanished from the little man's face. 'Get movin', I said! Faster, faster . . . one-two, one-two.'

As I stumbled forward over the black earth, between borders of sooty rhododendrons and tired grass, I just couldn't believe it. It was all too sudden. Three days ago I was in Darrowby and half of me was still back there, back with Helen. And another part was still looking out of the rear window of the taxi at the green hills receding behind the tiled roofs into the morning sunshine; still standing in the corridor of the train as the flat terrain of southern England slid past and a great weight built up steadily in my chest.

My first introduction to the RAF was at Lord's cricket ground. Masses of forms to fill, medicals, then the issue of an enormous pile of kit. I was billeted in a block of flats in St John's Wood – luxurious before the lush fittings had been removed. But they couldn't take away the heavy bathroom ware and one of our blessings was the unlimited hot water gushing at our touch into the expensive surroundings.

After that first crowded day I retired to one of those green-tiled sanctuaries and lathered myself with a new bar of a famous toilet soap which Helen had put in my bag. I have never been able to use that soap since. Scents are too evocative and the merest whiff jerks me back to that first night away from my wife, and to the feeling I had then. It was a dull, empty ache which never really went away.

On the second day we marched endlessly; lectures, meals, inoculations. I was used to syringes but the very sight of them was too much for many of my friends. Especially when the doctor took the blood samples; one look at the dark fluid flowing from their veins and the young men toppled quietly from their chairs, often four or five in a row while the orderlies, grinning cheerfully, bore them away.

We ate in the London Zoo and our meals were made interesting by the chatter of monkeys and the roar of lions in the background. But in between it was march, march, march, with our new boots giving us hell.

And on this third day the whole thing was still a blur. We had been wakened as on my first morning by the hideous 6 a.m. clattering of dustbin lids; I hadn't really expected a bugle but I found this noise intolerable. However, at the moment my only concern was that we had completed the circuit of the park. The gates were only a few yards ahead and I staggered up to them and halted among my groaning comrades.

'Round again, lads!' the corporal yelled, and as we stared at him aghast he smiled affectionately. 'You think this is tough? Wait till they get hold of you at ITW. I'm just kinda breakin' you in gently. You'll thank me for this later. Right, at the double! One-two, one-two!'

Bitter thoughts assailed me as I lurched forward once more. Another round of the park would kill me – there was not a shadow of a doubt about that. You left a loving wife and a happy home to serve king and country and this was how they treated you. It wasn't fair

The night before I had dreamed of Darrowby. I was back in old Mr Dakin's cow byre. The farmer's patient eyes in the long, drooping-moustached face looked down at me from his stooping height.

'It looks as though it's over wi' awd Blossom, then,' he

said, and rested his hand briefly on the old cow's back. It was an enormous, work-swollen hand. Mr Dakin's gaunt frame carried little flesh but the grossly thickened fingers bore testimony to a life of toil.

I dried off the needle and dropped it into the metal box where I carried my suture materials, scalpels and blades. 'Well, it's up to you of course, Mr Dakin, but this is the third time I've had to stitch her teats and I'm afraid it's going to keep on happening.'

'Aye, it's just the shape she is.' The farmer bent and examined the row of knots along the four-inch scar. 'By gaw, you wouldn't believe it could mek such a mess – just another cow standin' on it.'

'A cow's hoof is sharp,' I said. 'It's nearly like a knife coming down.'

That was the worst of very old cows. Their udders dropped and their teats became larger and more pendulous so that when they lay down in their stalls the vital milk-producing organ was pushed away to one side into the path of the neighbouring animals. If it wasn't Mabel on the right standing on it, it was Buttercup on the other side.

There were only six cows in the little cobbled byre with its low roof and wooden partitions and they all had names. You don't find cows with names any more and there aren't any farmers like Mr Dakin, who somehow scratched a living from a herd of six milkers plus a few calves, pigs and hens.

'Aye, well,' he said. 'Ah reckon t'awd lass doesn't owe me anythin'. Ah remember the night she was born, twelve years ago. She was out of awd Daisy and ah carried her out of this very byre on a sack and the snow was comin' down hard. Sin' then ah wouldn't like to count how many thousand gallons o' milk she's turned out – she's still givin' four a day. Naw, she doesn't owe me a thing.'

As if she knew she was the topic of conversation Blossom turned her head and looked at him. She was the classical picture of an ancient bovine; as fleshless as her owner, with jutting pelvic bones, splayed, overgrown feet and horns with a multitude of rings along their curving length. Beneath her, the udder, once high and tight, drooped forlornly almost to the floor.

She resembled her owner, too, in her quiet, patient demeanour. I had infiltrated her teat with a local anaesthetic before stitching but I don't think she would have moved if I hadn't used any. Stitching teats puts a vet in the ideal position to be kicked, with his head low down in front of the hind feet, but there was no danger with Blossom. She had never kicked anybody in her life.

Mr Dakin blew out his cheeks. 'Well, there's nowt else for it. She'll have to go. I'll tell Jack Dodson to pick 'er up for the fatstock market on Thursday. She'll be a bit tough for eatin' but ah reckon she'll make a few steak pies.'

He was trying to joke but he was unable to smile as he looked at the old cow. Behind him, beyond the open door, the green hillside ran down to the river and the spring sunshine touched the broad sweep of the shallows with a million dancing lights. A beach of bleached stones gleamed bonewhite against the long stretch of grassy bank which rolled up to the pastures lining the valley floor.

I had often felt that this smallholding would be an ideal place to live; only a mile outside Darrowby, but secluded, and with this heart-lifting vista of river and fell. I remarked on this once to Mr Dakin and the old man turned to me with a wry smile.

'Aye, but the view's not very sustainin',' he said.

It happened that I was called back to the farm on the following Thursday to 'cleanse' a cow and was in the byre when Dodson the drover called to pick up Blossom. He had collected a group of fat bullocks and cows from other farms and they stood, watched by one of his men, on the road high above.

'Nah then, Mr Dakin,' he cried as he bustled in. 'It's easy to see which one you want me to tek. It's that awd screw over there.'

He pointed at Blossom, and in truth the unkind description seemed to fit the bony creature standing between her sleek neighbours.

The farmer did not reply for a moment, then he went up between the cows and gently rubbed Blossom's forehead. 'Aye, this is the one, Jack.' He hesitated, then undid the chain round her neck. 'Off ye go, awd lass,' he murmured, and the old animal turned and made her way placidly from the stall.

'Aye, come on with ye!' shouted the dealer, poking his stick against the cow's rump.

'Doan't hit 'er!' barked Mr Dakin.

Dodson looked at him in surprise. 'Ah never 'it 'em, you know that. Just send 'em on, like,'

'Ah knaw, ah knaw, Jack, but you won't need your stick for this 'un. She'll go wherever ye want – allus has done.'

Blossom confirmed his words as she ambled through the door and, at a gesture from the farmer, turned along the track.

The old man and I stood watching as the cow made her way unhurriedly up the hill, Jack Dodson in his long khaki smock sauntering behind her. As the path wound behind a clump of sparse trees man and beast disappeared but Mr Dakin still gazed after them, listening to the clip-clop of the hooves on the hard ground.

When the sound died away he turned to me quickly. 'Right, Mr Herriot, we'll get on wi' our job, then. I'll bring your hot watter.'

The farmer was silent as I soaped my arm and inserted it into the cow. If there is one thing more disagreeable than removing the bovine afterbirth it is watching somebody else doing it, and I always try to maintain a conversation as I grope around inside. But this time it was hard work. Mr Dakin responded to my sallies on the weather, cricket and the price of milk with a series of grunts.

Holding the cow's tail he leaned on the hairy back and, empty-eyed, blew smoke from the pipe which like most farmers at a cleansing he had prudently lit at the outset. And of course, since the going was heavy, it just would happen that the job took much longer than usual. Sometimes a placenta simply lifted out but I had this one away from the

12

cotyledons one by one, returning every few minutes to the hot water and antiseptic to re-soap my aching arms.

But at last it was finished. I pushed in a couple of pessaries, untied the sack from my middle and pulled my shirt over my head. The conversation had died and the silence was almost oppressive as we opened the byre door.

Mr Dakin paused, his hand on the latch. 'What's that?' he said softly.

From somewhere on the hillside I could hear the clip-clop of a cow's feet. There were two ways to the farm and the sound came from a narrow track which joined the main road half a mile beyond the other entrance. As we listened a cow rounded a rocky outcrop and came towards us.

It was Blossom, moving at a brisk trot, great udder swinging, eyes fixed purposefully on the open door behind us.

'What the hangment ... ?' Mr Dakin burst out, but the old cow brushed past us and marched without hesitation into the stall which she had occupied for all those years. She sniffed enquiringly at the empty hay rack and looked round at her owner.

Mr Dakin stared back at her. The eyes in the weathered face were expressionless but the smoke rose from his pipe in a series of rapid puffs.

Heavy boots clattered suddenly outside and Jack Dodson panted his way through the door.

'Oh, you're there, ye awd beggar!' he gasped. 'Ah thought I'd lost ye!'

He turned to the farmer. 'By gaw, I'm sorry, Mr Dakin. She must 'ave turned off at t'top of your other path. Ah never saw her go.'

The farmer shrugged. 'It's awright, Jack. It's not your fault, ah should've told ye.'

'That's soon mended anyway.' The drover grinned and moved towards Blossom. 'Come on, lass, let's have ye out o' there again.'

But he halted as Mr Dakin held an arm in front of him.

There was a long silence as Dodson and I looked in surprise at the farmer who continued to gaze fixedly at the cow. There was a pathetic dignity about the old animal as she stood there against the mouldering timber of the partition, her eyes patient and undemanding. It was a dignity which triumphed over the unsightliness of the long upturned hooves, the fleshless ribs, the broken-down udder almost brushing the cobbles.

Then, still without speaking, Mr Dakin moved unhurriedly between the cows and a faint chink of metal sounded as he fastened the chain around Blossom's neck. Then he strolled to the end of the byre and returned with a forkful of hay which he tossed expertly into the rack.

This was what Blossom was waiting for. She jerked a mouthful from between the spars and began to chew with quiet satisfaction.

'What's to do, Mr Dakin?' the drover cried in bewilderment. 'They're waiting for me at t'mart!'

The farmer tapped out his pipe on the half door and began to fill it with black shag from a battered tin. 'Ah'm sorry to waste your time, Jack, but you'll have to go without 'er.'

'Without 'er . . . ? But . . . ?'

'Aye, ye'll think I'm daft, but that's how it is. T'awd lass has come 'ome and she's stoppin' 'ome.' He directed a look of flat finality at the drover.

Dodson nodded a couple of times then shuffled from the byre. Mr Dakin followed and called after him.

'Ah'll pay ye for your time, Jack. Put it down on ma bill.'

He returned, applied a match to his pipe and drew deeply.

'Mr Herriot,' he said as the smoke rose around his ears, 'do you ever feel when summat happens that it was meant to happen and that it was for t'best?'

'Yes, I do, Mr Dakin. I often feel that.'

'Aye well, that's how I felt when Blossom came down that hill.' He reached out and scratched the root of the cow's tail. 'She's allus been a favourite and by gaw I'm glad she's back.'

'But how about those teats? I'm willing to keep stitching them up, but. . . .'

'Nay, lad, ah've had an idea. Just came to me when you

were tekkin' away that cleansin' and I thowt I was ower late.'

'An idea?'

'Aye.' The old man nodded and tamped down the tobacco with his thumb. 'I can put two or three calves on to 'er instead of milkin' 'er. The old stable is empty – she can live in there where there's nobody to stand on 'er awd tits.'

I laughed. 'You're right, Mr Dakin. She'd be safe in the stable and she'd suckle three calves easily. She could pay her way.'

'Well, as ah said, it's matterless. After all them years she doesn't owe me a thing.' A gentle smile spread over the seamed face. 'Main thing is, she's come 'ome.'

My eyes were shut most of the time now as I blundered round the park and when I opened them a red mist swirled. But it is incredible what the human frame will stand and I blinked in disbelief as the iron gates appeared once more under their arch of sooty branches.

I had survived the second lap but an ordinary rest would be inadequate now. This time I would have to lie down. I felt sick.

'Good lads!' the corporal called out, cheerful as ever. 'You're doin' fine. Now we're just going to 'ave a little hoppin' on the spot.'

Incredulous wails rose from our demoralized band but the corporal was unabashed.

'Feet together now. Up! Up! Up! That's no good, come on, get some height into it! Up! Up!'

This was the final absurdity. My chest was a flaming cavern of agony. These people were supposed to be making us fit and instead they were doing irreparable damage to my heart and lungs.

'You'll thank me for this later, lads. Take my word for it. GET YOURSELVES OFF THE GROUND. UP! UP!'

Through my pain I could see the corporal's laughing face. The man was clearly a sadist. It was no good appealing to him.

And as, with the last of my strength, I launched myself into the air it came to me suddenly why I had dreamed about Blossom last night.

I wanted to go home, too.


# two


The fog swirled over the heads of the marching men; a London fog, thick, yellow, metallic on the tongue. I couldn't see the head of the column, only the swinging lantern carried by the leader.

This 6.30 a.m. walk to breakfast was just about the worst part of the day, when my morale was low and thoughts of home rose painfully.

We used to have fogs in Darrowby, but they were country fogs, different from this. One morning I drove out on my rounds with the headlights blazing against the grey curtain ahead, seeing nothing from my tight-shut box. But I was heading up the Dale, climbing steadily with the engine pulling against the rising ground, then quite suddenly the fog thinned to a shimmering silvery mist and was gone.

And there, above the pall, the sun was dazzling and the long green line of the fells rose before me, thrusting exultantly into a sky of summer blue.

Spellbound, I drove upwards into the bright splendour, staring through the windscreen as though I had never seen it all before; the bronze of the dead bracken spilling down the grassy flanks of the hills, the dark smudges of trees, the grey farmhouses and the endless pattern of walls creeping to the heather above.

I was in a rush as usual but I had to stop. I pulled up in a gateway, Sam jumped out and we went through into a field; and as the beagle scampered over the glittering turf I stood in the warm sunshine amid the melting frost and looked back at the dark damp blanket which blotted out the low country but left this jewelled world above it.

And, gulping the sweet air, I gazed about me gratefully at the clean green land where I worked and made my living.

I could have stayed there, wandering round, watching Sam exploring with waving tail, nosing into the shady corners where the sun had not reached and the ground was iron hard and the rime thick and crisp on the grass. But I had an appointment to keep, and no ordinary one – it was with a peer of the realm. Reluctantly I got back into the car.

I was due to start Lord Hulton's tuberculin test at 9.30 a.m. and as I drove round the back of the Elizabethan mansion to the farm buildings nearby I felt a pang of misgiving; there were no animals in sight. There was only a man in tattered blue dungarees hammering busily at a makeshift crush at the exit to the fold yard.

He turned round when he saw me and waved his hammer. As I approached I looked wonderingly at the slight figure with the soft fairish hair falling over his brow, at the holed cardigan and muck-encrusted wellingtons. You would have expected him to say, 'Nah then, Mr Herriot, how ista this mornin'?'

But he didn't, he said, 'Herriot, my dear chap, I'm most frightfully sorry, but I'm very much afraid we're not quite ready for you.' And he began to fumble with his tobacco pouch.

William George Henry Augustus, Eleventh Marquis of Hulton, always had a pipe in his mouth and he was invariably either filling it, cleaning it out with a metal reaming tool or trying to light it. I had never seen him actually smoking it. And at times of stress he attempted to do everything at once. He was obviously embarrassed at his lack of preparedness and when he saw me glance involuntarily at my watch he grew more agitated, pulling his pipe from his mouth and putting it back in again, tucking the hammer under his arm, rummaging in a large box of matches.

I gazed across to the rising ground beyond the farm buildings. Far off on the horizon I could make out tiny figures: galloping beasts, scurrying men; and faint sounds came down to me of barking dogs, irritated bellowings and shrill cries of 'Haow, haow!' 'Gerraway by!' 'Siddown, dog!'

I sighed. It was the old story. Even the Yorkshire aristocracy seemed to share this carefree attitude to time.

His lordship clearly sensed my feelings because his discomfort increased.

'It's too bad of me, old chap,' he said, spraying a few matchsticks around and dropping flakes of tobacco on the stone flags. 'I did promise to be ready for nine thirty but those blasted animals just won't cooperate.'

I managed a smile. 'Oh never mind, Lord Hulton, they seem to be getting them down the hill now and I'm not in such a panic this morning, anyway.'

'Oh splendid, splendid!' He attempted to ignite a towering mound of dark flake which spluttered feebly then toppled over the edge of his pipe. 'And come and see this! I've been rigging up a crush. We'll drive them in here and we'll really have 'em. Remember we had a spot of bother last time, what?'

I nodded. I did remember. Lord Hulton had only about thirty suckling cows but it had taken a three-hour rodeo to test them. I looked doubtfully at the rickety structure of planks and corrugated iron. It would be interesting to see how it coped with the moorland cattle.

I didn't mean to rub it in, but again I glanced unthinkingly at my watch and the little man winced as though he had received a blow.

'Dammit!' he burst out. 'What are they doing over there? Tell you what, I'll go and give them a hand!' Distractedly, he began to change hammer, pouch, pipe and matches from hand to hand, dropping them and picking them up, before finally deciding to put the hammer down and stuff the rest into his pockets. He went off at a steady trot and I thought as I had done so often that there couldn't be many noblemen in England like him.

If I had been a marquis, I felt, I would still have been in

bed or perhaps just parting the curtains and peering out to
see what kind of day it was. But Lord Hulton worked all the
time, just about as hard as any of his men. One morning I
arrived to find him at the supremely mundane task of 'plugging muck', standing on a manure heap, hurling steaming
forkfuls on to a cart. And he always dressed in rags. I suppose
he must have had more orthodox items in his wardrobe but
I never saw them. Even his tobacco was the great smoke of
the ordinary farmer – Redbreast Flake.

My musings were interrupted by the thunder of hooves
and wild cries; the Hulton herd was approaching. Within
minutes the fold yard was filled with milling creatures, steam
rising in rolling clouds from their bodies.

The marquis appeared round the corner of the building
at a gallop.

'Right, Charlie!' he yelled. 'Let the first one into the
crush!'

Panting with anticipation he stood by the nailed boards as
the men inside opened the yard gate. He didn't have to wait
long. A shaggy red monster catapulted from the interior,
appeared briefly in the narrow passage then emerged at about
fifty miles an hour from the other end with portions of his
lordship's creation dangling from its horns and neck. The
rest of the herd pounded close behind.

'Stop them! Stop them!' screamed the little peer, but it was
of no avail. A hairy torrent flooded through the opening and
in no time at all the herd was legging it back to the high land
in a wild stampede. The men followed them and within a few
moments Lord Hulton and I were standing there just as
before watching the tiny figures on the skyline, listening to
the distant 'Haow, haow!' 'Gerraway by!'

'I say,' he murmured despondently. 'It didn't work terribly well, did it?'

But he was made of stern stuff. Seizing his hammer he
began to bang away with undiminished enthusiasm and by
the time the beasts returned the crush was rebuilt and a
stout iron bar pushed across the front to prevent further
break-outs.

It seemed to solve the problem because the first cow, confronted by the bar, stood quietly and I was able to clip the hair on her neck through an opening between the planks. Lord Hulton, in high good humour, settled down on an upturned oil drum with my testing book on his knee.

'I'll do the writing for you,' he cried. 'Fire away, old chap!'

I poised my calipers. 'Eight, eight.' He wrote it down and the next cow came in.

'Eight, eight,' I said, and he bowed his head again.

The third cow arrived: 'Eight, eight.' And the fourth, 'Eight, eight.'

His lordship looked up from the book and passed a weary hand across his forehead.

'Herriot, dear boy, can't you vary it a bit? I'm beginning to lose interest.'

All went well until we saw the cow which had originally smashed the crush. She had sustained a slight scratch on her neck.

'I say, look at that!' cried the peer. 'Will it be all right?'

'Oh yes, it's nothing. Superficial.'

'Ah, good, but don't you think we should have something to put on it? Some of that. . . .'

I waited for it. Lord Hulton was a devotee of May and Baker's Propamidine Cream and used it for all minor cuts and grazes in his cattle. He loved the stuff. But unfortunately he couldn't say 'Propamidine'. In fact nobody on the entire establishment could say it except Charlie the farm foreman and he only thought he could say it. He called it 'Propopamide' but his lordship had the utmost faith in him.

'Charlie!' he bawled. 'Are you there, Charlie?'

The foreman appeared from the pack in the yard and touched his cap. 'Yes, m'lord.'

'Charlie, that wonderful stuff we get from Mr Herriot – you know, for cut teats and things. Pro . . . Pero . . . what the hell do you call it again?'

Charlie paused. It was one of his big moments. 'Propopamide, m'lord.'

The marquis, intensely gratified, slapped the knee of his

dungarees. 'That's it, Propopamide! Damned if I can get my tongue round it. Well done, Charlie!'

Charlie inclined his head modestly.

The whole test was a vast improvement on last time and we were finished within an hour and a half. There was just one tragedy. About half way through, one of the cows dropped down dead with an attack of hypomagnesaemia, a condition which often plagues sucklers. It was a sudden, painless collapse and I had no chance to do anything.

Lord Hulton looked down at the animal which had just stopped breathing. 'Do you think we could salvage her for meat if we bled her?'

'Well, it's typical hypomag. Nothing to harm anybody . . . you could try. It would depend on what the meat inspector says.'

The cow was bled, pulled into a van and the peer drove off to the abattoir. He came back just as we were finishing the test.

'How did you get on?' I asked him. 'Did they accept her?'

He hesitated. 'No . . . no, old chap,' he said sadly. 'I'm afraid they didn't.'

'Why? Did the meat inspector condemn the carcass?'

'Well . . . I never got as far as the meat inspector, actually . . . just saw one of the slaughtermen.'

'And what did he say?'

'Just two words, Herriot.'

'Two words . . . ?'

'Yes . . . "Bugger off!" '

I nodded. 'I see.' It was easy to imagine the scene. The tough slaughterman viewing the small, unimpressive figure and deciding that he wasn't going to be put out of his routine by some ragged farm man.

'Well, never mind, sir,' I said. 'You can only try.'

'True . . . true, old chap.' He dropped a few matches as he fumbled disconsolately with his smoking equipment.

As I was getting into the car I remembered about the Propamidine. 'Don't forget to call down for that cream, will you?'

'By Jove, yes! I'll come down for it after lunch. I have great faith in that Prom ... Pram ... Charlie! Damn and blast, what is it?'

Charlie drew himself up proudly. 'Propopamide, m'lord.'

'Ah yes, Propopamide!' The little man laughed, his good humour quite restored. 'Good lad, Charlie, you're a marvel!'

'Thank you, m'lord.' The foreman wore the smug expression of the expert as he drove the cattle back into the field.

It's a funny thing, but when you see a client about something you very often see him soon again about something else. It was only a week later, with the district still in the iron grip of winter, that my bedside phone jangled me from slumber.

After that first palpitation of the heart which I feel does vets no good at all I reached a sleepy hand from under the sheets.

'Yes?' I grunted.

'Herriot ... I say, Herriot ... is that you, Herriot?' The voice was laden with tension.

'Yes, it is, Lord Hulton.'

'Oh good ... good ... dash it, I do apologize. Frightfully bad show, waking you up like this ... but I've got something damn peculiar here.' A soft pattering followed which I took to be matches falling around the receiver.

'Really?' I yawned and my eyes closed involuntarily. 'In what way, exactly?'

'Well, I've been sitting up with one of my best sows. Been farrowing and produced twelve nice piglets, but there's something very odd.'

'How do you mean?'

'Difficult to describe, old chap ... but you know the ... er ... bottom aperture.... there's a bloody great long red thing hanging from it.'

My eyes snapped open and my mouth gaped in a soundless scream. Prolapsed uterus! Hard labour in cows, a pleasant exercise in ewes, impossible in sows.

'Long red ... ! When ... ? How ... ?' I was stammering pointlessly. I didn't have to ask.

'Just popped it out, dear boy. I was waiting for another piglet and whoops, there it was. Gave me a nasty turn.'

My toes curled tightly beneath the blankets. It was no good telling him that I had seen five prolapsed uteri in pigs in my limited experience and had failed in every case. I had come to the conclusion that there was no way of putting them back.

But I had to try. 'I'll be right out,' I muttered.

I looked at the alarm clock. It was five thirty. A horrible time, truncating the night's slumber yet eliminating any chance of a soothing return to bed for an hour before the day's work. And I hated turning out even more since my marriage. Helen was lovely to come back to, but by the same token it was a bigger wrench to leave her soft warm presence and venture into the inhospitable world outside.

And the journey to the Hulton farm was not enlivened by my memories of those five other sows. I had tried everything; full anaesthesia, lifting them upside down with pulleys, directing a jet from a hose on the everted organ, and all the time pushing, straining sweating over the great mass of flesh which refused to go back through that absurdly small hole. The result in each case had been the conversion of my patient into pork pies and a drastic plummeting of my self-esteem.

There was no moon and the soft glow from the piggery door made the only light among the black outlines of the buildings. Lord Hulton was waiting at the entrance and I thought I had better warn him.

'I have to tell you, sir, that this is a very serious condition. It's only fair that you should know that the sow very often has to be slaughtered.'

The little man's eyes widened and the corners of his mouth drooped.

'Oh, I say! That's rather a bore . . . one of my best animals. I . . . I'm rather attached to that pig.' He was wearing a polo-necked sweater of such advanced dilapidation that the hem hung in long woollen fronds almost to his knees, and as he tremblingly attempted to light his pipe he looked very vulnerable.

'But I'll do my very best,' I added hastily. 'There's always a chance.'

'Oh, good man!' In his relief, he dropped his pouch and as he stooped the open box of matches spilled around his feet. It was some time before we retrieved them and went into the piggery.

The reality was as bad as my imaginings. Under the single weak electric bulb of the pen an unbelievable length of very solid-looking red tissue stretched from the rear end of a massive white sow lying immobile on her side. The twelve pink piglets fought and worried along the row of teats; they didn't seem to be getting much.

As I stripped off and dipped my arms into the steaming bucket I wished with all my heart that the porcine uterus was a little short thing and not this horrible awkward shape. And it was a disquieting thought that tonight I had no artificial aids. People used all sorts of tricks and various types of equipment but here in this silent building there was just the pig, Lord Hulton and me. His lordship, I knew, was willing and eager, but he had helped me at jobs before and his usefulness was impaired by the fact that his hands were always filled with his smoking items and he kept dropping things.

I got down on my knees behind the animal with the feeling that I was on my own. And as soon as I cradled the mass in my arms the conviction flooded through me that this was going to be the same as all the others. The very idea of this lot going back whence it came was ridiculous and the impression was reinforced as I began to push. Nothing happened.

I had sedated the sow heavily and she wasn't straining much against me; it was just that the thing was so huge. By a supreme effort I managed to feed a few inches back into the vaginal opening but as soon as I relaxed it popped quietly out again. My strongest instinct was to call the whole thing off without delay; the end result would be the same and anyway I wasn't feeling very strong. In fact my whole being was permeated by the leaden-armed pervading weakness one feels when forced to work in the small hours.

I would try just once more. Lying flat, my naked chest

against the cold concrete I fought with the thing till my eyes popped and my breath gave out, but it had not the slightest effect and it made my mind up; I had to tell him.

Rolling over on my back I looked up at him, panting, waiting till I had the wind to speak. I would say, 'Lord Hulton, we are really wasting our time here. This is an impossible case. I am going back home now and I'll ring the slaughterhouse first thing in the morning.' The prospect of escape was beguiling; I might even be able to crawl in beside Helen for an hour. But as my mouth framed the words the little man looked down at me appealingly as though he knew what I was going to say. He tried to smile but darted anxious glances at me, at the pig and back again. From the other end of the animal a soft uncomplaining grunt reminded me that I wasn't the only one involved.

I didn't say anything. I turned back on to my chest, braced my feet against the wall of the pen and began again. I don't know how long I lay there, pushing, relaxing, pushing again as I gasped and groaned and the sweat ran steadily down my back. The peer was silent but I knew he was following my progress intently because every now and then I had to brush matches from the surface of the uterus.

Then for no particular reason the heap of flesh in my arms felt suddenly smaller. I glared desperately at the thing. There was no doubt about it, it was only half the size. I had to take a breather and a hoarse croak escaped me.

'God! I think it's going back!'

I must have startled Lord Hulton in mid fill because I heard a stifled 'What . . . what . . . oh I say, how absolutely splendid!' and a fragrant shower of tobacco cascaded from above.

This was it, then. Summoning the last of my energy for one big effort I blew half an ounce or so of Redbreast Flake from the uterine mucosa and heaved forward. And, miraculously, there was little resistance and I stared in disbelief as the great organ disappeared gloriously and wonderfully from sight. I was right behind it with my arm, probing frantically away up to the shoulder as I rotated my wrist again and again till both uterine cornua were fully involuted. When I was certain beyond doubt that everything was back in place I lay there for a few moments, my arm still deep inside the sow, my forehead resting on the floor. Dimly, through the mist of exhaustion I heard Lord Hulton's cries.

'Stout fella! Dash it, how marvellous! Oh stout fella!' He was almost dancing with joy.

One last terror assailed me. What if it came out again? Quickly I seized needle and thread and began to insert a few sutures in the vulva.

'Here, hold this!' I barked, giving him the scissors.

Stitching with the help of Lord Hulton wasn't easy. I kept pushing needle or scissors into his hands then demanding them back peremptorily, and it caused a certain amount of panic. Twice he passed me his pipe to cut the ends of my suture and on one occasion I found myself trying in the dim light to thread the silk through his reaming tool. His lordship suffered too, in his turn, because I heard the occasional stifled oath as he impaled a finger on the needle.

But at last it was done. I rose wearily to my feet and leaned against the wall, my mouth hanging open, sweat trickling into my eyes. The little man's eyes were full of concern as they roved over my limply hanging arms and the caked blood and filth on my chest.

'Herriot, my dear old chap, you're all in! And you'll catch pneumonia or something if you stand around half naked. You need a hot drink. Tell you what – get yourself cleaned up and dressed and I'll run down to the house for something.' He scurried swiftly away.

My aching muscles were slow to obey as I soaped and towelled myself and pulled on my shirt. Fastening my watch round my wrist I saw that it was after seven and I could hear the farm men clattering in the yard outside as they began their morning tasks.

I was buttoning my jacket when the little peer returned. He bore a tray with a pint mug of steaming coffee and two thick slices of bread and honey. He placed it on a bale of straw and pulled up an upturned bucket as a chair before hopping on to a meal bin where he sat like a pixie on a toad-stool with his arms around his knees, regarding me with keen anticipation.

'The servants are still abed, old chap,' he said. 'So I made this little bite for you myself.'

I sank on to the bucket and took a long pull at the coffee. It was black and scalding with a kick like a Galloway bullock and it spread like fire through my tired frame. Then I bit into the first slice of bread; home made, plastered thickly with farm butter and topped by a lavish layer of heather honey from the long row of hives I had often seen on the edge of the moor above. I closed my eyes in reverence as I chewed, then as I reached for the pint pot again I looked up at the small figure on the bin.

'May I say, sir, that this isn't a bite, it's a feast. It is all absolutely delicious.'

His face lit up with impish glee. 'Well, dash it . . . do you really think so? I'm so pleased. And you've done nobly, dear boy. Can't tell you how grateful I am.'

As I continued to eat ecstatically, feeling the strength ebbing back, he glanced uneasily into the pen.

'Herriot . . . those stitches. Don't like the look of them much. . . .'

'Oh yes,' I said. 'They're just a precaution. You can nick them out in a couple of days.'

'Splendid! But won't they leave a wound? We'd better put something on there.'

I paused in mid chew. Here it was again. He only needed his Propamidine to complete his happiness.

'Yes, old chap, we must apply some of that Prip . . . Prom . . . oh hell and blast, it's no good!' He threw back his head and bellowed, 'Charlie!'

The foreman appeared in the entrance, touching his cap. 'Morning, m'lord.'

'Morning, Charlie. See that this sow gets some of that wonderful cream on her. What the blazes d'you call it again?'

Charlie swallowed and squared his shoulders. 'Propopamide, m'lord.'

The little man threw his arms high in delight. 'Of course, of course! Propopamide! I wonder if I'll ever be able to get that word out?' He looked admiringly at his foreman. 'Charlie, you never fail – I don't know how you do it.'

Charlie bowed gravely in acknowledgement.

Lord Hulton turned to me. 'You'll let us have some more Propopamide, won't you, Herriot?'

'Certainly,' I replied. 'I think I have some in the car.'

Sitting there on the bucket amid the mixed aromas of pig and barley meal and coffee I could almost feel the waves of pleasure beating on me. His lordship was clearly enchanted by the whole business, Charlie was wearing the superior smile which always accompanied his demonstrations of lingual dexterity, and as for myself I was experiencing a mounting euphoria.

I could see into the pen and the sight was rewarding. The little pigs who had been sheltered in a large box during the operation were back with their mother, side by side in a long pink row as their tiny mouths enclosed the teats. The sow seemed to be letting her milk down, too, because there was no frantic scramble for position, just a rapt concentration.

She was a fine pedigree pig and instead of lying on the butcher's slab today she would be starting to bring up her family. As though reading my thoughts she gave a series of contented grunts and the old feeling began to bubble in me, the deep sense of fulfilment and satisfaction that comes from even the smallest triumph and makes our lives worth while.

And there was something else. A new thought stealing into my consciousness with a delicious fresh tingle about it. At this moment, who else in the length and breadth of Britain was eating a breakfast personally prepared and served by a marquis?

# three

I am afraid of dentists.

I am particularly afraid of strange dentists, so before I went into the RAF I made sure my teeth were in order. Everybody told me they were very strict about the aircrew's teeth and I didn't want some unknown prodding around in my mouth. There had to be no holes anywhere or they would start to ache away up there in the sky, so they said.

So before my call-up I went to old Mr Grover in Darrowby and he painstakingly did all that was necessary. He was good at his job and was always gentle and careful and didn't strike the same terror into me as other dentists. All I felt when I went to his surgery was a dryness of the throat and a quivering at the knees, and providing I kept my eyes tightly shut all the time I managed to get through the visit fairly easily.

My fear of dentists dates back to my earliest experiences in the twenties. As a child I was taken to the dread Hector McDarroch in Glasgow and he did my dental work right up to my teens. Friends of my youth tell me that he inspired a similar lasting fear in them, too, and in fact there must be a whole generation of Glaswegians who feel the same.

Of course you couldn't blame Hector entirely. The equipment in those days was primitive and a visit to any dental practitioner was an ordeal. But Hector, with his booming laugh, was so large and overpowering that he made it worse. Actually he was a very nice man, cheerful and good-natured, but the other side of him blotted it all out.

The electric drill had not yet been invented or if it had, it hadn't reached Scotland, and Hector bored holes in teeth with a fearsome foot-operated machine. There was a great wheel driven by a leather belt and this powered the drill, and as you lay in the chair two things dominated the outlook; the wheel whirring by your ear and Hector's huge knee pistoning almost into your face as he pedalled furiously.

He came from the far north and at the Highland games he

used to array himself in kilt and sporran and throw cabers around like matchsticks. He was so big and strong that I always felt hopelessly trapped in that chair with his bulk over me and the wheel grinding and the pedal thumping. He didn't exactly put his foot on my chest but he had me all right.

And it didn't worry him when he got into the sensitive parts with his drill; my strangled cries were of no avail and he carried on remorselessly to the end. I had the impression that Hector thought it was cissy to feel pain, or maybe he was of the opinion that suffering was good for the soul.

Anyway, since those days I've had a marked preference for small frail soft-spoken dentists like Mr Grover. I like to feel that if it came to a stand-up fight I would have a good chance of victory and escape. Also, Mr Grover understood that people were afraid, and that helped. I remember him chuckling when he told me about the big farm men who came to have their teeth extracted. Many a time, he said, he had gone across the room for his instruments and turned back to find the chair empty.

I still don't enjoy going to the dentist but I have to admit that the modern men are wonderful. I hardly see mine when I go. Just a brief glimpse of a white coat then all is done from behind. Fingers come round, things go in and out of my mouth but even when I venture to open my eyes I see nothing.

Hector McDarroch, on the other hand, seemed to take a pleasure in showing off his grisly implements, filling the long-needled syringe right in front of my eyes and squirting the cocaine ceilingwards a few times before he started on me. And worse, before an extraction he used to clank about in a tin box, producing a series of hideous forceps and examining them, whistling softly, till he found the right one.

So with all this in mind, as I sat in a long queue of airmen for the preliminary examination, I was thankful I had been to Mr Grover for a complete check-up. A dentist stood by a chair at the end of the long room and he examined the young men in blue one by one before calling out his findings to an orderly at a desk.

I derived considerable entertainment from watching the expressions on the lads' faces when the call went out. 'Three fillings, two extractions!' 'Eight fillings!' Most of them looked stunned, some thunderstruck, others almost tearful. Now and again one would try to expostulate with the man in white but it was no good; nobody was listening. At times I could have laughed out loud. Mind you, I felt a bit mean at being amused, but after all they had only themselves to blame. If only they had shown my foresight they would have had nothing to worry about.

When my name was called I strolled across, humming a little tune, and dropped nonchalantly into the chair. It didn't take the man long. He poked his way swiftly along my teeth then rapped out, 'Five fillings and one extraction!'

I sat bolt upright and stared at him in amazement.

'But ... but ...' I began to yammer, 'I had a check up by my own ...'

'Next, please,' murmured the dentist.

'But Mr Grover said ...'

'Next man! Move along!' bawled the orderly, and as I shuffled away I gazed appealingly at the white-coated figure. But he was reciting a list of my premolars and incisors and showed no interest.

I was still trembling when I was handed the details of my fate.

'Report at Regent Lodge tomorrow morning for the extraction,' the WAAF girl said.

Tomorrow morning! By God, they didn't mess about! And what the heck did it all mean, anyway? My teeth were perfectly sound. There was only that one with the bit of enamel chipped off. Mr Grover had pointed it out and said it wouldn't give any trouble. It was the tooth that held my pipe – surely it couldn't be that one.

But there came the disquieting thought that my opinion didn't matter. When my feeble protests were ignored back there it hit me for the first time that I wasn't a civilian any more.

Next morning the din from the dustbin lids had hardly

subsided when the grim realization drove into my brain. I was going to have a tooth out today! And very soon too. I passed the intervening hours in growing apprehension; morning parade, the march through the darkness to breakfast. The dried egg and fried bread were less attractive than ever and the grey day had hardly got under way before I was approaching the forbidding façade of Regent Lodge.

As I climbed the steps my palms began to sweat. I didn't like having my teeth drilled but extractions were infinitely worse. Something in me recoiled from the idea of having a part of myself torn away by force, even if it didn't hurt. But of course, I told myself as I walked along an echoing corridor, it never did hurt nowadays. Just a little prick, then nothing.

I was nurturing this comforting thought when I turned into a large assembly room with numbered doors leading from it. About thirty airmen sat around wearing a variety of expressions from sickly smiles to tough bravado. A chilling smell of antiseptic hung on the air. I chose a chair and settled down to wait. I had been in the armed forces long enough to know that you waited a long time for everything and I saw no reason why a dental appointment should be any different.

As I sat down the man on my left gave me a brief nod. He was fat, and greasy black hair fell over his pimpled brow. Though engrossed in picking his teeth with a match he gave me a long appraising stare before addressing me in rich cockney.

'What room you goin' in, mate?'

I looked at my card. 'Room four.'

'Blimey, mate, you've 'ad it!' He removed his matchstick and grinned wolfishly.

'Had it . . . ? What do you mean?'

'Well, haven't you 'eard? That's The Butcher in there.'

'The . . . The . . . Butcher?' I quavered.

'Yeh, that's what they call the dental officer in there.' He gave an expansive smile. 'He's a right killer, that bloke, I'll tell yer.'

I swallowed. 'Butcher . . . ? Killer . . . ? Oh come on. They'll all be the same, I'm sure.'

'Don't you believe it, mate. There's good an' there's bad, and that bloke's pure murder. It shouldn't be allowed.'

'How do you know, anyway?'

He waved an airy hand. 'Oh I've been 'ere a few times and I've heard some bleedin' awful screams comin' out of that room. Spoken to some of the chaps afterwards, too. They all call 'im The Butcher.'

I rubbed my hands on the rough blue of my trousers. 'Oh you hear these tales. I'm sure they're exaggerated'

'Well, you'll find out, mate.' He resumed his tooth picking. 'But don't say I didn't tell you.'

He went on about various things but I only half heard him. His name, it seemed, was Simkin, and he was not an aircrew cadet like the rest of us but a regular and a member of the groundstaff; he worked in the kitchens. He spoke scornfully of us raw recruits and pointed out that we would have to 'get some service in' before we were fit to associate with the real members of the Royal Air Force. I noticed, however, that despite his own years of allegiance he was still an AC2 like myself.

Almost an hour passed with my heart thumping every time the door of number four opened. I had to admit that the young men leaving that room all looked a bit shattered and one almost reeled out, holding his mouth with both hands.

'Cor! Look at that poor bugger!' Simkin drawled with ill-concealed satisfaction. 'Strike me! He's been through it, poor bleeder. I'm glad I'm not in your shoes, mate.'

I could feel the tension mounting in me. 'What room are you going into, anyway?' I asked.

He did a bit of deep exploration with his match. 'Room two, mate. I've been in there before. He's a grand bloke, one of the best. Never 'urts you.'

'Well you're lucky, aren't you?'

'Not lucky, mate.' He paused and stabbed his match at me. 'I know my way around, that's all. There's ways and means.' He allowed one eyelid to drop briefly.

The conversation was abruptly terminated as the dread door opened and a WAAF came out.

'AC2 Herriot!' she called.

I got up on shaking limbs and took a deep breath. As I set off I had a fleeting glimpse of the leer of pure delight on Simkin's face. He was really enjoying himself.

As I passed the portals my feeling of doom increased. The Butcher was another Hector McDarroch; about six feet two with rugby forward shoulders bulging his white coat. My flesh crept as he unleashed a hearty laugh and motioned me towards the chair.

As I sat down I decided to have one last try.

'Is this the tooth?' I asked, tapping the only possible suspect.

'It is indeed!' boomed The Butcher. 'That's the one.'

'Ah well,' I said with a light laugh. 'I'm sure I can explain. There's been some mistake. . . .'

'Yes . . . yes. . . .' he murmured, filling the syringe before my eyes and sending a few playful spurts into the air.

'There's just a bit of enamel off it, and Mr Grover said . . .'

The WAAF suddenly wound the chair back and I found myself in the semi-prone position with the white bulk looming over me.

'You see,' I gasped desperately. 'I need that tooth. It's the one that holds my . . .'

A strong finger was on my gum and I felt the needle going in. I resigned myself to my fate.

When he had inserted the local the big man put the syringe down. 'We'll just give that a minute or two,' he said, and left the room.

As soon as the door closed behind him the WAAF tiptoed over to me.

'This feller's loopy!' she whispered.

Half lying, I stared at her.

'Loopy . . . ? What d'you mean?'

'Crackers! Round the bend! No idea how to pull teeth!'

'But . . . but . . . he's a dentist isn't he . . . ?'

She pulled a wry face, 'Thinks he is! But he hasn't a clue!'

I had no time to explore this cheering information further because the door opened and the big man returned.

He seized a horrible pair of forceps and I closed my eyes as he started flexing his muscles.

I must admit I felt nothing. I knew he was twisting and tugging away up there but the local had mercifully done its job. I was telling myself that it would soon be over when I heard a sharp crack.

I opened my eyes. The Butcher was gazing disappointedly at my broken-off tooth in his forceps. The root was still in my gum.

Behind him the WAAF gave me a long 'I told you so' nod. She was a pretty little thing, but I fear the libido of the young men she encountered in here would be at a low ebb.

'Oh!' The Butcher grunted and began to rummage in a metal box. It took me right to the McDarroch days as he fished out one forceps after another, opened and shut them a few times then tried them on me.

But it was of no avail, and as the time passed I was the unwilling witness of the gradual transition from heartiness to silence, then to something like panic. The man was clearly whacked. He had no idea how to shift that root.

He must have been gouging for half an hour when an idea seemed to strike him. Pushing all the forceps to one side he almost ran from the room and reappeared shortly with a tray on which reposed a long chisel and a metal mallet.

At a sign from him the WAAF wound the chair back till I was completely horizontal. Seemingly familiar with the routine, she cradled my head in her arms in a practised manner and stood waiting.

This couldn't be true, I thought, as the man inserted the chisel into my mouth and poised the mallet; but all doubts were erased as the metal rod thudded against the remnants of my tooth and my head in turn shot back into the little WAAF's bosom. And that was how it went on. I lost count of time as The Butcher banged away and the girl hung on grimly to my jerking skull.

The thought uppermost in my mind was that I had always wondered how young horses felt when I knocked wolf teeth out of them. Now I knew.

When it finally stopped I opened my eyes, and though by this time I was prepared for anything I still felt slightly surprised to see The Butcher threading a needle with a length of suture silk. He was sweating and looking just a little desperate as he bent over yet again.

'Just a couple of stitches,' he muttered hoarsely, and I closed my eyes again.

When I left the chair I felt very strange indeed. The assault on my cranium had made me dizzy and the sensation of the long ends of the stitches tickling my tongue was distinctly odd. I'm sure that when I came out of the room I was staggering, and instinctively I pawed at my mouth.

The first man I saw was Simkin. He was where I had left him but he looked different as he beckoned excitedly to me. I went over and he caught at my tunic with one hand.

'What d'yer think, mate?' he gasped. 'They've changed me round and I've got to go into room four.' He gulped. 'You looked bloody awful comin' out there. What was it like?'

I looked at him Maybe there was going to be a gleam of light this morning. I sank into the chair next to him and groaned.

'By God, you weren't kidding! I've never met anybody like that – he's half killed me. They don't call him The Butcher for nothing!'

'Why . . . what . . . what did 'e do?'

'Nothing much. Just knocked my tooth out with a hammer and chisel, that's all.'

'Garn! You're 'avin' me on!' Simkin made a ghastly attempt to smile.

'Word of honour,' I said. 'Anyway, there's the tray coming out now. Look for yourself.'

He stared at the WAAF carrying the dreadful implements and turned very pale.

'Oh blimey! What . . . what else did 'e do?'

I held my jaw for a moment. 'Well he did something I've never seen before. He made such a great hole in my gum that he had to stitch me up afterwards.'

Simkin shook his head violently. 'Naow, I'm not 'avin' that! I don't believe yer!'

'All right,' I said. 'What do you think of this?'

I leaned forward, put my thumb under my lip and jerked it up to give him a close-up view of the long gash and the trailing blood-stained ends of the stitches.

He shrank away from me, lips trembling, eyes wide.

'Gawd!' he moaned. 'Oh Gawd . . . !'

It was unfortunate that the WAAF chose that particular moment to call out 'AC2 Simkin' piercingly from the doorway, because the poor fellow leaped as though a powerful electric current had passed through him. Then, head down, he trailed across the room. At the door he turned and gave me a last despairing look and I saw him no more.

This experience deepened my dread of the five fillings which awaited me. But I needn't have worried; they were trivial things and were efficiently and painlessly dealt with by RAF dentists very different from The Butcher.

And yet, many years after the war had ended, the man from room four stretched out a long arm from the past and touched me on the shoulder. I began to feel something sharp coming through the roof of my mouth and went to Mr Grover, who X-rayed me and showed me a pretty picture of that fateful root still there despite the hammer and chisel. He extracted it and the saga was ended.

The Butcher remained a vivid memory because, apart from my ordeal, I was constantly reminded of him by the dangerous wobbling of my pipe at the edge of that needless gap in my mouth. But I did have a small solace. I finished my visit to room four with a parting shaft which gave me a little comfort. As I tottered away I paused and addressed the big man's back as he prepared for his next victim.

'By the way,' I said. 'I've knocked out a lot of teeth just like you did there.'

He turned and stared at me. 'Really? Are you a dentist?'

'No,' I replied over my shoulder as I left. 'I'm a vet!'

# four

I like women better than men.

Mind you, I have nothing against men – after all, I am one myself – but in the RAF there were too many of them. Literally thousands, jostling, shouting, swearing; you couldn't get away from them. Some of them became my friends and have remained so until the present day, but the sheer earthy mass of them made me realize how my few months of married life had changed me.

Women are gentler, softer, cleaner, altogether nicer things and I, who always considered myself one of the boys, had come to the surprising conclusion that the companion I wanted most was a woman.

My impression that I had been hurled into a coarser world was heightened at the beginning of each day, particularly one morning when I was on fire picket duty and had the sadistic pleasure of rattling the dustbin lids and shouting 'Wakey-wakey!' along the corridors. It wasn't the cursing and the obscene remarks which struck deepest, it was the extraordinary abdominal noises issuing from the dark rooms. They reminded me of my patient, Cedric, and in an instant I was back in Darrowby answering the telephone.

The voice at the other end was oddly hesitant.

'Mr Herriot . . . I should be grateful if you would come and see my dog.' It was a woman, obviously upper class.

'Certainly. What's the trouble?'

'Well . . . he . . . er . . . he seems to suffer from . . . a certain amount of flatus.'

'I beg your pardon?'

There was a long pause. 'He has . . . excessive flatus.'

'In what way, exactly?'

'Well . . . I suppose you'd describe it as . . . windiness.' The voice had begun to tremble.

I thought I could see a gleam of light. 'You mean his stomach . . . ?'

'No, not his stomach. He passes . . . er . . . a considerable quantity of . . . wind from his . . . his . . .' A note of desperation had crept in.

'Ah, yes!' All became suddenly clear. 'I quite understand. But that doesn't sound very serious. Is he ill?'

'No, he's very fit in other ways.'

'Well then, do you think it's necessary for me to see him?'

'Oh yes, indeed, Mr Herriot. I wish you would come as soon as possible. It has become quite . . . quite a problem.'

'All right,' I said. 'I'll look in this morning. Can I have your name and address, please?'

'It's Mrs Rumney, The Laurels.'

The Laurels was a very nice house on the edge of the town standing back from the road in a large garden. Mrs Rumney herself let me in and I felt a shock of surprise at my first sight of her. It wasn't just that she was strikingly beautiful; there was an unworldly air about her. She would be around forty but had the appearance of a heroine in a Victorian novel – tall, willowy, ethereal. And I could understand immediately her hesitation on the phone. Everything about her suggested fastidiousness and delicacy.

'Cedric is in the kitchen,' she said. 'I'll take you through.'

I had another surprise when I saw Cedric. An enormous boxer hurled himself on me in delight, clawing at my chest with the biggest, horniest feet I had seen for a long time. I tried to fight him off but he kept at me, panting ecstatically into my face and wagging his entire rear end.

'Sit down, boy!' the lady said sharply, then, as Cedric took absolutely no notice, she turned to me nervously. 'He's so friendly.'

'Yes,' I said breathlessly, 'I can see that.' I finally managed to push the huge animal away and backed into a corner for safety. 'How often does this . . . excessive flatus occur?'

As if in reply an almost palpable sulphurous wave arose from the dog and eddied around me. It appeared that the excitement of seeing me had activated Cedric's weakness. I was up against the wall and unable to obey my first instinct to run for cover so I held my hand over my face for a few moments before speaking.

'Is that what you meant?'

Mrs Rumney waved a lace handkerchief under her nose and the faintest flush crept into the pallor of her cheeks.

'Yes,' she replied almost inaudibly. 'Yes . . . that is it.'

'Oh well,' I said briskly. 'There's nothing to worry about. Let's go into the other room and we'll have a word about his diet and a few other things.'

It turned out that Cedric was getting rather a lot of meat and I drew up a little chart cutting down the protein and adding extra carbohydrates. I prescribed a kaolin antacid mixture to be given night and morning and left the house in a confident frame of mind.

It was one of those trivial things and I had entirely forgotten it when Mrs Rumney phoned again.

'I'm afraid Cedric is no better, Mr Herriot.'

'Oh I'm sorry to hear that. He's still . . . er . . . still . . . yes . . . yes . . .' I spent a few moments in thought. 'I tell you what – I don't think I can do any more by seeing him at the moment, but I think you should cut out his meat completely for a week or two. Keep him on biscuits and brown bread rusked in the oven. Try him with that and vegetables and I'll give you some powder to mix in his food. Perhaps you'd call round for it.'

The powder was a pretty strong absorbent mixture and I felt sure it would do the trick, but a week later Mrs Rumney was on the phone again.

'There's absolutely no improvement, Mr Herriot.' The tremble was back in her voice. 'I . . . I do wish you'd come and see him again.'

I couldn't see much point in viewing this perfectly healthy animal again but I promised to call. I had a busy day and it was after six o'clock before I got round to The Laurels. There were several cars in the drive and when I went into the house I saw that Mrs Rumney had a few people in for drinks; people like herself – upper class and of obvious refinement. In fact I felt rather a lout in my working clothes among the elegant gathering.

Mrs Rumney was about to lead me through to the kitchen when the door burst open and Cedric bounded delightedly into the midst of the company. Within seconds an aesthetic-looking gentleman was frantically beating off the attack as the great feet ripped down his waistcoat. He got away at the cost of a couple of buttons and the boxer turned his attention to one of the ladies. She was in imminent danger of losing her dress when I pulled the dog off her.

Pandemonium broke out in the graceful room. The hostess's plaintive appeals rang out above the cries of alarm as the big dog charged around, but very soon I realized that a more insidious element had crept into the situation. The atmosphere in the room became rapidly charged with an unmistakable effluvium and it was clear that Cedric's unfortunate malady had reasserted itself.

I did my best to shepherd the animal out of the room but he didn't seem to know the meaning of obedience and I chased him in vain. And as the embarrassing minutes ticked away I began to realize for the first time the enormity of the problem which confronted Mrs Rumney. Most dogs break wind occasionally but Cedric was different; he did it all the time. And while his silent emanations were perhaps more treacherous there was no doubt that the audible ones were painfully distressing in a company like this.

Cedric made it worse, because at each rasping expulsion he would look round enquiringly at his back end then gambol about the room as though the fugitive zephyr was clearly visible to him and he was determined to corner it.

It seemed a year before I got him out of there. Mrs Rumney held the door wide as I finally managed to steer him towards it but the big dog wasn't finished yet. On his way out he cocked a leg swiftly and directed a powerful jet against an immaculate trouser leg.

After that night I threw myself into the struggle on Mrs Rumney's behalf. I felt she desperately needed my help, and I made frequent visits and tried innumerable remedies. I consulted my colleague Siegfried on the problem and he suggested a diet of charcoal biscuits. Cedric ate them in vast quantities and with evident enjoyment but they, like everything else, made not the slightest difference to his condition.

And all the time I pondered upon the enigma of Mrs Rumney. She had lived in Darrowby for several years but the townsfolk knew little about her. It was a matter of debate whether she was a widow or separated from her husband. But I was not interested in such things; the biggest mystery to me was how she ever got involved with a dog like Cedric.

It was difficult to think of any animal less suited to her personality. Apart from his regrettable affliction he was in every way the opposite to herself; a great thick-headed, rumbustious extrovert totally out of place in her gracious menage. I never did find out how they came together but on my visits I found that Cedric had one admirer at least.

He was Con Fenton, a retired farm worker who did a bit of jobbing gardening and spent an average of three days a week at The Laurels. The boxer romped down the drive after me as I was leaving and the old man looked at him with undisguised admiration.

'By gaw,' he said. 'He's a fine dog, is that!'

'Yes, he is, Con, he's a good chap, really.' And I meant it. You couldn't help liking Cedric when you got to know him. He was utterly amiable and without vice and he gave off a constant aura not merely of noxious vapours but of bonhomie. When he tore off people's buttons or sprinkled their trousers he did it in a spirit of the purest amity.

'Just look at them limbs!' breathed Con, staring rapturously at the dog's muscular thighs. 'By heck, 'e can jump ower that gate as if it weren't there. He's what ah call a dog!'

As he spoke it struck me that Cedric would be likely to appeal to him because he was very like the boxer himself; not over-burdened with brains, built like an ox with powerful shoulders and a big constantly-grinning face – they were two of a kind.

'Aye, ah allus likes it when t'missus lets him out in t'garden,' Con went on. He always spoke in a peculiar snuffling manner. 'He's grand company.'

I looked at him narrowly. No, he wouldn't be likely to notice Cedric's complaint since he always saw him out of doors.

On my way back to the surgery I brooded on the fact that I was achieving absolutely nothing with my treatment. And though it seemed ridiculous to worry about a case like this, there was no doubt the thing had begun to prey on my mind. In fact I began to transmit my anxieties to Siegfried. As I got out of the car he was coming down the steps of Skeldale House and he put a hand on my arm.

'You've been to The Laurels, James? Tell me,' he enquired solicitously, 'how is your farting boxer today?'

'Still at it, I'm afraid,' I replied, and my colleague shook his head in commiseration.

We were both defeated. Maybe if chlorophyll tablets had been available in those days they might have helped but as it was I had tried everything. It seemed certain that nothing would alter the situation. And it wouldn't have been so bad if the owner had been anybody else but Mrs Rumney; I found that even discussing the thing with her had become almost unbearable.

Siegfried's student brother Tristan didn't help, either. When seeing practice he was very selective in the cases he wished to observe, but he was immediately attracted to Cedric's symptoms and insisted on coming with me on one occasion. I never took him again because as we went in the big dog bounded from his mistress' side and produced a particularly sonorous blast as if in greeting.

Tristan immediately threw out a hand in a dramatic gesture and declaimed: 'Speak on, sweet lips that never told a lie!' That was his only visit. I had enough trouble without that.

I didn't know it at the time but a greater blow awaited me. A few days later Mrs Rumney was on the phone again.

'Mr Herriot, a friend of mine has such a sweet little Boxer bitch. She wants to bring her along to be mated with Cedric.'

'Eh?'

'She wants to mate her bitch with my dog.'

'With Cedric . . . ?' I clutched at the edge of the desk. It couldn't be true! 'And . . . and are you agreeable?'

'Yes, of course.'

I shook my head to dispel the feeling of unreality. I found it incomprehensible that anyone should want to reproduce Cedric, and as I gaped into the receiver a frightening vision floated before me of eight little Cedrics all with his complaint. But of course such a thing wasn't hereditary. I took a grip of myself and cleared my throat.

'Very well, then, Mrs Rumney, you'd better go ahead.'

There was a pause. 'But Mr Herriot, I want you to supervise the mating.'

'Oh really, I don't think that's necessary.' I dug my nails into my palm. 'I think you'll be all right without me.'

'Oh but I would be much happier if you were there. Please come,' she said appealingly.

Instead of emitting a long-drawn groan I took a deep breath.

'Right,' I said. 'I'll be along in the morning.'

All that evening I was obsessed by a feeling of dread. Another acutely embarrassing session was in store with this exquisite woman. Why was it I always had to share things like this with her? And I really feared the worst. Even the daftest dog, when confronted with a bitch in heat, knows instinctively how to proceed, but with a really ivory-skulled animal like Cedric I wondered. . . .

And next morning all my fears were realized. The bitch, Trudy, was a trim little creature and showed every sign of willingness to cooperate. Cedric, on the other hand, though obviously delighted to meet her, gave no hint of doing his part. After sniffing her over, he danced around her a few times, goofy-faced, tongue lolling. Then he had a roll on the lawn before charging at her and coming to a full stop, big feet outsplayed, head down, ready to play. I sighed. It was as I thought. The big chump didn't know what to do.

This pantomime went on for some time and, inevitably, the emotional strain brought on a resurgence of his symptoms. Frequently he paused to inspect his tail as though he had never heard noises like that before.

He varied his dancing routine with occasional headlong gallops round the lawn and it was after he had done about ten successive laps that he seemed to decide he ought to do something about the bitch. I held my breath as he approached her but unfortunately he chose the wrong end to commence operations. Trudy had put up with his nonsense with great patience but when she found him busily working away in the region of her left ear it was too much. With a shrill yelp she nipped him in the hind leg and he shot away in alarm.

After that whenever he came near she warned him off with bared teeth. Clearly she was disenchanted with her bridegroom and I couldn't blame her.

'I think she's had enough, Mrs Rumney,' I said.

I certainly had had enough and so had the poor lady, judging by her slight breathlessness, flushed cheeks and waving handkerchief.

'Yes . . . yes . . . I suppose you're right,' she replied.

So Trudy was taken home and that was the end of Cedric's career as a stud dog.

This last episode decided me. I had to have a talk with Mrs Rumney and a few days later I called in at The Laurels.

'Maybe you'll think it's none of my business,' I said. 'But I honestly don't think Cedric is the dog for you. In fact he's so wrong for you that he is upsetting your life.'

Mrs Rumney's eyes widened. 'Well . . . he is a problem in some ways . . . but what do you suggest?'

'I think you should get another dog in his place. Maybe a poodle or a corgi – something smaller, something you could control.'

'But Mr Herriot, I couldn't possibly have Cedric put down.' Her eyes filled quickly with tears. 'I really am fond of him despite his . . . despite everything.'

'No, no, of course not!' I said. 'I like him too. He has no malice in him. But I think I have a good idea. Why not let Con Fenton have him?'

'Con . . . ?'

'Yes, he admires Cedric tremendously and the big fellow would have a good life with the old man. He has a couple of fields behind his cottage and keeps a few beasts. Cedric could run to his heart's content out there and Con would be able to bring him along when he does the garden. You'd still see him three times a week.'

Mrs Rumney looked at me in silence for a few moments and I saw in her face the dawning of relief and hope.

'You know, Mr Herriot, I think that could work very well. But are you sure Con would take him?'

'I'd like to bet on it. An old bachelor like him must be lonely. There's only one thing worries me. Normally they only meet outside and I wonder how it would be when they were indoors and Cedric started to ... when the old trouble ... '

'Oh, I think that would be all right,' Mrs Rumney broke in quickly. 'When I go on holiday Con always takes him for a week or two and he has never mentioned any ... anything unusual ... in that way.'

I got up to go. 'Well, that's fine. I should put it to the old man right away.'

Mrs Rumney rang within a few days. Con had jumped at the chance of taking Cedric and the pair had apparently settled in happily together. She had also taken my advice and acquired a poodle puppy.

I didn't see the new dog till it was nearly six months old and its mistress asked me to call to treat it for a slight attack of eczema. As I sat in the graceful room looking at Mrs Rumney, cool, poised, tranquil, with the little white creature resting on her knee I couldn't help feeling how right and fitting the whole scene was. The lush carpet, the trailing velvet curtains, the fragile tables with their load of expensive china and framed miniatures. It was no place for Cedric.

Con Fenton's cottage was less than half a mile away and on my way back to the surgery, on an impulse I pulled up at the door. The old man answered my knock and his big face split into a delighted grin when he saw me.

'Come in, young man!' he cried in his strange snuffly voice. 'I'm right glad to see tha!'

I had hardly stepped into the tiny living room when a hairy form hurled itself upon me. Cedric hadn't changed a bit and I had to battle my way to the broken armchair by the fireside.

Con settled down opposite and when the boxer leaped to lick his face he clumped him companionably on the head with his fist.

'Siddown, ye great daft bugger,' he murmured with affection. Cedric sank happily on to the tattered hearthrug at his feet and gazed up adoringly at his new master.

'Well, Mr Herriot,' Con went on as he cut up some villainous-looking plug tobacco and began to stuff it into his pipe. 'I'm right grateful to ye for gettin' me this grand dog. By gaw, he's a topper and ah wouldn't sell 'im for any money. No man could ask for a better friend.'

'Well that's great, Con,' I said. 'And I can see that the big chap is really happy here.'

The old man ignited his pipe and a cloud of acrid smoke rose to the low, blackened beams. 'Aye, he's 'ardly ever inside. A gurt strong dog like 'im wants to work 'is energy off, like.'

But just at that moment Cedric was obviously working something else off because the familiar pungency rose from him even above the billowings from the pipe. Con seemed oblivious of it but in the enclosed space I found it overpowering.

'Ah well,' I gasped. 'I just looked in for a moment to see how you were getting on together. I must be on my way.' I rose hurriedly and stumbled towards the door but the red-olence followed me in a wave. As I passed the table with the remains of the old man's meal I saw what seemed to be the only form of ornament in the cottage, a cracked vase holding a magnificent bouquet of carnations. It was a way of escape and I buried my nose in their fragrance.

Con watched me approvingly. 'Aye, they're lovely flowers, aren't they? T'missus at Laurels lets me bring 'ome what I want and I reckon them carnations is me favourite.'

'Yes, they're a credit to you.' I still kept my nose among the blooms.

'There's only one thing,' the old man said pensively. 'Ah don't get t'full benefit of 'em.'

'How's that, Con?'

47

He pulled at his pipe a couple of times. 'Well, you can hear ah speak a bit funny, like?'

'No . . . no . . . not really.'

'Oh aye, ye know ah do. I've been like it since I were a lad. I 'ad a operation for adenoids and summat went wrong.'

'Oh, I'm sorry to hear that,' I said.

'Well, it's nowt serious, but it's left me lackin' in one way.'

'You mean . . . ?' A light was beginning to dawn in my mind, an elucidation of how man and dog had found each other, of why their relationship was so perfect, of the cert-ainty of their happy future together. It seemed like fate.

'Aye,' the old man went on sadly. 'I 'ave no sense of smell.'

# five

I think it was when I saw the London policeman wagging a finger at a scowling urchin that I thought of Wesley Binks and the time he put the firework through the surgery letter box.

It was what they used to call a 'banger' and it exploded at my feet as I hurried along the dark passage in answer to the door bell's ring, making me leap into the air in terror.

I threw open the front door and looked into the street. It was empty, but at the corner where the lamplight was re-flected in Robson's shop window I had a brief impression of a fleeing form and a faint echo of laughter. I couldn't do any-thing about it but I knew Wes was out there somewhere.

Wearily I trailed back into the house. Why did this lad persecute me? What could a ten-year-old boy possibly have against me? I had never done him any harm, yet I seemed to be the object of a deliberate campaign.

Or maybe it wasn't personal. It could be that he felt I

represented authority or the establishment in some way, or perhaps I was just convenient.

I was certainly the ideal subject for his little tricks of ringing the door bell and running away, because I dared not ignore the summons in case it might be a client, and also the consulting and operating rooms were such a long way from the front of the house. Sometimes I was dragged down from our bed-sitter under the tiles. Every trip to the door was an expedition and it was acutely exasperating to arrive there and see only a little figure in the distance dancing about and grimacing at me.

He varied this routine by pushing rubbish through the letter box, pulling the flowers from the tiny strip of garden we tried to cultivate between the flagstones and chalking rude messages on my car.

I knew I wasn't the only victim because I had heard complaints from others; the fruiterer who saw his apples disappear from the box in front of the shop, the grocer who unwillingly supplied him with free biscuits.

He was the town naughty boy all right, and it was incongruous that he should have been named Wesley. There was not the slightest sign in his behaviour of any strict Methodist upbringing. In fact I knew nothing of his family life – only that he came from the poorest part of the town, a row of 'yards' containing tumbledown cottages, some of them evacuated because of their condition.

I often saw him wandering about in the fields and lanes or fishing in quiet reaches of the river when he should have been in school. When he spotted me on these occasions he invariably called out some mocking remark and if he happened to be with some of his cronies they all joined in the laughter at my expense. It was annoying but I used to tell myself that there was nothing personal in it. I was an adult and that was enough to make me a target.

Wes's greatest triumph was undoubtedly the time he removed the grating from the coal cellar outside Skeldale House. It was on the left of the front steps and underneath it was a steep ramp down which the coalmen tipped their bags.

I don't know whether it was inspired intuition but he pinched the grating on the day of the Darrowby Gala. The festivities started with a parade through the town led by the Houlton Silver Band and as I looked down from the windows of our bed-sitter I could see them all gathering in the street below.

'Look, Helen,' I said. 'They must be starting the march from Trengate. Everybody I know seems to be down there.'

Helen leaned over my shoulder and gazed at the long lines of boy scouts, girl guides, ex-servicemen, with half the population of the town packed on the pavements, watching. 'Yes, it's quite a sight, isn't it? Let's go down and see them move off.'

We trotted down the long flights of stairs and I followed her out through the front door. And as I appeared in the entrance I was suddenly conscious that I was the centre of attention. The citizens on the pavements, waiting patiently for the parade to start, had something else to look at now. The little brownies and wolf cubs waved at me from their ranks and there were nods and smiles from the people across the road and on all sides.

I could divine their thoughts. 'There's t'young vitnery coming out of his house. Not long married, too. That's his missus next to him.'

A feeling of wellbeing rose in me. I don't know whether other newly married men feel the same, but in those early days I was aware of a calm satisfaction and fulfilment. And I was proud to be the 'vitnery' and part of the life of the town. There was my plate on the wall beside me, a symbol of my solid importance. I was a man of substance now, I had arrived.

Looking around me, I acknowledged the greeting with a few dignified little smiles, raising a gracious hand now and then rather like a royal personage on view. Then I noticed that Helen hadn't much room by my side, so I stepped to the left to where the grating should have been and slid gracefully down into the cellar.

It would be a dramatic touch to say I disappeared from

view; in fact I wish I had, because I would have stayed down there and avoided further embarrassment. But as it was I travelled only so far down the ramp and stuck there with my head and shoulders protruding into the street.

My little exhibition caused a sensation among the spectators. Nothing in the Gala parade could compete with this. One or two of the surrounding faces expressed alarm but loud laughter was the general response. The adults were almost holding each other up but the little brownies and wolf cubs made my most appreciative audience, breaking their ranks and staggering about helplessly in the roadway while their leaders tried to restore order.

I caused chaos, too, in the Houlton Silver Band, who were hoisting their instruments prior to marching off. If they had any ideas about bursting into tune they had to abandon them temporarily because I don't think any of them had breath to blow.

It was, in fact, two of the bandsmen who extricated me by linking their hands under my armpits. My wife was of no service at all in the crisis and I could only look up at her reproachfully as she leaned against the doorpost dabbing at her eyes.

It all became clear to me when I reached street level. I was flicking the coal dust from my trousers and trying to look unconcerned when I saw Wesley Binks doubled up with mirth, pointing triumphantly at me and at the hole over the cellar. He was quite near, jostling among the spectators, and I had my first close look at the wild-eyed little goblin who had plagued me. I may have made an unconscious movement towards him because he gave me a last malevolent grin and disappeared into the crowd.

Later I asked Helen about him. She could only tell me that Wesley's father had left home when he was about six years old, that his mother had remarried and the boy now lived with her and his stepfather.

Strangely, I had another opportunity to study him quite soon afterwards. It was about a week later and my feathers were still a little ruffled after the grating incident when I saw him sitting all alone in the waiting room. Alone, that is, except for a skinny black dog in his lap.

I could hardly believe it. I had often rehearsed the choice phrases which I would use on this very occasion but the sight of the animal restrained me; if he had come to consult me professionally I could hardly start pitching into him right away. Maybe later.

I pulled on a white coat and went in.

'Well, what can I do for you?' I asked coldly.

The boy stood up and his expression of mixed defiance and desperation showed that it had cost him something to enter this house.

'Summat matter wi' me dog,' he muttered.

'Right, bring him through.' I led the way along the passage to the consulting room.

'Put him on the table please,' I said, and as he lifted the little animal I decided that I couldn't let this opportunity pass. While I was carrying out my examination I would quite casually discuss recent events. Nothing nasty, no clever phrases, just a quiet probe into the situation. I was just about to say something like 'What's the idea of all those tricks you play on me?' when I took my first look at the dog and everything else fled from my mind.

He wasn't much more than a big puppy and an out-and-out mongrel. His shiny black coat could have come from a labrador and there was a suggestion of terrier in the pointed nose and pricked ears, but the long string-like tail and the knock-kneed fore limbs baffled me. For all that he was an attractive little creature with a sweetly expressive face.

But the things that seized my whole attention were the yellow blobs of pus in the corners of the eyes, the muco-purulent discharge from the nostrils and the photophobia which made the dog blink painfully at the light from the surgery window.

Classical canine distemper is so easy to diagnose but there is never any satisfaction in doing so.

'I didn't know you had a dog,' I said. 'How long have you had him?'

'A month. Feller got 'im from t'dog and cat home at Hartington and sold 'im to me.'

'I see.' I took the temperature and was not surprised to find it was 104 °F.

'How old is he?'

'Nine months.'

I nodded. Just about the worst age.

I went ahead and asked all the usual questions but I knew the answers already.

Yes, the dog had been slightly off colour for a week or two. No, he wasn't really ill, but listless and coughing occasionally. And of course it was not until the eyes and nose began to discharge that the boy became worried and brought him to see me. That was when we usually saw these cases – when it was too late.

Wesley imparted the information defensively, looking at me under lowered brows as though he expected me to clip his ear at any moment. But as I studied him any aggressive feelings I may have harboured evaporated quickly. The imp of hell appeared on closer examination to be a neglected child. His elbows stuck out through holes in a filthy jersey, his shorts were similarly ragged, but what appalled me most was the sour smell of his unwashed little body. I hadn't thought there were children like this in Darrowby.

When he had answered my questions he made an effort and blurted out one of his own.

'What's matter with 'im?'

I hesitated a moment. 'He's got distemper, Wes.'

'What's that?'

'Well, it's a nasty infectious disease. He must have got it from another sick dog.'

'Will 'e get better?'

'I hope so. I'll do the best I can for him.' I couldn't bring myself to tell a small boy of his age that his pet was probably going to die.

I filled a syringe with a 'mixed macterin' which we used at that time against the secondary invaders of distemper. It never did much good and even now with all our antibiotics we cannot greatly influence the final outcome. If you can catch a case in the early viral phase then a shot of hyperimmune serum is curative, but people rarely bring their dogs in until that phase is over.

As I gave the injection the dog whimpered a little and the boy stretched out a hand and patted him.

'It's awright, Duke,' he said.

'That's what you call him, is it – Duke?'

'Aye.' He fondled the ears and the dog turned, whipped his strange long tail about and licked the hand quickly. Wes smiled and looked up at me and for a moment the tough mask dropped from the grubby features and in the dark wild eyes I read sheer delight. I swore under my breath. This made it worse.

I tipped some boracic crystals into a box and handed it over. 'Use this dissolved in water to keep his eyes and nose clean. See how his nostrils are all caked and blocked up – you can make him a lot more comfortable.'

He took the box without speaking and almost with the same movement dropped three and sixpence on the table. It was about our average charge and resolved my doubts on that score.

'When'll ah bring 'im back?' he asked.

I looked at him doubtfully for a moment. All I could do was repeat the injections, but was it going to make the slightest difference?

The boy misread my hesitation.

'Ah can pay!' he burst out. 'Ah can get t'money!'

'Oh I didn't mean that, Wes. I was just wondering when it would be suitable. How about bringing him in on Thursday?'

He nodded eagerly and left with his dog.

As I swabbed the table with disinfectant I had the old feeling of helplessness. The modern veterinary surgeon does not see nearly as many cases of distemper as we used to, simply because most people immunize their puppies at the earliest possible moment. But back in the thirties it was only the fortunate dogs who were inoculated. The disease is so easy to prevent but almost impossible to cure.

The next three weeks saw an incredible change in Wesley Binks's character. He had built up a reputation as an idle scamp but now he was transformed into a model of industry, delivering papers in the mornings, digging people's gardens, helping to drive the beasts at the auction mart. I was perhaps the only one who knew he was doing it for Duke.

He brought the dog in every two or three days and paid on the nail. I naturally charged him as little as possible but the money he earned went on other things – fresh meat from the butcher, extra milk and biscuits.

'Duke's looking very smart today,' I said on one of the visits. 'I see you've been getting him a new collar and lead.'

The boy nodded shyly then looked up at me, dark eyes intent. 'Is 'e any better?'

'Well, he's about the same, Wes. That's how it goes – dragging on without much change.'

'When . . . when will ye know?'

I thought for a moment. Maybe he would worry less if he understood the situation. 'The thing is this. Duke will get better if he can avoid the nervous complications of distemper.'

'Wot's them?'

'Fits, paralysis and a thing called chorea which makes the muscles twitch.'

'Wot if he gets them?'

'It's a bad lookout in that case. But not all dogs develop them.' I tried to smile reassuringly. 'And there's one thing in Duke's favour – he's not a pure-bred. Cross-bred dogs have a thing called hybrid vigour which helps them to fight disease. After all, he's eating fairly well and he's quite lively, isn't he?'

'Aye, not bad.'

'Well then, we'll carry on. I'll give him another shot now.'

The boy was back in three days and I knew by his face he had momentous news.

'Duke's a lot better – 'is eyes and nose 'ave dried up and he's eatin' like a 'oss!' He was panting with excitement.

I lifted the dog on to the table. There was no doubt he was

enormously improved and I did my best to join in the rejoicing.

'That's great, Wes,' I said, but a warning bell was tinkling in my mind. If nervous symptoms were going to supervene, this was the time – just when the dog was apparently recovering.

I forced myself to be optimistic. 'Well now, there's no need to come back any more but watch him carefully and if you see anything unusual bring him in.'

The ragged little figure was overjoyed. He almost pranced along the passage with his pet and I hoped fervently that I would not see them in there again.

That was on the Friday evening and by Monday I had put the whole thing out of my head and into the category of satisfying memories when the boy came in with Duke on the lead.

I looked up from the desk where I was writing in the day book. 'What is it, Wes?'

'He's dotherin'.'

I didn't bother going through to the consulting room but hastened from behind the desk and crouched on the floor, studying the dog intently. At first I saw nothing, then as I watched I could just discern a faint nodding of the head. I placed my hand on the top of the skull and waited. And it was there; the slight but regular twitching of the temporal muscles which I had dreaded.

'I'm afraid he's got chorea, Wes.' I said.

'What's that?'

'It's one of the things I was telling you about. Sometimes they call it St Vitus' Dance. I was hoping it wouldn't happen.'

The boy looked suddenly small and forlorn and he stood there silent, twisting the new leather lead between his fingers. It was such an effort for him to speak that he almost closed his eyes.

'Will 'e die?'

'Some dogs do get over it, Wes. 'I didn't tell him that I had seen it happen only once. 'I've got some tablets which might help him. I'll get you some.'

I gave him a few of the arsenical tablets I had used in my only cure. I didn't even know if they had been responsible but I had nothing more to offer.

Duke's chorea pursued a text book course over the next two weeks. All the things which I had feared turned up in a relentless progression. The twitching spread from his head to his limbs, then his hindquarters began to sway as he walked.

His young master brought him in repeatedly and I went through the motions, trying at the same time to make it clear that it was all hopeless. The boy persisted doggedly, rushing about meanwhile with his paper deliveries and other jobs, insisting on paying though I didn't want his money. Then one afternoon he called in.

'Ah couldn't bring Duke,' he muttered. 'Can't walk now. Will you come and see 'im?'

We got into my car. It was a Sunday, about three o'clock and the streets were quiet. He led me up the cobbled yard and opened the door of one of the houses.

The stink of the place hit me as I went in. Country vets aren't easily sickened but I felt my stomach turning. Mrs Binks was very fat and a filthy dress hung shapelessly on her as she slumped, cigarette in mouth, over the kitchen table. She was absorbed in a magazine which lay in a clearing among mounds of dirty dishes and her curlers nodded as she looked up briefly at us.

On the couch under the window her husband sprawled asleep, open-mouthed, snoring out the reek of beer. The sink, which held a further supply of greasy dishes, was covered in a revolting green scum. Clothes, newspapers and nameless rubbish littered the floor and over everything a radio blasted away at full strength.

The only clean new thing was the dog basket in the corner. I went across and bent over the little animal. Duke was now prostrate and helpless, his body emaciated and jerking uncontrollably. The sunken eyes had filled up again with pus and gazed apathetically ahead.

'Wes,' I said. 'You've got to let me put him to sleep.'

He didn't answer, and as I tried to explain, the blaring radio drowned my words. I looked over at his mother.

'Do you mind turning the radio down?' I asked.

She jerked her head at the boy and he went over and turned the knob. In the ensuing silence I spoke to him again.

'It's the only thing, believe me. You can't let him die by inches like this.'

He didn't look at me. All his attention was fixed desperately on his dog. Then he raised a hand and I heard his whisper.

'Awright.'

I hurried out to the car for the Nembutal.

'I promise you he'll feel no pain,' I said as I filled the syringe. And indeed the little creature merely sighed before lying motionless, the fateful twitching stilled at last.

I put the syringe in my pocket. 'Do you want me to take him away, Wes?'

He looked at me bewilderedly and his mother broke in.

'Aye, get 'im out. Ah never wanted t'bloody thing 'ere in t'first place.' She resumed her reading.

I quickly lifted the little body and went out. Wes followed me and watched as I opened the boot and laid Duke gently on top of my black working coat.

As I closed the lid he screwed his knuckles into his eyes and his body shook. I put my arm across his shoulders, and as he leaned against me for a moment and sobbed I wondered if he had ever been able to cry like this – like a little boy with somebody to comfort him.

But soon he stood back and smeared the tears across the dirt on his cheeks.

'Are you going back into the house, Wes?' I asked.

He blinked and looked at me with a return of his tough expression.

'Naw!' he said and turned and walked away. He didn't look back and I watched him cross the road, climb a wall and trail away across the fields towards the river.

And it has always seemed to me that at that moment Wes walked back into his old life. From then on there were no more odd jobs or useful activities. He never played any more tricks on me but in other ways he progressed into more serious misdemeanours. He set barns on fire, was up before the magistrates for theft and by the time he was thirteen he was stealing cars.

Finally he was sent to an approved school and then he disappeared from the district. Nobody knew where he went and most people forgot him. One person who didn't was the police sergeant.

'That young Wesley Binks,' he said to me ruminatively. 'He was a wrong 'un if ever I saw one. You know, I don't think he ever cared a damn for anybody or any living thing in his life.'

'I know how you feel, sergeant,' I replied, 'But you're not entirely right. There was one living thing . . .'

# six

Tristan would never have won any prizes as an exponent of the haute cuisine.

We got better food in the RAF than most people in wartime Britain but it didn't compare with the Darrowby fare. I suppose I had been spoiled; first by Mrs Hall, then by Helen. There were only brief occasions at Skeldale House when we did not eat like kings and one of those was when Tristan was installed as temporary cook.

It began one morning at breakfast in the days when I was still a bachelor and Tristan and I were taking our places at the mahogany dining table. Siegfried bustled in, muttered a greeting and began to pour his coffee. He was unusually distrait as he buttered a slice of toast and cut into one of the rashers on his plate, then after a minute's thoughtful chewing he brought down his hand on the table with a suddenness that made me jump.

'I've got it!' he exclaimed.

'Got what?' I enquired.

Siegfried put down his knife and fork and wagged a finger at me. 'Silly, really, I've been sitting here puzzling about what to do and it's suddenly clear.'

'Why, what's the trouble?'

'It's Mrs Hall,' he said. 'She's just told me her sister has been taken ill and she has to go and look after her. She thinks she'll be away for a week and I've been wondering who I could get to look after the house.'

'I see.'

'Then it struck me.' He sliced a corner from a fried egg. 'Tristan can do it.'

'Eh?' His brother looked up, startled, from his *Daily Mirror*. 'Me?'

'Yes, you! You spend a lot of time on your arse. A bit of useful activity would be good for you.'

Tristan looked at him warily. 'What do you mean – useful activity?'

'Well, keeping the place straight,' Siegfried said. 'I wouldn't expect perfection but you could tidy up each day, and of course prepare the meals.'

'Meals?'

'That's right.' Siegfried gave him a level stare. 'You can cook, can't you?'

'Well, er, yes . . . I can cook sausage and mash.'

Siegfried waved an expansive hand. 'There you are, you see, no problem. Push over those fried tomatoes, will you, James?'

I passed the dish silently. I had only half heard the conversation because part of my mind was far away. Just before breakfast I had had a phone call from Ken Billings, one of our best farmers, and his words were still echoing in my head.

'Mr Herriot, that calf you saw yesterday is dead. That's the third 'un I've lost in a week and I'm flummoxed. I want ye out here this mornin' to have another look round.'

I sipped my coffee absently. He wasn't the only one who was flummoxed. Three fine calves had shown symptoms of acute gastric pain, I had treated them and they had died.

That was bad enough but what made it worse was that I hadn't the faintest idea what was wrong with them.

I wiped my lips and got up quickly. 'Siegfried, I'd like to go to Billings' first. Then I've got the rest of the round you gave me.'

'Fine, James, by all means.' My boss gave me a sweet and encouraging smile, balanced a mushroom on a piece of fried bread and conveyed it to his mouth. He wasn't a big eater but he did love his breakfast.

On the way to the farm my mind beat about helplessly. What more could I do than I had already done? In these obscure cases one was driven to the conclusion that the animal had eaten something harmful. At times I had spent hours roaming around pastures looking for poisonous plants but that was pointless with Billings's calves because they had never been out; they were mere babies of a month old.

I had carried out post mortem examinations of the dead animals but had found only a non-specific gastro-enteritis. I had sent kidneys to the laboratory for lead estimation with negative result; like their owner, I was flummoxed.

Mr Billings was waiting for me in his yard.

'Good job I rang you!' he said breathlessly. 'There's another 'un startin'.'

I rushed with him into the buildings and found what I expected and dreaded; a small calf kicking at its stomach, getting up and down, occasionally rolling on its straw bed. Typical abdominal pain. But why?

I went over it as with the others. Temperature normal, lungs clear, only rumenal atony and extreme tenderness as I palpated the abdomen.

As I was putting the thermometer back in its case the calf suddenly toppled over and went into a frothing convulsion. Hastily I injected sedatives, calcium, magnesium, but with a feeling of doom. I had done it all before.

'What the hell is it?' the farmer asked, voicing my thoughts.

I shrugged. 'It's acute gastritis, Mr Billings, but I wish I knew the cause. I could swear this calf has eaten some irritant or corrosive poison.'

'Well, dang it, they've nobbut had milk and a few nuts.' The farmer spread his hands. 'There's nothing they can get to hurt them.'

Again, wearily, I went through the old routine; ferreting around in the calf pen, trying to find some clue. An old paint tin, a burst packet of sheep dip. It was amazing, the things you came across in the clutter of a farm building.

But not at Mr Billings's place. He was meticulously tidy, particularly with his calves, and the window sills and shelves were free from rubbish. It was the same with the milk buckets, scoured to spotless cleanliness after every feed.

Mr Billings had a thing about his calves. His two teenage sons were fanatically keen on farming and he encouraged them in all the agricultural skills; but he fed the calves himself.

'Feeding them calves is t'most important job in stock rearing,' he used to say. 'Get 'em over that first month and you're half way there.'

And he knew what he was talking about. His charges never suffered from the normal ailments of the young; no scour, no joint ill, no pneumonia. I had often marvelled at it, but it made the present disaster all the more unbearable.

'All right,' I said with false breeziness as I left. 'Maybe this one won't be so bad. Give me a ring in the morning.'

I did the rest of my round in a state of gloom and at lunch I was still so preoccupied that I wondered what had happened when Tristan served the meal. I had entirely forgotten about Mrs Hall's absence.

However, the sausage and mash wasn't at all bad and Tristan was lavish with his helpings. The three of us cleaned our plates pretty thoroughly, because morning is the busiest working time in practice and I was always famished by midday.

My mind was still on Mr Billings's problem during the afternoon calls and when we sat down to supper I was only mildly surprised to find another offering of sausage and mash.

'Same again, eh?' Siegfried grunted, but he got through his plateful and left without further comment.

The next day started badly. I came into the dining room to find the table bare and Siegfried stamping around.

'Where the hell is our breakfast?' he burst out. 'And where the hell is Tristan?'

He pounded along the passage and I heard his shouts in the kitchen 'Tristan! Tristan!'

I knew he was wasting his time. His brother often slept in and it was just a bit more noticeable this morning.

My boss returned along the passage at a furious gallop and I steeled myself for some unpleasantness as the young man was rousted from his bed. But Tristan, as usual, was master of the situation. Siegfried had just begun to take the stairs three at a time when his brother descended from the landing, knotting his tie with perfect composure. It was uncanny. He always got more than his share of sleeping time but was rarely caught between the sheets.

'Sorry, chaps,' he murmured. 'Afraid I overslept.'

'Yes, that's all right!' shouted Siegfried. 'But how about our bloody breakfast? I gave you a job to do!'

Tristan was contrite. 'I really do apologize, but I was up late last night, peeling potatoes.'

His brother's face flushed. 'I know all about that!' he barked. 'You didn't start till after closing time at the Drovers!'

'Well, that's right.' Tristan swallowed and his face assumed the familiar expression of pained dignity. 'I did feel a bit dry last night. Think it must have been all the cleaning and dusting I did.'

Siegfried did not reply. He shot a single exasperated look at the young man then turned to me. 'We'll have to make do with bread and marmalade this morning, James. Come through to the kitchen and we'll...'

The jangling telephone cut off his words. I lifted the receiver and listened and it must have been the expression on my face which stopped him in the doorway.

'What's the matter, James?' he asked as I came away from the phone. 'You look as though you've had a kick in the belly.'

I nodded. 'That's how I feel. That calf is nearly dead at

Billings's and there's another one ill. I wish you'd come out there with me, Siegfried.'

My boss stood very still as he looked over the side of the pen at the little animal. It didn't seem to know where to put itself, rising and lying down, kicking at some inward pain, writhing its hindquarters from side to side. As he watched it fell on its side and began to thrash around with all four limbs.

'James,' he said quietly. 'That calf has been poisoned.'

'That's what I thought, but how?'

Mr Billings broke in. 'It's no good talkin' like that, Mr Farnon. We've been over this place time and time again and there's nowt for them to get.'

'Well, we'll go over it again.' Siegfried stalked around the calf house as I had done and when he returned his face was expressionless.

'Where do you get the nuts from? he grunted, crumbling one of the cubes between his fingers.

Mr Billings threw his arms wide. 'From t'local mill. Ryders' best. You can't fault them, surely.'

Siegfried said nothing. Ryders were noted for their meticulous preparation of cattle food. He went over the sick calf with stethoscope and thermometer, digging his fingers into the hairy abdominal wall, staring impassively at the calf's face to note its reaction. He did the same with my patient of yesterday whose glazing eyes and cold extremities told their grim tale. Then he gave the calves almost the same treatment as I had and we left.

He was silent for the first half mile, then he beat the wheel suddenly with one hand. 'There's an irritant poison there, James! As sure as God made little apples there is. But I'm damned if I know where it's coming from.'

Our visit had taken a long time and we returned to Skeldale House for lunch. Like myself, his mind was still wrestling with Mr Billing's problem and he hardly winced as Tristan placed a steaming plateful of sausage and mash before him. Then, as he prodded the mash with a fork, he appeared to come to the surface.

'God almighty!' he exclaimed. 'Have we got this again?'

Tristan smiled ingratiatingly. 'Yes, indeed. Mr Johnson told me they were a particularly fine batch of sausages today. Definitely superior, he said.'

'Is that so?' His brother gave him a sour glance. 'Well, they look the bloody same to me. Like supper yesterday – and like lunch.' His voice began to rise, then he subsided.

'Oh, what the hell,' he muttered, and began to toy listlessly with the food. Clearly those calves had drained him and I knew how he felt.

I got through my share without much difficulty – I've always liked sausage and mash.

But my boss is a resilient character and when we met in the late afternoon he was bursting with his old spirit.

'That call to Billings's shook me, James, I can tell you.' he said. 'But I've revisited a few of my other cases since then and they're all improving nicely. Raises the morale tremendously. Here, let me get you a drink.'

He reached into the cupboard above the mantelpiece for the gin bottle and after pouring a couple of measures he looked benignly at his brother who was tidying the sitting room.

Tristan was making a big show, running a carpet sweeper up and down, straightening cushions, flicking a duster at everything in sight. He sighed and panted with effort as he bustled around, the very picture of a harassed domestic. He needed only a mob cap and frilly apron to complete the image.

We finished our drinks and Siegfried immersed himself in the *Veterinary Record* as savoury smells began to issue from the kitchen. It was about seven o'clock when Tristan put his head round the door.

'Supper is on the table,' he said.

My boss put down the *Record*, rose and stretched expansively. 'Good, I'm ready for it, too.'

I followed him into the dining room and almost cannoned into his back as he halted abruptly. He was staring in disbelief at the tureen in the middle of the table.

'Not bloody sausage and mash again!' he bellowed.

Tristan shuffled his feet. 'Well, er, yes – it's very nice really.'

'Very nice! I'm beginning to dream about the blasted stuff. Can't you cook anything else?'

'Well, I told you.' Tristan looked wounded. 'I told you I could cook sausage and mash.'

'Yes, you did!' shouted his brother. 'But you didn't say you couldn't cook anything else BUT sausage and bloody mash!'

Tristan made a non-committal gesture and his brother sank wearily down at the table.

'Go on, then,' he sighed. 'Dish it out and heaven help us.'

He took a small mouthful from his plate then gripped at his stomach and emitted a low moan. 'This stuff is killing me. I don't think I'll ever be the same after this week.'

The following day opened in dramatic fashion. I had just got out of bed and was reaching for my dressing gown when an explosion shook the house. It was a great 'WHUFF' which rushed like a mighty wind through passages and rooms, rattling the windows and leaving an ominous silence in its wake.

I dashed out to the landing and ran into Siegfried, who stared wide-eyed at me for a moment before galloping downstairs.

In the kitchen Tristan was lying on his back amid a litter of pans and dishes. Several rashers of bacon and a few smashed eggs nestled on the flags.

'What the hell's going on?' Siegfried shouted.

His brother looked up at him with mild interest. 'I really don't know. I was lighting the fire and there was a bang.'

'Lighting the fire . . . ?'

'Yes, I've had a little difficulty these last two mornings. The thing wouldn't go. I think the chimney needs sweeping. These old houses . . .'

'Yes, yes!' Siegfried burst out. 'We know, but what the hell happened?'

Tristan sat up. Even then, among the debris with smuts all over his face, he still retained his poise. 'Well, I thought I'd hurry things along a bit,' (His agile mind was forever seeking new methods of conserving energy.) 'I soaked a piece of cotton wool in ether and chucked that in.'

'Ether?'

'Well yes, it's inflammable, isn't it?'

'Inflammable!' His brother was pop-eyed. 'It's bloody well explosive! It's a wonder you didn't blow the whole place up.'

Tristan rose and dusted himself off. 'Ah well, never mind. I'll soon have breakfast ready.'

'You can forget that.' Siegfried took a long shuddering breath then went over to the bread tin, extracted a loaf and began to saw at it. 'The breakfast's on the floor, and anyway, by the time you've cleared up this mess we'll be gone. Bread and marmalade all right for you, James?'

We went out together again. My boss had arranged that Ken Billings should postpone his calf feeding till we got there so that we could witness the process.

It wasn't a happy arrival. Both the calves had died and the farmer's eyes held a look of desperation.

Siegfried's jaw clenched tight for a moment then he motioned with his hand. 'Please carry on, Mr Billings. I want to see you feed them.'

The nuts were always available for the little animals but we watched intently as the farmer poured the milk into the buckets and the calves started to drink. The poor man had obviously given up hope and I could tell by his apathetic manner that he hadn't much faith in this latest ploy.

Neither had I, but Siegfried prowled up and down like a caged panther as though willing something to happen. The calves raised white-slobbered muzzles enquiringly as he hung over them but they could offer no more explanation of the mystery than I could myself.

I looked across the long row of pens. There were still more than thirty calves left in the building and the terrible thought arose that the disease might spread through all of them. My mind was recoiling when Siegfried stabbed a finger at one of the buckets.

'What's that?' he snapped.

The farmer and I went over and gazed down at a circular black object about half an inch across floating on the surface of the milk.

'Bit o' muck got in somehow,' Mr Billings mumbled. 'I'll 'ave it out.' He put his hand into the bucket.

'No, let me!' Siegfried carefully lifted the thing, shook the milk from his fingers and studied it with interest.

'This isn't muck,' he murmured. 'Look, it's concave – like a little cup.' He rubbed a corner between thumb and forefinger. 'I'll tell you what it is, it's a scab. Where the heck has it come from?'

He began to examine the neck and head of the calf, then became very still as he handled one of the little horn buds. 'There's a raw surface here. You can see where the scab belongs.' He placed the dark cup over the bud and it fitted perfectly.

The farmer shrugged. 'Aye, well, I can understand that. I disbudded all the calves about a fortnight sin'.'

'What did you use, Mr Billings?' My colleague's voice was soft.

'Oh, some new stuff. Feller came round sellin' it. You just paint it on – it's a lot easier than t'awd caustic stick.'

'Have you got the bottle?'

'Aye, it's in t'house. I'll get it.'

When the farmer returned Siegfried read the label and handed the bottle to me.

'Butter of antimony, Jim. Now we know.'

'But ... what are you on about?' asked the farmer bewilderedly.

Siegfried looked at him sympathetically. 'Antimony is a deadly poison, Mr Billings. Oh, it'll burn your horn buds off, all right, but if it gets among the food, that's it.'

The farmer's eyes widened. 'Yes, dang it, and when they put their heads down to drink that's just when the scabs would fall off!'

'Exactly,' Siegfried said. 'Or they maybe knocked the horn buds on the sides of the bucket. Anyway, let's make sure the others are safe.'

We went round all the calves, removing the lethal crusts and scrubbing the buds clean, and when we finally drove away we knew that the brief but painful episode of the Billings calves was over.

In the car, my colleague put his elbow on the wheel and drove with his chin cupped in his hands. He often did this when in contemplative mood and it never failed to unnerve me.

'James,' he said, 'I've never seen anything like that before. It really is one for the book.'

His words were prophetic, for as I write about it now I realize that it has never been repeated in the thirty-five years that have passed since then.

At Skeldale House we parted to go our different ways. Tristan, no doubt anxious to redeem himself after the morning's explosive beginning, was plying mop and bucket and swabbing the passage with the zeal of one of Nelson's sailors.

But when Siegfried drove away, the activity stopped abruptly and as I was leaving with my pockets stuffed with the equipment for my round I glanced into the sitting room and saw the young man stretched in his favourite chair.

I went in and looked with some surprise at a pan of sausages balanced on the coals.

'What's this?' I asked.

Tristan lit a Woodbine, shook out his *Daily Mirror* and put his feet up. 'Just prepared lunch, old lad.'

'In here?'

'Yes, Jim, I've had enough of that hot stove – there's no comfort through there. And anyway, the kitchen's such a bloody long way away.'

I gazed down at the reclining form. 'No need to ask what's on the menu?'

'None at all, old son.' Tristan loked up from his paper with a seraphic smile.

I was about to leave when a thought struck me. 'Where are the potatoes?'

'In the fire.'

'In the fire!'

'Yes, I just popped them in there to roast for a while. They're delicious that way.'

'Are you sure?'

'Absolutely, Jim. I'll tell you – you'll fall in love with my cooking all over again.'

I didn't get back till nearly one o'clock. Tristan was not in the sitting room but a haze of smoke hung on the air and a reek like a garden bonfire prickled in my nostrils.

I found the young man in the kitchen. His *savoir faire* had vanished and he was prodding desperately at a pile of coal black spheres.

I stared at him. 'What are those?'

'The bloody potatoes, Jim! I fell asleep for a bit and this happened!'

He gingerly sawed through one of the objects. In the centre of the carbonaceous ball I could discern a small whitish marble which seemed to be all that remained of the original vegetable.

'Hell's bells, Triss! What are you going to do?'

He gave me a stricken glance. 'Hack out the centres and mash 'em up together. It's all I CAN do.'

This was something I couldn't bear to watch. I went upstairs, had a wash then took my place at the dining table. Siegfried was already seated and I could see that the little triumph of the morning had cheered him. He greeted me jovially.

'James, wasn't that the damndest thing at Ken Billings'? It's so satisfying to get it cleared up.'

But his smile froze as Tristan appeared and set down the tureens before him. From one peeped the inevitable sausages and the other contained an amorphous dark grey mass liberally speckled with black foreign bodies of varying size.

'What in the name of God,' he enquired with ominous quiet, 'is this?'

His brother swallowed. 'Sausage and mash,' he said lightly.

Siegfried gave him a cold look. 'I am referring to this.' He poked warily at the dark mound.

'Well, er, it's the potatoes.' Tristan cleared his throat. 'Got a little burnt, I'm afraid.'

My boss made no comment. With dangerous calm he spooned some of the material on to his plate, raised a forkful and began to chew slowly. Once or twice he winced as a particularly tough fragment of carbon cracked between his molars, then he closed his eyes and swallowed.

For a moment he was still, then he grasped his midriff with both hands, groaned and jumped to his feet.

'No, that's enough!' he cried. 'I don't mind investigating poisonings on the farms but I object to being poisoned myself in my own home!' He strode away from the table and paused at the door. 'I'm going over to the Drovers for lunch.'

As he left another spasm seized him. He clutched his stomach again and looked back.

'Now I know just how those poor bloody calves felt!'

# seven

I suppose it was a little thoughtless of me to allow my scalpel to flash and flicker quite so close to Rory O'Hagan's fly buttons.

The incident came back to me as I sat in my room in St John's Wood reading Black's *Veterinary Dictionary*. It was a bulky volume to carry around and my RAF friends used to rib me about my 'vest pocket edition', but I had resolved to keep reading it in spare moments to remind me of my real life.

I had reached the letter 'C' and as the word 'Castration' looked up at me from the page I was jerked back to Rory.

I was castrating pigs. There were several litters to do and I was in a hurry and failed to notice the Irish farm worker's mounting apprehension. His young boss was catching the little animals and handing them to Rory who held them upside down, gripped between his thighs with their legs apart, and as I quickly incised the scrotums and drew out the testicles my blade almost touched the rough material of his trouser crutch.

'For God's sake, have a care, Mr Herriot!' he gasped at last.

I looked up from my work. 'What's wrong, Rory?'

'Watch what you're doin' with that bloody knife! You're whippin' it round between me legs like a bloody Red Indian. You'll do me a mischief afore you've finished!'

'Aye, be careful, Mr Herriot,' the young farmer cried. 'Don't geld Rory instead of the pig. His missus ud never forgive ye.' He burst into a loud peal of laughter, the Irishman grinned sheepishly and I giggled.

That was my undoing because the momentary inattention sent the blade slicing across my left forefinger. The razor-sharp edge went deep and in an instant the entire neighbourhood seemed flooded with my blood. I thought I would never staunch the flow. The red ooze continued, despite a long session of self-doctoring from the car boot, and when I finally drove away my finger was swathed in the biggest, clumsiest dressing I had ever seen. I had finally been forced to apply a large pad of cotton wool held in place with an enormous length of three-inch bandage.

It was dark when I left the farm: about five o'clock on a late December day, the light gone early and the stars beginning to show in a frosty sky. I drove slowly, the enormous finger jutting upwards from the wheel, pointing the way between the headlights like a guiding beacon. I was within half a mile of Darrowby with the lights of the little town beginning to wink between the bare roadside branches when a car approached, went past, then I heard a squeal of brakes as it stopped and began to double back.

It passed me again, drew into the side and I saw a frantically waving arm. I pulled up and a young man jumped from the driving seat and ran towards me.

He pushed his head in at the window. 'Are you the vet?' His voice was breathless, panic-stricken.

'Yes, I am.'

'Oh thank God! We're passing through on the way to Manchester and we've been to your surgery ... they said you were out this way ... described your car. Please help us!'

'What's the trouble?'

'It's our dog ... in the back of the car. He's got a ball stuck in his throat. I ... I think he might be dead.'

I was out of my seat and running along the road before he had finished. It was a big white saloon and in the darkness of the back seat a wailing chorus issued from several little heads silhoutted against the glass.

I tore open the door and the wailing took on words.

'Oh Benny, Benny, Benny ... !'

I dimly discerned a large dog spread over the knees of four small children. 'Oh Daddy, he's dead, he's dead!'

'Let's have him out,' I gasped, and as the young man pulled on the forelegs I supported the body, which slid and toppled on to the tarmac with a horrible limpness.

I pawed at the hairy form. 'I can't see a bloody thing! Help me pull him round.'

We dragged the unresisting bulk into the headlights' glare and I could see it all. A huge, beautiful collie in his luxuriant prime, mouth gaping, tongue lolling, eyes staring lifelessly at nothing. He wasn't breathing.

The young father took one look then gripped his head with both hands. 'Oh God, oh God. ...' From within the car I heard the quiet sobbing of his wife and the piercing cries from the back. 'Benny ... Benny. ...'

I grabbed the man's shoulder and shouted at him. 'What did you say about a ball?'

'It's in his throat ... I've had my fingers in his mouth for ages but I couldn't move it.' The words came mumbling up from beneath the bent head.

I pushed my hand into the mouth and I could feel it all right. A sphere of hard solid rubber not much bigger than a golf ball and jammed like a cork in the pharynx, effectively blocking the trachea. I scrabbled feverishly at the wet smoothness but there was nothing to get hold of. It took me about three seconds to realize that no human agency would ever get the ball out that way and without thinking I withdrew my hands, braced both thumbs behind the angle of the lower jaw and pushed.

The ball shot forth, bounced on the frosty road and rolled sadly on to the grass verge. I touched the corneal surface of the eye. No reflex. I slumped to my knees, burdened by the hopeless regret that I hadn't had the chance to do this just a bit sooner. The only function I could perform now was to take the body back to Skeldale House for disposal. I couldn't allow the family to drive to Manchester with a dead dog. But I wished fervently that I had been able to do more, and as I passed my hand along the richly coloured coat over the ribs the vast bandaged finger stood out like a symbol of my helplessness.

It was when I was gazing dully at the finger, the heel of my hand resting in an intercostal space, that I felt the faintest flutter from below.

I jerked upright with a hoarse cry. 'His heart's still beating! He's not gone yet!' I began to work on the dog with all I had. And out there in the darkness of that lonely country road it wasn't much. No stimulant injections, no oxygen cylinders or intratracheal tubes. But I depressed his chest with my palms every three seconds in the old-fashioned way, willing the dog to breathe as the eyes still stared at nothing. Every now and then I blew desperately down the throat or probed between the ribs for that almost imperceptible beat.

I don't know which I noticed first, the slight twitch of an eyelid or the small lift of the ribs which pulled the icy Yorkshire air into his lungs. Maybe they both happened at once but from that moment everything was dreamlike and wonderful. I lost count of time as I sat there while the breathing became deep and regular and the animal began to be aware of his surroundings; and by the time he started to look around him and twitch his tail tentatively I realized suddenly that I was stiff-jointed and almost frozen to the spot.

74

With some difficulty I got up and watched in disbelief as the collie staggered to his feet. The young father ushered him round to the back where he was received with screams of delight.

The man seemed stunned. Throughout the recovery he had kept muttering, 'You just flicked that ball out . . . just flicked it out. Why didn't I think of that . . .?' And when he turned to me before leaving he appeared to be still in a state of shock.

'I don't . . . I don't know how to thank you,' he said huskily. 'It's a miracle.' He leaned against the car for a second. 'And now what is your fee? How much do I owe you?'

I rubbed my chin. I had used no drugs. The only expenditure had been time.

'Five bob,' I said. 'And never let him play with such a little ball again.'

He handed the money over, shook my hand and drove away. His wife, who had never left her place, waved as she left, but my greatest reward was in the last shadowy glimpse of the back seat where little arms twined around the dog, hugging him ecstatically, and in the cries, thankful and joyous, fading into the night.

'Benny . . . Benny . . . Benny. . . .'

Vets often wonder after a patient's recovery just how much credit they might take. Maybe it would have got better without treatment – it happened sometimes; it was difficult to be sure.

But when you know without a shadow of a doubt that, even without doing anything clever, you have pulled an animal back from the brink of death into the living, breathing world, it is a satisfaction which lingers, flowing like balm over the discomforts and frustrations of veterinary practice, making everything right.

Yet, in the case of Benny the whole thing had an unreal quality. I never even glimpsed the faces of those happy children nor that of their mother huddled in the front seat. I had a vague impression of their father but he had spent most of the time with his head in his hands. I wouldn't have known him if I met him in the street. Even the dog, in the unnatural glare of the headlights, was a blurred memory.

It seemed the family had the same feeling because a week later I had a pleasant letter from the mother. She apologized for skulking out of the way so shamelessly, she thanked me for saving the life of their beloved dog who was now prancing around with the children as though nothing had happened, and she finished with the regret that she hadn't even asked me my name.

Yes, it had been a strange episode, and not only were those people unaware of my name but I'd like to bet they would fail to recognize me if they saw me again.

In fact, looking back at the affair, the only thing which stood out unequivocal and substantial was my great white-bound digit which had hovered constantly over the scene, almost taking on a personality and significance of its own. I am sure that is what the family remembered best about me because of the way the mother's letter began.

'Dear Vet with the bandaged finger . . .'

# eight

My stint in London was nearing its end. Our breaking-in weeks were nearly over and we waited for news of posting to Initial Training Wing.

The air was thick with rumours. We were going to Aberystwyth in Wales; too far away for me, I wanted the north. Then we were going to Newquay in Cornwall; worse still. I was aware that the impending birth of AC2 Herriot's child did not influence the general war strategy but I still wanted to be as near to Helen as possible at the time.

The whole London phase is blurred in my memory. Possibly because everything was so new and different that the impressions could not be fully absorbed, and also perhaps because I was tired most of the time. I think we were all tired. Few of us were used to being jerked from slumber at 6 a.m. every morning and spending the day in continual physical activity. If we weren't being drilled we were being marched to meals, to classes, to talks. I had lived in a motor car for a few years and the rediscovery of my legs was painful.

There were times, too, when I wondered what it was all about. Like all the other young men I had imagined that after a few brisk preliminaries I would be sitting in an aeroplane, learning to fly, but it turned out that this was so far in the future that it was hardly mentioned. At the ITW we would spend months learning navigation, principles of flight, morse and many other things.

I was thankful for one blessing. I had passed the mathematics exam. I have always counted on my fingers and still do and I had been so nervous about this that I went to classes with the ATC in Darrowby before my call-up, dredging from my schooldays horrific calculations about trains passing each other at different speeds and water running in and out of bath tubs. But I had managed to scrape through and felt ready to face anything.

There were some unexpected shocks in London. I didn't anticipate spending days mucking out some of the dirtiest piggeries I had ever seen. Somebody must have had the idea of converting all the RAF waste food into pork and bacon and of course there was plenty of labour at hand. I had a strong feeling of unreality as, with other aspiring pilots, I threw muck and swill around hour after hour.

There was another time I had the same feeling. One night three of us decided to go to the cinema. We took pains to get to the front of the queue for the evening meal so that we would be in time for the start of the picture. When the doors of the huge dining room at the zoo were thrown open we were first in, but a sergeant cook met us in the entrance with:

'I want three volunteers for dishwashing - you, you and you,' and marched us away.

He probably had a kind heart because he patted our shoulders as we climbed miserably into greasy dungarees.

'Never mind, lads,' he said. 'I'll see you get a real good meal afterwards.'

My friends were taken somewhere else and I found myself alone in a kind of dungeon at the end of a metal chute. Very soon dirty plates began to cascade down the chute and my job was to knock the food remains off them and transfer them to a mechanical washer.

The menu that night was cottage pie and chips, a combination which has remained engraved on my memory. For more than two hours I stood at bay while a nonstop torrent of crockery poured down on me; thousands and thousands of plates, every one bearing a smear of cottage pie, a blob of cold gravy, a few adhering chips.

As I reeled around in the meaty steam a little tune tinkled repetitively in my mind; it was the song Siegfried and I were forever singing as we waited to enter the RAF, the popular jingle which in our innocence we thought typified the new life ahead.

If I only had wings,
Oh what a difference it would make to things,
All day long I'd be in the sky, up on high,
Talking to the birdies that pass me by.

But in this reeking cavern with my hands, face, hair and every pore of my skin impregnated with cottage pie and chips, those birdies seemed far away.

At last, however, the plates began to slow down and finally stopped coming. The sergeant came in beaming and congratulated me on doing a fine job. He led me back to the dining hall, vast and empty save for my two friends. They both wore bemused, slightly stunned expressions and I am pretty sure I looked the same.

'Sit down here, lads,' the sergeant said. We took our places side by side in a corner with the bare boards of the table stretching away into the distance. 'I told you you'd get a real good meal, didn't I? Well, here it is.' He slid three heaped platefuls in front of us.

'There y'are,' he said. 'Cottage pie and chips, double helpin's!'

The following day I might have felt more disenchanted than ever, but news of the posting blotted out all other feelings. It seemed too good to be true – I was going to Scarborough. I had been there and I knew it as a beautiful seaside resort, but that wasn't why I was so delighted. It was because it was in Yorkshire.

# nine

As we marched out of the station into the streets of Scarborough I could hardly believe I was back in Yorkshire. But if there had been any doubt in my mind it would have been immediately resolved by my first breath of the crisp, tangy air. Even in winter there had been no 'feel' to the soft London air and I half closed my eyes as I followed the tingle all the way down to my lungs.

Mind you, it was cold. Yorkshire is a cold place and I could remember the sensation almost of shock at the start of my first winter in Darrowby.

It was after the first snow and I followed the clanging ploughs up the Dale, bumping along between high white mounds till I reached old Mr Stokill's gate. With my fingers on the handle I looked through the glass at the new world beneath me. The white blanket rolled down the hillside and lapped over the roofs of the dwelling and outbuildings of the little farm. Beyond, it smoothed out and concealed the familiar features, the stone walls bordering the fields, the stream on the valley floor, turning the whole scene into something unknown and exciting.

But the thrill I felt at the strange beauty was swept away as I got out and the wind struck me. It was an Arctic blast screaming from the east, picking up extra degrees of cold as it drove over the frozen white surface. I was wearing a heavy overcoat and woollen gloves but the gust whipped its way right into my bones. I gasped and leaned my back against the car while I buttoned the coat up under my chin, then I struggled forward to where the gate shook and rattled. I fought it open and my feet crunched as I went through.

Coming round the corner of the byre I found Mr Stokill forking muck on to a heap, making a churned brown trail across the whiteness.

'Now then,' he muttered along the side of a half-smoked cigarette. He was over seventy but still ran the smallholding single-handed. He told me once that he had worked as a farm hand for six shillings a day for thirty years, yet still managed to save enough to buy his own little place. Maybe that was why he didn't want to share it.

'How are you, Mr Stokill?' I said, but just then the wind tore through the yard, clutching icily at my face, snatching my breath away so that I turned involuntarily to one side with an explosive 'Aaahh!'

The old farmer looked at me in surprise, then glanced around as though he had just noticed the weather.

'Aye, blows a bit thin this mornin', lad.' Sparks flew from the end of his cigarette as he leaned for a moment on the fork.

He didn't seem to have much protection against the cold. A light khaki smock fluttered over a ragged navy waistcoat, clearly once part of his best suit, and his shirt bore neither collar nor stud. The white stubble on his fleshless jaw was a reproach to my twenty-four years and suddenly I felt an inadequate city-bred softie.

The old man dug his fork into the manure pile and turned towards the buildings. 'Ah've got a nice few cases for ye to see today. Fust 'un's in 'ere.' He opened a door and I staggered gratefully into a sweet bovine warmth where a few shaggy little bullocks stood hock deep in straw.

'That's the youth we want.' He pointed to a dark roan

standing with one hind foot knuckled over. 'He's been on three legs for a couple o' days. Ah reckon he's got foul.'

I walked up to the little animal but he took off at a speed which made light of his infirmity.

'We'll have to run him into the passage. Mr Stokill,' I said. 'Just open the gate, will you?'

With the rough timbers pushed wide I got behind the bullock and sent him on to the opening. It seemed as though he was going straight through but at the entrance he stopped peeped into the passage and broke away. I galloped a few times round the yard after him, then had another go. The result was the same. After half a dozen tries I wasn't cold any more. I'll back chasing young cattle against anything else for working up a sweat, and I had already forgotten the uncharitable world outside. And I could see I was going to get warmer still because the bullock was beginning to enjoy the game, kicking up his heels and frisking around after each attempt.

I put my hands on my hips, waited till I got my breath back then turned to the farmer.

'This is hopeless. He'll never go in there,' I said. 'We'd maybe better try to get a rope on him.'

'Nay, lad, there's no need for that. We'll get him through t'gate right enough.' The old man ambled to one end of the yard and returned with an armful of clean straw. He sprinkled it freely in the gate opening and beyond in the passage, then turned to me. 'Now send 'im on.'

I poked a finger into the animal's rump and he trotted forward, proceeded unhesitatingly between the posts and into the passage.

Mr Stokill must have noticed my look of bewilderment.

'Aye, 'e just didn't like t'look of them cobbles. Once they was covered over he was awright.'

'Yes ... yes ... I see.' I followed the bullock slowly through.

He was indeed suffering from foul of the foot, the mediaeval term given because of the stink of the necrotic tissue between the cleats, and I didn't have any antibiotics or sulphonamides to treat it. It is so nice and easy these days to give an injection, knowing that the beast will be sound in a day or two. But all I could do was wrestle with the lunging hind foot, dressing the infected cleft with a crude mixture of copper sulphate and Stockholm tar and finishing with a pad of cotton wool held by a tight bandage. When I had finished I took off my coat and hung it on a nail. I didn't need it any more.

Mr Stokill looked approvingly at the finished job. 'Capital, capital,' he murmured. 'Now there's some little pigs in this pen got a bit o' scour. I want you to give 'em a jab wi' your needle.'

We had various *E coli* vaccines which sometimes did a bit of good in these cases and I entered the pen hopefully. But I left in a hurry because the piglets' mother didn't approve of a stranger wandering among her brood and she came at me open-mouthed, barking explosively. She looked as big as a donkey and when the cavernous jaws with the great yellowed teeth brushed my thigh I knew it was time to go. I hopped rapidly into the yard and crashed the door behind me.

I peered back ruminatively into the pen. 'We'll have to get her out of there before I can do anything, Mr Stokill.'

'Aye, you're right, young man, ah'll shift 'er.' He began to shuffle away.

I held up a hand. 'No, it's all right, I'll do it.' I couldn't let this frail old man go in there and maybe get knocked down and savaged, and I looked around for a means of protection. There was a battered shovel standing against a wall and I seized it.

'Open the door, please,' I said. 'I'll soon have her out.'

Once more inside the pen I held the shovel in front of me and tried to usher the huge sow towards the door. But my efforts at poking her rear end were fruitless; she faced me all the time, wide-mouthed and growling as I circled. When she got the blade of the shove between her teeth and began to worry it I called a halt.

As I left the pen I saw Mr Stokill dragging a large object over the cobbles.

'What's that?' I asked.

'Dustbin,' the old man grunted in reply.

'Dustbin! What on earth . . .?'

He gave no further explanation but entered the pen. As the sow came at him he allowed her to run her head into the bin then, bent double, he began to back her towards the open door. The animal was clearly baffled. Suddenly finding herself in this strange dark place she naturally tried to retreat from it and all the farmer did was guide her.

Before she knew what was happening she was out in the yard. The old man calmly removed the bin and beckoned to me. 'Right you are, Mr Herriot, you can get on now.'

It had taken about twenty seconds.

Well, that was a relief, and anyway I knew what to do next. Lifting a sheet of corrugated iron which the farmer had ready I rushed in among the little pigs. I would pen them in a corner and the job would be over in no time.

But their mother's irritation had been communicated to the family. It was a big litter and there were sixteen of them hurtling around like little pink racehorses. I spent a long time diving frantically after them, jamming the sheet at a bunch only to see half of them streaking out the other end, and I might have gone on indefinitely had I not felt a gentle touch on my arm.

'Haud on, young man, haud on.' The old farmer looked at me kindly. 'If you'll nobbut stop runnin' after 'em they'll settle down. Just bide a minute.'

Slightly breathless, I stood by his side and listened as he addressed the little creatures.

'Giss-giss, giss-giss,' murmured Mr Stokill without moving. 'Giss-giss, giss-giss.'

The piglets slowed their headlong gallop to a trot, then, as though controlled by telepathy, they all stopped at once and stood in a pink group in one corner.

'Giss-giss,' said Mr Stokill approvingly, advancing almost imperceptibly with the sheet. 'Giss-giss.'

He unhurriedly placed the length of metal across the corner and jammed his foot against the bottom.

'Now then, put the toe of your wellington against t'other end and we 'ave 'em,' he said quietly.

After that the injection of the litter was a matter of a few minutes. Mr Stokill didn't say, 'Well, I'm teaching you a thing or two today, am I not?' There was no hint of triumph or self-congratulation in the calm old eyes. All he said was, 'I'm keepin' you busy this mornin', young man. I want you to look at a cow now. She's got a pea in her tit.'

'Peas' and other obstructions in the teats were very common in the days of hand milking. Some of them were floating milk calculi, others tiny pedunculated tumours, injuries to the teat lining, all sorts of things. It was a whole diverting little field in itself and I approached the cow with interest.

But I didn't get very near before Mr Stokill put his hand on my shoulder.

'Just a minute, Mr Herriot, don't touch 'er tit yet or she'll clout ye. She's an awd bitch. Wait a minute till ah rope 'er.'

'Oh right,' I said. 'But I'll do it.'

He hesitated. 'Ah reckon I ought to . . .'

'No, no, Mr Stokill that's quite unnecessary, I know how to stop a cow kicking.' I said primly. 'Kindly hand me that rope.'

'But . . . she's a bugger . . . kicks like a 'oss. She's a right good milker but . . .'

'Don't worry,' I said, smiling. 'I'll stop her little games.'

I began to unwind the rope. It was good to be able to demonstrate that I did know something about handling animals even though I had been qualified for only a few months. And it made a change to be told before and not after the job that a cow was a kicker. A cow once kicked me nearly to the other end of the byre and as I picked myself up the farmer said unemotionally, 'Aye, she's allus had a habit o' that.'

Yes, it was nice to be warned, and I passed the rope round the animal's body in front of the udder and pulled it tight in a slip knot. Just like they taught us at college. She was a scrawny red shorthorn with a woolly poll and she regarded me with a contemplative eye as I bent down.

'All right, lass,' I said soothingly, reaching under her and gently grasping the teat. I squirted a few jets of milk then something blocked the end. Ah yes, there it was, quite large and unattached. I felt sure I could work it through the orifice without cutting the sphincter.

I took a firmer grip, squeezed tightly and immediately a cloven foot shot out like a whip lash and smacked me solidly on the knee. It is a particularly painful spot to be kicked and I spent some time hopping round the byre and cursing in a fervent whisper.

The farmer followed me anxiously. 'Ee, ah'm sorry, Mr Herriot, she's a right awd bugger. Better let me . . .'

I held up a hand. 'No, Mr Stokill. I already have her roped. I just didn't tie it tight enough, that's all.' I hobbled back to the animal, loosened the knot then retied it, pulling till my eyes popped. When I had finished, her abdomen was lifted high and nipped in like a wasp-waisted Victorian lady of fashion.

'That'll fix you,' I grunted, and bent to my work again. A few spurts of milk then the thing was at the teat end again, a pinkish-white object peeping through the orifice. A little extra pressure and I would be able to fish it out with the hypodermic needle I had poised ready. I took a breath and gripped hard.

This time the hoof caught me half way up the shin bone. She hadn't been able to get so much height into it but it was just as painful. I sat down on a milking stool, rolled up my trouser leg and examined the roll of skin which hung like a diploma at the end of a long graze where the sharp hoof had dragged along.

'Now then, you've 'ad enough, young man.' Mr Stokill removed my rope and gazed at me with commiseration. 'Ordinary methods don't work with this 'un. I 'ave to milk her twice a day and ah knaw.'

He fetched a soiled length of plough cord which had obviously seen much service and fastened it round the cow's hock. The other end had a hook which he fitted into a ring on the byre wall. It was just the right length to stretch taut, pulling the leg slightly back.

The old man nodded. 'Now try.'

With a feeling of fatalism I grasped the teat again. And it was as if the cow knew she was beaten. She never moved as I nipped hard and winkled out the offending obstruction. She couldn't do a thing about it.

'Ah, thank ye, lad,' the farmer said. 'That's champion. Been bothering me a bit has that. Didn't know what it was.' He held up a finger. 'One last job for ye. A young heifer with a bit o' stomach trouble, ah think. Saw her last night and she was a bit blown. She's in an outside buildin'.'

I put on my coat and we went out to where the wind welcomed us with savage glee. As the knife-like blast hit me, whistling up my nose and making my eyes water, I cowered in the lee of the stable.

'Where is this heifer?' I gasped.

Mr Stokill did not reply immediately. He was lighting another cigarette, apparently oblivious of the elements. He clamped the lid on an ancient brass lighter and jerked his thumb.

'Across the road. Up there.'

I followed his gesture over the buried walls, across the narrow roadway between the ploughed-out snow dunes to where the fell rose steeply in a sweep of broken white to join the leaden sky. Unbroken, that is, except for a tiny barn, a grey stone speck just visible on the last airy swell hundreds of feet up where the hillside joined the moorland above.

'Sorry,' I said, still crouching against the wall. 'I can't see anything.'

The old man, lounging in the teeth of the wind, looked at me in surprise. 'You can't? Why, t'barn's good enough to see, isn't it?'

'The barn?' I pointed a shaking finger at the heights. 'You mean that building? The heifer's surely not in there!'

'Aye, she is. Ah keep a lot o' me young beasts in them spots.'

'But . . . but . . .' I was gabbling now. 'We'll never get up there! That snow's three feet deep!'

He blew smoke pleasurably from his nostrils. 'We will, don't tha worry. Just hang on a second.'

He disappeared into the stable and after a few moments I peeped inside. He was saddling a fat brown cob and I stared as he led the little animal out, climbed stiffly on to a box and mounted.

Looking down at me he waved cheerfully. 'Well, let's be goin'. Have you got your stuff?'

Bewilderedly I filled my pockets. A bottle of bloat mixture, a trochar and cannula, a packet of gentian and nux vomica. I did it in the dull knowledge that there was no way I could get up that hill.

On the other side of the road an opening had been dug and Mr Stokill rode through. I slithered in his wake, looking up hopelessly at the great smooth wilderness rearing above us.

Mr Stokill turned in the saddle. 'Get haud on t'tail,' he said.

'I beg your pardon?'

'Get a haud of 'is tail.'

As in a dream I seized the bristly hairs.

'No, both 'ands,' the farmer said patiently.

'That's grand, lad. Now 'ang on.'

He clicked his tongue, the cob plodded resolutely forward and so did I.

And it was easy! The whole world fell away beneath us as we soared upwards, and leaning back and enjoying it I watched the little valley unfold along its twisting length until I could see away into the main Dale with the great hills billowing round and white into the dark clouds.

At the barn the farmer dismounted. 'All right, young man?'

'All right, Mr Stokill.' As I followed him into the little building I smiled to myself. This old man had once told me that he left school when he was twelve, whereas I had spent most of the twenty-four years of my life in study. Yet when I looked back on the last hour or so I could come to only one conclusion.

He knew a lot more than I did.

# ten

I had plenty of company for Christmas that year. We were billeted in the Grand Hotel, the massive Victorian pile which dominated Scarborough in turreted splendour from its eminence above the sea, and the big dining room was packed with several hundred shouting airmen. The iron discipline was relaxed for a few hours to let the Yuletide spirit run free.

It was so different from other Christmases I had known that it ought to have remained like a beacon in my mind, but I know that my strongest memory of Christmas will always be bound up with a certain little cat.

I first saw her when I was called to see one of Mrs Ainsworth's dogs, and I looked in some surprise at the furry black creature sitting before the fire.

'I didn't know you had a cat,' I said.

The lady smiled. 'We haven't, this is Debbie.'

'Debbie?'

'Yes, at least that's what we call her. She's a stray. Comes here two or three times a week and we give her some food. I don't know where she lives but I believe she spends a lot of her time around one of the farms along the road.'

'Do you ever get the feeling that she wants to stay with you?'

'No.' Mrs Ainsworth shook her head. 'She's a timid little thing. Just creeps in, has some food then flits away. There's something so appealing about her but she doesn't seem to want to let me or anybody into her life.'

I looked again at the little cat. 'But she isn't just having food today.'

'That's right. It's a funny thing but every now and again she slips through here into the lounge and sits by the fire for a few minutes. It's as though she was giving herself a treat.'

'Yes ... I see what you mean.' There was no doubt there was something unusual in the attitude of the little animal. She was sitting bolt upright on the thick rug which lay before the fireplace in which the coals glowed and flamed. She made no effort to curl up or wash herself or do anything other than gaze quietly ahead. And there was something in the dusty black of her coat, the half-wild scrawny look of her, that gave me a clue. This was a special event in her life, a rare and wonderful thing; she was lapping up a comfort undreamed of in her daily existence.

As I watched she turned, crept soundlessly from the room and was gone.

'That's always the way with Debbie,' Mrs Ainsworth laughed. 'She never stays more than ten minutes or so, then she's off.'

She was a plumpish, pleasant-faced woman in her forties and the kind of client veterinary surgeons dream of; well off, generous, and the owner of three cosseted basset hounds. And it only needed the habitually mournful expressions of one of the dogs to deepen a little and I was round there post haste. Today one of the bassets had raised its paw and scratched its ear a couple of times and that was enough to send its mistress scurrying to the phone in great alarm.

So my visits to the Ainsworth home were frequent but undemanding, and I had ample opportunity to look out for the little cat which had intrigued me. On one occasion I spotted her nibbling daintily from a saucer at the kitchen door. As I watched she turned and almost floated on light footsteps into the hall then through the lounge door.

The three bassets were already in residence, draped snoring on the fireside rug, but they seemed to be used to Debbie because two of them sniffed her in a bored manner and the third merely cocked a sleepy eye at her before flopping back on the rich pile.

Debbie sat among them in her usual posture; upright, intent, gazing absorbedly into the glowing coals. This time I tried to make friends with her. I approached her carefully but she leaned away as I stretched out my hand. However, by patient wheedling and soft talk I managed to touch her and gently stroked her cheek with one finger. There was a moment when she responded by putting her head on one side and rubbing back against my hand but soon she was ready to leave. Once outside the house she darted quickly along the road then through a gap in a hedge and the last I saw was the little black figure flitting over the rain-swept grass of a field.

'I wonder where she goes,' I murmured half to myself.

Mrs Ainsworth appeared at my elbow. 'That's something we've never been able to find out.'

It must have been nearly three months before I heard from Mrs Ainsworth, and in fact I had begun to wonder at the bassets' long symptomless run when she came on the phone.

It was Christmas morning and she was apologetic. 'Mr Herriot, I'm so sorry to bother you today of all days. I should think you want a rest at Christmas like anybody else.' But her natural politeness could not hide the distress in her voice.

'Please don't worry about that,' I said. 'Which one is it this time?'

'It's not one of the dogs. It's . . . Debbie.'

'Debbie? She's at your house now?'

'Yes . . . but there's something wrong. Please come quickly.'

Driving through the market place I thought again that Darrowby on Christmas Day was like Dickens come to life; the empty square with the snow thick on the cobbles and hanging from the eaves of the fretted lines of roofs; the shops closed and the coloured lights of the Christmas trees winking at the windows of the clustering houses, warmly inviting against the cold white bulk of the fells behind.

Mrs Ainsworth's home was lavishly decorated with tinsel and holly, rows of drinks stood on the sideboard and the rich aroma of turkey and sage and onion stuffing wafted from the kitchen. But her eyes were full of pain as she led me through to the lounge.

Debbie was there all right, but this time everything was different. She wasn't sitting upright in her usual position; she was stretched quite motionless on her side, and huddled close to her lay a tiny black kitten.

I looked down in bewilderment. 'What's happened here?'

'It's the strangest thing,' Mrs Ainsworth replied. 'I haven't seen her for several weeks then she came in about two hours ago – sort of staggered into the kitchen, and she was carrying the kitten in her mouth. She took it through to the lounge and laid it on the rug and at first I was amused. But I could see all was not well because she sat as she usually does, but for a long time – over half an hour – then she lay down like this and she hasn't moved.'

I knelt on the rug and passed my hand over Debbie's neck and ribs. She was thinner than ever, her fur dirty and mud-caked. She did not resist as I gently opened her mouth. The tongue and mucous membranes were abnormally pale and the lips ice-cold against my fingers. When I pulled down her eyelid and saw the dead white conjunctiva a knell sounded in my mind.

I palpated the abdomen with a grim certainty as to what I would find and there was no surprise, only a dull sadness as my fingers closed around a hard lobulated mass deep among the viscera. Massive lymphosarcoma. Terminal and hopeless. I put my stethoscope on her heart and listened to the increasingly faint, rapid beat then I straightened up and sat on the rug looking sightlessly into the fireplace, feeling the warmth of the flames on my face.

Mrs Ainsworth's voice seemed to come from afar. 'Is she ill, Mr Herriot?'

I hesitated. 'Yes . . . yes, I'm afraid so. She has a malignant growth.' I stood up. 'There's absolutely nothing I can do. I'm sorry.'

'Oh!' Her hand went to her mouth and she looked at me wide-eyed. When at last she spoke her voice trembled. 'Well, you must put her to sleep immediately. It's the only thing to do. We can't let her suffer.'

'Mrs Ainsworth,' I said. 'There's no need. She's dying now – in a coma – far beyond suffering.'

She turned quickly away from me and was very still as she fought with her emotions. Then she gave up the struggle and dropped on her knees beside Debbie.

'Oh, poor little thing!' she sobbed and stroked the cat's

head again and again as the tears fell unchecked on the matted fur. 'What she must have come through. I feel I ought to have done more for her.'

For a few moments I was silent, feeling her sorrow, so discordant among the bright seasonal colours of this festive room. Then I spoke gently.

'Nobody could have done more than you,' I said. 'Nobody could have been kinder.'

'But I'd have kept her here – in comfort. It must have been terrible out there in the cold when she was so desperately ill – I daren't think about it. And having kittens, too – I . . . I wonder how many she did have?'

I shrugged. 'I don't suppose we'll ever know. Maybe just this one. It happens sometimes. And she brought it to you, didn't she?'

'Yes . . . that's right . . . she did . . . she did.' Mrs Ainsworth reached out and lifted the bedraggled black morsel. She smoothed her finger along the muddy fur and the tiny mouth opened in a soundless miaow. 'Isn't it strange? She was dying and she brought her kitten here. And on Christmas Day.'

I bent and put my hand on Debbie's heart. There was no beat.

I looked up. 'I'm afraid she's gone.' I lifted the small body, almost feather light, wrapped it in the sheet which had been spread on the rug and took it out to the car.

When I came back Mrs Ainsworth was still stroking the kitten. The tears had dried on her cheeks and she was bright-eyed as she looked at me.

'I've never had a cat before,' she said.

I smiled. 'Well it looks as though you've got one now.'

And she certainly had. That kitten grew rapidly into a sleek handsome cat with a boisterous nature which earned him the name of Buster. In every way he was the opposite to his timid little mother. Not for him the privations of the secret outdoor life; he stalked the rich carpets of the Ainsworth home like a king and the ornate collar he always wore added something more to his presence.

On my visits I watched his development with delight but the occasion which stays in my mind was the following Christmas Day, a year from his arrival.

I was out on my rounds as usual. I can't remember when I haven't had to work on Christmas Day because the animals have never got round to recognizing it as a holiday; but with the passage of the years the vague resentment I used to feel has been replaced by philosophical acceptance. After all as I tramped around the hillside barns in the frosty air I was working up a better appetite for my turkey than all the millions lying in bed or slumped by the fire; and this was aided by the innumerable aperitifs I received from the hospitable farmers.

I was on my way home, bathed in a rosy glow. I had consumed several whiskies – the kind the inexpert Yorkshiremen pour as though it was ginger ale – and I had finished with a glass of old Mrs Earnshaw's rhubarb wine which had seared its way straight to my toenails. I heard the cry as I was passing Mrs Ainsworth's house.

'Merry Christmas, Mr Herriot!' She was letting a visitor out of the front door and she waved at me gaily. 'Come in and have a drink to warm you up.'

I didn't need warming up but I pulled in to the kerb without hesitation. In the house there was all the festive cheer of last year and the same glorious whiff of sage and onion which set my gastric juices surging. But there was not the sorrow; there was Buster.

He was darting up to each of the dogs in turn, ears pricked, eyes blazing with devilment, dabbing a paw at them then streaking away.

Mrs Ainsworth laughed. 'You know, he plagues the life out of them. Gives them no peace.'

She was right. To the bassets, Buster's arrival was rather like the intrusion of an irreverent outsider into an exclusive London club. For a long time they had led a life of measured grace; regular sedate walks with their mistress, superb food in ample quantities and long snoring sessions on the rugs and armchairs. Their days followed one upon another in unruffled calm. And then came Buster.

He was dancing up to the youngest dog again, sideways

this time, head on one side, goading him. When he started boxing with both paws it was too much even for the basset. He dropped his dignity and rolled over with the cat in a brief wrestling match.

'I want to show you something.' Mrs Ainsworth lifted a hard rubber ball from the sideboard and went out to the garden, followed by Buster. She threw the ball across the lawn and the cat bounded after it over the frosted grass, the muscles rippling under the black sheen of his coat. He seized the ball in his teeth, brought it back to his mistress, dropped it at her feet and waited expectantly. She threw it and he brought it back again.

I gasped incredulously. A feline retriever!

The bassets looked on disdainfully. Nothing would ever have induced them to chase a ball, but Buster did it again and again as though he would never tire of it.

Mrs Ainsworth turned to me. 'Have you ever seen anything like that?'

'No,' I replied. 'I never have. He is a most remarkable cat.'

She snatched Buster from his play and we went back into the house where she held him close to her face, laughing as the big cat purred and arched himself ecstatically against her cheek.

Looking at him, a picture of health and contentment, my mind went back to his mother. Was it too much to think that that dying little creature with the last of her strength had carried her kitten to the only haven of comfort and warmth she had ever known in the hope that it would be cared for there? Maybe it was.

But it seemed I wasn't the only one with such fancies. Mrs Ainsworth turned to me and though she was smiling her eyes were wistful.

'Debbie would be pleased,' she said.

I nodded. 'Yes, she would . . . It was just a year ago today she brought him, wasn't it?'

'That's right.' She hugged Buster to her again. 'The best Christmas present I ever had.'

# eleven

I stared in disbelief at the dial of the weighing machine. Nine stone seven pounds! I had lost two stones since joining the RAF. I was cowering in my usual corner in Boots' chemist's shop in Scarborough, where I had developed the habit of a weekly weigh-in to keep a morbid eye on my progressive emaciation. It was incredible and it wasn't all due to the tough training.

On our arrival in Scarborough we had a talk from our Flight Commander, Flt Lieut Barnes. He looked us over with a contemplative eye and said, 'You won't know yourselves when you leave here.' That man wasn't kidding.

We were never at rest. It was PT and Drill, PT and Drill, over and over. Hours of bending and stretching and twisting down on the prom in singlets and shorts while the wind whipped over us from the wintry sea. Hours of marching under the bellowings of our sergeant; quick march, slow march, about turn. We even marched to our navigation classes, bustling along at the RAF quick time, arms swinging shoulder high.

They marched us regularly to the top of Castle Hill where we fired off every conceivable type of weapon; twelve bores, ·22 rifles, revolvers, Browning machine guns. We even stabbed at dummies with bayonets. In between they had us swimming, playing football or rugby or running for miles along the beach and on the cliff tops towards Filey.

At first I was too busy to see any change in myself, but one morning after a few weeks our flight was coming to the end of a five-mile run. We dropped down from the Spa to a long stretch of empty beach and the sergeant shouted, 'Right, sprint to those rocks! Let's see who gets there first!'

We all took off on the last hundred yards' dash and I was mildly surprised to find that the first man past the post was myself – and I wasn't really out of breath. That was when the realization hit me. Mr Barnes had been right. I didn't know myself.

When I left Helen I was a cosseted young husband with a little double chin and the beginnings of a spare tyre, and now I was a lithe, tireless greyhound. I was certainly fit, but there was something wrong. I shouldn't have been as thin as this. Another factor was at work.

In Yorkshire when a man goes into a decline during his wife's pregnancy they giggle behind their hands and say he is 'carrying' the baby. I never laugh at these remarks because I am convinced I 'carried' my son.

I base this conclusion on a variety of symptoms. It would be an exaggeration to say I suffered from morning sickness, but my suspicions were certainly aroused when I began to feel a little queasy in the early part of the day. This was followed by a growing uneasiness as Helen's time drew near and a sensation, despite my physical condition, of being drained and miserable. With the onset in the later stages of unmistakable labour pains in my lower abdomen all doubts were resolved and I knew I had to do something about it.

I had to see Helen. After all, she was just over that hill which I could see from the top windows of the Grand. Maybe that wasn't strictly true, but at least I was in Yorkshire and a bus would take me to her in three hours. The snag was that there was no leave from ITW. They left us in no doubt about that. They said the discipline was as tough as a Guards regiment and the restrictions just as rigid. I would get compassionate leave when the baby was born, but I couldn't wait till then. The grim knowledge that any attempt to dodge off unofficially would be like a minor desertion and would be followed by serious consequences, even prison, didn't weigh with me.

As one of my comrades put it: 'One bloke tried it and finished up in the Glasshouse. It isn't worth it, mate.'

But it was no good. I am normally a law-abiding citizen but I had not a single scruple. I had to see Helen. A surreptitious study of the timetables revealed that there was a bus at 2 p.m. which got to Darrowby at five o'clock, and another leaving Darrowby at six which arrived in Scarborough at nine. Six hours travelling to have one hour with Helen. It was worth it.

At first I couldn't see a way of getting to the bus station at two o'clock in the afternoon because we were never free at that time, but my chance came quite unexpectedly. One Friday lunchtime we learned that there were no more classes that day but we were confined to the Grand till evening. Most of my friends collapsed thankfully on to their beds, but I slunk down the long flights of stone stairs and took up a position in the foyer where I could watch the front door.

There was a glass-fronted office on one side of the entrance where the SPs sat and kept an eye on all departures. There was only one on duty today and I waited till he turned and moved to the back of the room then I walked quietly past him and out into the square.

That part had been almost too easy, but I felt naked and exposed as I crossed the deserted space between the Grand and the hotels on the opposite side. It was better once I had rounded the corner and I set off at a brisk pace for the west. All I needed was a little bit of luck and as I pressed, dry-mouthed, along the empty street it seemed I had found it. The shock when I saw the two burly SPs strolling towards me was like a blow but was immediately followed by a strange calm.

They would ask me for the pass I didn't have, then they would want to know what I was doing there. It wouldn't be much good telling them I had just popped out for a breath of air – this street led to both the bus and railway stations and it wouldn't need a genius to rumble my little game. Anyway, there was no cover here, no escape, and I wondered idly if there had ever been a veterinary surgeon in the Glasshouse. Maybe I was about to set up some kind of a record.

Then behind me I heard the rhythmic tramp of marching feet and the shrill ''eft 'ight, 'eft 'ight,' that usually went with it. I turned and saw a long blue column approaching with a corporal in charge. As they swung past me I looked again at the SPs and my hear gave a thud. They were laughing into each other's faces at some private joke; they hadn't seen me. Without thinking I tagged on to the end of the marching men and within a few seconds was past the SPs unnoticed.

With my mind working with the speed of desperation, it seemed I would be safest where I was till I could break away in the direction of the bus station. For a while I had a glorious feeling of anonymity, then the corporal, still shouting, glanced back. He faced to the front again then turned back more slowly for another look. He appeared to find something interesting because he shortened his stride till he was marching opposite me..

As he looked me up and down I examined him in turn from the corner of my eye. He was a shrivelled, runtish creature with fierce little eyes glinting from a pallid, skull-like face. It was some time before he spoke.

'Who the — hell are you?' he enquired conversationally. It was the number one awkward question but I discerned the faintest gleam of hope; he had spoken in the unmistakable harsh, glottal accent of my home town.

'Herriot, corporal. Two flight, four squadron,' I replied in my broadest Glasgow.

'Two flight, four . . . ! This is one flight, three squadron. What the — hell are ye daein' here?'

Arms swinging high, staring rigidly ahead, I took a deep breath. Concealment was futile now.

'Tryin' to get tae see ma wife, corp. She's havin' a baby soon.'

I glanced quickly at him. His was not the kind of face to reveal weakness by showing surprise but his eyes widened fractionally. 'Get tae see yer wife? Are ye — daft or whit?'

'It's no' far, corp. She lives in Darrowby. Three hours in the bus. Ah wid be back tonight.'

'Back tonight! Ye want yer — heid examinin'!'

'I've got tae go!'

'Eyes front!' he screamed suddenly at the men before us. ''eft 'ight, 'eft 'ight!' Then he turned and studied me as though I were an unbelievable phenomenon. He was interesting to me, too, as a typical product of the bad times in Glasgow between the wars. Stunted, undernourished, but as tough and belligerent as a ferret.

'D'ye no' ken,' he said at length, 'that ye get — leave when yer wife has the wean?'

'Aye, but ah canna' wait that long. Gimme a break, corp.'

'Give ye a — break! D'ye want tae get me — shot?'

'No, corp, just want tae get to the bus station.'

'Jesus! Is that a'?' He gave me a final incredulous look before quickening his steps to the head of the column. When he returned he surveyed me again.

'Whit part o' Glesca are ye frae?'

'Scotstounhill,' I replied. 'How about you?'

'Govan.'

I turned my head slightly towards him. 'Rangers supporter, eh?'

He did not change expression, but an eyebrow flickered and I knew I had him.

'Whit a team!' I murmured reverently. 'Many's the time I've stood on the terraces at Ibrox.'

He said nothing and I began to recite the names of the great Rangers team of the thirties. 'Dawson, Gray, McDonald, Meiklejohn, Simpson, Brown.' His eyes took on a dreamy expression and by the time I had intoned 'Archibald, Marshall, English, McPhail and Morton,' there was something near to a wistful smile on his lips.

Then he appeared to shake himself back to normality.

''Eft 'ight, 'eft 'ight!' he bawled. 'C'mon, c'mon, pick it up!' Then he muttered to me from the corner of his mouth. 'There's the — bus station. When we march past it run like — !'

He took off again, shouting to the head of the flight, I saw the buses and the windows of the waiting room on my left and dived across the road and through the door. I snatched off my cap and sat trembling among a group of elderly farmers and their wives. Through the glass I could see the long lines of blue moving away down the street and I could still hear the shouts of the corporal.

But he didn't turn round and I saw only his receding back, the narrow shoulders squared, the bent legs stepping it out in time with his men. I never saw him again but to this day I wish I could take him to Ibrox and watch the Rangers with him and maybe buy him a half and half pint at one of the Govan pubs. It wouldn't have mattered if he had turned out to be a Celtic supporter at that decisive moment because I had the Celtic team on my tongue all ready to trot out, starting with Kennaway, Cook, McGonigle. It is not the only time my profound knowledge of football has stood me in good stead.

Sitting on the bus, still with my cap on my lap to avoid attracting attention, it struck me that the whole world changed within a mile or two as we left the town. Back there the war was everywhere, filling people's minds and eyes and thoughts; the teeming thousands of uniformed men, the RAF and army vehicles, the almost palpable atmosphere of anticipation and suspense. And suddenly it all just stopped.

It vanished as the wide sweep of grey-blue sea fell beneath the rising ground behind the town, and as the bus trundled westward I looked out on a landscape of untroubled peace. The long moist furrows of the new-turned soil glittered under the pale February sun, contrasting with the gold stubble fields and the grassy pastures where sheep clustered around their feeding troughs. There was no wind and the smoke rose straight from the farm chimneys and the bare branches of the roadside trees were still as they stretched across the cold sky.

There were many things that pulled at me. A man in breeches and leggings carrying on his shoulder a bale of hay to some outlying cattle; a group of farm men burning hedge clippings and the fragrance of the wood smoke finding its way into the bus. The pull was stronger as the hours passed and the beginnings of my own familiar countryside began to appear beyond the windows. Maybe it was a good thing I didn't see Darrowby; Helen's home was near the bus route and I dropped off well short of the town.

She was alone in the house and she turned her head as I walked into the kitchen. The delight on her face was mixed with astonishment; in fact I know we were both astonished, she because I was so skinny and I because she was so fat. Helen, with the baby only two weeks away, was very large indeed, but not too large for me to get my arms around her, and we stood there in the middle of the flagged floor clasped together for a long time with neither of us saying much.

She cooked me egg and chips and sat by me while I ate. We carried on a rather halting conversation and it came to me with a bump that my mind had been forced on to different tracks since I had left her. In those few months my brain had become saturated with the things of my new life – even my mouth was full of RAF slang and jargon. In our bed-sitter we used to talk about my cases, the funny things that happened on my rounds, but now, I thought helplessly, there wasn't much point in telling her that AC2 Phillips was on jankers again, that vector triangles were the very devil, that Don McGregor thought he had discovered the secret of Sergeant Hynd's phenomenally shiny boots.

But it really didn't matter. My worries melted as I looked at her. I had been wondering if she was well and there she was, bouncing with energy, shining-eyed, rosy-cheeked and beautiful. There was only one jarring note and it was a strange one. Helen was wearing a 'maternity dress' which expanded with the passage of time by means of an opening down one side. Anyway, I hated it. It was blue with a high red collar and I thought it cheap-looking and ugly. I was aware that austerity had taken over in England and that a lot of things were shoddy, but I desperately wished my wife had something better to wear. In all my life there have been very few occasions when I badly wanted more money and that was one of them, because on my wage of three shillings a day as an AC2 I was unable to drape her with expensive clothes.

The hour winged past and it seemed no time at all before I was back on the top road waiting in the gathering darkness for the Scarborough bus. The journey back was a bit dreary as the blacked-out vehicle bumped and rattled its way through the darkened villages and over the long stretches of anonymous countryside. It was cold, too, but I sat there happily with the memory of Helen wrapped around me like a warm quilt.

The whole day had been a triumph. I had got away by a lucky stroke and there would be no problem getting back into the Grand because one of my pals would be on sentry duty and it would be a case of 'pass friend'. Closing my eyes in the gloom I could still feel Helen in my arms and I smiled to myself at the memory of her bounding healthiness. She looked marvellous, the egg and chips tasted wonderful, everything was great.

Except that one discord which jangled still. Oh, how I hated that dress!


# twelve

'Hey you! Where the 'ell d'you think you're goin'?'

Coming from the RAF Special Police it was a typical mode of address and the man who barked it out wore the usual truculent expression.

'Extra navigation class, corporal,' I replied.

'Lemme see your pass!'

He snatched it from my hand, read it and returned it without looking at me. I slunk out into the street feeling like a prisoner on parole.

Not all the SPs were like that but I found most of them lacking in charm. And it brought home to me with a rush something which had been slowly dawning on me ever since I joined the Air Force; that I had been spoiled for quite a long time now. Spoiled by the fact that I had always been treated with respect because I was a veterinary surgeon, a member of an honourable profession. And I had taken it entirely for granted.

Now I was an AC2, the lowest form of life in the RAF, and the 'Hey you!' was a reflection of my status. The Yorkshire farmers don't rush out and kiss you, but their careful friendliness and politeness is something which I have valued even more since my service days. Because that was when I stopped taking it for granted.

Mind you, you have to put up with a certain amount of

cheek in most jobs, and veterinary practice is no exception. Even now I can recall the glowering face of Ralph Beamish the racehorse trainer, as he watched me getting out of my car.

'Where's Mr Farnon?' he grunted.

My toes curled. I had heard that often enough, especially among the horse fraternity around Darrowby.

'I'm sorry, Mr Beamish, but he'll be away all day and I thought I'd better come along rather than leave it till tomorrow.'

He made no attempt to hide his disgust. He blew out his fat, purpled cheeks, dug his hands deep in his breeches pockets and looked at the sky with a martyred air.

'Well come on, then.' He turned and stumped away on his short, thick legs towards one of the boxes which bordered the yard. I sighed inwardly as I followed him. Being an unhorsey vet in Yorkshire was a penance at times, especially in a racing stable like this which was an equine shrine. Siegfried, apart altogether from his intuitive skill, was able to talk the horse language. He could discuss effortlessly and at length the breeding and points of his patients; he rode, he hunted, he even looked the part with his long aristocratic face, clipped moustache and lean frame.

The trainers loved him and some, like Beamish, took it as a mortal insult when he failed to come in person to minister to their valuable charges.

He called to one of the lads who opened a box door.

'He's in there,' he muttered. 'Came in lame from exercise this morning.'

The lad led out a bay gelding and there was no need to trot the animal to diagnose the affected leg; he nodded down on his near fore in an unmistakable way.

'I think he's lame in the shoulder,' Beamish said.

I went round the other side of the horse and picked up the off fore. I cleaned out the frog and sole with a hoof knife; there was no sign of bruising and no sensitivity when I tapped the handle of the knife against the horn.

I felt my way over the coronet to the fetlock and after

some palpation I located a spot near the distal end of the metacarpus which was painful on pressure.

I looked up from my crouching position. 'This seems to be the trouble, Mr Beamish. I think he must have struck into himself with his hind foot just there.'

'Where?' The trainer leaned over me and peered down at the leg. 'I can't see anything.'

'No, the skin isn't broken, but he flinches if you press here.'

Beamish prodded the place with a stubby forefinger.

'Well, he does,' he grunted. 'But he'd flinch anywhere if you squeeze him like you're doing.'

My hackles began to rise at his tone but I kept my voice calm. 'I'm sure that's what it is. I should apply a hot anti-phlogistine poultice just above the fetlock and alternate with a cold hose on it twice a day.'

'Well, I'm just as sure you're wrong. It's not down there at all. The way that horse carries his leg he's hurt his shoulder.' He gestured to the lad. 'Harry, see that he gets some heat on that shoulder right away.'

If the man had struck me I couldn't have felt worse. I opened my mouth to argue but he was walking away.

'There's another horse I want you to look at,' he said. He led the way into a nearby box and pointed to a big brown animal with obvious signs of blistering on the tendons of a fore limb.

'Mr Farnon put a red blister on that leg six months ago. He's been resting in here ever since. He's going sound now – d'you think he's ready to go out?'

I went over and ran my fingers over the length of the flexor tendons, feeling for signs of thickening. There was none. Then I lifted the foot and as I explored further I found a tender area in the superficial flexor.

I straightened up. 'He's still a bit sore,' I said. 'I think it would be safer to keep him in for a bit longer.'

'Can't agree with you,' Beamish snapped. He turned to the lad. 'Turn him out, Harry.'

I stared at him. Was this a deliberate campaign to make me

feel small? Was he trying to rub in the fact that he didn't think much of me? Anyway, he was beginning to get under my skin and I hoped my burning face wasn't too obvious.

'One thing more,' Beamish said. 'There's a horse through here been coughing. Have a look at him before you go.'

We went through a narrow passage into a smaller yard and Harry entered a box and got hold of a horse's head collar. I followed him, fishing out my thermometer.

As I approached the animal's rear end he laid back his ears, whickered and began to caper around. I hesitated, then nodded to the lad.

'Lift his fore leg while I take his temperature, will you?' I said.

The lad bent down and seized the foot but Beamish broke in. 'Don't bother, Harry, there's no need for that. He's quiet as a sheep.'

I paused for a moment. I felt I was right but my stock was low on this establishment. I shrugged, lifted the tail and pushed the thermometer into the rectum.

The two hind feet hit me almost simultaneously but as I sailed backwards through the door I remember thinking quite clearly that the one on the chest had made contact fractionally before the one on the abdomen. But my thoughts were rapidly clouded by the fact that the lower hoof had landed full on my solar plexus.

Stretched on the concrete of the yard I gasped and groaned in a frantic search for breath. There was a moment when I was convinced I was going to die but at last a long wailing respiration came to my aid and I struggled painfully into a sitting position. Through the open door I could see Harry hanging on to the horse's head and staring at me with frightened eyes. Mr Beamish, on the other hand, showed no interest in my plight; he was anxiously examining the horse's hind feet one after the other. Obviously he was worried lest they may have sustained some damage by coming into contact with my nasty hard ribs.

Slowly I got up and drew some long breaths. I was shaken but not really hurt. And I suppose it was instinct that had made me hang on to my thermometer; the delicate tube was still in my hand.

My only emotion as I went back into the box was cold rage.

'Lift that bloody foot like I told you!' I shouted at the unfortunate Harry.

'Right, sir! Sorry, sir!' He bent, lifted the foot and held it cupped firmly in his hands.

I turned to Beamish to see if he had any observation to make, but the trainer was silent, gazing at the big animal expressionlessly.

This time I took the temperature without incident. It was 101°F. I moved to the head and opened the nostril with finger and thumb, revealing a slight muco-purulent discharge. Sub-maxillary and post-pharyngeal glands were normal.

'He's got a bit of a cold,' I said. 'I'll give him an injection and leave you some sulphonamide – that's what Mr Farnon uses in these cases.' If my final sentence reassured him in any way he gave no sign, watching dead-faced as I injected 10 cc of Prontosil.

Before I left I took a half-pound packet of sulphonamide from the car boot. 'Give him three ounces of this immediately in a pint of water, then follow it with one and a half ounces night and morning and let us know if he isn't a lot better in two days.'

Mr Beamish received the medicine unsmilingly and as I opened the car door I felt a gush of relief that the uncomfortable visit was at an end. It seemed to have lasted a long time and there had been no glory for me in it. I was starting the engine when one of the little apprentices panted up to the trainer.

'It's Almira, sir. I think she's chokin'!'

'Choking!' Beamish stared at the boy then whipped round to me. 'Almira's the best filly I have. You'd better come!'

It wasn't over yet, then. With a feeling of doom I hurried after the squat figure back into the yard where another lad stood by the side of a beautiful chestnut filly. And as I saw her a cold hand closed around my heart. I had been dealing with trivia but this was different.

She stood immobile, staring ahead with a peculiar intensity. The rise and fall of her ribs was accompanied by a rasping, bubbling wheeze and at each intake her nostrils flared wildly. I had never seen a horse breathe like this. And there were other things; saliva drooled from her lips and every few seconds she gave a retching cough.

I turned to the apprentice. 'When did this start?'

'Not long ago, sir. I saw her an hour since and she were as right as a bobbin.'

'Are you sure?'

'Aye, I was givin' 'er some hay. There was nowt ailin' her then.'

'What the devil's wrong with her?' Beamish exclaimed.

Well, it was a good question and I didn't have a clue to the answer. As I walked bemusedly round the animal, taking in the trembling limbs and terrified eyes, a jumble of thoughts crowded my brain. I had seen 'choking' horses – the dry choke when the gullet becomes impacted with food – but they didn't look like this. I felt my way along the course of the oesophagus and it was perfectly clear. And anyway the respiration was quite different. This filly looked as though she had some obstruction in her airflow. But what . . . ? And how . . . ? Could there be a foreign body in there? Just possible, but that was something else I had never seen.

'Well, damn it, I'm asking you! What is it? What d'you make of her?' Mr Beamish was becoming impatient and I couldn't blame him.

I was aware that I was slightly breathless. 'Just a moment while I listen to her lungs.'

'Just a moment!' the trainer burst out. 'Good God, man, we haven't got many moments! This horse could die!'

He didn't have to tell me. I had seen that ominous trembling of the limbs before and now the filly was beginning to sway a little. Time was running out.

Dry mouthed, I auscultated the chest. I knew there was nothing wrong with her lungs – the trouble seemed to be in the throat area – but it gave me a little more time to think. Even with the stethoscope in my ears I could still hear Beamish's voice.

'It would have to be this one! Sir Eric Horrocks gave five thousand pounds for her last year. She's the most valuable animal in my stables. Why did this have to happen?'

Groping my way over the ribs, my heart thudding, I heartily agreed with him. Why in heaven's name did I have to walk into this nightmare? And with a man like Beamish who had no faith in me.

He stepped forward and clutched my arm. 'Are you sure Mr Farnon isn't available?'

'I'm sorry,' I replied huskily. 'He's over thirty miles away.'

The trainer seemed to shrivel within himself. 'That's it then. We're finished. She's dying.'

And he was right. The filly had begun to reel about, the breathing louder and more stertorous than ever, and I had difficulty in keeping the stethoscope on her chest wall. It was when I was resting my hand on her flank to steady her that I noticed the little swelling under the skin. It was a circular plaque, like a penny pushed under the tissue. I glanced sharply at it. Yes, it was clearly visible. And there was another one higher up on the back . . . and another and another. My heart gave a quick double thump . . . so that was it.

'What am I going to tell Sir Eric?' the trainer groaned. 'That his filly is dead and the vet didn't know what was wrong with her?' He glared desperately around him as though in the faint hope that Siegfried might magically appear from nowhere.

I called over my shoulder as I trotted towards the car. 'I never said I didn't know. I do know. She's got urticaria.'

He came shambling after me. 'Urti . . . what the blazes is that?'

'Nettlerash,' I replied, fumbling among my bottles for the adrenalin.

'Nettlerash!' His eyes widened. 'But that couldn't cause all this!'

I drew 5 cc of the adrenalin into the syringe and started back. 'It's nothing to do with nettles. It's an allergic condition, usually pretty harmless, but in a very few cases it causes oedema of the larynx – that's what we've got here.'

It was difficult to raise the vein as the filly staggered around, but she came to rest for a few seconds and I dug my thumb into the jugular furrow. As the big vessel came up tense and turgid I thrust in the needle and injected the adrenalin. Then I stepped back and stood by the trainer's side.

Neither of us said anything. The spectacle of the toiling animal and the harrowing sound of the breathing absorbed us utterly.

The grim knowledge that she was on the verge of suffocation appalled me and when she stumbled and almost fell the hand in my pocket gripped more tightly on the scalpel which I had taken from my car along with the adrenalin. I knew only too well that tracheotomy was indicated here but I didn't have a tube with me. If the filly did go off her legs I should have to start cutting into her windpipe, but I put the thought away from me. For the moment I had to depend on the adrenalin.

Beamish stretched out a hand in a helpless gesture. 'It's hopeless, isn't it?' he whispered.

I shrugged. 'There's a small chance. If the injection can reduce the fluid in the larynx in time . . . we'll just have to wait.'

He nodded and I could read more than one emotion in his face; not just the dread of breaking the news to the famous owner but the distress of a horse-lover as he witnessed the plight of the beautiful animal.

At first I thought it was imagination, but it seemed that the breathing was becoming less stertorous. Then as I hovered in an agony of uncertainty I noticed that the salivation was diminishing; she was able to swallow.

From that moment events moved with unbelievable rapidity. The symptoms of allergies appear with dramatic suddenness but mercifully they often disappear as quickly following treatment. Within fifteen minutes the filly looked almost normal. There was still a slight wheeze in her respirations but she was looking around her, quite free from distress.

Beamish, who had been watching like a man in a daze, pulled a handful of hay from a bale and held it out to her. She snatched it eagerly from his hand and began to eat with great relish.

'I can't believe it,' the trainer muttered almost to himself. 'I've never seen anything work as fast as that injection.'

I felt as though I was riding on a pink cloud with all the tension and misery flowing from me in a joyful torrent. Thank God there were moments like this among the traumas of veterinary work; the sudden transition from despair to triumph, from shame to pride.

I almost floated to the car and as I settled in my seat Beamish put his face to the open window.

'Mr Herriot . . .' He was not a man to whom gracious speech came easily and his cheeks, roughened and weathered by years of riding on the open moor, twitched as he sought for words. 'Mr Herriot, I've been thinking . . . you don't have to be a horsey man to cure horses, do you?'

There was something like an appeal in his eyes as we gazed at each other. I laughed suddenly and his expression relaxed.

'That's right,' I said, and drove away.

# thirteen

Do dogs have a sense of humour?

I felt I needed all mine as I stood on guard outside the Grand. It was after midnight, with a biting wind swirling across the empty square, and I was so cold and bored that it was a relief even to slap the butt of my rifle in salute as a solitary officer went by.

Wryly I wondered how, after my romantic ideas of training to be a pilot, I came to be defending the Grand Hotel at Scarborough against all comers. No doubt there was something comic in the situation and I suppose that was what set my mind wandering in the direction of Farmer Bailes' dog, Shep.

Mr Bailes' little place was situated about half way along Highburn village and to get into the farmyard you had to walk twenty yards or so between five-foot walls. On the left was the neighbouring house, on the right the front garden of the farm. In this garden Shep lurked for most of the day.

He was a huge dog, much larger than the average collie. In fact I am convinced he was part Alsatian because though he had a luxuriant black and white coat there was something significant in the massive limbs and in the noble brown-shaded head with its upstanding ears. He was quite different from the stringy little animals I saw on my daily round.

As I walked between the walls my mind was already in the byre, just visible at the far end of the yard. Because one of the Bailes cows, Rose by name, had the kind of obscure digestive ailment which interferes with veterinary surgeons' sleep. They are so difficult to diagnose. This animal had begun to grunt and go off her milk two days ago and when I had seen her yesterday I had flitted from one possibility to the other. Could be a wire. But the fourth stomach was contracting well and there were plenty of rumenal sounds. Also she was eating a little hay in a half-hearted way.

Could it be impaction . . . ? Or a partial torsion of the gut . . . ? There was abdominal pain without a doubt and that nagging temperature of $102.5°$ – that was damn like a wire. Of course I could settle the whole thing by opening the cow up, but Mr Bailes was an old-fashioned type and didn't like the idea of my diving into his animal unless I was certain of my diagnosis. And I wasn't – there was no getting away from that.

Anyway, I had built her up at the front end so that she was standing with her fore feet on a half door and had given her a strong oily purgative. 'Keep the bowels open and trust in

God,' an elderly colleague had once told me. There was a lot in that.

I was half way down the alley between the walls with the hope bright before me that my patient would be improved when from nowhere an appalling explosion of sound blasted into my right ear. It was Shep again.

The wall was just the right height for the dog to make a leap and bark into the ear of the passers by. It was a favourite gambit of his and I had been caught before; but never so successfully as now. My attention had been so far away and the dog had timed his jump to a split second so that his bark came at the highest point, his teeth only inches from my face. And his voice befitted his size, a great bull bellow surging from the depths of his powerful chest and booming from his gaping jaws.

I rose several inches into the air and when I descended, heart thumping, head singing, I glared over the wall. But as usual all I saw was the hairy form bounding away out of sight round the corner of the house.

That was what puzzled me. Why did he do it? Was he a savage creature with evil designs on me or was it his idea of a joke? I never got near enough to him to find out.

I wasn't in the best of shape to receive bad news and that was what awaited me in the byre. I had only to look at the farmer's face to know that the cow was worse.

'Ah reckon she's got a stoppage,' Mr Bailes muttered gloomily.

I gritted my teeth. The entire spectrum of abdominal disorders were lumped as 'stoppages' by the older race of farmers. 'The oil hasn't worked, then?'

'Nay, she's nobbut passin' little hard bits. It's a proper stoppage, ah tell you.'

'Right, Mr Bailes,' I said with a twisted smile. 'We'll have to try something stronger.' I brought in from my car the gastric lavage outfit I loved so well and which has so sadly disappeared from my life. The long rubber stomach tube, the wooden gag with its leather straps to buckle behind the horns. As I pumped in the two gallons of warm water rich in formalin and sodium chloride I felt like Napoleon sending in the Old Guard at Waterloo. If this didn't work nothing would.

And yet I didn't feel my usual confidence. There was something different here. But I had to try. I had to do something to start this cow's insides functioning because I did not like the look of her today. The soft grunt was still there and her eyes had begun to retreat into her head – the worst sign of all in bovines. And she had stopped eating altogether.

Next morning I was driving down the single village street when I saw Mrs Bailes coming out of the shop. I drew up and pushed my head out of the window.

'How's Rose this morning, Mrs Bailes?'

She rested her basket on the ground and looked down at me gravely. 'Oh, she's bad, Mr Herriot. Me husband thinks she's goin' down fast. If you want to find him you'll have to go across the field there. He's mendin' the door in that little barn.'

A sudden misery enveloped me as I drove over to the gate leading into the field. I left the car in the road and lifted the latch.

'Damn! Damn! Damn!' I muttered as I trailed across the green. I had a nasty feeling that a little tragedy was building up here. If this animal died it would be a sickening blow to a small farmer with ten cows and a few pigs. I should be able to do something about it and it was a depressing thought that I was getting nowhere.

And yet, despite it all, I felt peace stealing into my soul. It was a large field and I could see the barn at the far end as I walked with the tall grass brushing my knees. It was a meadow ready for cutting and suddenly I realized that it was high summer, the sun was hot and that every step brought the fragrance of clover and warm grass rising about me into the crystal freshness of the air. Somewhere nearby a field of broad beans was in full flower and as the exotic scent drifted across I found myself inhaling with half-closed eyes as though straining to discern the ingredients of the glorious melange.

And then there was the silence; it was the most soothing thing of all. That and the feeling of being alone. I looked drowsily around at the empty green miles sleeping under the sunshine. Nothing stirred, there was no sound.

Then without warning the ground at my feet erupted in an incredible blast of noise. For a dreadful moment the blue sky was obscured by an enormous hairy form and a red mouth went 'WAAAHH!' in my face. Almost screaming, I staggered back and as I glared wildly I saw Shep disappearing at top speed towards the gate. Concealed in the deep herbage right in the middle of the field he had waited till he saw the whites of my eyes before making his assault.

Whether he had been there by accident or whether he had spotted me arriving and slunk into position I shall never know, but from his point of view the result must have been eminently satisfactory because it was certainly the worst fright I have ever had. I live a life which is well larded with scares and alarms, but this great dog rising bellowing from that empty landscape was something on its own. I have heard of cases where sudden terror and stress has caused involuntary evacuation of the bowels and I know without question that this was the occasion when I came nearest to suffering that unhappy fate.

I was still trembling when I reached the barn and hardly said a word as Mr Bailes led me back across the road to the farm.

And it was like rubbing it in when I saw my patient. The flesh had melted from her and she stared at the wall apathetically from sunken eyes. The doom-laden grunt was louder.

'She must have a wire!' I muttered. 'Let her loose for a minute, will you?'

Mr Bailes undid the chain and Rose walked along the byre. At the end she turned and almost trotted back to her stall, jumping quite freely over the gutter. My Bible in those days was Udall's *Practice of Veterinary Medicine* and the great man stated therein that if a cow moved freely she was unlikely to have a foreign body in her reticulum. I pinched her withers and she didn't complain . . . it had to be something else.

'It's worst stoppage ah've seen for a bit,' said Mr Bailes. 'Ah gave her a dose of some right powerful stuff this mornin' but it's done no good.'

I passed a weary hand over my brow. 'What was that, Mr Bailes?' It was always a bad sign when the client started using his own medicine.

The farmer reached to the cluttered windowsill and handed me a bottle. 'Doctor Hornibrook's Stomach Elixir. A sovereign remedy for all diseases of cattle.' The Doctor, in top hat and frock coat, looked confidently out at me from the label as I pulled out the cork and took a sniff. I blinked and staggered back with watering eyes. It smelt like pure ammonia but I was in no position to be superior about it.

'That dang grunt!' The farmer hunched his shoulders. 'What's cause of it?'

It was no good my saying it sounded like a circumscribed area of peritonitis because I didn't know what was behind it.

I decided to have one last go with the lavage. It was still the strongest weapon in my armoury but this time I added two pounds of black treacle to the mixture. Nearly every farmer had a barrel of the stuff in his cow house in those days and I had only to go into the corner and turn the tap.

I often mourn the passing of the treacle barrel because molasses was a good medicine for cattle, but I had no great hopes this time. The clinical instinct I was beginning to develop told me that something inside this animal was fundamentally awry.

It was not till the following afternoon that I drove into Highburn. I left the car outside the farm and was about to walk between the walls when I paused and stared at a cow in the field on the other side of the road. It was a pasture next to the hayfield of yesterday and that cow was Rose. There could be no mistake – she was a fine deep red with a distinctive white mark like a football on her left flank.

I opened the gate and within seconds my cares dropped from me. She was wonderfully, miraculously improved, in fact she looked like a normal animal. I walked up to her and scratched the root of her tail. She was a docile creature and merely looked round at me as she cropped the grass; and her eyes were no longer sunken but bright and full.

She seemed to take a fancy to a green patch further into the field and began to amble slowly towards it. I followed, entranced, as she moved along, shaking her head impatiently against the flies, eager for more of the delicious herbage. The grunt had disappeared and her udder hung heavy and turgid between her legs. The difference since yesterday was incredible.

As the wave of relief flooded through me I saw Mr Bailes climbing over the wall from the next field. He would still be mending that barn door.

As he approached I felt apang of commiseration. I had to guard against any display of triumph. He must be feeling just a bit silly at the moment after showing his lack of faith in me yesterday with his home remedies and his general attitude. But after all the poor chap had been worried – I couldn't blame him. No, it wouldn't do to preen myself unduly.

'Ah, good morning to you, Mr Bailes,' I said expansively. 'Rose looks fine today, doesn't she?'

The farmer took off his cap and wiped his brow. 'Aye, she's a different cow, all right.'

'I don't think she needs any more treatment,' I said. I hesitated. Perhaps one little dig would do no harm. 'But it's a good thing I gave her that extra lavage yesterday.'

'Yon pumpin' job?' Mr Bailes raised his eyebrows. 'Oh that had nowt to do with it.'

'What . . . what do you mean? It cured her, surely.'

'Nay, lad, nay, Jim Oakley cured her.'

'Jim . . . what on earth . . . ?'

'Aye, Jim was round 'ere last night. He often comes in of an evenin' and he took one look at the cow and told me what to do. Ah'll tell you she was like dyin' – that pumpin' job hadn't done no good at all. He told me to give her a bloody good gallop round t'field.'

'What!'

'Aye, that's what he said. He'd seen 'em like that afore and a good gallop put 'em right. So we got Rose out here and did as he said and by gaw it did the trick. She looked better right away.'

I drew myself up. 'And who,' I asked frigidly, 'is Jim Oakley?'

'He's t'postman, of course.'

'The postman!'

'Aye, but he used to keep a few beasts years ago. He's a very clever man wi' stock, is Jim.'

'No doubt, but I assure you, Mr Bailes...'

The farmer raised a hand. 'Say no more, lad. Jim put 'er right and there's no denyin' it. I wish you'd seen 'im chasin' 'er round. He's as awd as me, but by gaw 'e did go. He can run like'ell, can Jim.' He chuckled reminiscently.

I had had about enough. During the farmer's eulogy I had been distractedly scratching the cow's tail and had soiled my hand in the process. Mustering the remains of my dignity I nodded to Mr Bailes.

'Well, I must be on my way. Do you mind if I go into the house to wash my hands?'

'You go right in,' he replied. 'T'missus will get you some hot water.'

Walking back down the field the cruel injustice of the thing bore down on me increasingly. I wandered as in a dream through the gate and across the road. Before entering the alley between the walls I glanced into the garden. It was empty. Shuffling beside the rough stones I sank deeper into my misery. There was no doubt I had emerged from that episode as a complete Charlie. No matter where I looked I couldn't see a gleam of light.

It seemed to take a long time to reach the end of the wall and I was about to turn right towards the door of the farm kitchen when from my left I heard the sudden rattle of a chain then a roaring creature launched itself at me, bayed once, mightily, into my face and was gone.

This time I thought my heart would stop. With my defences at their lowest I was in no state to withstand Shep. I had quite forgotten that Mrs Bailes occasionally tethered him in the kennel at the entrance to discourage unwelcome visitors, and as I half lay against the wall, the blood thundering in my ears, I looked dully at the long coil of chain on the cobbles.

I have no time for people who lose their temper with animals but something snapped in my mind then. All my frustration burst from me in a torrent of incoherent shouts and I grabbed the chain and began to pull on it frenziedly. That dog which had tortured me was there in that kennel. For once I knew where to get at him and this time I was going to have the matter out with him. The kennel would be about ten feet away and at first I saw nothing. There was only the dead weight on the end of the chain. Then as I hauled inexorably a nose appeared, then a head, then all of the big animal hanging limply by his collar. He showed no desire to get up and greet me but I was merciless and dragged him inch by inch over the cobbles till he was lying at my feet.

Beside myself with rage, I crouched, shook my fist under his nose and yelled at him from a few inches' range.

'You big bugger! If you do that to me again I'll knock your bloody head off! Do you hear me, I'll knock your bloody head clean off!'

Shep rolled frightened eyes at me and his tail flickered apologetically between his legs. When I continued to scream at him he bared his upper teeth in an ingratiating grin and finally rolled on his back where he lay inert with half-closed eyes.

So now I knew. He was a softie. All his ferocious attacks were just a game. I began to calm down but for all that I wanted him to get the message.

'Right, mate,' I said in a menacing whisper. 'Remember what I've said!' I let go the chain and gave a final shout. 'Now get back in there!'

Shep, almost on his knees, tail tucked well in, shot back into his kennel and I turned toward the farmhouse to wash my hands.

The memory of my discomfiture fermented in the back of

my mind for some time. I had no doubt then that I had been unfairly judged, but I am older and wiser now and in retrospect I think I was wrong.

The symptoms displayed by Mr Bailes' cow were typical of displacement of the abomasum (when the fourth stomach slips round from the right to the left side) and it was a condition that was just not recognized in those early days.

At the present time we correct the condition by surgery – pushing the displaced organ back to the right side and tacking it there with sutures. But sometimes a similar result can be obtained by casting the cow and rolling her over, so why not by making her run . . . ? I freely admit that I have many times adopted Jim Oakley's precept of a 'bloody good gallop', often with spectacular results. To this day I frequently learn things from farmers, but that was one time when I learned from a postman.

I was surprised when, about a month later, I received another call to one of Mr Bailes' cows. I felt that after my performance with Rose he would have called on the services of Jim Oakley for any further trouble. But no, his voice on the phone was as polite and friendly as ever, with not a hint that he had lost faith. It was strange. . . .

Leaving my car outside the farm I looked warily into the front garden before venturing between the walls. A faint tinkle of metal told me that Shep was lurking there in his kennel and I slowed my steps; I wasn't going to be caught again. At the end of the alley I paused, waiting, but all I saw was the end of a nose which quietly withdrew as I stood there. So my outburst had got through to the big dog – he knew I wasn't going to stand any more nonsense from him.

And yet, as I drove away after the visit I didn't feel good about it. A victory over an animal is a hollow one and I had the uncomfortable feeling that I had deprived him of his chief pleasure. After all, every creature is entitled to some form of recreation and though Shep's hobby could result in the occasional heart failure it was, after all, his thing and part of him. The thought that I had crushed something out of his life was a disquieting one. I wasn't proud.

So that when, later that summer, I was driving through Highburn I paused in anticipation outside the Bailes farm. The village street, white and dusty, slumbered under the afternoon sun. In the blanketing silence nothing moved – except for one small man strolling towards the opening between the walls. He was fat and very dark – one of the tinkers from a camp outside the village – and he carried an armful of pots and pans.

From my vantage point I could see through the railings into the front garden where Shep was slinking noiselessly into position beneath the stones. Fascinated, I watched as the man turned unhurriedly into the opening and the dog followed the course of the disembodied head along the top of the wall.

As I expected it all happened half way along. The perfectly timed leap, the momentary pause at the summit then the tremendous 'WOOF!' into the unsuspecting ear.

It had its usual effect. I had a brief view of flailing arms and flying pans followed by a prolonged metallic clatter, then the little man reappeared like a projectile, turned right and sped away from me up the street. Considering his almost round physique he showed an astonishing turn of speed, his little legs pistoning, and he did not pause till he disappeared into the shop at the far end of the village.

I don't know why he went in there because he wouldn't find any stronger restorative than ginger pop.

Shep, apparently well satisfied, wandered back over the grass and collapsed in a cool patch where an apple tree threw its shade over the grass; head on paws he waited in comfort for his next victim.

I smiled to myself as I let in the clutch and moved off. I would stop at the shop and tell the little man that he could collect his pans without the slightest fear of being torn limb from limb, but my overriding emotion was one of relief that I had not cut the sparkle out of the big dog's life.

Shep was still having his fun.

# fourteen

I suppose once you embark on a life of crime it gets easier all the time. Making a start is the only hard bit.

At any rate, that is how it seemed to me as I sat in the bus, playing hookey again. There had been absolutely no trouble about dodging out of the Grand, the streets of Scarborough had been empty of SPs and nobody had given me a second look as I strolled casually into the bus station.

It was Saturday, 13 February. Helen was expecting our baby this week-end. It could happen any time and I just didn't see how I could sit here these few miles away and do nothing. I had no classes today or tomorrow so I would miss nothing and nobody would miss me. It was, I told myself, a mere technical offence, and anyway I had no option. Like the first time, I just had to see Helen.

And it wouldn't be long now, I thought, as I hurried up to the familiar doorway of her home. I went inside and gazed disappointedly at the empty kitchen – somehow I had been sure she would be standing there waiting for me with her arms wide. I shouted her name but nothing stirred in the house. I was still there, listening, when her father came through from an inner room.

'You've got a son,' He said.

I put my hand on the back of a chair. 'What . . . ?'

'You've got a son.' He was so calm.

'When . . . ?'

'Few minutes ago. Nurse Brown's just been on the phone. Funny you should walk in.'

As I leaned on the chair he gave me a keen look. 'Would you like a drop of whisky?'

'Whisky? No – why?'

'Well you've gone a bit white, lad, that's all. Anyway, you'd better have something to eat.'

'No, no, no thanks, I've got to get out there.'

He smiled. 'There's no hurry, lad. Anyway, they won't

want anybody there too soon. Better eat something.'

'Sorry, I couldn't. Would you – would you mind if I borrowed your car?'

I was still trembling a little as I drove away. If only Mr Alderson had led up to it gradually – he might have said, 'I've got some news for you,' or something like that, but his direct approach had shattered me. When I pulled up outside Nurse Brown's it still hadn't got through to me that I was a father.

Greenside Nursing Home sounded impressive, but it was in fact Nurse Brown's dwelling house. She was State Registered and usually had two or three of the local women in at a time to have their babies.

She opened the door herself and threw up her hands. 'Mr Herriot! It hasn't taken you long! Where did you spring from?' She was a cheerfully dynamic little woman with mischievous eyes.

I smiled sheepishly. 'Well, I just happened to drop in on Mr Alderson and got the news.'

'You might have given us time to get the little fellow properly washed,' she said. 'But never mind, come up and see him. He's a fine baby – nine pounds.'

Still in a dreamlike state I followed her up the stairs of the little house into a small bedroom. Helen was there, in the bed, looking flushed.

'Hello,' she said.

I went over and kissed her.

'What was it like?' I enquired nervously.

'Awful,' Helen replied without enthusiasm. Then she nodded towards the cot beside her.

I took my first look at my son. Little Jimmy was brick red in colour and his face had a bloated, dissipated look. As I hung over him he twisted his tiny fists under his chin and appeared to be undergoing some mighty internal struggle. His face swelled and darkened as he contorted his features then from deep among the puffy flesh his eyes fixed me with a baleful glare and he stuck his tongue out of the corner of his mouth.

'My God!' I exclaimed.

The nurse looked at me, startled. 'What's the matter?'

'Well, he's a funny-looking little thing, isn't he?'

'What!' She stared at me furiously. 'Mr Herriot, how can you say such a thing? He's a beautiful baby!'

I peered into the cot again. Jimmy greeted me with a lopsided leer, turned purple and blew a few bubbles.

'Are you sure he's all right?' I said.

There was a tired giggle from the bed but Nurse Brown was not amused.

'All right! What exactly do you mean?' She drew herself up stiffly.

I shuffled my feet. 'Well, er – is there anything wrong with him?'

I though she was going to strike me 'Anything . . . how dare you! Whatever are you talking about? I've never heard such nonsense!' She turned appealingly towards the bed, but Helen, a weary smile on her face, had closed her eyes.

I drew the enraged little woman to one side. 'Look, Nurse, have you by chance got any others on the premises?'

'Any other what?' she asked icily.

'Babies – new babies. I want to compare Jimmy with another one.'

Her eyes widened. 'Compare him! Mr Herriot, I'm not going to listen to you any longer – I've lost patience with you!'

'I'm asking you, Nurse,' I repeated. 'Have you any more around?'

There was a long pause as she looked at me as though I was something new and incredible. 'Well – there's Mrs Dewburn in the next room. Little Sidney was born about the same time as Jimmy.'

'Can I have a look at him?' I gazed at her appealingly.

She hesitated then a pitying smile crept over her face. 'Oh you . . . you . . . just a minute, then.'

She went into the other room and I heard a mumble of voices. She reappeared and beckoned to me.

Mrs Dewburn was the butcher's wife and I knew her well. The face on the pillow was hot and tired like Helen's.

'Eee, Mr Herriot, I didn't expect to see you. I thought you were in the army.'

'RAF, actually, Mrs Dewburn. I'm on – er – leave at the moment.'

I looked in the cot. Sidney was dark red and bloated, too, and he, also, seemed to be wrestling with himself. The inner battle showed in a series of grotesque facial contortions culminating in a toothless snarl.

I stepped back involuntarily. 'What a beautiful child,' I said.

'Yes, isn't he lovely,' said his mother fondly.

'He is indeed, gorgeous.' I took another disbelieving glance into the cot. 'Well, thank you very much, Mrs Dewburn. It was kind of you to let me see him.'

'Not at all, Mr Herriot, it's nice of you to take an interest.'

Outside the door I took a long breath and wiped my brow. The relief was tremendous. Sidney was even funnier than Jimmy.

When I returned to Helen's room Nurse Brown was sitting on the bed and the two women were clearly laughing at me. And of course, looking back, I must have appeared silly. Sidney Dewburn and my son are now two big, strong, remarkably good-looking young men, so my fears were groundless.

The little nurse looked at me quizzically. I think she had forgiven me.

'I suppose you think all your calves and foals are beautiful right from the moment they are born?'

'Well yes,' I replied. 'I have to admit it – I think they are.'

As I have said before, ideas do not come readily to me, but on the bus journey back to Scarborough a devilish scheme began to hatch in my brain.

I was due for compassionate leave, but why should I take it now? Helen would be in the Nursing Home for a fortnight and there didn't seem any sense in my mooning round Darrowby on my own. The thing to do would be to send myself a telegram a fortnight from now announcing the birth, and we would be able to spend my leave together.

It was interesting how my moral scruples dissolved in the face of this attraction, but anyway, I told myself, where was the harm? I wasn't scrounging anything extra, I was just altering the time. The RAF or the war effort in general would suffer no mortal blow. Long before the darkened vehicle had rolled into the town I had made up my mind and on the following day I wrote to a friend in Darrowby and arranged about the telegram.

But I wasn't such a hardened criminal as I thought, because as the days passed doubts began to creep in. The rules at ITW were rigidly strict. I would be in trouble if I was found out. But the prospect of a holiday with Helen blotted out all other considerations.

When the fateful day arrived my room mates and I were stretched on our beds after lunch when a great voice boomed along the corridor.

'AC2 Herriot! Come on, let's have you, Herriot!'

My stomach lurched. Somehow I hadn't reckoned on Flight Sergeant Blackett coming into this. I had thought maybe an LAC or a corporal, even one of the sergeants might have handled it, not the great man himself.

Flight Sergeant Blackett was an unsmiling martinet of immense natural presence which a gaunt six feet two inch frame, wide bony shoulders and a craggy countenance did nothing to diminish. It was usually the junior NCOs who dealt with our misdemeanours, but if Flight Sergeant Blackett ever took a hand it was a withering experience.

I heard it again. The same bull bellow which echoed over our heads on the square every morning.

'Herriot! Let's be having you, Herriot!'

I was on my way at a brisk trot out of the room and along the polished surface of the corridor. I came to a halt stiffly in front of the tall figure.

'Yes, Flight Sergeant.'

'You Herriot?'

'Yes, Flight Sergeant.'

The telegram between his fingers scuffed softly against the blue serge of his trousers as he swung his hand to and fro. My pulse rate accelerated painfully as I waited.

'Well now, lad, I'm pleased to tell you that your wife has had her baby safely.' He raised the telegram to his eyes. 'It says 'ere, "A boy, both well. Nurse Brown." Let me be the first to congratulate you.' He held out his hand and as I took it he smiled. Suddenly he looked very like Gary Cooper.

'Now you'll want to get off right away and see them both, eh?'

I nodded dumbly. He must have thought I was an unemotional character.

He put a hand on my shoulder and guided me into the orderly room.

'Come on, you lot, get movin'!' The organ tones rolled over the heads of the airmen seated at the tables. 'This is important. Got a brand new father 'ere. Leave pass, railway warrant, pay, double quick!'

'Right, Flight. Very good, Flight.' The typewriters began to tap.

The big man went over to a railway timetable on the wall. 'You haven't far to go, anyway. Let's see – Darrowby, Darrowby . . . yes, there's a train out of here for York at three twenty.' He looked at his watch. 'You ought to make that if you get your skates on.'

A deepening sense of shame threatened to engulf me when he spoke again.

'Double back to your room and get packed. We'll have your documents ready.'

I changed into my best blue, filled my kit bag and threw it over my shoulder, then hurried back to the orderly room.

The Flight Sergeant was waiting. He handed me a long envelope. 'It's all there, son, and you've got plenty of time.' He looked me up and down, walked round me and straightened the white flash in my cap. 'Yes, very smart. We've got to have you lookin' right for your missus, haven't we?' He gave me the Gary Cooper smile again. He was a handsome, kind-eyed man and I'd never noticed it.

He strolled with me along the corridor. 'This'll be your first 'un, of course?'

'Yes, Flight.'

He nodded. 'Well, it's a great day for you. I've got three

of 'em, meself. Getting big now but I miss 'em like hell with this ruddy war. I really envy you, walking in that door tonight and seeing your son for the very first time.'

Guilt drove through me in a searing flood and as we halted at the top of the stairs I was convinced my shifty eyes and furtive glances would betray me. But he wasn't really looking at me.

'You know, lad,' he said softly, gazing somewhere over my head. 'This is the best time of your life coming up.'

We weren't allowed to use the main stairways and as I clattered down the narrow stone service stairs I heard the big voice again.

'Give my regards to them both.'

I had a wonderful time with Helen, walking for miles, discovering the delights of pram pushing, with little Jimmy miraculously improved in appearance. Everything was so much better than if I had taken my leave at the official time and there is no doubt my plan was a success.

But I was unable to gloat about it. The triumph was dimmed and to this day I have reservations about the whole thing.

Flight Sergeant Blackett spoiled it for me.

# fifteen

'You must have to be a bit of an idiot to be a country vet.' The young airman was laughing as he said it, but I felt there was some truth in his words. He had been telling me about his job in civil life and when I described my own working hours and conditions he had been incredulous.

There was one time I would have agreed with him wholeheartedly. It was nine o'clock on a filthy wet night and I was still at work. I gripped the steering wheel more tightly and shifted in my seat, groaning softly as my tired muscles complained.

Why had I entered this profession? I could have gone in for something easier and gentler – like coalmining or lumberjacking. I had started feeling sorry for myself three hours ago, driving across Darrowby market place on the way to a calving. The shops were shut and even through the wintry drizzle there was a suggestion of repose, of work done, of firesides and books and drifting tobacco smoke. I had all those things, plus Helen, back there in our bed-sitter.

I think the iron really entered when I saw the carload of young people setting off from the front of the Drovers; three girls and three young fellows, all dressed up and laughing and obviously on their way to a dance or party. Everybody was set for comfort and a good time; everybody except Herriot, rattling towards the cold wet hills and the certain prospect of toil.

And the case did nothing to raise my spirits. A skinny little heifer stretched on her side in a ramshackle open-fronted shed littered with old tin cans, half bricks and other junk; it was difficult to see what I was stumbling over since the only light came from a rusty oil lamp whose flame flickered and dipped in the wind.

I was two hours in that shed, easing out the calf inch by inch. It wasn't a malpresentation, just a tight fit, but the heifer never rose to her feet and I spent the whole time on the floor, rolling among the bricks and tins, getting up only to shiver my way to the water bucket while the rain hurled itself icily against the shrinking flesh of my chest and back.

And now here I was, driving home frozen-faced with my skin chafing under my clothes and feeling as though a group of strong men had been kicking me enthusiastically from head to foot for most of the evening. I was almost drowning in self-pity when I turned into the tiny village of Copton. In the warm days of summer it was idyllic, reminding me always of a corner of Perthshire, with its single street hugging the lower slopes of a green hillside and a dark drift of trees spreading to the heathery uplands high above.

But tonight it was a dead black place with the rain sweeping across the headlights against the tight-shut houses; except for a faint glow right in the middle where the light from the village pub fell softly on the streaming roadway. I stopped the car under the swinging sign of the Fox and Hounds and on an impulse opened the door. A beer would do me good.

A pleasant warmth met me as I went into the pub. There was no bar counter, only high-backed settles and oak tables arranged under the whitewashed walls of what was simply a converted farm kitchen. At one end a wood fire crackled in an old black cooking range and above it the tick of a wall clock sounded above the murmur of voices. It wasn't as lively as the modern places but it was peaceful.

'Now then, Mr Herriot, you've been workin',' my neighbour said as I sank into the settle.

'Yes, Ted, how did you know?'

The man glanced over my soiled mackintosh and the wellingtons which I hadn't bothered to change on the farm. 'Well, that's not your Sunday suit, there's blood on your nose end and cow shit on your ear.' Ted Dobson was a burly cowman in his thirties and his white teeth showed suddenly in a wide grin.

I smiled too and plied my handkerchief. 'It's funny how you always want to scratch your nose at times like that.'

I looked around the room. There were about a dozen men drinking from pint glasses, some of them playing dominoes. They were all farm workers, the people I saw when I was called from my bed in the darkness before dawn; hunched figures they were then, shapeless in old greatcoats, cycling out to the farms, head down against the wind and rain, accepting the facts of their hard existence. I often thought at those times that this happened to me only occasionally, but they did it every morning.

And they did it for thirty shillings a week; just seeing them here made me feel a little ashamed.

Mr Waters, the landlord, whose name let him in for a certain amount of ribbing, filled my glass, holding his tall jug high to produce the professional froth.

'There y'are, Mr Herriot, that'll be sixpence. Cheap at 'alf the price.'

Every drop of beer was brought up in that jug from the wooden barrels in the cellar. It would have been totally impracticable in a busy establishment, but the Fox and Hounds was seldom bustling and Mr Waters would never get rich as a publican. But he had four cows in the little byre adjoining this room, fifty hens pecked around in his long back garden and he reared a few litters of pigs every year from his two sows.

'Thank you, Mr Waters.' I took a deep pull at the glass. I had lost some sweat despite the cold and my thirst welcomed the flow of rich nutty ale. I had been in here a few times before and the faces were all familiar. Especially old Albert Close, a retired shepherd who sat in the same place every night at the end of the settle hard against the fire.

He sat as always, his hands and chin resting on the tall crook which he had carried through his working days, his eyes blank. Stretched half under the seat, half under the table lay his dog, Mick, old and retired like his master. The animal was clearly in the middle of a vivid dream; his paws pedalled the air spasmodically, his lips and ears twitched and now and then he emitted a stifled bark.

Ted Dobson nudged me and laughed. 'Ah reckon awd Mick's still rounding up them sheep.'

I nodded. There was little doubt the dog was reliving the great days, crouching and darting, speeding in a wide arc round the perimeter of the field at his master's whistle. And Albert himself. What lay behind those empty eyes? I could imagine him in his youth, striding the windy uplands, covering endless miles over moor and rock and beck, digging that same crook into the turf at every step. There were no fitter men than the Dales shepherds, living in the open in all weathers, throwing a sack over their shoulders in snow and rain.

And there was Albert now, a broken, arthritic old man gazing apathetically from beneath the ragged peak of an ancient tweed cap. I noticed he had just drained his glass and I walked across the room.

'Good evening, Mr Close,' I said.

He cupped an ear with his hand and blinked up at me. 'Eh?'

I raised my voice to a shout. 'How are you, Mr Close?'

'Can't complain, young man,' he murmured. 'Can't complain.'

'Will you have a drink?'

'Aye, thank ye.' He directed a trembling finger at his glass. 'You can put a drop i' there, young man.'

I knew a drop meant a pint and beckoned to the landlord who plied his jug expertly. The old shepherd lifted the recharged glass and looked up at me.

'Good 'ealth,' he grunted.

'All the best,' I said and was about to return to my seat when the old dog sat up. My shouts at his master must have wakened him from his dream because he stretched sleepily, shook his head a couple of times and looked around him. And as he turned and faced me I felt a sudden sense of shock.

His eyes were terrible. In fact I could hardly see them as they winked painfully at me through a sodden fringe of pus-caked lashes. Rivulets of discharge showed dark and ugly against the white hair on either side of the nose.

I stretched my hand out to him and the dog wagged his tail briefly before closing his eyes and keeping them closed. It seemed he felt better that way.

I put my hand on Albert's shoulder. 'Mr Close, how long has he been like this?'

'Eh?'

I increased my volume. 'Mick's eyes. They're in a bad state.'

'Oh aye.' The old man nodded in comprehension. 'He's got a bit o' caud in 'em. He's allus been subjeck to it ever since 'e were a pup.'

'No, it's more than cold, it's his eyelids.'

'Eh?'

I took a deep breath and let go at the top of my voice.

'He's got turned-in eyelids. It's rather a serious thing.'

The old man nodded again. 'Aye, 'e lies a lot wi' his head at foot of t'door. It's draughty there.'

'No, Mr Close!' I bawled. 'It's got nothing to do with that. It's a thing called entropion and it needs an operation to put it right.'

'That's right, young man.' He took a sip at his beer. 'Just a bit o' caud. Ever since he were a pup he's been subjeck . . .'

I turned away wearily and returned to my seat. Ted Dobson looked at me enquiringly.

'What was that about?'

'Well, it's a nasty thing, Ted. Entropion is when the eyelids are turned in and the lashes rub against the eyeball. Causes a lot of pain, sometimes ulceration or even blindness. Even a mild case is damned uncomfortable for a dog.'

'I see,' Ted said ruminatively. 'Ah've noticed awd Mick's had mucky eyes for a long time but they've got worse lately.'

'Yes, sometimes it happens like that, but often it's congenital. I should think Mick has had a touch of it all his life but for some reason it's suddenly developed to this horrible state.' I turned again towards the old dog, sitting patiently under the table, eyes still tight shut.

'He's sufferin' then?'

I shrugged my shoulders. 'Well, you know what it's like if you have a speck of dust in your eyes or even one lash turned in. I should say he feels pretty miserable.'

'Poor awd beggar. Ah never knew it was owt like that.' He drew on his cigarette. 'And could an operation cure it?'

'Yes, Ted, it's one of the most satisfying jobs a vet can do. I always feel I've done a dog a good turn when I've finished.'

'Aye, ah bet you do. It must be a nice feelin'. But it'll be a costly job, ah reckon?'

I smiled wryly. 'It depends how you look at it. It's a fiddly business and takes time. We usually charge about a pound for it.' A human surgeon would laugh at a sum like that, but it would still be too much for old Albert.

For a few moments we were both silent, looking across the room at the old man, at the threadbare coat, the long tatter of trouser bottoms falling over the broken boots. A pound was two weeks of the old age pension. It was a fortune.

Ted got up suddenly. 'Any road, somebody ought to tell 'im. Ah'll explain it to 'im.'

He crossed the room. 'Are ye ready for another, Albert?'

The old shepherd glanced at him absently then indicated his glass, empty again. 'Aye, ye can put a drop i' there, Ted.'

The cowman waved to Mr Waters then bent down. 'Did ye understand what Mr Herriot was tellin' ye, Albert?' he shouted.

'Aye .. aye .. Mick's got a bit o' caud in 'is eyes.'

'Nay, 'e hasn't! it's nowt of t'soart! It's a en . . . a en . . . summat different.'

'Keeps gettin' caud in 'em.' Albert mumbled, nose in glass.

Ted yelled in exasperation. 'Ye daft awd divil! Listen to what ah'm sayin' – ye've got to take care of 'im and . . .'

But the old man was far away. 'Ever sin 'e were a pup . . . allus been subjeck to it . . .'

Though Mick took my mind off my own troubles at the time, the memory of those eyes haunted me for days. I yearned to get my hands on them. I knew an hour's work would transport the old dog into a world he perhaps had not known for years, and every instinct told me to rush back to Copton, throw him in the car and bear him back to Darrowby for surgery. I wasn't worried about the money but you just can't run a practice that way.

I regularly saw lame dogs on farms, skinny cats on the streets and it would have been lovely to descend on each and every one and minister to them out of my knowledge. In fact I had tried a bit of it and it didn't work.

It was Ted Dobson who put me out of my pain. He had

come in to the town to see his sister for the evening and he stood leaning on his bicycle in the surgery doorway, his cheerful, scrubbed face gleaming as if it would light up the street.

He came straight to the point. 'Will ye do that operation on awd Mick, Mr Herriot?'

'Yes, of course, but . . . how about . . . ?'

'Oh that'll be right. T'lads at Fox and Hounds are seein' to it. We're takin' it out of the club money.'

'Club money?'

'Aye, we put in a bit every week for an outin' in t'summer. Trip to t'seaside or summat like.'

'Well it's extremely kind of you, Ted, but are you quite sure? Won't any of them mind?'

Ted laughed. 'Nay, it's nowt, we won't miss a quid. We drink ower much on them do's anyway.' He paused. 'All t'lads want this job done – it's been gettin' on our bloody nerves watchin' t'awd dog ever since you told us about 'im.'

'Well, that's great,' I said. 'How will you get him down?'

'Me boss is lendin' me 'is van. Wednesday night be all right?'

'Fine.' I watched him ride away then turned back along the passage. It may seem to modern eyes that a lot of fuss had been made over a pound but in those days it was a very substantial sum, and some idea may be gained from the fact that four pounds a week was my commencing salary as a veterinary surgeon.

When Wednesday night arrived it was clear that Mick's operation had become something of a gala occasion. The little van was crammed with regulars from the Fox and Hounds and others rolled up on their bicycles.

The old dog slunk fearfully down the passage to the operating room, nostrils twitching at the unfamiliar odours of ether and antiseptic. Behind him trooped the noisy throng of farm men, their heavy boots clattering on the tiles.

Tristan, who was doing the anaesthesia, hoisted the dog on the table and I looked around at the unusual spectacle of rows of faces regarding me with keen anticipation. Normally I am not in favour of lay people witnessing operations but since these men were sponsoring the whole thing they would have to stay.

Under the lamp I got my first good look at Mick. He was a handsome, well-marked animal except for those dreadful eyes. As he sat there he opened them a fraction and peered at me for a painful moment before closing them against the bright light; that, I felt, was how he spent his life, squinting carefully and briefly at his surroundings. Giving him the intravenous barbiturate was like doing him a favour, ridding him of his torment for a while.

And when he was stretched unconscious on his side I was able to carry out my first examination. I parted the lids, wincing at the matted lashes, awash with tears and discharge; there was a long-standing keratitis and conjunctivitis but with a gush of relief I found that the cornea was not ulcerated.

'You know,' I said. 'This is a mess, but I don't think there's any permanent damage.'

The farm men didn't exactly break into a cheer but they were enormously pleased. The carnival air was heightened as they chattered and laughed and when I poised my scalpel it struck me that I had never operated in such a noisy environment.

But I felt almost gleeful as I made the first incision; I had been looking forward so much to this moment. Starting with the left eye I cut along the full length parallel to the margin of the lid then made a semicircular sweep of the knife to include half an inch of the tissue above the eye. Seizing the skin with forceps I stripped it away, and as I drew the lips of the bleeding wound together with stitches I noticed with intense gratification how the lashes were pulled high and away from the corneal surface they had irritated, perhaps for years.

I cut away less skin from the lower lid – you never need to take so much there – then started on the right eye. I was slicing away happily when I realized that the noise had subsided; there were a few mutterings, but the chaff and laughter had died. I glanced up and saw big Ken Appleton, the horseman from Laurel Grove; it was natural that he should catch my eye, because he was six feet four and built like the Shires he cared for.

'By gaw, it's 'ot in 'ere,' he whispered, and I could see he meant it because sweat was streaming down his face.

I was engrossed in my work or I would have noticed that he wasn't only sweating but deadly pale. I was stripping the skin from the eyelid when I heard Tristan's yell.

'Catch him!'

The big man's surrounding friends supported him as he slid gently to the floor and he stayed there, sleeping peacefully, till I had inserted the last stitch. Then as Tristan and I cleaned up and put the instruments away he began to look around him and his companions helped him to his feet. Now that the cutting was over the life had returned to the party and Ken came in for some leg-pulling; but his was not the only white face.

'I think you could do with a drop of whisky, Ken,' Tristan said. He left the room and returned with a bottle which, with typical hospitality, he dispensed to all. Beakers, measuring glasses and test tubes were pressed into service and soon there was a boisterous throng around the sleeping dog. When the van finally roared off into the night the last thing I heard was the sound of singing from the packed interior.

They brought Mick back in ten days for removal of the stitches. The wounds had healed well but the keratitis had still not cleared and the old dog was still blinking painfully. I didn't see the final result of my work for another month.

It was when I was again driving home through Copton from an evening call that the lighted doorway of the Fox and Hounds recalled me to the little operation which had been almost forgotten in the rush of new work. I went in and sat down among the familiar faces.

Things were uncannily like before. Old Albert Close in his usual place, Mick stretched under the table, his twitching feet testifying to another vivid dream. I watched him closely until I could stand it no longer. As if drawn by a magnet I crossed the room and crouched by him.

'Mick!' I said. 'Hey, wake up, boy!'

The quivering limbs stilled and there was a long moment when I held my breath as the shaggy head turned towards me. Then with a kind of blissful disbelief I found myself gazing into the wide, clear, bright eyes of a young dog.

Warm wine flowed richly through my veins as he faced me, mouth open in a panting grin, tail swishing along the stone flags. There was no inflammation, no discharge, and the lashes, clean and dry, grew in a soft arc well clear of the corneal surface which they had chafed and rasped for so long. I stroked his head and as he began to look around him eagerly I felt a thrill of utter delight at the sight of the old animal exulting in his freedom, savouring the new world which had opened to him. I could see Ted Dobson and the other men smiling conspiratorially as I stood up.

'Mr Close,' I shouted. 'Will you have a drink?'

'Aye, you can put a drop i' there, young man.'

'Mick's eyes are a lot better.'

The old man raised his glass. 'Good 'ealth. Aye, it were nobbut a bit o' caud.'

'But Mr Close . . . !'

'Nasty thing, is caud in t'eyes. T'awd feller keeps lyin' in that door'ole and ah reckon he'll get it again. Ever since 'e were a pup 'e's been subjeck . . .'

# sixteen

As I bent over the wash basin in the 'ablutions' and went into another violent paroxysm of coughing I had a growing and uncomfortable conviction that I was a mere pawn.

The big difference between my present existence and my

old life as a vet was that I used to make up my own mind as to how I would do things, whereas in the RAF all the decisions which affected me were made by other people. I didn't much like being a pawn because the lives of us lowly airmen were ruled by a lot of notions and ideas dreamed up by individuals so exalted that we never knew them.

And so many of these ideas seemed crazy to me.

For instance, who decided that all our bedroom windows should be nailed open throughout a Yorkshire winter so that the healthy mist could swirl straight from the black ocean and settle icily on our beds as we slept? The result was an almost one hundred per cent incidence of bronchitis in our flight, and in the mornings the Grand Hotel sounded like a chest sanatorium with a harrowing chorus of barks and wheezes.

The cough seized me again, racking my body, threatening to dislodge my eyeballs. It was a temptation to report sick but I hadn't done it yet. Most of the lads stuck it out till they had roaring fevers before going sick and by now, at the end of February, nearly all of them had spent a few days in hospital. I was one of the few who hadn't. Maybe there was a bit of bravado in my stand – because most of them were eighteen- or nineteen-year-olds and I was a comparatively old man in my twenties – but there were two other reasons. Firstly, it was very often after I had got dressed and been unable to eat breakfast that I felt really ill. But by then it was too late. You had to report sick before seven o'clock or suffer till next day.

Another reason was that I didn't like the look of the sick parade. As I went out to the corridor with my towel round my shoulders a sergeant was reading a list and inflating his lungs at the same time.

'Get on parade, the sick!' he shouted. 'C'mon, c'mon, let's be 'avin' you!'

From various doors an unhappy group of invalids began to appear, shuffling over the linoleum, each draped with his 'small kit', haversack containing pyjamas, canvas shoes, knife, fork, spoon, etc.

The sergeant unleashed another bellow. 'Get into line, there! Come on, you lot, hurry it up, look lively!'

I looked at the young men huddled there, white-faced and trembling. Most of them were coughing and spluttering and one of them clutched his abdomen as though he had a ruptured appendix.

'Parade!' bawled the sergeant. 'Parade, atten-shun! Parade stan'-at ease! Atten-shun! Le-eft turn! Qui-ick march! 'Eft-'ight, 'eft-'ight, 'eft-'ight, 'eft-'ight!'

The hapless band trailed wearily off. They had a march of nearly a mile through the rain to the sick quarters in another hotel above the Spa, and as I turned into my room it was with a renewed resolve to hang on as long as possible.

Another thing that frightened us all for a spell was the suggestion, drifting down from somewhere on high, that it wasn't enough to go jogging around Scarborough on our training runs; we ought to stop every now and then and do a bit of shadow boxing like fighters. This idea seemed too outrageous to be true but we had it from the sergeant himself, who came with us on our runs. Some VIP had passed it down, claiming that it would instil belligerence in us. We were thoroughly alarmed for a while, including the sergeant, who had no desire to be seen in charge of a bunch of apparent lunatics dancing around punching at the air. Mercifully, somebody had the strength to resist this one and the whole thing fell through.

But of all these brilliant schemes the one I remember best was the one that decided we had to scream at the end of our physical training session. Apart from running miles all over the place, we had long periods of PT down on the rain-swept prom with the wind cutting in from the sea on our goose-pimpled limbs. We became so good at these exercises that it was decided to put on a show for a visiting air marshal. Not only our flight but several squadrons all performing in unison in front of the Grand.

We trained for months for the big day, doing the same movements over and over again till we were perfect. At first the barrel-chested PT sergeant shouted instructions at us all the time, then as we got better all he did was call out 'Exercise three, commence.' And finally it all became so much a part of our being that he merely sounded a tiny peep on his whistle at the beginning of each exercise.

By spring we were really impressive. Hundreds of men in shorts and singlets swinging away as one out there on the square, with the PT sergeant up on the balcony above the doorway where he would stand with the air marshal on the day. The thing that made it so dramatic was the utter silence; the forest of waving limbs and swaying bodies with not a sound but the peep of the whistle.

Everything was lovely till somebody had the idea of the screaming. Up till then we had marched silently from the square at the end of the session, but that was apparently not good enough. What we had to do now was count up to five at the end of the last exercise, then leap into the air, scream at the top of our voices and run off the square at top speed.

And I had to admit that it seemed quite a brainwave. We tried it a few times, then we began to put our hearts into it, jumping high, yelling like dervishes then scuttling away into the various openings among the hotels around the square.

It must have looked marvellous from the balcony. The great mass of white-clad men going through the long routine in a cathedral hush, a few seconds of complete immobility at the end then the whole concourse erupting with a wild yell and disappearing, leaving the empty square echoing. And this last touch had another desirable aspect; it was further proof of our latent savagery. The enemy would have quaked at that chilling sound.

The sergeant had a little trouble with a lad in my flight, a tall gangling red-haired youth called Cromarty who stood in the line in front of me a few feet to my right. Cromarty seemed unable to enter into the spirit of the thing.

'Come on, lad,' the sergeant said one day. 'Put a bit of devil into it! You got to sound like a killer. You're floating up and down there like a ruddy fairy godmother.'

Cromarty did try, but the thing seemed to embarrass him. He gave a little hop, an apologetic jerk of his arms and a feeble cry.

The sergeant ran his hand through his hair. 'No, no, lad! You've got to let yourself go!' He looked around him. 'Here, Devlin, come out and show 'im how it's done.'

Devlin, a grinning Irishman, stepped forward. The scream was the high point of his day. He stood relaxed for a moment then without warning catapulted himself high in the air, legs and arms splayed, head back, while a dreadful animal cry burst from his gaping mouth.

The sergeant took an involuntary step backwards. 'Thanks, Devlin, that's fine,' he said a little shakily, then he turned to Cromarty. 'Now you see how I want it, boy, just like that. So work at it.'

Cromarty nodded. He had a long, serious face and you could see he wanted to oblige. After that I watched him each day and there was no doubt he was improving. His inhibitions were gradually being worn down.

It seemed that nature was smiling on our efforts because the great day dawned with blue skies and warm sunshine. Every man among the hundreds who marched out into the square had been individually prepared. Newly bathed, fresh haircut, spotless white shorts and singlet. We waited in our motionless lines before the newly painted door of the Grand while, on the balcony above, gold braid glinted on the air marshal's cap.

He stood among a knot of the top RAF brass of Scarborough, while in one corner I could see our sergeant, erect in long white flannels, his great chest sticking out further than ever. Beneath us the sea shimmered and the golden bay curved away to the Filey cliffs.

The sergeant raised his hand. 'Peep' went the whistle and we were off.

There was something exhilarating about being part of this smooth machine. I had a wonderful sense of oneness with the arms and legs which moved with mine all around. It was effortless. We had ten exercises to do and at the end of the first we stood rigid for ten seconds, then the whistle piped and we started again.

The time passed too quickly as I revelled in our perfection. At the end of exercise nine I came to attention, waiting for the whistle, counting under my breath. Nothing stirred, the silence was profound. Then, from the motionless ranks, as unexpected as an exploding bomb, Cromarty in front of me launched himself upwards in a tangle of flailing limbs and red hair and unleashed a long bubbling howl. He had put so much into his leap that he seemed to take a long time to come down and even after his descent the shattering sound echoed on.

Cromarty had made it at last. As fierce and warlike a scream, as high a jump as ever the sergeant could desire. The only snag was that he was too soon.

When the whistle went for the last exercise a lot of people didn't hear it because of the noise and many others were in a state of shock and came in late. Anyway, it was a shambles and the final yell and scuttle a sad anticlimax. I myself, though managing to get a few inches off the ground, was unable to make any sound at all.

Had Cromarty not been serving in the armed forces of a benign democracy he would probably have been taken quietly away and shot. As it was, there was really nothing anybody could do to him. NCOs weren't even allowed to swear at the men.

I felt for the PT sergeant. There must have been a lot he wanted to say but he was grievously restricted. I saw him with Cromarty later. He put his face close to the young man's.

'You ... you ...' His features worked as he fought for words 'You THING you!'

He turned and walked away with bowed shoulders. At that moment I'm sure he felt like a pawn too.

# seventeen

There is no doubt that when I looked back at my life in Darrowby I was inclined to bathe the whole thing in a rosy glow, but occasionally the unhappy things came to mind.

That man, distraught and gasping on the surgery steps. 'It's no good, I can't bring him in. He's as stiff as a board!'

My stomach lurched. It was another one. 'Jasper, you mean?'

'Yes, he's in the back of my car, right here.'

I ran across the pavement and opened the car door. It was as I feared; a handsome Dalmation stretched in a dreadful tetanic spasm, spine arched, head craning desperately backward, legs like four wooden rods groping at nothing.

I didn't wait to talk but dashed back into the house for syringe and drugs.

I leaned into the car, tucked some papers under the dog's head, injected the apomorphine and waited.

The man looked at me with anxious eyes. 'What is it?'

'Strychnine poisoning, Mr Bartle. I've just given an emetic to make him vomit.' As I spoke the animal brought up the contents of his stomach on to the paper.

'Will that put him right?'

'It depends on how much of the poison has been absorbed.' I didn't feel like telling him that it was almost invariably fatal, that in fact I had treated six dogs in the last week with the same condition and they had all died. 'We'll just have to hope.'

He watched me as I filled another syringe with barbiturate. 'What are you doing now?'

'Anaesthetising him.' I slipped the needle into the radial vein and as I slowly trickled the fluid into the dog's bloodstream the taut muscles relaxed and he sank into a deep slumber.

'He looks better already,' Mr Bartle said.

'Yes, but the trouble is when the injection wears off he

may go back into a spasm. As I say, it all depends on how much of the strychnine has got into his system. Keep him in a quiet place with as little noise as possible. Any sound can bring on a spasm. When he shows signs of coming out of it give me a ring.'

I went back into the house. Seven cases in a week! It was tragic and scarcely believable, but there was no doubt left in my mind now. This was malicious. Some psychopath in our little town was deliberately putting down poison to kill dogs. Strychnine poisoning was something that cropped up occasionally. Gamekeepers and other people used the deadly drug to kill vermin, but usually it was handled with great care and placed out of reach of domestic pets. Trouble started when a burrowing dog came across the poison by accident. But this was different.

I had to warn pet owners somehow. I lifted the phone and spoke to one of the reporters on the *Darrowby and Houlton Times*. He promised to put the story in the next edition, along with advice to keep dogs on their leads and otherwise supervise pets more carefully.

Then I rang the police. The sergeant listened to my account. 'Right, Mr Herriot, I agree with you that there's some crackpot going around and we'll certainly investigate this matter. If you'll just give me the names of the dog owners involved . . . thank you . . . thank you. We'll see these people and check round the local chemists to see if anybody has been buying strychnine lately. And of course we'll keep our eyes open for anybody acting suspiciously.'

I came away from the phone feeling that I might have done something to halt the depressing series of events, but I couldn't rid myself of a gloomy apprehension that more trouble was round the corner. But my mood lightened when I saw Johnny Clifford in the waiting room.

Johnny always made me feel better because he was invariably optimistic and wore a cheerful grin which never altered, even though he was blind. He was about my own age and he sat there in his habitual pose, one hand on the head of his guide dog, Fergus.

'Is it inspection time again already, Johnny?' I asked.

'Aye, it is that, Mr Herriot, it's come round again. It's been a quick six months.' He laughed and held out his card.

I squatted and looked into the face of the big Alsatian sitting motionless and dignified by his master's side. 'Well, and how's Fergus these days?'

'Oh he's in grand fettle. Eatin' well and full of life.' The hand on the head moved round to the ears and at the other end the tail did a bit of sweeping along the waiting-room floor.

As I looked at the young man, his face alight with pride and affection, I realized afresh what this dog meant to him. He had told me that when his failing sight progressed to total blindness in his early twenties he was filled with a despair which did not lessen until he was sent to train with a guide dog and met Fergus; because he found something more than another living creature to act as his eyes, he found a friend and companion to share every moment of his days.

'Well, we'd better get started,' I said. 'Stand up a minute, old lad, while I take your temperature.' That was normal and I went over the big animal's chest with a stethoscope, listening to the reassuringly steady thud of the heart. As I parted the hair along the neck and back to examine the skin I laughed.

'I'm wasting my time here, Johnny. You've got his coat in perfect condition.'

'Aye, never a day goes by but he gets a good groomin'.'

I had seen him at it, brushing and combing tirelessly to bring extra lustre to the sleek swathes of hair. The nicest thing anybody could say to Johnny was, 'That's a beautiful dog you've got.' His pride in that beauty was boundless even though he had never seen it himself.

Treating guide dogs for the blind has always seemed to me to be one of a veterinary surgeon's most rewarding tasks. To be in a position to help and care for these magnificent animals is a privilege, not just because they are highly trained and valuable but because they represent in the ultimate way something which has always lain near the core and centre of my life: the mutually depending, trusting and loving association between man and animal.

Meeting these blind people was a humbling experience which sent me about my work with a new appreciation of my blessings.

I opened the dog's mouth and peered at the huge gleaming teeth. It was dicing with danger to do this with some Alsatians, but with Fergus you could haul the great jaws apart and nearly put your head in and he would only lick your ear. In fact he was at it now. My cheek was nicely within range and he gave it a quick wipe with his large wet tongue.

'Hey, just a minute, Fergus!' I withdrew and plied my handkerchief. 'I've had a wash this morning. And anyway, only little dogs lick – not big tough Alsatians.'

Johnny threw back his head and gave a great peal of laughter. 'There's nowt tough about him, he's the softest dog you could ever meet.'

'Well, that's the way I like them.' I said. I reached for a tooth scaler. 'There's just a bit of tartar on one of his back teeth. I'll scrape it off right now.'

When I was finished I looked in the ears with an auroscope. There was no canker but I cleaned out a little wax.

Then I went round the feet, examining paws and claws. They always fascinated me, these feet; wide, enormous, with great spreading toes. They had to be that size to support the big body and the massive bones of the limbs.

'All correct except that one funny claw, Johnny.'

'Aye, you allus have to trim that 'un don't you? I could feel it was growin' long again.'

'Yes, that toe seems to be slightly crooked or it would wear down like the others with all the walking he does. You have a great time going walks all day, don't you, Fergus?'

I dodged another attempted lick and closed my clippers around the claw. I had to squeeze till my eyes popped before the overgrown piece shot away with a loud crack.

'By gosh, we'd go through some clippers if all dogs had claws like that,' I gasped. 'It just about does them in every time he calls.'

Johnny laughed again and dropped his hand on the great head with that gesture which said so much.

I took the card and entered my report on the dog's health along with the things I had done. Then I dated it and handed it back. 'That's it for this time, Johnny. He's in excellent order and there's nothing more I need do to him.'

'Thank you, Mr Herriot. See you next time round, then.' The young man took hold of the harness and I followed the two of them along the passage and out of the front door. I watched as Fergus halted by the kerb and waited till a car had passed before crossing the road.

They hadn't gone very far along the road when a woman with a shopping bag stopped them. She began to chatter animatedly, looking down repeatedly at the big dog. She was talking about Fergus and Johnny rested his hand on the noble head and nodded and smiled. Fergus was his favourite topic.

Shortly after midday Mr Bartle rang to say Jasper showed signs of returning spasms and before sitting down to lunch I rushed round to his house and repeated the barbiturate injection. Mr Bartle owned one of the local mills, producing cattle food for the district. He was a very bright man indeed.

'Mr Herriot,' he said. 'Please don't misunderstand me. I have every faith in you, but isn't there anything else you can do? I am so very fond of this dog.'

I shrugged helplessly. 'I'm sorry, but I can't do any more.'

'But is there no antidote to this poison?'

'No, I'm afraid there isn't.'

'Well . . .' He looked down with drawn face at the unconscious animal. 'What's going on? What's happening to Jasper when he goes stiff like he did? I'm only a layman but I like to understand things.'

'I'll try to explain it,' I said. 'Strychnine is absorbed into the nervous system and it increases the conductivity of the spinal cord.'

'What does that mean?'

'It means that the muscles become more sensitive to outside stimuli so that the slightest touch or sound throws them into violent contractions.'

'But why does a dog stretch out like that?'

'Because the extensor muscles are stronger than the flexors, causing the back to be arched and the legs extended.'

He nodded. 'I see, but . . . I believe it is usually fatal. What is it that . . . that kills them?'

'They die of asphyxia due to paralysis of the respiratory centre or contraction of the diaphragm.'

Maybe he wanted to ask more, but it was painful for him and he stayed silent.

'There's one thing I'd like you to know, Mr Bartle,' I said. 'It is almost certainly not a painful condition.'

'Thank you.' He bent and briefly stroked the sleeping dog. 'So nothing more can be done?'

I shook my head. 'The barbiturate keeps the spasms in abeyance and we'll go on hoping he hasn't absorbed too much strychnine. I'll call back later, or you can ring me if he gets worse. I can be here in a few minutes.'

Driving away, I pondered on the irony that made Darrowby a paradise for dog killers as well as dog lovers. There were grassy tracks everywhere; wandering by the river's edge, climbing the fell-sides and coiling green and tempting among the heather on the high tops. I often felt sympathy for pet owners in the big cities, trying to find places to walk their dogs. Here in Darrowby we could take our pick. But so could the poisoner. He could drop his deadly bait un-observed in a hundred different places.

I was finishing the afternoon surgery when the phone rang. It was Mr Bartle.

'Has he started the spasms again?' I asked.

There was a pause. 'No, I'm afraid Jasper is dead. He never regained consciousness.'

'Oh . . . I'm very sorry.' I felt a dull despair. That was the seventh death in a week.

'Well, thank you for your treatment, Mr Herriot. I'm sure nothing could have saved him.'

I hung up the phone wearily. He was right. Nothing or nobody could have done any good in this case, but it didn't help. If you finish up with a dead animal there is always the feeling of defeat.

Next day I was walking on to a farm when the farmer's wife called to me. 'I have a message for you to ring back to the surgery.'

I heard Helen's voice at the other end. 'Jack Brimham has just come in with his dog. I think it's another strychnine case.'

I excused myself and drove back to Darrowby at top speed. Jack Brimham was a builder. He ran a one-man business and whatever job he was on – repairing roofs or walls or chimneys – his little white rough-haired terrier went with him, and you could usually see the little animal nosing among the piles of bricks, exploring in the surrounding fields.

Jack was a friend, too. I often had a beer with him at the Drovers' Arms and I recognized his van outside the surgery. I trotted along the passage and found him leaning over the table in the consulting room. His dog was stretched there in that attitude which I dreaded.

'He's gone, Jim,' he muttered.

I looked at the shaggy little body. There was no movement, the eyes stared silently. The legs, even in death, strained across the smooth surface of the table. It was pointless, but I slipped my hand inside the thigh and felt for the femoral artery. There was no pulse.

'I'm sorry, Jack,' I said.

He didn't answer for a moment. 'I've been readin' about this in the paper, Jim, but I never thought it would happen to me. It's a bugger, isn't it?'

I nodded. He was a craggy-faced man, a tough Yorkshireman with a humour and integrity which I liked and a soft place inside which his dog had occupied. I did not know what to say to him.

'Who's doin' this?' he said, half to himself.

'I don't know, Jack. Nobody knows.'

'Well I wish I could have five minutes with him, that's all.'
He gathered the rigid little form into his arms and went
out.

My troubles were not over for that day. It was about 11
p.m. and I had just got into bed when Helen nudged me.

'I think there's somebody knocking at the front door,
Jim.'

I opened the window and looked out. Old Boardman, the
lame veteran of the first war who did odd jobs for us, was
standing on the steps.

'Mr Herriot,' he called up to me. 'I'm sorry to bother you
at this hour, but Patch is ill.'

I leaned further out. 'What's he doing?'

'He's like a bit o' wood – stiff like, and laid on 'is side.'

I didn't bother to dress, just pulled my working corduroys
over my pyjamas and went down the stairs two at a time. I
grabbed what I needed from the dispensary and opened the
front door. The old man, in shirt sleeves, caught at my arm.

'Come quickly, Mr Herriot!' He limped ahead of me to
his little house about twenty yards away in the lane round
the corner.

Patch was like all the others. The fat spaniel I had seen so
often waddling round the top yard with his master was in that
nightmare position on the kitchen floor, but he had vomited,
which gave me hope. I administered the intravenous injection but as I withdrew the needle the breathing stopped.

Mrs Boardman, in nightgown and slippers, dropped on her
knees and stretched a trembling hand towards the motionless
animal.

'Patch . . .' She turned and stared at me, wide-eyed. 'He's
dead!'

I put my hand on the old woman's shoulder and said some
sympathetic words. I thought grimly that I was getting good
at it. As I left I looked back at the two old people. Boardman
was kneeling now by his wife and even after I had closed the
door I could hear their voices: 'Patch . . . oh Patch.'

I almost reeled over the few steps to Skeldale House and
before going in I stood in the empty street breathing the cool

air and trying to calm my racing thoughts. With Patch gone, the thing was getting very near home. I saw that dog every day. In fact all the dogs that had died were old friends – in a little town like Darrowby you came to know your patients personally. Where was it going to end?

I didn't sleep much that night and over the next few days I was obsessed with apprehension. I expected another poisoning with every phone call and took care never to let my own dog, Sam, out of the car in the region of the town. Thanks to my job I was able to exercise him miles away on the summits of the fells, but even there I kept him close to me.

By the fourth day I was beginning to feel more relaxed. Maybe the nightmare was over. I was driving home in the late afternoon past the row of grey cottages at the end of the Houlton Road when a woman ran waving into the road.

'Oh, Mr Herriot,' she cried when I stopped. 'I was just goin' to t'phone box when I saw you.'

I pulled up by the kerb. 'It's Mrs Clifford, isn't it?'

'Yes, Johnny's just come in and Fergus 'as gone queer. Collapsed and laid on t'floor.'

'Oh no!' An icy chill drove through me and for a moment I stared at her, unable to move. Then I threw open the car door and hurried after Johnny's mother into the end cottage. I halted abruptly in the little room and stared down in horror. The very sight of the splendid dignified animal scrabbling helplessly on the linoleum was a desecration, but strychnine is no respecter of such things.

'Oh God!' I breathed. 'Has he vomited, Johnny?'

'Aye, me mum said he was sick in t'back garden when we came in.' The young man was sitting very upright in a chair by the side of his dog. Even now there was a half smile on his face, but he looked strained as he put out his hand in the old gesture and failed to find the head that should have been there.

The bottle of barbiturate wobbled in my shaking hand as I filled the syringe. I tried to put away the thought that I was doing what I had done to all the others – all the dead ones. At my feet Fergus panted desperately, then as I bent over him he suddenly became still and went into the horrible distinctive spasm, the great limbs I knew so well straining frantically into space, the head pulled back grotesquely over the spine.

This was when they died, when the muscles were at full contraction. As the barbiturate flowed into the vein I waited for signs of relaxation but saw none. Fergus was about twice as heavy as any of the other victims I had treated and the plunger went to the end of the syringe without result.

Quickly I drew in another dose and began to inject it, my tension building as I saw how much I was administering. The recommended dose was 1 cc per 5 lb body weight and beyond that you could kill the animal. I watched the gradations on the glass barrel of the syringe and my mouth went dry when the dose crept far beyond the safety limit. But I knew I had to relieve this spasm and continued to depress the plunger relentlessly.

I did it in the grim knowledge that if he died now I would never know whether to blame the strychnine or myself for his death.

The big dog had received more than a lethal amount before peace began to return to the taut body and even then I sat back on my heels, almost afraid to look in case I had brought about his end. There was a long agonizing moment when he lay still and apparently lifeless then the rib cage began to move almost imperceptibly as the breathing recommenced.

Even then I was in suspense. The anaesthesia was so deep that he was only just alive, yet I knew that the only hope was to keep him that way. I sent Mrs Clifford out to phone Siegfried that I would be tied up here for a while, then I pulled up a chair and settled down to wait.

The hours passed as Johnny and I sat there, the dog stretched between us. The young man discussed the case calmly and without self-pity. There was no suggestion that this was anything more than a pet animal lying at his feet – except for the tell-tale reaching for the head that was no longer there.

Several times Fergus showed signs of going into another spasm and each time I sent him back into his deep, deep insensibility, pushing him repeatedly to the brink with a fateful certainty that it was the only way.

It was well after midnight when I came sleepily out into the darkness. I felt drained. Watching the life of the friendly, clever, face-licking animal flicker as he lay inert and unheeding had been a tremendous strain, but I had left him sleeping – still anaesthetized but breathing deeply and regularly. Would he wake up and start the dread sequence again? I didn't know and I couldn't stay any longer. There was a practice with other animals to attend to.

But my anxiety jerked me into early wakefulness next morning. I tossed around till seven thirty telling myself this wasn't the way to be a veterinary surgeon, that you couldn't live like this. But my worry was stronger than the voice of reason and I slipped out before breakfast to the roadside cottage.

My nerves were like a bowstring as I knocked on the door. Mrs Clifford answered and I was about to blurt out my enquiries when Fergus trotted from the inner room.

He was still a little groggy from the vast dosage of barbiturate but he was relaxed and happy, the symptoms had gone, he was himself again. With a gush of pure joy I knelt and took the great head between my hands. He slobbered at me playfully with his wet tongue and I had to fight him off.

He followed me into the living room where Johnny was seated at the table, drinking tea. He took up his usual position, sitting upright and proud by his master's side.

'You'll have a cup, Mr Herriot?' Mrs Clifford asked, poising the teapot.

'Thanks, I'd love one, Mrs Clifford,' I replied.

No tea ever tasted better and as I sipped I watched the young man's smiling face.

'What a relief, Mr Herriot! I sat up with him all night, listenin' to the chimes of the church clock. It was just after four when I knew we'd won because I heard 'im get to his feet and sort o' stagger about. I stopped worryin' then, just listened to 'is feet patterin' on the linoleum. It was lovely!'

He turned his head to me and I looked at the slightly up-turned eyes in the cheerful face.

'I'd have been lost without Fergus,' he said softly. 'I don't know how to thank you.'

But as he unthinkingly rested his hand on the head of the big dog who was his pride and delight I felt that the gesture alone was all the thanks I wanted.

That was the end of the strychnine poisoning outbreak in Darrowby. The older people still talk about it, but nobody ever had the slightest clue to the identity of the killer and it is a mystery to this day.

I feel that the vigilance of the police and the publicity in the press frightened this twisted person off, but anyway it just stopped and the only cases since then have been accidental ones.

To me it is a sad memory of failure and frustration. Fergus was my only cure and I'm not sure why he recovered. Maybe the fact that I pushed the injection to dangerous levels because I was desperate had something to do with it, or maybe he just didn't pick up as much poison as the others. I'll never know.

But over the years when I saw the big dog striding majestically in his harness, leading his master unerringly around the streets of Darrowby, I always had the same feeling.

If there had to be just one saved, I'm glad it was him.

# eighteen

A tender nerve twinged as the old lady passed me the cup of tea. She looked just like Mrs Beck.

One of the local churches was having a social evening to entertain us lonely airmen and as I accepted the cup and sat down I could hardly withdraw my eyes from the lady's face.

Mrs Beck! I could see her now standing by the surgery window.

'Oooh, I never thought you were such a 'eartless man, Mr Herriot.' Her chin trembled and she looked up at me reproachfully.

'But Mrs Beck,' I said. 'I assure you I am not being in the least heartless. I just cannot carry out a major operation on your cat for ten shillings.'

'Well, I thought you would've done it for a poor widder woman like me.'

I regarded her thoughtfully, taking in the small compact figure, the healthy cheeks, the neat helmet of grey hair pulled tightly into a bun. Was she really a poor widow? There was cause for doubt. Her next-door neighbour in Rayton village was a confirmed sceptic.

'It's all a tale, Mr Herriot,' he had said. 'She tries it on wi' everybody, but I'll tell you this – she's got a long stockin'. Owns property all over t'place.'

I took a deep breath. 'Mrs Beck. We often do work at reduced rates for people who can't afford to pay, but this is what we call a luxury operation.'

'Luxury!' The lady was aghast. 'Eee, ah've been tellin' you how Georgina keeps havin' them kittens. She's at it all the time and it's gettin' me down. Ah can't sleep for worryin' when t'next lot's comin'.' She dabbed her eyes.

'I understand and I'm sorry. I can only tell you again that the only way to prevent this trouble is to spay your cat and the charge is one pound.'

'Nay, I can't afford that much!'

I spread my hands. 'But you are asking me to do it for half the price. That's ridiculous. This operation involves the removal of the uterus and ovaries under a general anaesthetic. You just can't do a job like that for ten shillings.'

'Oh, you are cruel!' She turned and looked out of the window and her shoulders began to shake. 'You won't even take pity on a poor widder.'

This had been going on for ten minutes and it began to dawn on me that I was in the presence of a stronger character than myself. I glanced at my watch – I should have been on my round by now and it was becoming increasingly obvious that I wasn't going to win this argument.

I sighed. Maybe she really was a poor widow. 'All right, Mrs Beck, I'll do it for ten shillings, just this once. Will Tuesday afternoon be all right for you?'

She swung round from the window, her face crinkling magically into a smile. 'That'll suit me grand! Eee, that's right kind of you.' She tripped past me and I followed her along the passage.

'Just one thing,' I said as I held the front door open for her. 'Don't give Georgina any food from midday on Monday. She must have an empty stomach when you bring her in.'

'Bring 'er in?' She was a picture of bewilderment. 'But I 'aven't got no car. I thought you'd be collectin' her.'

'Collecting! But Rayton's five miles away!'

'Yes, and bring 'er back afterwards, too. I 'ave no transport.'

'Collect . . . operate on her . . . take her back! All for ten shillings!'

She was still smiling but a touch of steel glinted in her eyes. 'Well, that's what you agreed to charge – ten shillings.'

'But . . . but . . .'

'Oh now you're startin' again.' The smile faded and she put her head on one side. 'And I'm only a poor . . .'

'Okay, okay,' I said hastily. 'I'll call on Tuesday.'

And when Tuesday afternoon came round I cursed my

softness. If that cat had been brought in I could have operated on her at two o'clock and been out on the road doing my farm calls by two thirty. I didn't mind working at a loss for half an hour, but how long was this business going to take?

On my way out I glanced through the open door of the sitting room. Tristan was supposed to be studying but was sleeping soundly in his favourite chair. I went in and looked down at him, marvelling at the utter relaxation, seen only in a dedicated sleeper. His face was as smooth and untroubled as a baby's, the *Daily Mirror*, open at the comic strips, had fallen across his chest and a burnt-out Woodbine hung from one dangling hand.

I shook him gently. 'Like to come with me, Triss? I've got to pick up a cat.'

He came round slowly, stretching and grimacing, but his fundamental good nature soon reasserted itself.

'Certainly, Jim,' he said with a final yawn. 'It will be a pleasure.'

Mrs Beck lived half way down the left side of Rayton village. I read 'Jasmine Cottage' on the brightly painted gate, and as we went up the garden path the door opened and the little woman waved gaily.

'Good afternoon, gentlemen, I'm right glad to see you both.' She ushered us into the living-room among good, solid-looking furniture which showed no sign of poverty. The open cupboard of a mahogany sideboard gave me a glimpse of glasses and bottles. I managed to identify Scotch, cherry brandy and sherry before she nudged the door shut with her knee.

I pointed to a cardboard box loosely tied with string. 'Ah, good, you've got her in there, have you?'

'Nay, bless you, she's in t'garden. She allus has a bit of play out there of an afternoon.'

'In the garden, eh?' I said nervously. 'Well, please get her in, we're in rather a hurry.'

We went through a tiled kitchen to the back door. Most of these cottages had a surprising amount of land behind them and Mrs Beck's patch was in very nice order. Flower beds bordered a smooth stretch of lawn and the sunshine drew glittering colours from the apples and pears among the branches of the trees.

'Georgina,' carolled Mrs Beck. 'Where are you, my pet?'

No cat appeared and she turned to me with a roguish smile. 'I think the little imp's playin' a game with us. She does that, you know.'

'Really?' I said without enthusiasm. 'Well, I wish she'd show herself. I really don't have much . . .'

At that moment a very fat tabby darted from a patch of chrysanthemums and flitted across the grass into a clump of rhododendrons with Tristan in close pursuit. The young man dived among the greenery and the cat emerged from the other end at top speed, did a couple of laps of the lawn then shot up a gnarled tree.

Tristan, eyes gleaming in anticipation, lifted a couple of windfall apples from the turf. 'I'll soon shift the bugger from there, Jim,' he whispered and took aim.

I grabbed his arm. 'For heaven's sake, Triss!' I hissed. 'You can't do that. Put those things down.'

'Oh . . . all right.' He dropped the apples and made for the tree. 'I'll get hold of her for you, anyway.'

'Wait a minute.' I seized his coat as he passed. 'I'll do it. You stay down here and try to catch her if she jumps.'

Tristan looked disappointed but I gave him a warning look. The way the cat had moved, it struck me that it only needed a bit of my colleague's ebullience to send the animal winging into the next county. I began to climb the tree.

I like cats, I've always liked them, and since I feel that animals recognize this in a person I have usually been able to approach and handle the most difficult types. It is not too much to say that I prided myself on my cat technique; I didn't foresee any trouble here.

Puffing slightly, I reached the top branch and extended a hand to the crouching animal.

'Pooss-pooss,' I cooed, using my irresistible cat tone.

Georgina eyed me coldly and gave no answering sign other than a higher arching of the back.

I leaned further along the branch. 'Pooss-pooss, pooss-pooss.' My voice was like molten honey, my finger near her face. I would rub her cheek ever so gently and she would be mine. It never failed.

'Pah!' replied Georgina warningly but I took no heed and touched the fur under her chin.

'Pah-pah!' Georgina spat and followed with a lightning left hook which opened a bloody track across the back of my hand.

Muttering fervently, I retreated and nursed my wounds. From below Mrs Beck gave a tinkling laugh.

'Oh, isn't she a little monkey! She's that playful, bless her.'

I snorted and began to ease my way along the branch again. This time, I thought grimly, I would dispense with finesse. The quick grab was indicated here.

As though reading my thoughts the little creature tripped to the end of the branch and as it bent low under her weight she dropped lightly to the grass.

Tristan was on her in a flash, throwing himself full length and seizing her by the hind leg. Georgina whipped round and unhesitatingly sank her teeth into his thumb but Tristan's core of resilience showed. After a single howl of agony he changed his grip at lightning speed to the scruff of the neck.

A moment later he was standing upright holding a dangling fighting fury high in the air.

'Right, Jim,' he called happily. 'I have her.'

'Good lad! Hang on!' I said breathlessly and slithered down the tree as quickly as I could. Too quickly, in fact, as an ominous ripping sound announced the removal of a triangular piece of my jacket elbow.

But I couldn't bother with trifles. Ushering Tristan at a gallop into the house I opened the cardboard box. There were no sophisticated cat containers in those days and it was a tricky job to enclose Georgina, who was lashing out in all directions and complaining bitterly in a bad-tempered wail.

It took a panting ten minutes to imprison the cat but even with several yards of rough twine round the floppy cardboard I still didn't feel very secure as I bore it to the car.

Mrs Beck raised a finger as we were about to drive away. I carefully explored my lacerated hand and Tristan sucked his thumb as we waited for her to speak.

'Mr Herriot, I 'ope you'll be gentle with 'er,' she said anxiously. 'She's very timid, you know.'

We had covered barely half a mile before sounds of strife arose from the back.

'Get back! Get in there. Get back, you bugger!'

I glanced behind me. Tristan was having trouble. Georgina clearly didn't care for the motion of the car and from the slits in the box clawed feet issued repeatedly; on one occasion an enraged spitting face got free as far as the neck. Tristan kept pushing everything back with great resolution but I could tell from the rising desperation of his cries that he was fighting a losing battle.

I heard the final shout with a feeling of inevitability.

'She's out, Jim! The bugger's out!'

Well this was great. Anybody who has driven a car with a hysterical cat hurtling around the interior will appreciate my situation. I crouched low over the wheel as the furry creature streaked round the sides or leaped clawing at the roof or windscreen with Tristan lunging vainly after her.

But cruel fate had not finished with us yet. My colleague's gasps and grunts from the rear ceased for a moment to be replaced by a horrified shriek.

'The bloody thing's shitting, Jim! She's shitting everywhere!'

The cat was obviously using every weapon at her disposal and he didn't have to tell me. My nose was way ahead of him, and I frantically wound down the window. But I closed it just as quickly at the rising image of Georgina escaping and disappearing into the unknown.

I don't like to think of the rest of that journey. I tried to breathe through my mouth and Tristan puffed out dense clouds of Woodbine smoke but it was still pretty terrible.

Just outside Darrowby I stopped the car and we made a concerted onslaught on the animal; at the cost of a few more wounds, including a particularly painful scratch on my nose, we cornered her and fastened her once more in the box.

Even on the operating table Georgina had a few tricks left. We were using ether and oxygen as anaesthetic and she was particularly adept at holding her breath while the mask was on her face then returning suddenly to violent life when we thought she was asleep. We were both sweating when she finally went under.

I suppose it was inevitable, too, that she should be a difficult case. Ovaro-hysterectomy in the cat is a fairly straight-forward procedure and nowadays we do innumerable cases uneventfully, but in the thirties, particularly in country practice, it was infrequently done and consequently a much larger undertaking.

I personally had my own preferences and aversions in this field. For instance, I found thin cats easy to do and fat cats difficult. Georgina was extremely fat.

When I opened her abdomen an ocean of fat welled up at me, obscuring everything, and I spent a long nerve-racking period lifting out portions of bowel or omentum with my forceps, surveying them gloomily and stuffing them back in again. A great weariness had begun to creep over me by the time I at last managed to grip the pink ovary between the metallic jaws and drew forth the slender string of uterus. After that it was routine, but I still felt a strange sense of exhaustion as I inserted the last stitch.

I put the sleeping cat into the box and beckoned to Tristan. 'Come on, let's get her home before she comes round.' I was starting along the passage when he put his hand on my arm.

'Jim,' he said gravely. 'You know I'm your friend.'

'Yes, Triss, of course.'

'I'd do anything for you, Jim.'

'I'm sure you would.'

He took a deep breath. 'Except one thing. I'm not going back in that bloody car.'

I nodded dully. I really couldn't blame him.

'That's all right,' I said. 'I'll be off, then.'

Before leaving I sprinkled the interior with pine-smelling disinfectant but it didn't make much difference. In any case my main emotion was the hope that Georgina wouldn't wake up before I got to Rayton, and that was shattered before I had crossed Darrowby market place. The hair prickled on the back of my neck as an ominous droning issued from the box on the rear seat. It was like the sound of a distant swarm of bees but I knew what it meant; the anaesthetic was wearing off.

Once clear of the town I put my foot on the boards. This was something I rarely did because whenever I pushed my vehicle above forty miles an hour there was such a clamour of protest from engine and body that I always feared the thing would disintegrate around me. But at this moment I didn't care. Teeth clenched, eyes staring, I hurtled forward, but I didn't see the lonely strip of tarmac or the stone walls flitting past; all my attention was focused behind me, where the swarm of bees was getting nearer and the tone angrier.

When it developed into a bad-tempered yowling and was accompanied by the sound of strong claws tearing at cardboard I began to tremble. As I thundered into Rayton village I glanced behind me. Georgina was half out of the box. I reached back and grasped her scruff and when I stopped at the gate of Jasmine Cottage I pulled on the brake with one hand and lifted her on to my lap with the other.

I sagged in the seat, my breath escaping in a great explosion of relief; and my stiff features almost bent into a smile as I saw Mrs Beck pottering in her garden.

She took Georgina from me with a cry of joy but gasped in horror when she saw the shaven area and the two stitches on the cat's flank.

'Oooh, my darlin'! What 'ave those nasty men been doin' to you?' She hugged the animal to her and glared at me.

'She's all right, Mrs Beck, she's fine,' I said. 'You can give her a little milk tonight and some solid food tomorrow. There's nothing to worry about.'

She pouted. 'Oh, very well. And now . . .' She gave me a sidelong glance. 'I suppose you'll want your money?'

'Well, er . . .'

'Wait there, then. I'll get it.' She turned and went into the house.

Standing there, leaning against the reeking car, feeling the sting of the scratches on my hands and nose and examining the long tear on my jacket elbow I felt physically and emotionally spent. All I had done this afternoon was spay a cat but I had nothing more to offer.

Apathetically I watched the lady coming down the path. She was carrying a purse. At the gate she stopped and faced me.

'Ten shillin's, wasn't it?'

'That's right.'

She rummaged in the purse for some time before pulling out a ten-shilling note which was regarded sadly.

'Oh Georgina, Georgina, you *are* an expensive pussy,' she soliloquized.

Tentatively I began to extend my hand but she pulled the note away. 'Just a minute, I'm forgettin'. You 'ave to take the stitches out, don't you?'

'Yes, in ten days.'

She set her lips firmly. 'Well there's plenty of time to pay ye then – ye'll be here again.'

'Here again . . . ? But you can't expect . . .'

'I allus think it's unlucky to pay afore a job's finished,' she said. 'Summat terrible might happen to Georgina.'

'But . . . but . . .'

'Nay, ah've made up me mind,' she said. She replaced the money and snapped the purse shut with an air of finality before turning towards the house. Halfway up the path she looked over her shoulder and smiled.

'Aye, that's what I'll do. I'll pay ye when ye come back.'

# nineteen

We were ready to march away from Scarborough. And it was ironical that we were leaving just when the place was beginning to smile on us.

In the May sunshine we stood on parade outside the Grand at 7 a.m. as we had done throughout the Yorkshire winter, mostly in darkness, often with the icy rain blowing in our faces. But now I felt a pang of regret as I looked over the heads at the wide beautiful bay stretching beneath its cliffs to the far headland, the sand clean-washed and inviting, the great blue expanse of sea shimmering and glittering and over everything the delicious sea-smell of salt and seaweed, raising memories of holidays and happy things lost in the war.

'Atten-shun!' Flight Sergeant Blackett's bellow rolled over us as we stiffened in our ranks, every man carrying full kit, our packs braced with sheets of cardboard to give the sharp, rectangular look, hair cut short, boots gleaming, buttons shining like gold. Without our knowing, No. ten ITW had moulded us into a smart, disciplined unit, very different from the shambling, half-baked crew of six months ago. We had all passed our exams and were no longer AC2s but Leading Aircraftmen, and as LAC Herriot my wage had rocketed from three shillings to a dizzying seven and threepence a day.

'Right turn!' Again the roar. 'By the left qui-ick march!'

Arms high, moving as one, we swung past the front of the Grand for the last time. I shot a parting glance at the great building – like a dignified Victorian lady stripped of her finery – and I made a resolve. I would come back some day, when the war was over, and see the Grand Hotel as it should be.

And I did, too. Years later, Helen and I sat in deep arm-chairs in the lounge where the SPs had barked. Waiters padded over the thick carpets with tea and muffins while a string orchestra played selections from *Rose Marie*.

And in the evening we dined in the elegant room with its long unbroken line of window looking down on the sea. This room had been the cold open terrace where I learned to read the Aldis lamp flickering from the lighthouse, but now we sat in luxurious warmth eating grilled sole and watching the lights of the harbour and town beginning to wink in the gathering dusk.

But that was very much in the future as the tramping feet echoed along Huntriss Row on the way to the station and the long lines of blue left the emptying square. We didn't know where we were going, everything was uncertain.

Black's *Veterinary Dictionary* dug into my back through the layer of cardboard. It was an unwieldy article but it reminded me of good days and gave me hope of more to come.

# twenty

'It's the same the whole world over, it's the poor wot gets the blame. It's the rich wot gets the pleasure . . .'

We were on a 'toughening course', living under canvas in the depths of Shropshire, and this was one of the occasions when we were all gathered together – hundreds of sunburned men – in a huge marquee waiting to be addressed by a visiting air commodore.

Before the great man arrived the platform was occupied by a lascivious sergeant who was whittling away the time by leading us in a succession of bawdy ditties accompanied by gestures. 'It's the rich wot gets the . . .', but instead of 'pleasure' he made a series of violent pumping movements with his forearm.

I was intrigued by the reaction of the airman on my right. He was a slim, pink-faced lad of about nineteen and his lank fair hair fell over his face as he jumped up and down. He was really throwing himself into it, bawling out the indelicate words, duplicating the sergeant's gesticulations with maniacal glee. He was, I had recently learned, the son of a bishop.

We had been joined on this course by the Oxford University Air Squadron. They were a group of superior and delicately nurtured young men and since I had spent three full days peeling potatoes with them I had come to know most of them very well. 'Spud bashing' is an unequalled method of becoming familiar with one's fellow men and as, hour after hour, we filled countless bins with our produce, the barriers crumbled steadily until at the end of three days we didn't have many secrets from each other.

The bishop's son had found something hilarious in the idea of a qualified veterinary surgeon leaving his practice to succour his country by removing the skins from thousands of tubers. And I, on the other hand, derived some reward from watching his antics. He was a charming and likeable lad but he seized avidly on anything with the faintest salacious slant. They say parsons' sons are a bit wild when let off the leash, and I suppose an escapee from a bishop's palace is even more susceptible to the blandishments of the big world.

I looked at him again. All around him men were yelling their heads off, but his voice, mouthing the four-letter words with relish, rang above the rest and he followed the actions of the conducting sergeant like a devoted acolyte.

It was all so different from Darrowby. My early days in the RAF with all the swearing and uninhibited conversation made me realize, perhaps for the first time, what kind of a community I had left behind me. Because I often think that one of the least permissive societies in the history of mankind was the agricultural community of rural Yorkshire in the thirties. Among the farmers anything to do with sex or the natural functions was unmentionable.

It made my work more difficult because if the animal's ailment had the slightest sexual connotation its owner would refuse to go into details if Helen or our secretary Miss

Harbottle answered the phone. 'I want the vet to come and see a cow,' was as far as they would go.

Today's case was typical and I looked at Mr Hopps with some irritation.

'Why didn't you say your cow wasn't coming into season? There's a new injection for that now but I haven't got it with me. I can't carry everything in my car, you know.'

The farmer studied his feet. 'Well, it was a lady on t'phone and I didn't like to tell 'er that Snowdrop wasn't bullin'.' He looked up at me sheepishly. 'Can't you do owt about it, then?'

I sighed. 'Maybe I can. Bring me a bucket of hot water and some soap.'

As I lathered my arm I felt a twinge of disappointment. I'd have liked to try that new Prolan injection. But on the other hand there was a certain interest in these rectal examinations.

'Hold her tail, please,' I said, and began to work my hand carefully past the anal ring.

We were doing a lot of this lately. The profession had awakened quite suddenly to the fact that bovine infertility was no longer an impenetrable mystery. We were carrying out more and more of these examinations, and as I say, they had a strange fascination.

Siegfried put it with his usual succinctness one morning.

'James,' he said. 'There is more to be learned up a cow's arse than in many an encyclopaedia.'

And, groping my way into this animal, I could see what he meant. Through the rectal wall I gripped the uterine cervix, then I worked along the right horn. It felt perfectly normal, as did the fallopian tube when I reached it. In another moment the ovary rested between my fingers like a walnut; but it was a walnut with a significant bulge and I smiled to myself. That swelling was the corpus luteum, the 'yellow body' which was exerting its influence on the ovary and preventing the initiation of the normal oestral cycle.

I squeezed gently on the base of the bulge and felt it part from the ovary and swim off into space. That was lovely – just what was required – and I looked happily along the cow's back at the farmer.

'I think I've put things right, Mr Hopps. She should come on within the next day or two and you can get her served right away.'

I withdrew my arm, smeared with filth almost to the shoulder, and began to swill it with the warm water. This was the moment when young people with dewy-eyed ambitions to be veterinary surgeons usually decided to be lawyers or nurses instead. A lot of teenagers came round with me to see practice and it seemed to me that the sooner they witnessed the realities of the job the better it would be for them. A morning's pregnancy diagnoses or something similar had a salutary effect in sorting out the sheep from the goats.

As I left the farm I had the satisfied feeling that I had really done something, and a sensation of relief that Mr Hopps' delicacy hadn't resulted in an abortive visit.

It was strange, but when I returned to the surgery I immediately encountered another example of the same thing.

Mr Pinkerton, a smallholder, was sitting in the office next to Miss Harbottle's desk. By his side sat his farm collie.

'Well, what can I do for you, Mr Pinkerton?' I asked as I closed the door behind me.

The farmer hesitated. 'It's me dog – 'e isn't right.'

'What do you mean? Is he ill?' I bent down and stroked the shaggy head and as the dog leaped up in delight his tail began to beat a booming tom-tom rhythm against the side of the desk.

'Nay, nay, he's right enough in 'imself.' The man was clearly ill at ease.

'Well, what's the trouble? He looks the picture of health to me.'

'Aye, but ah'm a bit worried. Ye see it's 'is . . .' He glanced furtively towards Miss Harbottle. 'It's 'is pencil.'

'What d'you say?'

A faint flush mounted in Mr Pinkerton's thin cheeks. Again he shot a terrified glance at Miss Harbottle. 'It's 'is . . . pencil. There's summat matter with 'is pencil.' He indicated by the merest twitch of his forefinger somewhere in the direction of the animal's belly.

I looked. 'I'm sorry, but I can't see anything unusual.'

'Ah, but there is.' The farmer's face twisted in an agony of embarrassment and he pushed his face close to mine. 'There's summat there,' he said in a hoarse whisper. 'Summat comin' from 'is . . . 'is pencil.'

I got down on my knees and had a closer look, and suddenly all became clear.

'Is that what you mean?' I pointed to a tiny blob of semen on the end of the prepuce.

He nodded dumbly, his face a study in woe.

I laughed. 'Well you can stop worrying. That's nothing abnormal. You might call it an overflow. He's just a young dog, isn't he?'

'Aye, nobbut eighteen months.'

'Well, that's it. He's just too full of the joys. Plenty of good food and maybe not a lot of work to do, eh?'

'Aye, he gets good grub. Nowt but the best. And you're right – I 'aven't much work for him.'

'Well, there you are.' I held out a hand. 'Just cut down his diet and see he gets more exercise and this thing will sort itself out.'

Mr Pinkerton stared at me. 'But aren't you goin' to do anything to 'is . . . 'is . . .' Again he cast an anguished glance at our secretary.

'No, no,' I said. 'I assure you there's nothing wrong with his . . . er . . . pencil. No local trouble at all.'

I could see he was still totally unconvinced so I threw in another ploy. 'I tell you what. I'll give you some mild sedative tablets for him. They'll help a bit.'

I went through to the dispensary and counted the tablets into a box. Back in the office I handed them to the farmer with a confident smile, but his face registered only a deepening misery. Obviously I hadn't explained the thing clearly enough and as I led him along the passage to the front door I talked incessantly, putting the whole business into simple words which I was sure he would understand.

As he stood on the doorstep I gave him a final comforting pat on the shoulder and though I was almost breathless with my own babbling I thought it best to sum up the entire oration before he left.

'So there you are,' I said with a light laugh. 'Reduce his food, see that he gets plenty of work and exercise and give him one of the tablets night and morning.'

The farmer's mouth drooped until I thought he would burst into tears then he turned and trailed down the steps into the street. He took a couple of indeterminate strides then swung round and his voice rose in a plaintive wail.

'But Mr Herriot . . . 'ow about 'is pencil?'

And when little Mr Gilby crashed moaning on the cobbles of his byre floor, my first thought was that it was unfair that it should happen to him of all people.

Because the natural delicacy and reticence of the times were embodied in him to an extreme degree. Even his physical make-up had something ethereal about it; nine stones of tiny bones, taut skin with no fat and a gentle, innocent face, almost child-like despite his fifty years. Nobody had ever heard Mr Gilby swear or use a vulgar expression; in fact he was the only farmer I have ever known who talked about cow's 'manure'.

Besides, as a strict methodist he didn't drink or indulge in worldly pleasures and had never been known to tell a lie. Altogether he was so good that I would have regarded him with deep suspicion if he had been anybody else. But I had come to know Mr Gilby. He was a nice little man, he was as honest as the day. I would have trusted him with my life.

That was why I was so sad to see him lying there. It had happened so quickly. We had just come into the byre and he pointed to a black Angus Cross cow almost opposite the door.

'That's 'er. Got a touch o'cold, I think.' He knew I would want to take the temperature and grasped the tail before putting one foot across the channel so that he could slide between the cow and her neighbour. That was when it happened; when his legs were wide apart in the worst possible position.

In a way I wasn't surprised because that tail had been swishing bad-temperedly as we came in, and I am always a bit wary of black cows anyway. She didn't seem to like our sudden entry and lashed out with her right hind foot with the speed of light, catching him with her flinty hoof full in the crutch as his legs were splayed. He was wearing only frayed, much-washed overall trousers and the protection was nil.

I winced as the foot went home with an appalling thud, but Mr Gilby showed no emotion at all. He dropped as though on the receiving end of a firing squad and lay motionless on the hard stones, his hands clutched between his legs. It was only after several seconds that he began to moan softly.

As I hurried to his aid I felt it was wrong that I should be witnessing this disintegration of his modest façade. The little farmer, I was sure, would rather have died than be caught in this inelegant position, grovelling on the floor gripping frantically at an unmentionable area. I kneeled on the cobbles and patted his shoulder while he fought his inner battle with his agony.

After a while he felt well enough to sit up and I put my arm around him and supported him while perspiration bedewed the greenish pallor of his face. That was when the embarrassment began to creep in, because though he had removed his hands from their compromising position he was clearly deeply ashamed at being caught in a coarse attitude.

I felt strangely helpless. The little man couldn't relieve his feelings in the usual way by cursing the animal and fate in general, nor could I help him to laugh the thing off with a few earthy remarks. This sort of thing happens now and then in the present day and usually gives rise to a certain amount of ripe comment, often embracing the possible effect on the victim's future sex life. It all helps.

But here in Mr Gilby's byre there was only an uncomfortable silence. After a time the colour began to return to his cheeks and the little man struggled slowly to his feet. He took a couple of deep breaths then looked at me unhappily. Obviously he thought he owed me some explanation, even apology, for his tasteless behaviour.

As the minutes passed the tension rose. Mr Gilby's mouth twitched once or twice as though he were about to speak but he seemed unable to find the words. At length he appeared to come to a decision. He cleared his throat, looked around him carefully then put his lips close to my ear. He clarified the whole situation by one hoarsely whispered, deeply confidential sentence.

'Right in the privates, Mr Herriot.'

I referred earlier to the prevailing shyness about the natural functions and this did indeed give rise to problems.

One slight difficulty which all country vets encounter is that there comes a time on a long round when they have to urinate. When I first came to Yorkshire it seemed the most natural thing in the world for me to retire to a corner of a cow byre to relieve myself and it was utterly incomprehensible that anybody of my own sex should find this embarrassing. But it soon became obvious that the farmers were shuffling their feet, looking pointedly in the opposite direction or showing other signs of unease.

My attempts to laugh the incident off met with no success. Jocular remarks thrown over my shoulder like 'Just wringing out a kidney' or 'This method gives instant relief', were greeted with serious nods and mutterings of 'Aye . . . aye . . . aye . . . that's right.' I often had to resort to sneaking into some deserted outhouse as soon as I arrived, but very often the farmer would burst in and catch me in the act and retreat bashfully.

The farmers themselves added to my difficulties by their hospitable custom of pushing large mugs of tea into my hand at every opportunity. At times I shrank from causing offence in the buildings and when under stress took refuge in the open countryside. But even this was fraught with peril, because though I always selected a deserted road with the moors stretching empty to the far horizon the landscape within seconds invariably became black with cars, all driven by women and all bearing down on me at high speed.

I recall with quaking shame one occasion when a carload of middle-aged spinsters stopped and questioned me at length about the quickest way to Darrowby while a dark pool spread accusingly around my feet.

But I suppose there are exceptions to every rule, and there was one time when the reaction to my predicament was different. I had consumed my usual quota of tea and on top of this one kind chap had opened a couple of pint bottles of brown ale after a sweating session castrating calves in a tin-roofed shed. By the time I arrived at old Mr Ainsley's I was in dire straits.

But there was nobody around. I tiptoed into the byre, slunk into a corner and blessedly opened the flood gates. I was in mid flow when I heard the clatter of heavy boots on the cobbles behind me. The old man, shoulders hunched, hands in pockets, was standing there watching me.

Oh dear, it had happened again, but I wasn't going to stop now. With a sickly smile I looked over my shoulder at him.

'Sorry to make free with your cow house like this, Mr Ainsley,' I said in what I hoped was a light, bantering tone. 'But I had no option. When I have to go I just have to go. Maybe I have a weak bladder or something.'

The old man regarded me impassively for a few moments then he nodded his head several times.

'Aye, ah knaw, ah knaw,' he said gloomily. 'You're like me, Mr Herriot. Ah's allus pissin'.'

# twenty-one

Little pictures kept floating up into my mind. Memories from the very early days at Skeldale House. Before the RAF, before Helen . . .

Siegfried and I were at breakfast in the big dining-room. My colleague looked up from a letter he was reading.

'James, do you remember Stewie Brannan?'

I smiled. 'I could hardly forget. That was quite a day at Brawton races.' I would always carry a vivid recollection of Siegfried's amiable college chum with me.

'Yes . . . yes, it was.' Siegfried nodded briefly. 'Well I've got a letter from him here. He's got six kids now, and though he doesn't complain, I don't think life is exactly a picnic working in a dump like Hensfield. Especially when he knocks a bare living out of it.' He pulled thoughtfully at the lobe of his ear. 'You know, James, it would be rather nice if he could have a break. Would you be willing to go through there and run his practice for a couple of weeks so that he could take his family on holiday?'

'Certainly. Glad to. But you'll be a bit pushed here on your own, won't you?'

Siegfried waved a hand. 'It'll do me good. Anyway it's the quiet time for us. I'll write back today.'

Stewie grasped the opportunity eagerly and within a few days I was on the road to Hensfield. Yorkshire is the biggest county in England and it must be the most varied. I could hardly believe it when, less than two hours after leaving the clean grassy fells and crystal air of Darrowby, I saw the forest of factory chimneys spouting from the brown pall of grime.

This was the industrial West Riding and I drove past mills as dark and satanic as any I had dreamed of, past long rows of dreary featureless houses where the workers lived. Everything was black; houses, mills, walls, trees, even the surrounding hillsides, smeared and soiled from the smoke which drifted across the town from a hundred belching stacks.

Stewie's surgery was right in the heart of it, a gloomy edifice in a terrace of sooty stone. As I rang the bell I read the painted board: 'Stewart Brannan MRCVS, Veterinary Surgeon and Canine Specialist.' I was wondering what the Royal College would think about the last part when the door opened and my colleague stood before me.

He seemed to fill the entrance. If anything he was fatter than before, but that was the only difference. Since it was August I couldn't expect him to be wearing his navy nap overcoat, but otherwise he was as I remembered him in Darrowby; the big, meaty, good-natured face, the greasy black hair slicked across the brow which always seemed to carry a gentle dew of perspiration.

He reached out, grabbed my hand and pulled me delightedly through the doorway.

'Jim! Great to see you!' He put an arm round my shoulders as we crossed a dark hallway. 'It's so good of you to help me out like this. The family are thrilled - they're all in the town shopping for the holiday. We've got fixed up in a flat at Blackpool.' His permanent smile widened.

We went into a room at the back where a rickety kitchen-type table stood on brown linoleum. I saw a sink in one corner, a few shelves with bottles and a white-painted cupboard. The atmosphere held a faint redolence of carbolic and cat's urine.

'This is where I see the animals,' Stewie said contentedly. He looked at his watch. 'Twenty past five - I have a surgery at five thirty. I'll show you round till then.'

It didn't take long because there wasn't much to see. I knew there was a more fashionable veterinary firm in Hensfield and that Stewie made his living from the poor people of the town; the whole set-up was an illustration of practice on a shoestring. There didn't seem to be more than one of anything - one straight suture needle, one curved needle, one pair of scissors, one syringe. There was a sparse selection of drugs and an extraordinary array of dispensing bottles and jars. These bottles were of many strange shapes - weird things which I had never seen in a dispensary before.

Stewie seemed to read my thoughts. 'It's nothing great, Jim. I haven't a smart practice and I don't make a lot, but we manage to clear the housekeeping and that's the main thing.'

The phrase was familiar. 'Clear the housekeeping' – that was how he had put it when I first met him at Brawton races. It seemed to be the lodestar of his life.

The end of the room was cut off by a curtain which my colleague drew to one side.

'This is what you might call the waiting room.' He smiled as I looked in some surprise at half a dozen wooden chairs arranged round the three walls. 'No high-powered stuff, Jim, no queues into the streets, but we get by.'

Some of Stewie's clients were already filing in; two little girls with a black dog, a cloth-capped old man with a terrier on a string, a teenage boy carrying a rabbit in a basket.

'Right,' the big man said. 'We'll get started,' He pulled on a white coat, opened the curtain and said, 'First, please.'

The little girls put their dog on the table. He was a long-tailed mixture of breeds and he stood trembling with fear, rolling his eyes apprehensively at the white coat.

'All right, lad,' Stewie murmured. 'I'm not going to hurt you.' He stroked and patted the quivering head before turning to the girls. 'What's the trouble, then?'

'It's 'is leg, 'e's lame,' one of them replied.

As if in confirmation the little dog raised a fore leg and held it up with a pitiful expression. Stewie engulfed the limb with his great hand and palpated it with the utmost care. And it struck me immediately – the gentleness of this shambling bear of a man.

'There's nothing broken,' he said. 'He's just sprained his shoulder. Try to rest it for a few days and rub this in night and morning.'

He poured some whitish liniment from a Winchester bottle into one of the odd-shaped bottles and handed it over.

One of the little girls held out her hand and unclasped her fingers to reveal a shilling in her palm.

'Thanks,' said Stewie without surprise. 'Goodbye.'

He saw several other cases, then as he was on his way to the curtain two grubby urchins appeared through the door at the other end of the room. They carried a clothes basket containing a widely varied assortment of glassware.

Stewie bent over the basket, lifting out HP sauce bottles, pickle jars, ketchup containers and examining them with the air of a connoisseur. At length he appeared to come to a decision.

'Threepence,' he said.

'Sixpence,' said the urchins in unison.

'Fourpence,' grunted Stewie.

'Sixpence,' chorused the urchins.

'Fivepence,' my colleague muttered doggedly.

'Sixpence!' There was a hint of triumph in the cry.

Stewie sighed. 'Go on then.' He passed over the coin and began to stack the bottles under the sink.

'I just scrape off the labels and give them a good boil up, Jim.'

'I see.'

'It's a big saving.'

'Yes, of course.' The mystery of the strangely shaped dispensing bottles was suddenly resolved.

It was six thirty when the last client came through the curtain. I had watched Stewie examining each animal carefully, taking his time and treating their conditions ably within the confines of his limited resources. His charges were all around a shilling to two shillings and it was easy to see why he only just cleared the housekeeping.

One other thing I noticed; the people all seemed to like him. He had no 'front' but he was kind and concerned. I felt there was a lesson there.

The last arrival was a stout lady with a prim manner and a very correct manner of speech.

'My dog was bit last week,' she announced, 'and I'm afraid the wound is goin' antiseptic.'

'Ah yes.' Stewie nodded gravely. The banana fingers explored the tumefied area on the animal's neck with a gossamer touch. 'It's quite nasty, really. He could have an abscess there if we're not careful.'

He took a long time over clipping the hair away, swabbing out the deep puncture with peroxide of hydrogen. Then he puffed in some dusting powder, applied a pad of cotton wool and secured it with a bandage. He followed with an anti-staphylococcal injection and finally handed over a sauce bottle filled to the rim with acriflavine solution.

'Use as directed on the label,' he said, then stood back as the lady opened her purse expectantly.

A long inward struggle showed in the occasional twitches of his cheeks and flickerings of his eyelids but finally he squared his shoulders.

'That,' he said resolutely, 'will be three and sixpence.'

It was a vast fee by Stewie's standards, but probably the minimum in other veterinary establishments, and I couldn't see how he could make any profit from the transaction.

As the lady left, a sudden uproar broke out within the house. Stewie gave me a seraphic smile.

'That'll be Meg and the kids. Come and meet them.'

We went out to the hall and into an incredible hubbub. Children shouted, screamed and laughed, spades and pails clattered, a large ball thumped from wall to wall and above it all a baby bawled relentlessly.

Stewie moved into the mob and extracted a small woman.

'This,' he murmured with quiet pride, 'is my wife.' He gazed at her like a small boy admiring a film star.

'How do you do,' I said.

Meg Brannan took my hand and smiled. Any glamour about her existed only in her husband's eye. A ravaged prettiness still remained but her face bore the traces of some tough years. I could imagine her life of mother, housewife, cook, secretary, receptionist and animal nurse.

'Oh, Mr Herriot, it is good of you and Mr Farnon to help us out like this. We're so looking forward to going away.' Her eyes held a faintly desperate gleam but they were kind.

I shrugged. 'Oh it's a pleasure, Mrs Brannan. I'm sure I'll enjoy it and I hope you all have a marvellous holiday.' I really meant it – she looked as though she needed one.

I was introduced to the children but I never really got them sorted out. Apart from the baby, who yelled indefatigably from leather lungs, I think there were three little boys and two little girls, but I couldn't be sure – they moved around too quickly.

The only time they were silent was for a brief period at supper when Meg fed them and us from a kind of cauldron in which floated chunks of mutton, potatoes and carrots. It was very good, too, and was followed by a vast blancmange with jam on top.

The tumult broke out again very soon as the youngsters raced through their meal and began to play in the room. One thing I found disconcerting was that two biggest boys kept throwing a large, new, painted ball from one to the other across the table as we ate. The parents said nothing about it – Meg, I felt, because she had stopped caring, and Stewie because he never had cared.

Only once when the ball whizzed past my nose and almost carried away a poised spoonful of blancmange did their father remonstrate.

'Now then, now then,' he murmured absently, and the throwing was re-sited more towards the middle of the table.

Next morning I saw the family off. Stewie had changed his dilapidated Austin Seven for a large rust-encrusted Ford V Eight. Seated at the wheel he waved and beamed through the cracked side windows with serene contentment. Meg, by his side, managed a harassed smile and at the other windows an assortment of dogs and children fought for a vantage point. As the car moved away a pram, several suitcases and a cot swayed perilously on the roof, the children yelled, the dogs barked, the baby bawled, then they were gone.

As I re-entered the house the unaccustomed silence settled around me, and with the silence came a faint unease. I had to look after this practice for two weeks and the memory of the thinly furnished surgery was not reassuring. I just didn't have the tools to tackle any major problem.

But it was easy to comfort myself. From what I had seen this wasn't the sort of place where dramatic things happened. Stewie had once said he made most of his living by castrating tom cats and I supposed if you threw in a few ear cankers and minor ailments that would be about it.

The morning surgery seemed to confirm this impression; a few humble folk led in nondescript pets with mild conditions and I happily dispensed a series of Bovril bottles and meat paste jars containing Stewie's limited drug store.

I had only one difficulty and that was with the table, which kept collapsing when I lifted the animals on to it. For some obscure reason it had folding legs held by metal struts underneath and these were apt to disengage at crucial moments, causing the patient to slide abruptly to the floor. After a while I got the hang of the thing and kept one leg jammed against the struts throughout the examination.

It was about 10.30 a.m. when I finally parted the curtains and found the waiting room empty and only the distinctive cat–dog smell lingering on the air. As I locked the door it struck me that I had very little to do till the afternoon surgery. At Darrowby I would have been dashing out to start the long day's driving round the countryside, but here almost all the work was done at the practice house.

I was wondering how I would put the time in after the single outside visit on the book when the door bell rang. Then it rang again followed by a frantic pounding on the wood. I hurried through the curtain and turned the handle. A well dressed young couple stood on the step. The man held a Golden Labrador in his arms and behind them a caravan drawn by a large gleaming car stood by the kerb.

'Are you the vet?' the girl gasped. She was in her twenties, auburn haired, extremely attractive, but her eyes were terrified.

I nodded. 'Yes – yes, I am. What's the trouble?'

'It's our dog.' The young man's voice was hoarse, his face deathly pale. 'A car hit him.'

I glanced over the motionless yellow form. 'Is he badly hurt?'

There were a few moments of silence then the girl spoke almost in a whisper. 'Look at his hind leg.'

I stepped forward and as I peered into the crook of the

man's arm a freezing wave drove through me. The limb was hanging off at the hock. Not fractured but snapped through the joint and dangling from what looked like a mere shred of skin. In the bright morning sunshine the white ends of naked bones glittered with a sickening lustre.

It seemed a long time before I came out of my first shock and found myself staring stupidly at the animal. And when I spoke the voice didn't sound like my own.

'Bring him in,' I muttered, and as I led the way back through the odorous waiting room the realization burst on me that I had been wrong when I thought that nothing ever happened here.

# twenty-two

I held the curtains apart as the young man staggered in and placed his burden on the table.

Now I could see the whole thing; the typical signs of a road accident; the dirt driven savagely into the glossy gold of the coat, the multiple abrasions. But that mangled leg wasn't typical. I had never seen anything like it before.

I dragged my eyes round to the girl. 'How did it happen?'

'Oh, just in a flash.' The tears welled in her eyes. 'We are on a caravanning holiday. We had no intention of staying in Hensfield' – (I could understand that) – 'but we stopped for a newspaper, Kim jumped out of the car and that was it.'

I looked at the big dog stretched motionless on the table. I reached out a hand and gently ran my fingers over the noble outlines of the head.

'Poor old lad,' I murmured and for an instant the beautiful hazel eyes turned to me and the tail thumped briefly against the wood.

'Where have you come from?' I asked.

'Surrey,' the young man replied. He looked rather like the

prosperous young stockbroker that the name conjured up.

I rubbed my chin. 'I see . . .' A way of escape shone for a moment in the tunnel. 'Perhaps if I patch him up you could get him back to your own vet there.'

He looked at his wife for a moment then back at me. 'And what would they do there? Amputate his leg?'

I was silent. If an animal in this condition arrived in one of those high-powered southern practices with plenty of skilled assistance and full surgical equipment that's what they probably would do. It would be the only sensible thing.

The girl broke in on my thoughts. 'Anyway, if it's at all possible to save his leg something has to be done right now. Isn't that so?' She gazed at me appealingly.

'Yes,' I said huskily. 'That's right.' I began to examine the dog. The abrasions on the skin were trivial. He was shocked but his mucous membranes were pink enough to suggest that there was no internal haemorrhage. He had escaped serious injury except for that terrible leg.

I stared at it intently, appalled by the smooth glistening articular surfaces of the tibio-tarsal joint. There was something obscene in its exposure in a living animal. It was as though the hock had been broken open by brutal inquisitive hands.

I began a feverish search of the premises, pulling open drawers, cupboards, opening tins and boxes. My heart leaped at each little find; a jar of catgut in spirit, a packet of lint, a sprinkler tin of iodoform, and – treasure trove indeed – a bottle of barbiturate anaesthetic.

Most of all I needed antibiotics, but it was pointless looking for those because they hadn't been discovered yet. But I did hope fervently for just an ounce or two of sulphanilamide. and there I was disappointed, because Stewie's menage didn't stretch to that. It was when I came upon the box of plaster of paris bandages that something seemed to click.

At that time in the late thirties the Spanish civil war was vivid in people's minds. In the chaos of the later stages there had been no proper medicaments to treat the terrible wounds. They had often been encased in plaster and left, in the grim phrase, to 'stew in their own juice'. Sometimes the results were surprisingly good.

I grabbed the bandages. I knew what I was going to do. Gripped by a fierce determination I inserted the needle into the radial vein and slowly injected the anaesthetic. Kim blinked, yawned lazily and went to sleep. I quickly laid out my meagre armoury then began to shift the dog into a better position. But I had forgotten about the table and as I lifted the hind quarters the whole thing gave way and the dog slithered helplessly towards the floor.

'Catch him!' At my frantic shout the man grabbed the inert form, then I reinserted the slots in their holes and got the wooden surface back on the level.

'Put your leg under there,' I gasped, then turned to the girl. 'And would you please do the same at the other end. This table mustn't fall over once I get started.'

Silently they complied and as I looked at them, each with a leg jammed against the underside, I felt a deep sense of shame. What sort of place did they think this was?

But for a long time after I forgot everything. First I put the joint back in place, slipping the ridges of the tibial-tarsal trochlea into the grooves at the distal end of the tibia as I had done so often in the anatomy lab at college. And I noticed with a flicker of hope that some of the ligaments were still intact and, most important, that a few good blood vessels still ran down to the lower part of the limb.

I never said a word as I cleaned and disinfected the area, puffed iodoform into every crevice and began to stitch. I stitched interminably, pulling together shattered tendons, torn joint capsule and fascia. It was a warm morning and as the sun beat on the surgery window the sweat broke out on my forehead. By the time I had sutured the skin a little river was flowing down my nose and dripping from the tip. Next, more iodoform, then the lint and finally two of the plaster bandages, making a firm cast above the hock down over the foot.

I straightened up and faced the young couple. They had never moved from their uncomfortable postures as they held the table upright but I gazed at them as though seeing them for the first time.

I mopped my brow and drew a long breath. 'Well, that's it. I'd be inclined to leave it as it is for a week, then wherever you are let a vet have a look at it.'

They were silent for a moment then the girl spoke. 'I would rather you saw it yourself.' Her husband nodded agreement.

'Really?' I was amazed. I had thought they would never want to see me, my smelly waiting room or my collapsible table again.

'Yes, of course we would,' the man said. 'You have taken such pains over him. Whatever happens we are deeply grateful to you, Mr Brannan.'

'Oh, I'm not Mr Brannan, he's on holiday. I'm his locum, my name is Herriot.'

He held out his hand. 'Well thank you again, Mr Herriot. I am Peter Gillard and this is my wife. Marjorie.'

We shook hands and he took the dog in his arms and went out to the car.

For the next few days I couldn't keep Kim's leg out of my mind. At times I felt I was crazy trying to salvage a limb that was joined to the dog only by a strip of skin. I had never met anything remotely like it before and in unoccupied moments that hock joint with all its imponderables would float across my vision.

There were plenty of these moments because Stewie's was a restful practice. Apart from the three daily surgeries there was little activity, and in particular the uncomfortable pre-breakfast call so common in Darrowby was unknown here.

The Brannans had left the house and me in the care of Mrs Holroyd, an elderly widow of raddled appearance who slouched around in a flowered overall down which ash cascaded from a permanently dangling cigarette. She wasn't a good riser but she soon had me trained, because after a few mornings when I couldn't find her I began to prepare my own breakfast and that was how it stayed.

However, at other times she looked after me very well. She was what you might call a good rough cook and pushed large tasty meals at me regularly with a 'There y'are, luv,' watching me impassively till I started to eat. The only thing that disturbed me was the long trembling finger of ash which always hung over my food from the cigarette that was part of her.

Mrs Holroyd also took telephone messages when I wasn't around. There weren't many outside visits but two have stuck in my memory.

The first was when I looked on the pad and read, 'Go to Mr Pimmarov to see bulldog,' in Mrs Holroyd's careful back-sloped script.

'Pimmarov?' I asked her. 'Was he a Russian gentleman?'

'Dunno, luv, never asked 'im.'

'Well – did he sound foreign? I mean did he speak broken English?'

'Nay, luv, Yorkshire as me, 'e were.'

'Ah well, never mind, Mrs Holroyd. What's his address?'

She gave me a surprised look. 'How should ah know? He never said.'

'But . . . but Mrs Holroyd. How can I visit him when I don't know where he lives?'

'Well you'll know best about that, luv.'

I was baffled. 'But he must have told you.'

'Now then, young man, Pimmarov was all 'e told me. Said you would know.' She stuck out her chin, her cigarette quivered and she regarded me stonily. Maybe she had had similar sessions with Stewie, but she left me in no doubt that the interview was over.

During the day I tried not to think about it but the knowledge that somewhere in the neighbourhood there was an ailing bulldog that I could not succour was worrying. I just hoped it was nothing fatal.

A phone call at 7 p.m. resolved my fears.

'Is that t'vet?' The voice was gruff and grumpy.

'Yes . . . speaking.'

'Well, ah've been waitin' all day for tha. When are you comin' to see ma flippin' bulldog?'

A light glimmered. But still . . . that accent . . . no suggestion of the Kremlin . . . not a hint of the Steppes.

'Oh, I'm terribly sorry,' I gabbled. 'I'm afraid there's been a little misunderstanding. I'm doing Mr Brannan's work and I don't know the district. I do hope your dog isn't seriously ill.'

'Nay, nay, nobbut a bit o' cough, but ah want 'im seein' to.'

'Certainly, certainly, I'll be right out, Mr . . . er . . .'

'Pym's ma name and ah live next to t'post office in Roff village.'

'Roff?'

'Aye, two miles outside Hensfield.'

I sighed with relief. 'Very good, Mr Pym, I'm on my way.'

'Thank ye.' The voice sounded mollified. 'Well, tha knows me now, don't tha – Pym o' Roff.'

The light was blinding. 'Pym o' Roff!' Such a simple explanation.

A lot of Mrs Holroyd's messages were eccentric but I could usually interpret them after some thought. However one bizarre entry jolted me later in the week. It read simply: 'Johnson, 12, Back Lane, Smiling Harry Syphilis.'

I wrestled with this for a long time before making a diffident approach to Mrs Holroyd.

She was kneading dough for scones and didn't look up as I entered the kitchen.

'Ah, Mrs Holroyd.' I rubbed my hands nervously. 'I see you have written down that I have to go to Mr Johnson's.'

'That's right, luv.'

'Well, er . . . fine, but I don't quite understand the other part – the Smiling Harry Syphilis.'

She shot a sidelong glance at me. 'Well that's 'ow you spell that word, isn't it? Ah looked it up once in a doctor's book in our 'ouse,' she said defensively.

'Oh yes, of course, yes, you've spelled it correctly. It's just the Smiling . . . and the Harry.'

Her eyes glinted dangerously and she blew a puff of smoke at me. 'Well, that's what t'feller said. Repeated it three times. Couldn't make no mistake.'

'I see. But did he mention any particular animal?'

'Naw, 'e didn't. That was what 'e said. That and no more.'
A grey spicule of ash toppled into the basin and was immediately incorporated in the scones. 'Ah do ma best, tha knows!'

'Of course you do, Mrs Holroyd,' I said hastily. 'I'll just pop round to Back Lane now.'

And Mr Johnson put everything right within seconds as he led me to a shed on his allotment.

'It's me pig, guvnor. Covered wi' big red spots. Reckon it's swine erysipelas.'

Only he pronounced it arrysipelas and he did have a slurring mode of speech. I really couldn't blame Mrs Holroyd.

Little things like that enlivened the week but the tension still mounted as I awaited the return of Kim. And even when the seventh day came round I was still in suspense because the Gillards did not appear at the morning surgery. When they failed to show up at the afternoon session I began to conclude that they had had the good sense to return south to a more sophisticated establishment. But at five thirty they were there.

I knew it even before I pulled the curtains apart. The smell of doom was everywhere, filling the premises, and when I went through the curtains it hit me; the sickening stink of putrefaction.

Gangrene. It was the fear which had haunted me all week and now it was realized.

There were about half a dozen other people in the waiting room, all keeping as far away as possible from the young couple who looked up at me with strained smiles. Kim tried to rise when he saw me but I had eyes only for the dangling useless hind limb where my once stone-hard plaster hung in sodden folds.

Of course it had to happen that the Gillards were last in and I was forced to see all the other animals first. I examined them and prescribed treatment in a stupor of misery and shame. What had I done to that beautiful dog out there? I had been crazy to try that experiment. A gangrenous leg meant that even amputation might be too late to save his life. Death from septicaemia was likely now and what the hell could I do for him in this ramshackle surgery?

When at last it was their turn the Gillards came in with Kim limping between them, and it was an extra stab to realize afresh what a handsome animal he was. I bent over the great golden head and for a moment the friendly eyes looked into mine and the tail waved.

'Right,' I said to Peter Gillard, putting my arms under the chest. 'You take the back end and we'll lift him up.'

As we hoisted the heavy dog on to the table the flimsy structure disintegrated immediately, but this time the young people were ready for it and thrust their legs under the struts like a well-trained team till the surface was level again.

With Kim stretched on his side I fingered the bandage. It usually took time and patience with a special saw to remove a plaster but this was just a stinking pulp. My hand shook as I cut the bandage lengthways with scissors and removed it.

I had steeled myself against the sight of the cold dead limb with its green flesh but though there was pus and serous fluid everywhere the exposed flesh was a surprising, healthy pink. I took the foot in my hand and my heart gave a great bound. It was warm and so was the leg, right up to the hock. There was no gangrene.

Feeling suddenly weak I leaned against the table. 'I'm sorry about the terrible smell. All the pus and discharge have been decomposing under the bandage for a week but despite the mess it's not as bad as I feared.'

'Do you . . . do you think you can save his leg?' Marjorie Gillard's voice trembled.

'I don't know. I honestly don't know. So much has to happen. But I'd say it was a case of so far so good.'

I cleaned the area thoroughly with spirit, gave a dusting of iodoform and applied fresh lint and two more plaster bandages.

'You'll feel a lot more comfortable now, Kim,' I said, and the big dog flapped his tail against the wood at the sound of his name.

I turned to his owners. 'I want him to have another week in plaster, so what would you like to do?'

'Oh, we'll stay around Hensfield,' Peter Gillard replied. 'We've found a place for our caravan by the river – it's not too bad.'

'Very well, till next Saturday, then.' I watched Kim hobble out, holding his new white cast high, and as I went back into the house relief flowed over me in a warm wave.

But at the back of my mind the voice of caution sounded. There was still a long way to go . . .

# twenty-three

The second week went by without incident. I had a mildly indecent postcard from Stewie and a view of Blackpool Tower from his wife. The weather was scorching and they were having the best holiday of their lives. I tried to picture them enjoying themselves but I had to wait a few weeks for the evidence – a snap taken by a beach photographer. The whole family were standing in the sea, grinning delightedly into the camera as the wavelets lapped round their ankles. The children brandished buckets and spades, the baby dangled bandy legs towards the water, but it was Stewie who fascinated me. A smile of blissful contentment beamed from beneath a knotted handkerchief, sturdy braces supported baggy flannel trousers rolled decorously calf high. He was the archetype of the British father on holiday.

The last event of my stay in Hensfield was a visit to the local greyhound track. Stewie had an appointment there every other Friday to inspect the dogs.

The Hensfield stadium was not prepossessing from the outside. It had been built in a natural hollow in the sooty hills and was surrounded by ramshackle hoardings.

It was a cool night and as I drove down to the entrance I could hear the tinny blaring from the loudspeakers. It was George Formby singing 'When I'm Cleaning Windows' and strumming on his famous ukelele.

There are all kinds of greyhound tracks. My own experience had been as a student, accompanying vets who officiated under the auspices of the National Greyhound Racing Club, but this was an unlicensed or 'flapping' track, and vastly different. I know there are many highly reputable flapping tracks but this one had a seedy air. It was, I thought wryly, just the sort of place that would be under the care of Stewie.

First I had to go to the manager's office. Mr Coker was a hard-eyed man in a shiny pin-striped suit and he nodded briefly before giving me a calculating stare.

'Your duties here are just a formality,' he said, twisting his features into a smile. 'There'll be nothing to trouble you.'

I had the impression that he was assessing me with quiet satisfaction, looking me up and down, taking in my rumpled jacket and slacks, savouring my obvious youth and inexperience. He kept the smile going as he stubbed out his cigar. 'Well, I hope you'll have a pleasant evening.'

'Thank you,' I replied, and left.

I met the judge, timekeeper and other officials then went down to a long glass-fronted bar overlooking the track. Quite suddenly I felt I was in an alien environment. The place was rapidly filling up and the faces around me were out of a different mould from the wholesome rural countenances of Darrowby. There seemed to be a large proportion of fat men in camel coats with brassy blondes in tow. Shifty-looking characters studied race cards and glared intently at the flickering numbers on the tote board.

I looked at my watch. It was time to inspect the dogs for the first race. 'When I'm cleanin' winders!' bawled George Formby as I made my way round the edge of the track to the paddock, a paved enclosure with a wire-netting surround. Five dogs were being led round the perimeter and I stood in the centre and watched them for a minute or two. Then I halted them and went from one to the other, looking at their

eyes, examining their mouths for salivation and finally pal-
pating their abdomens.

They all appeared bright and normal except number four
which seemed rather full in the stomach region. A greyhound
should only have a light meal on the morning of a race and
nothing thereafter and I turned to the man who was holding
the animal.

'Has this dog been fed within the last hour or two?' I asked.

'No,' he replied. 'He's had nothing since breakfast.'

As I passed my fingers over the abdomen again I had the
feeling that several of the onlookers were watching me with
unusual intentness. But I dismissed it as imagination and
passed on to the next animal.

Number four was second favourite but from the moment
it left its trap it was flagging. It finished last and from the
darkness on the far side of the track a storm of booing broke
out. I was able to make out some of the remarks which came
across on the night air. 'Open your bloody eyes, vet!' was
one of them. And here, in the long, brightly lit bar I could
see people nudging each other and looking at me.

I felt a thrill of anger. Maybe some of those gentlemen
down there thought they could cash in on Stewie's absence.
I probably looked a soft touch to them.

My next visit to the paddock was greeted with friendly
nods and grins from all sides. In fact there was a strong
atmosphere of joviality. When I went round the dogs all was
well until I came to number five and this time I couldn't be
mistaken. Under my probing fingers the stomach bulged
tensely and the animal gave a soft grunt as I squeezed.

'You'll have to take this dog out of the race,' I said. 'He's
got a full stomach.'

The owner was standing by the kennel lad.

'Can't 'ave!' he burst out. 'He's had nowt!'

I straightened up and looked him full in the face but his
eyes were reluctant to meet mine. I knew some of the tricks;
a couple of pounds of steak before the race; a bowlful of
bread crumbs and two pints of milk – the crumbs swelled
beautifully within a short time.

'Would you like me to vomit him?' I began to move away. 'I've got some washing soda in my car – we'll soon find out.'

The man held up a hand. 'Naw, naw, I don't want you messin' about with me dog.' He gave me a malevolent glare and trailed sulkily away.

I had only just got back to the bar when I heard the announcement over the loudspeakers. 'Will the vet please report to the manager's office.'

Mr Coker looked up from his desk and glared at me through a haze of cigar smoke. 'You've taken a dog out of the race!'

'That's right, I'm sorry, but his stomach was full.'

'But damn it . . . I' He stabbed a finger at me then subsided and forced a tortured smile across his face. 'Now, Mr Herriot, we have to be reasonable in these matters. I've no doubt you know your job, but don't you think there's just a chance you could be wrong?' He waved his cigar expansively. 'After all, anybody can make a mistake, so perhaps you would be kind enough to reconsider.' He stretched his smile wider.

'No, I'm sorry, Mr Coker, but that would be impossible.'

There was a long pause. 'That's your last word, then?'

'It is.'

The smile vanished and he gave me a threatening stare.

'Now look,' he said. 'You've mucked up that race and it's a serious matter. I don't want any repetition, do you understand?' He ground his cigar out savagely and his jaw jutted. 'So I hope we won't have any more trouble like this.'

'I hope so, too, Mr Coker,' I said as I went out.

It seemed a long way down to the paddock on my next visit. It was very dark now and I was conscious of the hum of the crowd, the shouts of the bookies and George and his ukelele still going full blast. 'Oh, don't the wind blow cold!' he roared.

This time it was dog number two. I could feel the tension as I examined him and found the same turgid belly.

'This one's out,' I said, and apart from a few black looks there was no argument.

They say bad news travels fast and I had hardly started my

return journey when George was switched off and the loudspeaker asked me to report to the manager's office.

Mr Coker was no longer at his desk. He was pacing up and down agitatedly and when he saw me he did another length of the room before coming to a halt. His expression was venomous and it was clear he had decided that the tough approach was best.

'What the bloody hell do you think you're playing at?' he barked. 'Are you trying to ruin this meeting?'

'No,' I replied. 'I've just taken out another dog which was unfit to run. That's my job. That's what I'm here for.'

His face flushed deep red. 'I don't think you know what you're here for. Mr Brannan goes off on holiday and leaves us at the mercy of a young clever clogs like you, throwing your weight about and spoiling people's pleasure. Wait till I see him!'

'Mr Brannan would have done just the same as I have. Any veterinary surgeon would.'

'Rubbish! Don't tell me what it's all about – you're still wet behind the ears.' He advanced slowly towards me. 'But I'll tell you this, I've had enough! So get it straight, once and for all – no more of this nonsense. Cut it out!'

I felt my heart thudding as I went down to see the dogs for the next race. As I examined the five animals the owners and kennel lads fixed me with a hypnotic stare as though I were some strange freak. My pulse began to slow down when I found there were no full stomachs this time and I glanced back in relief along the line. I was about to walk away when I noticed that number one looked a little unusual. I went back and bent over him, trying to decide what it was about him that had caught my attention. Then I realized what it was – he looked sleepy. The head was hanging slightly and he had an air of apathy.

I lifted his chin and looked into his eyes. The pupils were dilated and every now and then there was a faint twitch of nystagmus. There was absolutely no doubt about it – he had received some kind of sedative. He had been doped.

The men in the paddock were very still as I stood upright.

For a few moments I gazed through the wire netting at the brightly lit green oval, feeling the night air cold on my cheeks. George was still at it on the loudspeakers.

'Oh Mr Wu,' he trilled. 'What can I do?'

Well I knew what I had to do, anyway. I tapped the dog on the back.

'This one's out,' I said.

I didn't wait for the announcement and was half way up the steps to the manager's office before I heard the request for my presence blared across the stadium.

When I opened the door I half expected Mr Coker to rush at me and attack me and I was surprised when I found him sitting at his desk, his head buried in his hands. I stood there on the carpet for some time before he raised a ghastly countenance to me.

'Is it true?' he whispered despairingly. 'Have you done it again?'

I nodded. 'Afraid so.'

His lips trembled but he didn't say anything, and after a brief, disbelieving scrutiny he sank his head in his hands again.

I waited for a minute or two but when he stayed like that, quite motionless, I realized that the audience was at an end and took my leave.

I found no fault with the dogs for the next race and as I left the paddock an unaccustomed peace settled around me. I couldn't understand it when I heard the loudspeaker again – 'Will the vet please report . . .' But this time it was to the paddock and I wondered if a dog had been injured. Anyway, it would be a relief to do a bit of real vetting for a change.

But when I arrived there were no animals to be seen; only two men cradling a fat companion in their arms.

'What's this?' I asked one of them.

'Ambrose 'ere fell down the steps in the stand and skinned 'is knee.'

I stared at him. 'But I'm a vet, not a doctor.'

'Ain't no doctor on the track,' the man mumbled. 'We reckoned you could patch 'im up.'

Ah well, it was a funny night. 'Put him over on that bench,' I said.

I rolled up the trouser to reveal a rather revolting fat dimpled knee. Ambrose emitted a hollow groan as I touched a very minor abrasion on the patella.

'It's nothing much,' I said. 'You've just knocked a bit of skin off.'

Ambrose looked at me tremblingly. 'Aye, but it could go t'wrong way, couldn't it? I don't want no blood poisonin'.'

'All right, I'll put something on it.' I looked inside Stewie's medical bag. The selection was limited but I found some tincture of iodine and I poured a little on a pad of cotton wool and dabbed the wound.

Ambrose gave a shrill yelp. 'Bloody 'ell, that 'urts! What are you doin' to me?' His foot jerked up and rapped me sharply on the elbow.

Even my human patients kicked me, it seemed. I smiled reassuringly. 'Don't worry, it won't sting for long. I'll put a bandage on now.'

I bound up the knee, rolled down the trouser and patted the fat man's shoulder. 'There you are – good as new.'

He got off the bench, nodded, then grimacing painfully, prepared to leave. But an afterthought appeared to strike him and he pulled a handful of change from his pocket. He rummaged among it with a forefinger before selecting a coin which he pressed into my palm.

'There y'are,' he said.

I looked at the coin. It was a sixpence, the fee for my only piece of doctoring of my own species. I stared stupidly at it for a long time and when I finally looked up with the half-formed idea of throwing Ambrose's honorarium back at his head the man was limping into the crowd and was soon lost to sight.

Back in the bar I was gazing apathetically through the glass at the dogs parading round the track when I felt a hand on my arm. I turned and recognized a man I had spotted earlier in the evening. He was one of a group of three men and three women, the men dark, tight-suited, foreign-looking, the women loud and over-dressed. There was something sinister about them and I remembered thinking they could have passed without question as members of the Mafia.

The man put his face close to mine and I had a brief impression of black, darting eyes and a predatory smile.

'Is number three fit ?' he whispered.

I couldn't understand the question. He seemed to know I was the vet and surely it was obvious that if I had passed the dog I considered him fit.

'Yes,' I replied. 'Yes, he is.'

The man nodded vigorously and gave me a knowing glance from hooded eyes. He returned and held a short, intimate conversation with his friends, then they all turned and looked over at me approvingly.

I was bewildered, then it struck me that they may have thought I was giving them an inside tip. To this day I am not really sure but I think that was it because when number three finished nowhere in the race their attitude changed dramatically and they flashed me some black glares which made them look more like the Mafia than ever.

Anyway I had no more trouble down at the paddock for the rest of the evening. No more dogs to take out, which was just as well, because I had made enough enemies for one night.

After the last race I looked around the long bar. Most of the tables were occupied by people having a final drink, but I noticed an empty one and sank wearily into a chair. Stewie had asked me to stay for half an hour after the finish to make sure all the dogs got away safely and I would stick to my bargain even though what I wanted most in the world was to get away from here and never come back.

George was still in splendid voice on the loudspeakers. 'I always get to bed by half past nine,' he warbled, and I felt strongly that he had a point there.

Along the bar counter were assembled most of the people with whom I had clashed; Mr Coker and other officials and dog owners. There was a lot of nudging and whispering and I didn't have to be told the subject of their discussion. The

Mafia, too, were doing their bit with fierce side glances and I could almost feel the waves of antagonism beating against me.

My gloomy thoughts were interrupted by the arrival of a bookie and his clerk. The bookie dropped into a chair opposite me and tipped out a huge leather bag on to the table. I had never seen so much money in my life. I peered at the man over a mountain of fivers and pounds and ten-shilling notes while little streams and tributaries of coins ran down its flanks.

The two of them began a methodical stacking and counting of the loot while I watched hypnotically. They had eroded the mountain to about half its height when the bookie caught my eye. Maybe he thought I looked envious or poverty-stricken or just miserable because he put his finger behind a stray half crown and flicked it expertly across the smooth surface in my direction.

'Get yourself a drink, son,' he said.

It was the second time I had been offered money during the last hour and I was almost as much taken aback as the first time. The bookie looked at me expressionlessly for a moment then he grinned. He had an attractively ugly, good-natured face that I liked instinctively and suddenly I felt grateful to him, not for the money but for the sight of a friendly face. It was the only one I had seen all evening.

I smiled back. 'Thanks,' I said. I lifted the half crown and went over to the bar.

I awoke next morning with the knowledge that it was my last day at Hensfield. Stewie was due back at lunch time.

When I parted the now familiar curtains at the morning surgery I still felt a vague depression, a hangover from my unhappy night at the dog track.

But when I looked into the waiting room my mood lightened immediately. There was only one animal among the odd assortment of chairs but that animal was Kim, massive, golden and beautiful, sitting between his owners, and when he saw me he sprang up with swishing tail and laughing mouth.

There was none of the smell which had horrified me before but as I looked at the dog I could sniff something else – the sweet, sweet scent of success. Because he was touching the ground with that leg; not putting any weight on it but definitely dotting it down as he capered around me.

In an instant I was back in my world again and Mr Cöker and the events of last night were but the dissolving mists of a bad dream.

I could hardly wait to get started.

'Get him on the table,' I cried, then began to laugh as the Gillards automatically pushed their legs against the collapsible struts. They knew the drill now.

I had to restrain myself from doing a dance of joy when I got the plaster off. There was a bit of discharge but when I cleaned it away I found healthy granulation tissue everywhere. Pink new flesh binding the shattered joint together, smoothing over and hiding the original mutilation.

'Is his leg safe now?' Marjorie Gillard asked softly.

I looked at her and smiled. 'Yes, it is. There's no doubt about it now.' I rubbed my hand under the big dog's chin and the tail beat ecstatically on the wood. 'He'll probably have a stiff joint but that won't matter, will it?'

I applied the last of Stewie's bandages then we hoisted Kim off the table.

'Well, that's it,' I said. 'Take him to your own vet in another fortnight. After that I don't think he'll need a bandage at all.'

The Gillards left on their journey back to the south and a couple of hours later Stewie and his family returned. The children were very brown; even the baby, still bawling resolutely, had a fine tan. The skin had peeled off Meg's nose but she looked wonderfully relaxed. Stewie, in open necked shirt and with a face like a boiled lobster, seemed to have put on weight.

'That holiday saved our lives, Jim,' he said. 'I can't thank you enough, and please tell Siegfried how grateful we are.' He looked fondly at his turbulent brood flooding through the house, then as an afterthought he turned to me.

'Is everything all right in the practice?'

'Yes, Stewie, it is. I had my ups and downs of course.'

He laughed. 'Don't we all.'

'We certainly do, but everything's fine now.'

And everything did seem fine as I drove away from the smoke. I watched the houses thin and fall away behind me till the whole world opened out clean and free and I saw the green line of the fells rising over Darrowby.

I suppose we all tend to remember the good things but as it turned out I had no option. The following Christmas I had a letter from the Gillards with a packet of snapshots showing a big golden dog clearing a gate, leaping high for a ball, strutting proudly with a stick in his mouth. There was hardly any stiffness in the leg, they said; he was perfectly sound.

So even now when I think of Hensfield the thing I remember best is Kim.

# twenty-four

There was a lot of shouting in the RAF. The NCOs always seemed to be shouting at me or at somebody else and a lot of them had impressively powerful voices. But for sheer volume I don't think any of them could beat Len Hampson.

I was on the way to Len's farm and on an impulse I pulled up the car and leaned for a moment on the wheel. It was a hot still day in late summer and this was one of the softer corners of the Dales, sheltered by the enclosing fells from the harsh winds which shrivelled all but the heather and the tough moorland grass.

Here, great trees, oak, elm and sycamore in full rich leaf, stood in gentle majesty in the green dips and hollows, their branches quite still in the windless air.

In all the grassy miles around me I could see no movement, nor could I hear anything except the fleeting hum of a bee and the distant bleating of a sheep.

Through the open window drifted the scents of summer; warm grass, clover and the sweetness of hidden flowers. But in the car they had to compete with the all-pervading smell of cow. I had spent the last hour injecting fifty wild cattle and I sat there in soiled breeches and sweat-soaked shirt looking out sleepily at the tranquil landscape.

I opened the door and Sam jumped out and trotted into a nearby wood. I followed him into the cool shade, into the damp secret fragrance of pine needles and fallen leaves which came from the dark heart of the crowding boles. From somewhere in the branches high above I could hear that most soothing of sounds, the cooing of a woodpigeon.

Then, although the farm was two fields away, I heard Len Hampson's voice. He wasn't calling the cattle home or anything like that. He was just conversing with his family as he always did in a long tireless shout.

I drove on to the farm and he opened the gate to let me into the yard.

'Good morning, Mr Hampson,' I said.

'NOW THEN, MR HERRIOT,' he bawled. 'IT'S A GRAND MORNIN'.'

The blast of sound drove me back a step but his three sons smiled contentedly. No doubt they were used to it.

I stayed at a safe distance. 'You want me to see a pig.'

'AYE, A GOOD BACON PIG. GONE RIGHT OFF. IT HASN'T ATE NOWT FOR TWO DAYS.'

We went into the pig pen and it was easy to pick out my patient. Most of the big white occupants careered around at the sight of a stranger, but one of them stood quietly in a corner.

It isn't often a pig will stand unresisting as you take its temperature but this one never stirred as I slipped the thermometer into its rectum. There was only a slight fever but the animal had the look of doom about it; back slightly arched, unwilling to move, eyes withdrawn and anxious.

I looked up at Len Hampson's red-faced bulk leaning over the wall of the pen.

'Did this start suddenly or gradually?' I asked.

'RIGHT SUDDEN!' In the confined space the full throated yell was deafening. 'HE WERE AS RIGHT AS NINEPENCE ON MONDAY NIGHT AND LIKE THIS ON TUESDAY MORNIN'.'

I felt my way over the pig's abdomen. The musculature was tense and boardlike and the abdominal contents were difficult to palpate because of this, but the whole area was tender to the touch.

'I've seen them like this before,' I said. 'This pig has a ruptured bowel. They do it when they are fighting or jostling each other, especially when they are full after a meal.'

'WHAT'S GOIN' TO 'APPEN THEN?'

'Well, the food material has leaked into the abdomen, causing peritonitis. I've opened up pigs like this and they are a mass of adhesions – the abdominal organs all growing together. I'm afraid the chances of recovery are very small.'

He took off his cap, scratched his bald head and replaced the tattered headgear. 'THAT'S A BUGGER. GOOD PIG 'AN ALL. IS IT 'OPELESS?' He still gave tongue at the top of his voice despite his disappointment.

'Yes, I'm afraid it's pretty hopeless. They usually eat very little and just waste away. It would really be best to slaughter him.'

'NAY, AH DON'T LIKE THAT MUCH! AH ALLUS LIKE TO 'AVE A GO. ISN'T THERE SUMMAT WE CAN DO? WHERE THERE'S LIFE THERE'S 'OPE, THA KNAWS.'

I smiled. 'I suppose there's always some hope, Mr Hampson.'

'WELL THEN, LET'S GET ON. LET'S TRY!'

'All right.' I shrugged. 'He's not really in acute pain – more discomfort – so I suppose there's no harm in treating him. I'll leave you a course of powders.'

As I pushed my way from the pen I couldn't help noticing the superb sleek condition of the other pigs.

'My word,' I said. 'These pigs are in grand fettle. I've never seen a better lot. You must feed them well.'

It was a mistake. Enthusiasm added many decibels to his volume.

'*Aye!*' he bellowed. 'YOU'VE GOT TO GIVE STOCK A BIT O' GOOD STUFF TO MEK 'EM DO RIGHT!'

My head was still ringing when I reached the car and opened the boot. I handed over a packet of my faithful sulphonamide powders. They had done great things for me but I didn't expect much here.

It was strange that I should go straight from the chief shouter of the practice to the chief whisperer. Elijah Wentworth made all his communications *sotto voce*.

I found Mr Wentworth hosing down his cow byre and he turned and looked at me with his habitual serious expression. He was a tall thin man, very precise in his speech and ways, and though he was a hard-working farmer he didn't look like one. This impression was heightened by his clothes which were more suited to office work than his rough trade.

A fairly new trilby hat sat straight on his head as he came over to me. I was able to examine it thoroughly because he came so close that we were almost touching noses.

He took a quick look around him. 'Mr Herriot,' he whispered, 'I've got a real bad case.' He spoke always as though every pronouncement was of the utmost gravity and secrecy.

'Oh I'm sorry to hear that. What's the trouble?'

'Fine big bullock, Mr Herriot. Goin' down fast.' He moved in closer till he could murmur directly into my ear. 'I suspect TB.' He backed away, face drawn.

'That doesn't sound so good,' I said. 'Where is he?'

The farmer crooked a finger and I followed him into a loose box. The bullock was a Hereford Cross and should have weighed about ten hundredweight, but was gaunt and emaciated. I could understand Mr Wentworth's fears, but I was beginning to develop a clinical sense and it didn't look like TB to me.

'Is he coughing?' I asked.

'No, never coughs, but he's a bit skittered.'

I went over the animal carefully and there were a few things – the submaxillary oedema, the pot-bellied appearance, the pallor of the mucous membranes – which made diagnosis straightforward.

'I think he's got liver fluke, Mr Wentworth. I'll take a dung sample and have it examined for fluke eggs but I want to treat him right away.'

'Liver fluke? Where would he pick that up?'

'Usually from a wet pasture. Where has he been running lately?'

The farmer pointed through the door. 'Over yonder. I'll show you.'

I walked with him a few hundred yards and through a couple of gates into a wide flat field lying at the base of the fell. The squelchy feel of the turf and the scattered tufts of bog grass told the whole story.

'This is just the place for it,' I said. 'As you know, it's a parasite which infests the liver, but during its life cycle it has to pass through a snail and that snail can only live where there is water.'

He nodded slowly and solemnly several times then began to look around him and I knew he was going to say something. Again he came very close then scanned the horizon anxiously. In all directions the grassland stretched empty and bare for miles but he still seemed worried he might be overheard.

We were almost cheek to cheek as he breathed the words into my ear. 'Ah know who's to blame for this.'

'Really? Who is that?'

He made another swift check to ensure that nobody had sprung up through the ground then I felt his hot breath again. 'It's me landlord.'

'How do you mean?'

'Won't do anything for me.' He brought his face round and looked at me wide-eyed before taking up his old position by my ear. 'Been goin' to drain this field for years but done nowt.'

I moved back. 'Ah well, I can't help that, Mr Wentworth.

In any case there's other things you can do. You can kill the snails with copper sulphate – I'll tell you about that later – but in the meantime I want to dose your bullock.'

I had some hexachlorethane with me in the car and I mixed it in a bottle of water and administered it to the animal. Despite his bulk he offered no resistance as I held his lower jaw and poured the medicine down his throat.

'He's very weak, isn't he?' I said.

The farmer gave me a haggard look. 'He is that. I doubt he's a goner.'

'Oh don't give up hope, Mr Wentworth. I know he looks terrible but if it is fluke then the treatment will do a lot for him. Let me know how he goes on.'

It was about a month later, on a market day, and I was strolling among the stalls which packed the cobbles. In front of the entrance to the Drovers' Arms the usual press of farmers stood chatting among themselves, talking business with cattle dealers and corn merchants, while the shouts of the stallholders sounded over everything.

I was particularly fascinated by the man in charge of the sweet stall. He held up a paper bag and stuffed into it handfuls of assorted sweetmeats while he kept up a nonstop brazen-voiced commentary.

'Lovely peppermint drops! Delicious liquorice allsorts! How about some sugar candies! A couple o' bars o' chocolate! Let's 'ave some butterscotch an' all! Chuck in a beautiful slab o' Turkish Delight!' Then holding the bulging bag aloft in triumph ''ere! 'ere! Who'll give me a tanner for the lot?'

Amazing, I thought as I moved on. How did he do it? I was passing the door of the Drovers when a familiar voice hailed me.

'HEY! MR HERRIOT!' There was no mistaking Len Hampson. He hove in front of me, red-faced and cheerful. 'REMEMBER THAT PIG YE DOCTORED FOR ME?' He had clearly consumed a few market-day beers and his voice was louder than ever.

The packed mass of farmers pricked up their ears. There is nothing so intriguing as the ailments of another farmer's livestock.

'Yes, of course, Mr Hampson,' I replied.

'WELL 'E NEVER DID NO GOOD!' bawled Len.

I could see the farmers' faces lighting up. It is more interesting still when things go wrong.

'Really? Well I'm sorry.'

'NAW 'E DIDN'T. AH'VE NEVER SEEN A PIG GO DOWN AS FAST!'

'Is that so?'

'AYE, FLESH JUST MELTED OFF 'IM!'

'Oh, what a pity. But if you recall I rather expected . . .'

'WENT DOWN TO SKIN AND BONE 'E DID!' The great bellow rolled over the market place, drowning the puny cries of the stallholders. In fact the man with the sweets had suspended operations and was listening with as much interest as the others.

I looked around me uneasily. 'Well, Mr Hampson, I did warn you at the time . . .'

'LIKE A WALKIN' SKELETON 'E WERE! NEVER SEEN SUCH A OBJECK!'

I realized Len wasn't in the least complaining. He was just telling me, but for all that I wished he would stop.

'Well, thank you for letting me know,' I said. 'Now I really must be off . . .'

'AH DON'T KNOW WHAT THEM POWDERS WERE YOU GAVE 'IM.'

I cleared my throat. 'Actually they were . . .'

'THEY DID 'IM NO BLOODY GOOD ANY ROAD!'

'I see. Well as I say, I have to run . . .'

'AH GOT MALLOCK TO KNOCK 'IM ON T'HEAD LAST WEEK.'

'Oh dear . . .'

'FINISHED UP AS DOG MEAT, POOR BUGGER!'

'Quite . . . quite . . .'

'WELL, GOOD DAY TO YE, MR HERRIOT.' He turned and walked away, leaving a quivering silence behind him.

With an uncomfortable feeling that I was the centre of

attention I was about to retreat hastily when I felt a gentle hand on my arm. I turned and saw Elijah Wentworth.

'Mr Herriot,' he whispered. 'About that bullock.'

I stared at him, struck by the coincidence. The farmers stared, too, but expectantly.

'Yes, Mr Wentworth?'

'Well now, I'll tell you.' He came very near and breathed into my ear. 'It was like a miracle. He began to pick up straight away after you treated him.'

I stepped back. 'Oh marvellous! But speak up, will you, I can't quite hear you.' I looked around hopefully.

He came after me again and put his chin on my shoulder. 'Yes, I don't know what you gave 'im but it was wonderful stuff. I could hardly believe it. Every day I looked at 'im he had put on a bit more.'

'Great! But do speak a little louder,' I said eagerly.

'He's as fat as butter now.' The almost inaudible murmur wafted on my cheek. 'Ah'm sure he'll get top grade at the auction mart.'

I backed away again. 'Yes . . . yes . . . what was that you said?'

'I was sure he was dyin', Mr Herriot, but you saved him by your skill,' he said, but every word was pianissimo, sighed against my face.

The farmers had heard nothing and, their interest evaporating, they began to talk among themselves. Then as the man with the sweets started to fill his bags and shout again Mr Wentworth moved in and confided softly and secretly into my private ear.

'That was the most brilliant and marvellous cure I 'ave ever seen.'

# twenty-five

It must be unusual to feel senile in one's twenties, but it was happening to me. There were a few men of my own age among my RAF friends but for the most part I was surrounded by eighteen- and nineteen-year-olds.

It seemed that the selection boards thought this the optimum age for training pilots, navigators and air gunners and I often wondered how we elderly gentlemen had managed to creep in.

These boys used to pull my leg. The fact that I was not merely married but a father put me in the dotage class, and the saddest part was that I really did feel old in their company. They were all having the most marvellous time; chasing the local girls, drinking, going to dances and parties, carried along on the frothy insouciance which a war engenders. And I often thought that if it had all happened a few years earlier I would have been doing the same.

But it was no good now. Most of me was still back in Darrowby. During the day there was enough pressure to keep my mind occupied but in the evenings when I was off the leash all I wanted to do were the simple things I had done with Helen; the long games of bezique by the fireside in our bed-sitter, tense battles on the push-ha'penny board; we even used to throw rings at hooks on a board on the wall. Kids' games after a hard slog round the practice, but even now as I look down the years I know I have never found a better way of living.

It was when we were lying in bed one night that Helen brought up the subject of Granville Bennett.

'Jim,' she murmured sleepily. 'Mr Bennett phoned again today. And his wife rang last week. They keep asking us to have a meal with them.'

'Yes . . . yes . . .' I didn't want to talk about anything at that moment. This was always a good time. The dying flames sent lights and shadows dancing across the ceiling, Oscar

Rabin's band was playing *Deep Purple* on the bedside radio Ewan Ross gave us for a wedding present and I had just pulled off an unexpected victory at push-ha'penny. Helen was a dab hand at that game, urging the coins expertly up the board with the ball of her thumb, her lips pushed forward in a pout of concentration. Of course she had a lifetime of experience behind her while I was just learning, and it was inevitable that I seldom won. But I had done it tonight and I felt good.

My wife nudged me with her knee. 'Jim, I can't understand you. You never seem to do anything about it. And yet you say you like him.'

'Oh, I do, he's a grand chap, one of the best.' Everybody liked Granville, but at the same time there were many strong men who dived down alleys at the sight of him. I didn't like to tell Helen that every time I came into contact with him I got my wings singed. I fully realized that he meant well, that the whole thing was a natural extension of his extreme generosity. But it didn't help.

'And you said his wife was very nice, too.'

'Zoe? Oh yes, she's lovely.' And she was, too, but thanks to her husband she had never seen me in any other role than a drunken hulk. My toes curled under the blankets. Zoe was beautiful, kind and intelligent – just the kind of woman you wanted to observe you staggering and hiccuping all over the place. In the darkness I could feel the hot blush of shame on my cheeks.

'Well then,' Helen continued, with the persistence that is part of even the sweetest women. 'Why don't we accept their invitation? I'd rather like to meet them – and it's a bit embarrassing when they keep phoning.'

I turned on my side. 'Okay, we'll go one of these days, I promise.'

But if it hadn't been for the little papilloma on Sam's lip I don't think we would ever have got there. I noticed the thing – a growth smaller than a pea – near the left commissure when I was giving our beagle an illicit chocolate biscuit. It was a typical benign tumour and on anybody else's dog I should have administered a quick local and whipped it off in a minute. But since it was Sam I turned pale and phoned Granville.

I have always been as soppy as any old lady over my pets and I suspect many of my colleagues are the same. I listened apprehensively to the buzz-buzz at the far end, then the big voice came on the line.

'Bennett here.'

'Hello, Granville, it's . . .'

'Jim!' The boom of delight was flattering. 'Where have you been hiding yourself, laddie?'

He didn't know how near he was to the truth. I told him about Sam.

'Doesn't sound much, old son, but I'll have a look at him with pleasure. Tell you what. We've been trying to get you over here for a meal – why not bring the little chap with you?'

'Well . . .' A whole evening in Granville's hands – it was a daunting prospect.

'Now don't mess about, Jim. You know, there's a wonderful Indian restaurant in Newcastle. Zoe and I would love to take you both out there. It's about time we met your wife, isn't it?'

'Yes . . . of course it is. . . . Indian restaurant, eh?'

'Yes, laddie. Superb curries – mild, medium or blast your bloody head off. Onion bhajis, bhuna lamb, gorgeous nan bread.'

My mind was working fast. 'Sounds marvellous, Granville.' It did seem fairly secure. He was most dangerous on his own territory and it would take forty-five minutes' driving each way to Newcastle. Then maybe an hour and a half in the restaurant. I should be reasonably safe for most of the evening. There was just the bit at his house before we left – that was the only worry.

It was uncanny how he seemed to read my thoughts. 'Before we leave, Jim, we'll have a little session in my garden.'

'Your garden?' It sounded strange in November.

'That's right, old lad.'

Ah well, maybe he was proud of his late chrysanthemums, and I couldn't see myself coming to much harm there. 'Well, fine, Granville. Maybe Wednesday night?'

'Lovely, lovely, lovely – can't wait to meet Helen.'

Wednesday was one of those bright frosty late autumn days which turn misty in the afternoon and by six o'clock the countryside was blanketed by one of the thickest fogs I had ever seen in Yorkshire.

Creeping along in our little car, my nose almost on the windscreen, I muttered against the glass.

'God's truth, Helen, we'll never get to Newcastle tonight! I know Granville's some driver but you can't see ten yards out there.'

Almost at walking pace we covered the twenty miles to the Bennett residence and it was with a feeling of relief that I saw the brightly lit doorway rising out of the mirk.

Granville, as vast and impressive as ever, was there in the hall with arms outspread. Bashfulness had never been one of his problems and he folded my wife in a bear-like embrace.

'Helen, my pet,' he said and kissed her fondly and lingeringly. He stopped to take a breath, regarded her for a moment with deep appreciation then kissed her again.

I shook hands decorously with Zoe and the two girls were introduced. They made quite a picture standing there. An attractive woman is a gift from heaven and it was a rare bonus to see two of them in close proximity. Helen very dark and blue-eyed, Zoe brown-haired with eyes of greyish-green, but both of them warm and smiling.

Zoe had her usual effect on me. That old feeling was welling up; the desire to look my best, in fact better than my best. I cast a furtive glance at the hall mirror. Immaculately suited, clean shirted, freshly shaven, I was sure I projected the desired image of the clean-limbed young veterinary surgeon, the newly married man of high principles and impeccable behaviour.

I breathed a silent prayer of thanks that at last she was seeing me stone cold sober and normal. Tonight I would expunge all her squalid memories of me from her mind.

'Zoe, my sweet,' carolled Granville. 'Take Helen into the garden while I see Jim's dog.'

I blinked. The garden in this fog. I just didn't get it, but I was too anxious about Sam to give the thing much thought. I opened the car door and the beagle trotted into the house.

My colleague greeted him with delight. 'Come inside, my little man.' Then he hollered at the top of his voice. 'Phoebe! Victoria! Yoo-hoo! Come and meet cousin Sam!'

The obese Staffordshire bull terrier waddled in, closely followed by the Yorkie, who bared her teeth in an ingratiating smile at all present.

After the dogs had met and exchanted pleasantries Granville lifted Sam into his arms.

'Is that what you mean, Jim? Is that what you're worried about?'

I nodded dumbly.

'Good God, I could take a deep breath and blow the damn thing off!' He looked at me incredulously and smiled. 'Jim, old lad, why are you so daft about your dog?'

'Why do you call Phoebe Phoebles?' I countered swiftly.

'Oh well . . .' He cleared his throat. 'I'll get my equipment. Hang on a minute.'

He disappeared and came back with a syringe and scissors. About half a cc was enough to numb the part, then he snipped off the papilloma, applied some stypic and put the beagle on the floor. The operation took about two minutes but even in that brief spell his unique dexterity was manifest.

'That'll be ten guineas, Mr Herriot,' he murmured, then gave a shout of laughter. 'Come on, let's get into the garden. Sam will be quite happy with my dogs.'

He led me out of the back door and we stumbled through the fog by a rockery and rose bushes. I was just wondering how on earth he expected to show me anything in this weather when we came up against a stone outhouse. He threw open the door and I stepped into a brightly lit, sparkling Aladdin's cave.

It was quite simply a fully fitted bar. At the far end a polished counter with beer handles and, behind, a long row of bottles of every imaginable liquor. A fire crackled in the hearth and hunting prints, cartoons and bright posters looked down from the walls. It was completely authentic.

Granville saw my astonished face and laughed. 'All right, eh, Jim? I thought it would be a nice idea to have my own little pub in the garden. Rather cosy, isn't it?'

'Yes . . . yes indeed . . . charming.'

'Good, good.' My colleague slipped behind the counter. 'Now what are you going to have?'

Helen and Zoe took sherry and I made a quick decision to stick to one fairly harmless drink.

'Gin and tonic, please, Granville.'

The girls received a normal measure of sherry but when the big man took my glass over to the gin bottle hanging on the wall his hand seemed to be overcome by an uncontrollable trembling. The bottle was upended with one of those little optic attachments you push up with the rim of the glass to give a single measure.

But as I say, as Granville inserted the neck of the bottle into the glass his whole arm jerked repeatedly as though he were going into a convulsion. It was obvious that the result would be about six gins instead of one and I was about to remonstrate when he took the glass away and topped it up quickly with tonic, ice and sliced lemon.

I looked at it apprehensively. 'Rather a big one, isn't it?'

'Not at all, laddie, nearly all tonic. Well, cheers, so nice to see you both.'

And it certainly was. They were generous, warm people and veterinary folk like ourselves. I felt a gush of gratitude for the friendliness they had always shown me and as I sipped my drink, which was chokingly strong, I felt as I had often done that these contacts were one of the brightest rewards of my job.

Granville held out his hand. 'Have another, laddie.'

'Well, hadn't we better be getting on our way? It's a terrible night – in fact I don't see us ever getting to Newcastle in this fog.'

'Nonsense, old son.' He took my glass, reached up to the

gin bottle and again was seized with a series of violent tremors of the forearm. 'No problem, Jim. Straight along the north road – half an hour or so – know it like the back of my hand.'

The four of us stood around the fire. The girls clearly had a lot to say to each other and Granville and I, like all vets, talked shop. It is wonderful how easy veterinary practice is in a warm room with good company and a dollop of alcohol in the stomach.

'One for the road, Jim,' my colleague said.

'No really, Granville, I've had enough,' I replied firmly. 'Let's be off.'

'Jim, Jim.' The familiar hurt look was creeping over his face. 'There's no rush. Look, we'll just have this last one while I tell you about this gorgeous restaurant.'

Once more he approached the gin bottle and this time the rigor lasted so long I wondered if he had some history of malaria.

Glass in hand he expounded. 'It's not just the curry, the cooking in general is exquisite.' He put his fingers to his lips and blew a reverent kiss into space. 'The flavours are unbelievable. All the spices of the orient, Jim.'

He went on at length and I wished he would stop because he was making me hungry. I had had a hard day round the farms and had eaten very little with the evening's feast in view, and as my colleague waved his hand around and drew word pictures of how they blended the rare herbs with the meat and fish, then served it on a bed of saffron rice, I was almost drooling.

I was relieved when I got through the third massive drink and Granville squeezed round to the front of the bar as if ready to go. We were on our way out when a man's bulk loomed in the doorway.

'Raymond!' cried Granville in delight. 'Come in, I've been wanting you to meet Jim Herriot. Jim, this is one of my neighbours – likes a bit of gardening, don't you Raymond?'

The man replied with a fat chuckle. 'Right, old boy! Splendid garden, this!' Granville seemed to know a lot of large, red-faced hearty men and this was one more.

My friend was behind the counter again. 'We must just have one with Raymond.'

I felt trapped as he again pressed my glass against the bottle and went into another paroxysm, but the girls didn't seem to mind. They were still deep in conversation and seemed unaware of the passage of time or the ravages of hunger.

Raymond was just leaving when Tubby Pinder dropped in. He was another enthusiastic horticulturist and I wasn't surprised to see that he was large, red-faced and hearty.

We had to have one with Tubby and I noticed with some alarm that after another palsied replenishment of my glass he had to replace the empty gin bottle with a fresh one. If the first one had been full then I had consumed nearly all of it.

I could hardly believe it when at last we were in the hall putting on our coats. Granville was almost purring with contentment.

'You two are going to love this place. It will be a joy to lead you through the menu.'

Outside the fog was thicker than ever. My colleague backed his enormous Bentley from the garage and began to usher us inside with great ceremony. He installed Helen and Zoe in the back, clucking solicitously over them, then he helped me into the passenger seat in front as though I were a disabled old man, tucking my coat in, adjusting the angle of the seat for maximum comfort, showing me how the cigar lighter worked, lighting up the glove compartment, enquiring which radio programme I desired.

At last he himself was in residence behind the wheel, massive and composed. Beyond the windscreen the fog parted for a second to show a steep, almost vertical grassy bank opposite the house, then it closed down like a dirty yellow curtain cutting off everything.

'Granville,' I said. 'We'll never get to Newcastle in this. It's over thirty miles.'

He turned and gave me a gentle smile. 'Absolutely no problem, laddie. We'll be there in half an hour, sampling that wonderful food. Tandoori chicken, all the spices of the orient, old son. Don't worry about a thing – I really know these roads. No chance of losing my way.'

He started the engine and drove confidently off, but unfortunately instead of taking the orthodox route along the road he proceeded straight up the grassy bank. He didn't seem to notice as the nose of the great car rose steadily higher, but when we had achieved an angle of forty-five degrees Zoe broke in gently from the back.

'Granville, dear, you're on the grass.'

My colleague looked round in some surprise. 'Not at all, my love. The road slopes a little here if you remember.' He kept his foot on the throttle.

I said nothing as my feet rose and my head went back. There was a point when the Bentley was almost perpendicular and I thought we were going over backwards, then I heard Zoe again.

'Granville, darling.' There was a hint of urgency in her tone. 'You're going up the bank.'

This time it seemed her husband was prepared to concede a little.

'Yes . . . yes, my pet,' he murmured as we hung there, all four of us gazing up at the fog-shrouded sky. 'Possibly I have strayed a little on to the verge.'

He took his foot off the brake and the car shot backwards at frightening speed into the darkness. We were brought up by a grinding crunch from the rear.

Zoe again: 'You've hit Mrs Thompson's wall, dear.'

'Have I, sweetheart? Ah, one moment. We'll soon be on our way.'

With undiminished aplomb he let in his clutch and we surged forward powerfully. But only for two seconds. From the gloom ahead there sounded a dull crash followed by a tinkling of glass and metal.

'Darling,' Zoe piped. 'That was the thirty miles an hour sign.'

'Was it really, my angel?' Granville rubbed his hand on the window. 'You know, Jim, the visibility isn't too good.'

He paused for a moment. 'Perhaps it would be a good idea if we postponed our visit till another time.'

He manoeuvred the big car back into the garage and we got out. We had covered, I should think, about five yards on our journey to Newcastle.

Back in the garden bar, Granville was soon in full cry again. And I was all for it because my earlier trepidation had vanished entirely. I was floating in a happy haze and I offered no resistance as my colleague jerked and twitched more samples from the gin bottle.

Suddenly he held up a hand. 'I'm sure we're all starving. Let's have some hot dogs!'

'Hot dogs?' I cried. 'Splendid idea!' It was a long call from all the spices of the orient but I was ready for anything.

'Zoe, sweet,' he said. 'We can use the big can of saveloy sausages if you would just heat it up.'

His wife left for the kitchen and Helen touched my arm.

'Jim,' she said. 'Saveloys . . . ?'

I knew what she meant. I have a pretty good digestion but there are certain things I can't eat. A single saveloy was enough to bring my entire metabolism to a halt, but at that moment it seemed a pettifogging detail.

'Oh don't worry, Helen,' I whispered, putting my arm round her. 'They won't hurt me.'

When Zoe came back with the food Granville was in his element, slicing the juicy smoked sausages lengthways, slapping mustard on them and enclosing them in rolls.

As I bit into the first one I thought I had never tasted anything so delicious. Chewing happily I found it difficult to comprehend my previous ridiculous prejudice.

'Ready for another, old son?' Granville held up a loaded roll.

'Sure! These are absolutely marvellous. Best hot dogs I've ever tasted!' I munched it down quickly and reached for a third.

I think it was when I had downed five of them that my friend prodded me in the ribs.

'Jim, lad,' he said between chews. 'We want a drop of beer to wash these down, don't you agree?'

I waved an arm extravagantly. 'Of course we do! Bloody gin's no good for this job!'

Granville pulled two pints of draught. Powerful delicious ale which flowed in a cooling wave over my inflamed mucous membranes, making me feel I had been waiting for it all my life. We each had three pints and another hot dog or two while waves of euphoria billowed around me.

The occasional anxious glance from Helen didn't worry me in the least. She was making signs that it was time to go home, but the very idea was unthinkable. I was having the time of my life, the world was a wonderful place and this little private pub was the finest corner of it.

Granville put down a half-eaten roll. 'Zoe, my precious, it would be nice to have something sweet to top this off. Why don't you bring out some of those little gooey things you made yesterday?'

She produced a plateful of very rich-looking cakelets. I do not have a sweet tooth and normally skip this part of the meal but I bit into one of Zoe's creations with relish. It was beautifully made and I could detect chocolate, marzipan, caramel and other things.

It was when I was eating the third that matters began to deteriorate. I found that my merry chatter had died and it was Granville doing all the talking, and as I listened to him owlishly I was surprised to see his face becoming two faces which floated apart and came together repeatedly. It was an astonishing phenomenon and it was happening with everything else in the room.

And I wasn't feeling so healthy now. That boundless vigour was no longer surging through my veins and I felt only a great weariness and a rising nausea.

I lost count of time around then. No doubt the conversation went on among the four of us but I can't remember any of it and my next recollection was of the party breaking up. Granville was helping Helen on with her coat and there was a general air of cheerful departure.

'Ready, Jim?' my friend said briskly.

I nodded and got slowly to my feet and as I swayed he put his arm round me and assisted me to the door. Outside, the fog had cleared and a bright pattern of stars overhung the village, but the clean cold air only made me feel worse and I stumbled through the darkness like a sleepwalker. When I reached the car a long griping spasm drove through me, reminding me horribly of the sausages, the gin and the rest. I groaned and leaned on the roof.

'Maybe you'd better drive, Helen,' my colleague said. He was about to open the door when, with a dreadful feeling of helplessness, I began to slide along the metal.

Granville caught my shoulders. 'He'd be better in the back,' he gasped and began to lug me on to the seat. 'Zoe, sweetheart, Helen, love, grab a leg each, will you? Fine, now I'll get round the other side and pull him in.'

He trotted round to the far side, opened the door and hauled at my shoulders.

'Down a bit your side, Helen, dear. Now to me a little. Up a trifle your side, Zoe, pet. Now back to you a bit. Lovely, lovely.'

Clearly he was happy at his work. He sounded like an expert furniture remover and through the mists I wondered bitterly how many inert forms he had stuffed into their cars after an evening with him.

Finally they got me in, half lying across the back seat. My face was pressed against the side window and from the outside it must have been a grotesque sight with the nose squashed sideways and a solitary dead-mackerel eye staring sightlessly into the night.

With an effort I managed to focus and saw Zoe looking down at me anxiously. She gave a tentative wave of goodbye but I could produce only a slight twitch of the cheek in reply.

Granville kissed Helen fondly then slammed the car door. Moving back, he peered in at me and brandished his arms.

'See you soon, I hope, Jim. It's been a lovely evening!' His big face was wreathed in a happy smile and as we drove away my final impression was that he was thoroughly satisfied.

# twenty-six

Being away from Darrowby and living a different life I was able to stand back and assess certain things objectively. I asked myself many questions. Why, for instance, was my partnership with Siegfried so successful?

Even now, as we still jog along happily after thirty-five years, I wonder about it. I know I liked him instinctively when I first saw him in the garden at Skeldale House on that very first afternoon, but I feel there is another reason why we get on together.

Maybe it is because we are opposites. Siegfried's restless energy impels him constantly to try to alter things while I abhor change of any kind. A lot of people would call him brilliant, while not even my best friends would apply that description to me. His mind relentlessly churns out ideas of all grades – excellent, doubtful and very strange indeed. I, on the other hand, rarely have an idea of any sort. He likes hunting, shooting and fishing; I prefer football, cricket and tennis. I could go on and on – we are even opposite physical types – and yet, as I say, we get along.

This of course doesn't mean that we have never had our differences. Over the years there have been minor clashes on various points.

One, I recall, was over the plastic calcium injectors. They were something new so Siegfried liked them, and by the same token I regarded them with deep suspicion.

My doubts were nourished by my difficulties with them. Their early troubles have now been ironed out but at the beginning I found the things so temperamental that I abandoned them.

My colleague pulled me up about it when he saw me washing out my flutter valve by running the surgery tap through it.

'For God's sake, James, you're not still using that old thing, are you?'

'Yes, I'm afraid I am.'

'But haven't you tried the new plastics?'

'I have.'

'Well...?'

'Can't get away with them, Siegfried.'

'Can't... what on earth do you mean?'

I trickled the last drop of water through the tube, rolled it small and slipped it into its case. 'Well, the last time I used one the calcium squirted all over the place. And it's messy, sticky stuff. I had great white streaks down my coat.'

'But James!' He laughed incredulously. 'That's crazy! They're childishly simple to use. I haven't had the slightest trouble.'

'I believe you,' I said. 'But you know me. I haven't got a mechanical mind.'

'For heaven's sake, you don't need a mechanical mind. They're foolproof.'

'Not to me, they aren't. I've had enough of them.'

My colleague put his hand on my shoulder and his patient look began to creep across his face. 'James, James, you must persevere.' He raised a finger. 'There is another point at issue here, you know.'

'What's that?'

'The matter of asepsis. How do you know that length of rubber you have there is clean?'

'Well, I wash it through after use, I use a boiled needle, and...'

'But don't you see, my boy, you're only trying to achieve what already exists in the plastic pack. Each one is self-contained and sterilized.'

'Oh I know all about that, but what's the good of it if I can't get the stuff into the cow?' I said querulously.

'Oh piffle, James!' Siegfried assumed a grave expression. 'It only needs a little application on your part, and I must stress that you are behaving in a reactionary manner by being stubborn. I put it to you seriously that we have to move with the times and every time you use that antiquated outfit of yours it is a retrograde step.'

We stood, as we often did, eyeball to eyeball, in mutual

disagreement till he smiled suddenly. 'Look, you're going out now, aren't you, to see that milk-fever cow I treated at John Tillot's. I understand it's not up yet.'

'That's right.'

'Well, as a favour to me, will you give one of the new packs a try?'

I thought for a moment. 'All right, Siegfried, I'll have one more go.'

When I reached the farm I found the cow comfortably ensconced in a field, in the middle of a rolling yellow ocean of buttercups.

'She's had a few tries to get on 'er feet,' the farmer said. 'But she can't quite make it.'

'Probably just wants another shot.' I went to my car which I had driven, rocking and bumping, over the rig and furrow of the field, and took one of the plastic packs from the boot.

Mr Tillot raised his eyebrows when he saw me coming back. 'Is that one o' them new things?'

'Yes, it is, Mr Tillot, the very latest invention. All completely sterilized.'

'Ah don't care what it is, ah don't like it!'

'You don't?'

'Naw!'

'Well . . . why not?'

'Ah'll tell ye. Mr Farnon used one this mornin'. Some of the stuff went in me eye, some went in 'is ear 'ole and the rest went down 'is trousers. Ah don't think t'bloody cow got any!'

There was another time Siegfried had to take me to task. An old-age pensioner was leading a small mongrel dog along the passage on the end of a piece of string. I patted the consulting room table.

'Put him up here, will you?' I said.

The old man bent over slowly, groaning and puffing.

'Wait a minute.' I tapped his shoulder. 'Let me do it.' I hoisted the little animal on to the smooth surface.

'Thank ye, sir.' The man straightened up and rubbed his back and leg. 'I 'ave arthritis bad and I'm not much good at liftin'. My name's Bailey and I live at t'council houses.'

'Right, Mr Bailey, what's the trouble?'

'It's this cough. He's allus at it. And 'e kind of retches at t'end of it.'

'I see. How old is he?'

'He were ten last month.'

'Yes . . .' I took the temperature and carefully auscultated the chest. As I moved the stethoscope over the ribs Siegfried came in and began to rummage in the cupboard.

'It's a chronic bronchitis, Mr Bailey,' I said. 'Many older dogs suffer from it just like old folks.'

He laughed. 'Aye, ah'm a bit wheezy meself sometimes.'

'That's right, but you're not so bad, really, are you?'

'Naw, naw.'

'Well neither is your little dog. I'm going to give him an injection and a course of tablets and it will help him quite a bit. I'm afraid he'll never quite get rid of this cough, but bring him in again if it gets very bad.'

He nodded vigorously. 'Very good, sir. Thank ye kindly, sir.'

As Siegfried banged about in the cupboard I gave the injection and counted out twenty of the new M&B 693 tablets.

The old man gazed at them with interest then put them in his pocket. 'Now what do ah owe ye, Mr Herriot?'

I looked at the ragged tie knotted carefully over the frayed shirt collar, at the threadbare antiquity of the jacket. His trouser knees had been darned but on one side I caught a pink glimpse of the flesh through the material.

'No, that's all right, Mr Bailey. Just see how he goes on.'

'Eh?'

'There's no charge.'

'But . . .'

'Now don't worry about it – it's nothing, really. Just see he gets his tablets regularly.'

'I will, sir, and it's very kind of you. I never expected . . .'

'I know you didn't, Mr Bailey. Goodbye for now and bring him back if he's not a lot better in a few days.'

The sound of the old man's footsteps had hardly died away when Siegfried emerged from the cupboard. He brandished a pair of horse tooth forceps in my face. 'God, I've been ages hunting these down. I'm sure you deliberately hide things from me, James.'

I smiled but made no reply and as I was replacing my syringe on the trolley my colleague spoke again.

'James, I don't like to mention this, but aren't you rather rash, doing work for nothing?'

I looked at him in surprise. 'He was an old-age pensioner. Pretty hard up I should think.'

'Maybe so, but really, you know, you just cannot give your services free.'

'Oh but surely occasionally, Siegfried – in a case like this . . .'

'No, James, not even occasionally. It's just not practical.'

'But I've seen you do it – time and time again!'

'Me?' His eyes widened in astonishment. 'Never! I'm too aware of the harsh realities of life for that. Everything has become so frightfully expensive. For instance, weren't those M&B 693 tablets you were dishing out? Heaven help us, do you know those things are threepence each? It's no good – you must never work without charging.'

'But dammit, you're always doing it!' I burst out. 'Only last week there was that . . .'

Siegfried held up a restraining hand. 'Please, James, please. You imagine things, that's your trouble.'

I must have given him one of my most exasperated stares because he reached out and patted my shoulder.

'Believe me, my boy, I do understand. You acted from the highest possible motives and I have often been tempted to do the same. But you must be firm. These are hard times and one must be hard to survive. So remember in future – no more Robin Hood stuff, we can't afford it.'

I nodded and went on my way somewhat bemusedly, but I soon forgot the incident and would have thought no more about it had I not seen Mr Bailey about a week later.

His dog was once more on the consulting room table and

Siegfried was giving it an injection. I didn't want to interfere so I went back along the passage to the front office and sat down to write in the day book. It was a summer afternoon, the window was open and through a parting in the curtain I could see the front steps.

As I wrote I heard Siegfried and the old man passing on their way to the front door. They stopped on the steps. The little dog, still on the end of its string, looked much as it did before.

'All right, Mr Bailey,' my colleague said. 'I can only tell you the same as Mr Herriot. I'm afraid he's got that cough for life, but when it gets bad you must come and see us.'

'Very good, sir,' the old man put his hand in his pocket. 'And what is the charge, please?'

'The charge, oh yes ... the charge ...' Siegfried cleared his throat a few times but seemed unable to articulate. He kept looking from the mongrel dog to the old man's tattered clothing and back again. Then he glanced furtively into the house and spoke in a hoarse whisper.

'It's nothing, Mr Bailey.'

'But Mr Farnon, I can't let ye ...'

'Shh! Shh!' Siegfried waved a hand agitatedly in the old man's face. 'Not a word now! I don't want to hear any more about it.'

Having silenced Mr Bailey he produced a large bag.

'There's about a hundred M&B tablets in here,' he said, throwing an anxious glance over his shoulder. 'He's going to keep needing them, so I've given you a good supply.'

I could see my colleague had spotted the hole in the trouser knee because he gazed down at it for a long time before putting his hand in his jacket pocket.

'Hang on a minute.' He extracted a handful of assorted chattels. A few coins fell and rolled down the steps as he prodded in his palm among scissors, thermometers, pieces of string, bottle openers. Finally his search was rewarded and he pulled out a bank note.

'Here's a quid,' he whispered and again nervously shushed the man's attempts to speak.

Mr Bailey, realizing the futility of argument, pocketed the money.

'Well, thank ye, Mr Farnon. Ah'll take t'missus to Scarborough wi' that.'

'Good lad, good lad,' muttered Siegfried, still looking around him guiltily. 'Now off you go.'

The old man solemnly raised his cap and began to shuffle painfully down the street.

'Hey, hold on, there,' my colleague called after him. 'What's the matter? You're not going very well.'

'It's this dang arthritis. Ah go a long way in a long time.'

'And you've got to walk all the way to the council houses?' Siegfried rubbed his chin irresolutely. 'It's a fair step.' He took a last wary peep down the passage then beckoned with his hand.

'Look, my car's right here,' he whispered. 'Nip in and I'll run you home.'

Some of our disagreements were sharp and short.

I was sitting at the lunch table, rubbing and flexing my elbow. Siegfried, carving enthusiastically at a joint of roast mutton, looked up from his work.

'What's the trouble, James – rheumatism?'

'No, a cow belted me with her horn this morning. Right on the funny bone.'

'Oh, bad luck. Were you trying to get hold of her nose?'

'No, giving her an injection.'

My colleague, transporting a slice of mutton to my plate, paused in mid-air. 'Injecting her? Up there?'

'Yes, in the neck.'

'Is that where you do it?'

'Yes, always have done. Why?'

'Because if I may say so, it's rather a daft place. I always use the rump.'

'Is that so?' I helped myself to mashed potatoes. 'And what's wrong with the neck?'

'Well, you've illustrated it yourself, haven't you? It's too damn near the horns for a start.'

'Okay, well the rump is too damn near the hind feet.'

'Oh, come now, James, you know very well a cow very seldom kicks after a rump injection.'

'Maybe so, but once is enough.'

'And once is enough with a bloody horn, isn't it?'

I made no reply, Siegfried plied the gravy boat over both our plates and we started to eat. But he had hardly swallowed the first mouthful when he returned to the attack.

'Another thing, the rump is so handy. Your way you have to squeeze up between the cows.'

'Well, so what?'

'Simply that you get your ribs squashed and your toes stood on, that's all.'

'All right.' I spooned some green beans from the tureen. 'But your way you stand an excellent chance of receiving a faceful of cow shit.'

'Oh rubbish, James, you're just making excuses!' He hacked violently at his mutton.

'Not at all,' I said. 'It's what I believe. And anyway, you haven't made out a case against the neck.'

'Made out a case? I haven't started yet. I could go on indefinitely. For instance, the neck is more painful.'

'The rump is more subject to contamination,' I countered.

'The neck is often thinly muscled,' snapped Siegfried. 'You haven't got a nice pad there to stick your needle into.'

'No, and you haven't got a tail either,' I growled.

'Tail? What the hell are you talking about?'

'I'm talking about the bloody tail! It's all right if you have somebody holding it but otherwise it's a menace, lashing about.'

Siegfried gave a few rapid chews and swallowed quickly. 'Lashing about? What in God's name has that got to do with it?'

'Quite a lot,' I replied. 'I don't like a whack across the face from a shitty tail, even if you do.'

There was a heavy-breathing lull then my colleague spoke in an ominously quiet voice. 'Anything else about the tail?'

'Yes, there is. Some cows can whip a syringe out of your

hand with their tail. The other day one caught my big fifty cc and smashed it against a wall. Broken glass everywhere.'

Siegfried flushed slightly and put down his knife and fork. 'James, I don't like to speak to you in these terms, but I am bound to tell you that you are talking the most unmitigated balls, bullshit and poppycock.'

I gave him a sullen glare. 'That's your opinion, is it?'

'It is indeed, James.'

'Right.'

'Right.'

'Okay.'

'Very well.'

We continued our meal in silence.

But over the next few days my mind kept returning to the conversation. Siegfried has always had a persuasive way with him and the thought kept recurring that there might be a lot in what he said.

It was a week later that I paused, syringe in hand, before pushing between two cows. The animals, divining my intent as they usually did, swung their craggy hind ends together and blocked my way. Yes, by God, Siegfried had a point. Why should I fight my way in there when the other end was ready and waiting?

I came to a decision. 'Hold the tail, please,' I said to the farmer and pushed my needle into the rump.

The cow never moved and as I completed the injection and pulled the needle out I was conscious of a faint sense of shame. That lovely pad of gluteal muscle, the easy availability of the site – my colleague had been dead right and I had been a pig-headed fool. I knew what to do in future.

The farmer laughed as he stepped back across the dung channel. 'It's a funny thing how you fellers all have your different ways.'

'What do you mean?'

'Well, Mr Farnon was 'ere yesterday, injecting that cow over there.'

'He was?' A sudden light flashed in my mind. Could it be

that Siegfried was not the only convincing talker in our practice . . . ? 'What about it?'

'Just that 'e had a different system from you. He injected into the neck.'

# twenty-seven

I leaned on the handle of my spade, wiped away the sweat which had begun to run into my eyes and gazed around me at the hundreds of men scattered over the dusty green.

We were still on our toughening course. At least that's what they told us it was. I had a private suspicion that they just didn't know what to do with all the aircrews under training and that somebody had devised this method of getting us out of the way.

Anyway, we were building a reservoir near a charming little Shropshire town and a whole village of tents had sprung up to house us. Nobody was quite sure about the reservoir but we were supposed to be building something. They issued us with denim suits and pick-axes and spades and for hour after hour we pecked desultorily at a rocky hillside.

But, hot as I was, I couldn't help thinking that things could be a lot worse. The weather was wonderful and it was a treat to be in the open all day. I looked down the slope and away across the sweetly rolling countryside to where low hills rose in the blue distance; it was a gentler landscape than the stark fells and moors I had left behind in Yorkshire, but infinitely soothing.

And the roofs of the town showing above the trees held a rich promise. During the hours under the fierce sun, with the rock dust caking round our lips, we built up a gargantuan thirst which we nurtured carefully till the evening when we were allowed out of camp.

There, in cool taverns in the company of country folk, we

slaked it with pints of glorious rough cider. I don't suppose you would find any there now. It is mostly factory-made cider which is drunk in the South of England these days, but many of the pubs used to have their own presses where they squeezed the juice from the local apples.

To me, there was something disturbing about sleeping in a tent. Each morning when I awoke with the early sun beating on the thin walls it was as if I were back in the hills above the Firth of Clyde long before the war was dreamed of. There was something very evocative about the tent smell of hot canvas and rubber groundsheet and crushed grass and the flies buzzing in a little cloud at the top of the pole. I was jerked back in an instant to Rosneath and when I opened my eyes I half expected to find Alex Taylor and Eddie Hutchinson, the friends of my boyhood, lying there in their sleeping bags.

The three of us went camping at Rosneath every weekend from Easter to October, leaving the smoke and dirt of Glasgow behind us; and here in Shropshire, in the uncanny tent smell, when I closed my eyes I could see the little pinewood behind the tent and the green hillside running down to the burn and, far below, the long blue mirror of the Gareloch glinting under the great mountains of Argyll. They have desecrated Rosneath and the Gareloch now, but to me, as a boy, it was a fairyland which led me into the full wonder and beauty of the world.

It was strange that I should dwell on that period when I was in my teens because Alex was in the Middle East, Eddie was in Burma and I was in another tent with a lot of different young men. And it was as though the time between had been rubbed away and Darrowby and Helen and all my struggles in veterinary practice had never happened. Yet those years in Darrowby had been the most important of my life. I used to sit up and shake myself, wondering at how my thoughts had been mixed up by the war.

But as I say, I quite enjoyed Shropshire. The only snag was that reservoir, or whatever it was that we were hacking out of the face of the hill. I could never get really involved with it.

So that I pricked up my ears when our Flight Sergeant made an announcement one morning.

'Some of the local farmers want help with their harvest,' he called out at the early parade. 'Are there any volunteers?'

My hand was the first up and after a few moments' hesitation others followed, but none of my particular friends volunteered for the job. When everything had been sorted out I found I had been allotted to a farmer Edwards with three other airmen who were from a different flight and strangers to me.

Mr Edwards arrived the following day and packed the four of us into a typical big old-fashioned farmer's car. I sat in the front with him while the three others filled the back. He asked our names but nothing else, as though he felt that our station in civil life was none of his concern. He was about thirty-five with jet black hair above a sunburnt face in which his white teeth and clear blue eyes shone startlingly.

He looked us over with a good-humoured grin as we rolled into his farmyard.

'Well, here we are, lads,' he said. 'This is where we're going to put you through it.'

But I hardly heard him. I was looking around me at the scene which had been part of my life a few months ago. The cobbled yard, the rows of doors leading to cow byre, barn, pigsties and loose boxes. An old man was mucking out the byre and as the rich bovine smell drifted across, one of my companions wrinkled his nose. But I inhaled it like perfume.

The farmer led us all into the fields where a reaper and binder was at work, leaving the sheaves of corn lying in long golden swathes.

'Any of you ever done any stooking?' he asked.

We shook our heads dumbly.

'Never mind, you'll soon learn. You come with me, Jim.'

We spaced ourselves out in the big field, each of my colleagues with an old man while Mr Edwards took charge of me. It didn't take me long to realize that I had got the tough section.

The farmer grabbed a sheaf in each hand, tucked them

under his arms, walked a few steps and planted them on end, resting against each other. I did the same till there were eight sheaves making up a stook. He showed me how to dig the stalks into the ground so that they stood upright and sometimes he gave a nudge with his knee to keep them in the right alignment.

I did my best but often my sheaves would fall over and I had to dart back and replace them. And I noticed with some alarm that Mr Edwards was going about twice as fast as the three old men. We had nearly finished the row while they were barely half way along, and my aching arms and back told me I was in for a testing time.

We went on like that for about two hours; bending, lifting, bending, lifting and shuffling forward without an instant's respite. One of the strongest impressions I had gained when I first came into country practice was that farming was the hardest way of all of making a living, and now I was finding out for myself. I was about ready to throw myself down on the stubble when Mrs Edwards came over the field with her young son and daughter. They carried baskets with the ingredients for our ten o'clock break; crusty apple tart and jugs of cider.

The farmer watched me quizzically as I sank gratefully down and began to drink like a parched traveller in the desert. The cider, from his own press, was superb, and I closed my eyes as I swallowed. The right thing, it seemed to me, would be to lie here in the sunshine for the rest of the day with about a gallon of this exquisite brew by my side, but Mr Edwards had other ideas. I was still chewing at the solid crust when he grasped a fresh pair of sheaves.

'Right, lad, must get on,' he grunted, and I was back on the treadmill.

With a pause at lunchtime for bread, cheese and more cider we went on at breakneck speed all day. I have always been grateful to the RAF for what they did for my physical well-being. When I was called up there was no doubt I was going slightly to seed under Helen's beneficent regime. Too much good cooking and the discovery of the charms of an armchair; I was getting fat. But the RAF changed all that and I don't think I have ever slipped back.

After the six months at Scarborough I am certain I didn't carry a surplus pound. Marching, drilling, PT, running – I could trot five miles along the beach and cliffs without trouble. When I arrived in Shropshire I was really fit. But I wasn't as fit as Mr Edwards.

He was a compact bundle of power. Not very big but with the wiry durability I remembered in the Yorkshire farmers. He seemed tireless, hardly breaking sweat as he moved along the rows, corded brown arms bulging from the sleeves of a faded collarless shirt, slightly bowed legs stumping effortlessly.

The sensible thing would have been to tell him straight that I couldn't go at his pace, but some demon of pride impelled me to keep up with him. I am quite sure he didn't mean to rub it in. Like any other farmer he had a job to do and was anxious to get on with it. At the lunch break he looked at me with some commiseration as I stood there, shirt sticking to my back, mouth hanging open, ribs heaving.

'You're doin' fine, Jim,' he said, then, as if noticing my distress for the first time, he shifted his feet awkwardly. 'I know you city lads ain't used to this kind of work and . . . well . . . it's not a question of strength, it's just knowin' how to do it.'

When we drove back to camp that night I could hear my companions groaning in the back of the car. They, too, had suffered, but not as badly as me.

After a few days I did begin to get the knack of the thing and though it still tested me to the utmost I was never on the border of collapse again.

Mr Edwards noticed the improvement and slapped me playfully on the shoulder. 'What did I tell you? It's just knowin' how to do it!'

But a new purgatory awaited me when we started to load the corn on to the stack. Forking the sheaves up on to the cart, roping them there then throwing them again, higher and higher as the stack grew in size. I realized with a jolt that stooking had been easy.

Mrs Edwards joined in this part. She stood on the top of

the stack with her husband, expertly turning the sheaves towards him while he arranged them as they should be. I had the unskilled job way below, toiling as never before, back breaking, the handle of the fork blistering my palms.

I just couldn't go fast enough and Mr Edwards had to hop down to help me, grasping a fork and hurling the sheaves up with easy flicks of the wrist.

He looked at me as before and spoke the encouraging words. 'You're comin' along grand, Jim. It's just knowin' how to do it.'

But there were many compensations. The biggest was being among farming folk again. Mrs Edwards in her undemonstrative way was obviously anxious to show hospitality to these four rather bewildered city boys far from home, and set us down to a splendid meal every evening. She was dark like her husband, with large eyes which joined in her quick smile and a figure which managed to be thin and shapely at the same time. She hadn't much chance to get fat because she never stopped working. When she wasn't outside throwing the corn around like any man she was cooking and baking, looking after her children and scouring her great barn of a farmhouse.

Those evening meals were something to look forward to and remember. Steaming rabbit pies with fresh green beans and potatoes from the garden. Bilberry tarts and apple crumble and a massive jug of thick cream to pour ad lib. Home-baked bread and farm cheese.

The four of us revelled in the change from the RAF fare. It was said the aircrews got the best food in the services and I believed it, but after a while it all began to taste the same. Maybe it was the bulk cooking but it palled in time.

Sitting at the farm table, looking at Mrs Edwards serving us, at her husband eating stolidly and at the two children, a girl of ten whose dark eyes showed promise of her mother's attractiveness and a sturdy, brown-limbed boy of eight, the thought recurred; they were good stock.

The clever economists who tell us that we don't need British agriculture and that our farms should be turned into national parks seem to ignore the rather obvious snag that an unfriendly country could starve us into submission in a week. But to me a greater tragedy still would be the loss of a whole community of people like the Edwards.

It was late one afternoon and I was feeling more of a weakling than ever, with Mr Edwards throwing the sheaves around as though they were weightless while I groaned and strained. The farmer was called away to attend to a calving cow and as he hopped blithely from the stack he patted my shoulder as I leaned on my fork.

'Never mind, Jim,' he laughed. 'It's just knowin' how to do it.'

An hour later we were going into the kitchen for our meal when Mrs Edwards said, 'My husband's still on with that cow. He must be having difficulty with her.'

I hesitated in the doorway. 'Do you mind if I go and see how he's getting on?'

She smiled. 'All right, if you like. I'll keep your food warm for you.'

I crossed the yard and went into the byre. One of the old men was holding the tail of a big Red Poll and puffing his pipe placidly. Mr Edwards, stripped to the waist, had his arm in the cow up to the shoulder. But it was a different Mr Edwards. His back and chest glistened and droplets of sweat ran down his nose and dripped steadily from the end. His mouth gaped and he panted as he fought his private battle somewhere inside.

He turned glazed eyes in my direction. At first he didn't appear to see me in his absorption, then recognition dawned.

''Ullo, Jim,' he muttered breathlessly. 'I've got a right job on 'ere.'

'Sorry to hear that. What's the trouble?'

He began to reply then screwed up his face. 'Aaah! The old bitch! She's squeezin' the life out of me arm again! She'll break it afore she's finished!' He paused, head hanging down, to recover, then he looked up at me. 'The calf's laid wrong, Jim. There's just a tail comin' into the passage and I can't get the hind legs round.'

A breech. My favourite presentation but one which always defeated farmers. I couldn't blame them really because they had never had the opportunity to read Franz Benesch's classical work on *Veterinary Obstetrics* which explains the mechanics of parturition so lucidly. One phrase has always stuck in my mind: 'The necessity for simultaneous application of antagonistic forces'.

Benesch points out that in order to correct many malpresentations it is necessary to apply traction and repulsion at the same time, and to do that with one hand in a straining cow is impossible.

As though to endorse my thoughts Mr Edwards burst out once more. 'Dang it, I've missed it again! I keep pushin' the hock away then grabbin' for the foot but the old bitch just shoves it all back at me. I've been doin' this for an hour now and I'm about knackered.'

I never thought I would hear such words from this tough little man, but there was no doubt he had suffered. The cow was a massive animal with a back like a dining table and she was heaving the farmer back effortlessly every time she strained. We didn't see many Red Polls in Yorkshire but the ones I had met were self-willed and strong as elephants; the idea of pushing against one for an hour made me quail.

Mr Edwards pulled his arm out and stood for a moment leaning against the hair rump. The animal was quite unperturbed by the interference of this puny human but the farmer was a picture of exhaustion. He worked his dangling fingers gingerly then looked up at me.

'By God!' he grunted. 'She's given me some stick. I've got hardly any feelin' left in this arm.'

He didn't have to tell me. I had known that sensation many a time. Even Benesch in the midst of his coldly scientific 're-positions', 'retropulsions', 'malpositions' and 'counteracting pressures' so far unbends as to state that 'Great demands are made upon the strength of the operator'. Mr Edwards would agree with him.

The farmer took a long shuddering breath and moved over to the bucket of hot water on the floor. He washed his arms then turned back to the cow with something like dread on his face.

'Look,' I said. 'Please let me help you.'

He gave a pallid smile. 'Thanks, Jim, but there's nuthin' you can do. Those legs have got to come round.'

'That's what I mean. I can do it.'

'What . . .?'

'With a bit of help from you. Have you got a piece of binder twine handy?'

'Aye, we've got yards of it, lad, but I'm tellin' you you need experience for this job. You know nuthin' about . . .'

He stopped because I was already pulling my shirt over my head. He was too tired to argue in any case.

Hanging the shirt on a nail on the wall, bending over the bucket and soaping my arms with the scent of the antiseptic coming up to me brought a rush of memories which was almost overwhelming. I held out my hand and Mr Edwards wordlessly passed me a length of twine.

I soaked it in the water, then quickly tied a slip knot at one end and inserted my hand into the cow. Ah yes, there was the tail, so familiar, hanging between the calf's pelvic bones. Oh, I did love a breach, and I ran my hand with almost voluptuous satisfaction along the hair of the limb till I reached the tiny foot. It was a moment's work to push the loop over the fetlock and tighten it while I passed the free end between the digits of the cloven foot.

'Hold that,' I said to the farmer, 'and pull it steadily when I tell you.'

I put my hand on the hock and began to push it away from me into the uterus.

'Now pull,' I said. 'But carefully. Don't jerk.'

Like a man in a dream he did as I said and within seconds the foot popped out of the vulva.

'Hell!' said Mr Edwards.

'Now for the other one,' I murmured as I removed the loop.

I repeated the procedure, the farmer, slightly pop-eyed, pulling on the twine. The second little hoof, yellow and moist, joined its fellow on the outside almost immediately.

'Bloody hell!' said Mr Edwards.

'Right,' I said. 'Grab a leg and we'll have him out in a couple of ticks.'

We each took a hold and leaned back, but the big cow did the job for us, giving a great heave which deposited the calf wet and wriggling into my arms. I staggered back and dropped with it on to the straw.

'Grand bull calf, Mr Edwards,' I said. 'Better give him a rub down.'

The farmer shot me a disbelieving glance then twisted some hay into a wisp and began to dry off the little creature.

'If you ever get stuck with a breech presentation again,' I said, 'I'll show you what you ought to do. You have to push and pull at the same time and that's where the twine comes in. As you repel the hock with your hand somebody else pulls the foot round, but you'll notice I have the twine between the calf's cleats and that's important. That way it lifts the sharp little foot up and prevents injury to the vaginal wall.'

The farmer nodded dumbly and went on with his rubbing. When he had finished he looked up at me in bewilderment and his lips moved soundlessly a few times before he spoke.

'What the . . . how . . . how the heck do you know all that?'

I told him.

There was a long pause then he exploded.

'You young bugger! You kept that dark, didn't you?'

'Well . . . you never asked me.'

He scratched his head. 'Well, I don't want to be nosey with you lads that helps me. Some folks don't like it . . .' His voice trailed away.

We dried our arms and donned our shirts in silence. Before leaving he looked over at the calf, already making strenuous efforts to rise as its mother licked it.

'He's a lively little beggar,' he said. 'And we might have lost 'im. I'm right grateful to you.' He put an arm round my shoulders. 'Anyway, come on, Mister Veterinary Surgeon, and we'll 'ave some supper.'

Half way across the yard he stopped and regarded me ruefully. 'You know, I must have looked proper daft to you, fumblin' away inside there for an hour and damn near killin' myself, then you step up and do it in a couple of minutes. I feel as weak as a girl.'

'Not in the least, Mr Edwards,' I replied. 'It's ...' I hesitated a moment. 'It's not a question of strength, it's just knowing how to do it.'

He nodded, then became very still and the seconds stretched out as he stared at me. Suddenly his teeth shone as the brown face broke into an ever-widening grin which developed into a great shout of laughter.

He was still laughing helplessly when we reached the house and as I opened the kitchen door he leaned against the wall and wiped his eyes.

'You young divil!' he said. 'You really got a bit o' your own back there, didn't you?'

# twenty-eight

At last we were on our way to Flying School. It was at Windsor and that didn't seem far on the map, but it was a typical war-time journey of endless stops and changes and interminable waits. It went on all through the night and we took our sleep in snatches. I stole an hour's fitful slumber on the waiting-room table at a tiny nameless station and despite my hard pillowless bed I drifted deliciously back to Darrowby.

I was bumping along the rutted track to Nether Lees Farm, hanging on to the jerking wheel. I could see the house below me, its faded red tiles showing above the sheltering trees, and behind the buildings the scrubby hillside rose to the moor.

Up there the trees were stunted and sparse and dotted widely over the steep flanks. Higher still there was only scree and cliff and right at the top, beckoning in the sunshine, I saw the beginning of the moor – smooth, unbroken and bare.

A scar on the broad sweep of green showed where long ago they quarried the stones to build the massive farmhouses and the enduring walls which have stood against the unrelenting climate for hundreds of years. Those houses and those endlessly marching walls would still be there when I was gone and forgotten.

Helen was with me in the car. I loved it when she came with me on my rounds, and after the visit to the farm we climbed up the fell-side, panting through the scent of the warm bracken, feeling the old excitement as we neared the summit.

Then we were on the top, facing into the wide free moorland and the clean Yorkshire wind and the cloud shadows racing over the greens and browns. Helen's hand was warm in mine as we wandered among the heather through green islets nibbled to a velvet sward by the sheep. She raised a finger as a curlew's lonely cry sounded across the wild tapestry and the wonder in her eyes shone through the dark flurry of hair blowing across her face.

The gentle shaking at my shoulder pulled me back to wakefulness, to the hiss of steam and the clatter of boots. The table top was hard against my hip and my neck was stiff where it had rested on my pack.

'Train's in, Jim.' An airman was looking down at me. 'I hated to wake you – you were smiling.'

Two hours later, sweaty, unshaven, half asleep, laden with kit, we shuffled into the airfield at Windsor. Sitting in the wooden building we only half listened to the corporal giving us our introductory address. Then suddenly his words struck home.

'There's one other thing,' he said. 'Remember to wear your identity discs at all times. We had two prangs last week – couple of fellers burned beyond recognition and neither of 'em was wearing his discs. We didn't know who they were.' He spread his hands appealingly. 'This sort of thing makes a lot of work for us, so remember what I've told you.'

In a moment we were all wide awake and listening intently. Probably thinking as I was – that we had only been playing at being airmen up till now.

I looked through the window at the wind sock blowing over the long flat stretch of green, at the scattered aircraft, the fire tender, the huddle of low wooden huts. The playing was over now. This was where everything started.

James Herriot
Special Limited Edition
**Every Living Thing/If Only They Could Talk/It Shouldn't Happen to a Vet/Let Sleeping Vets Lie**
£7.99

**Four bestsellers in one great volume!**

For more than 25 years, James Herriot captivated millions of readers and television viewers with tales of the triumphs, disasters, pride and sometimes heartache that filled his life as a vet in the Yorkshire Dales.

Included here is the story that launched a legend, James Herriot's very first book, *If Only They Could Talk*. Also included are his second and third books, *It Shouldn't Happen to a Vet* and *Let Sleeping Vets Lie* – and his last, unforgettable bestseller, *Every Living Thing*.

'Enormous pleasure . . . the stories can be read and re-read' *Sunday Times*

'After an evening among his tales, anyone with as much as a dog or a budgerigar will feel they should move to Darrowby at once' *Yorkshire Post*

'It is a pleasure to be in James Herriot's company' *Observer*

Rumer Godden
Special Limited Edition
**Coromandel Sea Change/The Greengage
Summer/The River** £6.99

**Three classics for the price of one!**

Rumer Godden's genius for storytelling has captivated readers all over the world for nearly four decades. Acclaimed as 'one of the finest of living English novelists' (Orville Prescott) her stories have a timelessness and a haunting simplicity that have earned them the status of modern classics.

Now in one anthology, three of Rumer Godden's best-loved novels will delight her many fans and new readers alike. Included are *Coromandel Sea Change*, Rumer Godden's first Number 1 bestseller of the 1990s, a captivating love story set in Southern India at election time; *The Greengage Summer*, an evocative portrait of love and deceit in rural France which became a memorable film starring Kenneth More and Susannah York; and *The River*, a beautiful tribute to India and childhood, made into a film by the great French director Jean Renoir.

'Sheer enjoyment' *Guardian*

'The miracle is Godden's genius for storytelling' *Evening Standard*

'The prose is as simple and luminous as the fantasy is elaborate'
*Independent on Sunday*

Elizabeth Jane Howard
Special Limited Edition
**The Long View/The Sea Change** £4.99

Two beautiful stories for the price of one!

Loyalty . . . Passion . . . Discovery . . .

Elizabeth Jane Howard, bestselling author of The Cazalet Chronicle, dissects
love, marriage and relationships in two revealing – and wonderfully
entertaining – full length novels.

*The Long View*
Elizabeth Jane Howard's acclaimed fictional portrait of a contemporary
marriage – ingeniously constructed to give a very real view of the shifting
relationship between two people.

'If artistry lies in heightened awareness, this is it' *The Times*

*The Sea Change*
A classic story of compulsion – deftly unravelling the complex interactions
between two men and two women whose lives become entangled in
London, New York, and finally on a remote and mysterious Greek island.

'Beautifully written and richly perceptive' *Daily Telegraph*

Tom Sharpe
Special Collectors' Edition
**Blott On The Landscape/The Wilt Alternative/The
Great Pursuit**  £5.99

**Three classic bestsellers for the price of one!**

Tom Sharpe
'The loudest laughs in literary comedy'

Tom Sharpe's addictive cocktail of comedy and cruelty, sex and satire has
made him one of our most popular and widely-quoted authors. No part of
British life is safe from Sharpe's withering scrutiny.

Enjoy the mastery of Tom Sharpe in three of his most famous novels: *Blott
on the Landscape* and *The Great Pursuit*, each a classic masterpiece of
brainteasing British humour to rank alongside the best of P G Wodehouse
and Evelyn Waugh, and *The Wilt Alternative*, the third book in the riotously
funny series that began with *Wilt* and *Wilt on High*.

'Extremely funny. Mr Sharpe's dialogue is nifty . . . imaginative . . . and
enjoyable' *Spectator*

'A toppling house of comic cards that knock you flat. He is the funniest
writer for years' *Observer*

'A gust of raucous fun and unashamed entertainment, as well as biting
comment' *Sunday Express*

Dick Francis
Special Limited Edition
**Reflex/Comeback** £4.99

**Two champion thrillers for the price of one!**

'Dick Francis at his brilliant best' *Sporting Life*

A veterinary surgeon with a string of bloody accidents to his name . . .

. . . a murdered photographer, ready to send shockwaves through the racing
world with a legacy from beyond the grave.

From the undisputed champion of the racing crime thriller, two more classic
tales of murder, mystery and intrigue – set against the colourful background
of the Sport of Queens. *Reflex*, a fast-moving story of corruption and greed,
was one of Dick Francis's earliest triumphs. *Comeback*, set among the
Gloucestershire raceyards the former jockey knows so well, is the master's
30th consecutive Number 1 bestseller.

Dick Francis
'Still the best bet for a winning read' *Mail on Sunday*

'The finish had me sweating. The Gold Cup is tame by comparison'
*Evening Standard*

Colin Forbes
Special Limited Edition
**Shockwave/The Greek Key**  £4.99

Colin Forbes
'Has no equal' *Sunday Mirror*

From the number one name in adventure fiction, two non-stop action novels
– each featuring the legendary British agent, Tweed.

*Shockwave*
Target of a ruthless frame-up, Tweed is forced to flee into snowbound
Europe. Top security chiefs, once Tweed's friends, are alerted to arrest the
fugitive. The unknown enemy hires a top assassin. His mission: kill Tweed.
Reaching Swiss sanctuary via the icy Black Forest, Tweed turns at bay –
launching a savage counter-attack to unmask his hidden opponent . . .

*The Greek Key*
Murder – committed over forty years ago, is the detonator which triggers off
Tweed, Paula Grey and Newman in their quest for the Greek Key. Trapped in
a vortex of violence and death, Tweed begins to uncover a diabolical plot to
destroy *glasnost*. Only he can stop the terrorist, if he isn't already too late . . .

Douglas Reeman
Special Limited Edition
**The Iron Pirate/In Danger's Hour**  £4.99

Two bestselling naval adventures for the price of one!

Classic World War Two adventure from master storyteller Douglas Reeman

From the summer of 1944, from the killing grounds of the Atlantic and the Baltic, two electrifying bestsellers from the master storyteller of the sea.

*The Iron Pirate* is the story of Germany's last hope in the seaborne war – the crack heavy cruiser *Prinz Luitpold*. The men who hunted with her. And those who would see her destroyed . . .

And from the deadly waters of the Channel and the Mediterranean, *In Danger's Hour* tells of the unsung heroes of the 'little ships'. As D-Day approaches, fleet minesweeper HMS *Rob Roy* faces her most dangerous mission yet: a deadly challenge that will test captain and crew to the limits of endurance – and beyond . . .

'Vivid naval action at its most authentic' *Sunday Times*

Clare Francis
Special Limited Edition
**Requiem/Wolf Winter** £4.99

The best of Clare Francis, in two classic thrillers.

'Magnificent . . . move over Frederick Forsyth and Hammond Innes'
*Sunday Telegraph*

*Requiem*
The death of an innocent child leads to outcry about the environmental
vandalism of an American petro-chemical giant. A reclusive rock star and a
Green activist team up to stalk the enemy – but no one could foresee the
terror to come . . .

'Plenty of action, and more than enough murderous surprises' *Independent*

*Wolf Winter*
In the deadly chill of the Cold War, two Norwegians are gunned down after
straying into Soviet wilderness – killings that will bind three people together
in a web of treachery and passion . . .

'The spy thriller has rarely been better done' *New York Times*

Sue Grafton
The Omnibus
# D is for Deadbeat/E is for Evidence/F is for Fugitive
£5.99

*'My name is Kinsey Millhone. I'm a private investigator . . . female, single and self-employed, with a constitutional inability to work for anyone else. I'm a purist when it comes to justice, but I'll lie at the drop of a hat. Inconsistency has never troubled me . . .'*

## D is for Deadbeat

The day before Hallowe'en. He introduced himself as Alvin Limardo, which wasn't his real name. The job he hired Kinsey to do seemed simple enough . . . until his cheque bounced. By the time she caught up with him he was dead and Kinsey collected far more than she'd bargained for . . .

'D is for deft and diverting.' *Guardian*

## E is for Evidence

It was two days after Christmas when Kinsey Millhone received the bankslip showing a credit of $5000. The account number was correct but Kinsey hadn't made the deposit. Then came the phone call and suddenly everything became clear. The frame-up was working and Kinsey was trapped . . .

'Grafton crafts a crazy, credible puzzle with jigsaw finesse.' *Sunday Times*

## F is for Fugitive

Seventeen years had passed since Jean Timberlake's body had been found at the foot of the sea wall. At the time, Bailey Fowler, an ex-boyfriend, pleaded guilty to voluntary manslaughter. Now he'd changed his tune. Kinsey Millhone was called in to solve the case – then she stumbled on the dark secrets of a family's buried past . . .

'Kinsey Millhone is one of the most convincing private investigators in operation.' *Independent*

All Pan Books are available at your local bookshop or newsagent, or can be ordered direct from the publisher. Indicate the number of copies required and fill in the form below.

Send to:      Macmillan General Books C.S.
                Book Service By Post
                PO Box 29, Douglas I-O-M
                IM99 1BQ

or phone:      01624 675137, quoting title, author and credit card number.

or fax:         01624 670923, quoting title, author, and credit card number.

Please enclose a remittance* to the value of the cover price plus 75 pence per book for post and packing. Overseas customers please allow £1.00 per copy for post and packing.

*Payment may be made in sterling by UK personal cheque, Eurocheque, postal order, sterling draft or international money order, made payable to Book Service By Post.

Alternatively by Access/Visa/MasterCard

Card No.

Expiry Date

Signature      _____

Applicable only in the UK and BFPO addresses.

While every effort is made to keep prices low, it is sometimes necessary to increase prices at short notice. Pan Books reserve the right to show on covers and charge new retail prices which may differ from those advertised in the text or elsewhere.

NAME AND ADDRESS IN BLOCK CAPITAL LETTERS PLEASE

Name _____

Address _____

_____

_____

_____

3/95

Please allow 28 days for delivery.
Please tick box if you do not wish to receive any additional information. ☐